FLAT
ROOFING
DESIGN
& GOOD
PRACTICE

CIRIA

BRITISH
FLAT ROOFING
COUNCIL

Summary

This Guide deals with the design of flat roofs, where 'flat roof' means continuously-supported flat roofs up to 10° pitch.

It is aimed principally at **designer/specifiers**, and at site-based agents of the Employer (such as Clerks of Works), working on the design of new buildings or on refurbishment, replacement or repairs of existing flat roofs.

The guidance provided is for roofs in UK climatic conditions.

It is also intended to help **building owners** and those tenants with responsibilities for the condition of the building they occupy, in particular in clarifying the services they require or the instructions they might wish to give.

The purpose is to provide guidance based on existing good practice, from which designers, clients and others may select according to circumstances. It is not intended to define the responsibilities of any parties – or to relieve them – in a given contract.

Author: Arup Research & Development

Flat Roofing: Design and Good Practice

The British Flat Roofing Council and Construction Industry Research and Information Association, 1993

CIRIA reference: BOOK 15, 1993

This book is one of a series being produced by CIRIA on building elements of which
Wall Technology, Volumes A to G, *CIRIA Special Publication 87*, was published in 1992.

Keywords:
Flat roofs, design, maintenance, repair, refurbishment, details, bituminous membranes, mastic asphalt, polymeric single-ply membranes, copper, lead, thermal insulation

Reader Interest:
Architects, building surveyors, clerks of works, maintenance engineers, other building professionals, roofing contractors, roofing suppliers and students

CLASSIFICATION	
AVAILABILITY	Unrestricted
CONTENT	Guidance based on best practice
STATUS	Committee guided and refereed
USERS	Building designers, inspectors of building work, maintenance professionals

ISBNs: BFRC 0 9519075 0 6
       CIRIA 0 86017 345 3

Produced on Apple Macintosh using QuarkXpress, Adobe Photoshop, Aldus Freehand and Adobe Illustrator
Filmsetting by Inner Circle
Printed by Linneys Colour Print, Mansfield

Published by the British Flat Roofing Council,
38 Bridlesmith Gate, Nottingham, NG1 2GQ
and
the Construction Industry Research and Information Association,
6 Storey's Gate, Westminster, London, SW1P 3AU

CIRIA is the Construction Industry Research and Information Association. It is a non-profit-distributing, private sector organisation carrying out research and providing information for its members, who include all types of organisations concerned with construction, including clients, professional practices, contractors, suppliers, educational and research establishments, professional institutions, trade associations, central and local government.

CIRIA focuses on providing best practice guidance to professionals that is authoritative, convenient to use and relevant. Areas covered include construction practice, building design and materials, management, ground engineering, water engineering and environmental issues.

Through active participation, **CIRIA** members choose research and information projects of most value to them. Funding contributions are sought from member subscriptions and from government and other sources on a project by project basis. Detailed work is contracted to the best qualified organisation selected in competition, and each project is guided by a project steering group, which contains both individual specialists and representatives of different groups with experience or interest in the topic.

CIRIA offers a number of different participation routes as follows:

Core Programme Sponsorship. Core Programme members, who include many of the most significant construction firms, choose the programme of research projects and obtain privileged early access to results.

Construction Industry Environmental Forum. Run in association with BRE and BSRIA, the Forum provides a focus for cross-industry discussion and information on environmental matters.

Associates/Affiliates. Subscribers obtain copies of **CIRIA** open publications on favourable terms and get discounts on **CIRIA** seminars.

Support for individual projects. Organisations can participate financially and technically in single projects of interest to them.

Purchase of publications. **CIRIA** publications, together with selected publications from other sources, are available by mail order or on personal application.

Seminars/Conferences. CIRIA runs a number of events, often related to research projects or publications.

CIRIA News. A quarterly newsletter is available free on request.

BRITISH FLAT ROOFING COUNCIL

No construction professional can keep pace with every development in product, process and practice. Having access to current, independent information is crucial. For over a decade, the British Flat Roofing Council has acted as the single unbiased and authoritative voice on all aspects of flat roofing. Representing the manufacturers and contractors of the flat and low pitched roofing industry, the principal objectives of **BFRC** are as follows:

- to co-ordinate and disseminate the considerable fund of knowledge and expertise on flat roofing
- to raise standards of design, construction, performance and maintenance
- to promote research into flat roofing systems
- to extend the development, testing and use of new waterproofing materials
- to identify and eliminate as far as possible the cause of roofing failure
- to promote an awareness of the advantages of flat and low-pitched roofs.

A member of the UK Construction Industry Council and the International Waterproofing Association, **BFRC** is a major contributor to the European standards harmonisation programme and BSI committees. From its Nottingham office, the council **provides a comprehensive technical advisory service** for building owners, specifiers, contractors, educationalists and others. **BFRC**'s Technical Officer is a regular speaker at conference, seminar and CPD events.

The council actively promotes research into flat roofing. It is currently engaged in two research projects funded by the Science and Engineering Research Council, DoE and **BFRC** through the LINK Programme Construction, Maintenance and Refurbishment.

One project seeks to assess the life span characteristics and as built performance of flat roofing systems at Napier University of Edinburgh. Setting out to compare design versus as-built performance, evaluate diagnostic tools for non-destructive testing and to establish economic performance, it will provide appropriate guidelines for feedback of results to the design and contracting professions.

The second LINK project, headed by a team at Loughborough University of Technology, wishes to establish a knowledge-based computer system for flat roof diagnosis. The study collects together a broad spectrum of existing knowledge and understanding on flat roof design and materials, which is networked by 'rules' linking visible features with underlying causes.

BFRC, therefore, co-ordinates a considerable base of knowledge and experience from manufacturers, contractors and research establishments. It is dedicated to continually raising the standard of flat roofing systems in design, construction, performance and maintenance wherever independent, authoritative advice is of benefit.

For further details, please contact:
the Membership Manager, CIRIA, 6 Storey's Gate
London SW1P 3AU.
Tel: 071-222 8891. Fax: 071-222 1708.

For further details, please contact:
BFRC, 38 Bridlesmith Gate
Nottingham NG1 2GQ
Tel: 0602 507733. Fax: 0602 504122

Foreword

Gomera, Canary Islands

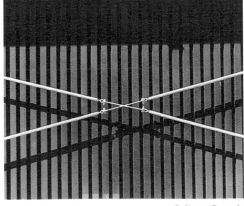

Reliance Controls

Some years ago I was asked to produce a planning strategy for an island called Gomera, which is part of the Spanish-speaking group of Canary Islands, lying close to the west coast of Africa. I went originally with a small team from our office to research the place. We were fascinated to discover that the indigenous buildings were of two distinct types, depending on where you were relative to the mountains which rose dramatically out of the centre of the island. The prevailing wind created a rain shadow over one side of the island and the buildings responded with pitched roofs covered with tiles. On the other side, which was noticeably warmer and drier, the structures were essentially flat-roofed. The platforms that they created were often shaded and used as outdoor rooms.

I was reminded of Gomera because recently our office has been designing a small factory in the South of Spain. Because the budget was very tight and the location was rural, we assumed that the most economical solution would be a variety of roof pitches covered with local tiles and walls of local block. Our intuitions proved to be wrong. No matter how many times the calculations were made, the cheapest solution always turned out to be a metal box with a low pitch or flat roof.

The word 'vernacular' when applied to architecture has in recent years taken on new and false meanings. To many it now conjures up a make-believe architecture of pitched roof pastiche; a misplaced attempt to create the image of a past that never really existed. The thatched cottage may appear quaint and rustic today, but in its heyday it was an advanced technology which used available materials in the most efficient and effective way possible. The true vernacular was always generated by the needs of people, the constraints of climate and the economy of means. Those buildings in Gomera were rooted in such realities; the existence of flat and pitched roofs on opposite sides of the island did not arise out of fashionable whim.

Today the materials and technologies of mass production and distribution are becoming universal to the extent that the true vernacular for certain building types is often the economical metal box. That is why, when put to the test, local tiles and blockwork were not affordable in the context of that factory in southern Spain. It reminds me of the time when I detailed the small factory for "Reliance Controls", nearly thirty years ago, and worked with product engineers to use profiled metal sheets stretched to their most economical limits. The building won the first award in Britain for industrial architecture and, in the media attention that followed, one writer, Ian Nairn, noted that "it was like discovering a lost vernacular".

Sadly the all-too-familiar metal box has become the building equivalent of fast food - a convenient short cut, but often divorced from contact with the place, its climate and any social or cultural connections. Without denying the growth of a global market for building products, these can, like any materials from an earlier tradition, be used with a sensitivity to the site and its context. The kind of information contained in this Guide is a valuable ingredient in that design process.

I have become increasingly concerned about the tendency for schools of architecture to separate the subject of design from technical studies and working drawings. For me that is a contradiction in terms - how can the design of something ever be considered as separate from the making of it? Surely both activities are interdependent. When I was a student of architecture, graduation from fourth to fifth year was conditional on successfully completing what was called The Four Day Test. For four days we produced, in the monastic silence of the examination room, the design, acoustic diagrams and working drawings for an auditorium. The only opportunity to "cheat" was by poring over volumes of Mitchell on Building Construction in the evenings, to be memorised for the following day. In these more liberal times I am sure that practices such as the Four Day Test would be frowned on as not fashionable. In the spirit of being proudly unfashionable, I warm to this Guide and recommend it and other similar Technical Handbooks.

I was recently the Chairman of a jury which was charged with singling out buildings for their innovative use of metal products. I was particularly impressed by one project, a new prison, which was dominated by clusters of steeply pitched roofs. Reading through the accompanying report the rationale became clear. It was explained that the steep pitches of smooth metal would be difficult to access and impossible to occupy for demonstrations in the event of a breakout. Furthermore there were no handholds and no sharp tiles to dislodge and use as weapons or projectiles. By coincidence I had flown past this building earlier that week without knowing what it was. It had caught my attention in the distance for the formal clarity of its many pitches on the skyline and the foil of its long horizontal walls set in rolling countryside - like a modern version of a medieval walled town.

I hold no personal brief for flat roofs against pitched roofs. There are no easy generalisations - they are each that fifth and important elevation. Looking down from any high-rise building in a city I am struck by the way we squander this fifth elevation. All too often it becomes an engineers' battleground - the last left-over space where the detritus of air conditioning finally takes root. Consider the lost opportunities to recreate those valuable site footprints in the sky as gardens for people. Or more prosaically, consider the scope for roofs which are perforated for natural light - to discover its dimension of poetry as well as its potential for saving energy.

With new and discreet ways of environmentally servicing buildings, the roof can revert to letting in the sun and keeping out the rain. When I was a student in the United States, I was told of a conversation between two businessmen who found that they both had buildings by the same very famous architect. One told the other that his roof leaked so badly that he had to move a bucket around the floor to contain the water. "That's nothing", the other replied, "you only have a one-bucket building - I have a two-bucket building".

In the cause of good building practice and the elimination of buckets I am pleased to recommend this work by Arup Research and Development.

Sir Norman Foster

Rooflight, Stansted Airport Terminal

Roof terrace to Willis Faber Dumas, Ipswich

Introduction 1

Using the Guide

Scope of the Guide

This Guide deals with the design of flat roofs, where 'flat roof' means **continuously-supported** flat roofs up to 10° pitch.

Target audience

It is aimed principally at **designer/specifiers**, and at site-based agents of the Employer (such as Clerks of Works), working on the design of new buildings or on refurbishment, replacement or repairs of existing flat roofs.

It is also intended to help **building owners** and those tenants with responsibilities for the condition of the building they occupy, in particular in clarifying the services they require or the instructions they might wish to give.

Limitations

The purpose is to provide guidance based on existing good practice, from which designers, clients and others may select according to circumstances. It is not intended to define the responsibilities of any parties – or to relieve them – in a given contract.

The guidance provided is for roofs in UK climatic conditions.

Nature of the Guide

The Guide is divided into Chapters; the Chapters are then divided into Units. The groupings of Chapters cover broad approaches; Units cover very specific tasks and topics.

The Guide has a number of key qualities, which together give it a distinct approach.

Authority

This Guide has drawn on a wide range of expertise:

- It was written and edited by designers and other technologists experienced in advising designers, contractors and specialist suppliers.
- It has involved major contributions by the **roofing industry** at large, notably major suppliers.
- Both text and illustration are based on a wide range of experience of good practice in design, manufacture, assembly and installation.
- The development of the Guide was overseen by a panel of technical experts from clients, universities, industry and designers.

Comprehensiveness

The Guide covers a full range of issues of new build and work to existing buildings:

- It shows how new build, replacement, refurbishment and repair works all require a design approach.
- It deals with the complete array of design requirements for a flat roof.

- It is comprehensive in its coverage of the principal roofing membrane materials.
- It acknowledges the **range** of people and organisations that may fill the role of 'the designer' for flat roofs - e.g. architects, surveyors, specialist sub-contractors, suppliers, etc.
- It is arranged to cater for designs by the principal designer, but also by others (e.g. nominated suppliers).

Reality of the design process

Whether experienced in flat roof design or not, most readers will use this Guide in their own way, turning to those points of entry they find most immediately useful.

The Guide therefore attempts to provide a flexible approach to fit in with the ways that designers work in practice, for example:

- It provides detailed guidance, but recognises that the designer must make the final **judgements** – based on the **specific** contract they are handling.
- It includes information important to the designer, presented to show what are the **critical** aspects.
- Information and issues are often presented as checklists, to save the reader having to scan extensively.
- Information is linked to **explanations**, to show how it relates to the **general principles** underlying the behaviour of flat roof assemblies.
- The Chapters follow a particular sequence, for convenience, but the reader can follow their own route through if preferred, using the comprehensive cross-referencing and visual index on every page.
- The main elements of design **selection** and **evaluation** are displayed to show a **recommended sequence** of decisions, but so that the designer can also use the information in their own preferred sequence.

Speed of use

The Guide includes many features for speed of use and ease of finding the right information, for example:

- Designers or other readers can refer to it selectively **at any stage of design or procurement**, and can quickly avoid information they do not require.
- The **complete cycle of designing, making and using the building** is displayed to locate the different components of the Guide and to show the reader how they can enter the cycle at any point.
- Many of its graphic features and layout are devised to achieve fast access, multiple prompts for cross-reference and easy ways for readers to pursue their own questions.
- Drawn details are annotated to draw the reader's attention quickly to the critical issues involved.

Chapter	1	2	3	4	5	6	7	8	9	10	11
Contents	Introduction	History	Regulatory Methods	Principles	Surveys	Constraints & Targets	Design Selection	Calculations	Detail Design Principles	Evaluation of Design	Built-up Roofing
Page	1	19	31	45	83	95	105	165	189	217	221

Project records

- A **Project Notebook** is provided, which includes blank pro formas (see also **Units 6.1** and **8.3**) to record critical information, decisions, etc. This is also part of an approach which may assist those involved with various forms of quality management procedures.

Indexing

The Guide does not provide a comprehensive subject index. Location of particular subjects is achieved in three ways:

- List of contents (**Unit 1.2**), which gives the titles, Unit reference number and page number for each Unit.
- Glossary of technical terms (**Unit 1.3**), where the most relevant Unit reference is usually given.
- Key subject index (**Unit 23.1**), which gives initial/principal location(s) of information on key subjects, a 'fast first search' index.

Basic components

The basic components of the Guide are Chapters and Units.

The Chapter

Chapters are based on the major distinct tasks faced by the designer or building owner. These are identified by the Chapter title. Each Chapter is then divided into Units.

The Unit

Units are designed as two-page spreads (occasionally multiples thereof), so that the reader can immediately see how much reading is involved. (They are described in greater detail overleaf.) They are arranged as concise blocks of information needed for the more detailed tasks involved in the main activity defined by the Chapter.

Structure of the Guide

The structure of the Guide is developed from the Units into Chapters and then into groupings of Chapters around even broader categories of information and guidance, as follows.

Background and principles

After a general review of flat roofs and roofing, and the regulatory framework within which they are made, the Guide explains the underlying principles of flat roof behaviour (**Chapter 4**). The information provided is essential to the designer, but many will already be familiar with it and will not always need to refresh their memory.

Design preliminaries

The next Chapters of the Guide provide the essential preliminaries to the design of a specific roof. This is achieved through a building survey (**Chapter 5**) and through definition of the design requirements – here termed 'constraints' and 'targets' – of the roof (**Chapter 6**).

Design selection

The 'core' of the Guide is the design selection, including, where appropriate, calculation checks (**Chapters 7, 8**). These Chapters separately consider each of the key design issues in the design.

At the front of the main design Chapter (**Chapter 7**) is a **design sequence flow diagram**, which shows the interactions of all aspects of the design and maintenance of flat roofs.

Detailed design (**Chapter 9**) is developed through analytical diagrams. These principles of detail are then developed for specific membrane materials:

- built-up roofing (**Chapter 11**)
- mastic asphalt (**Chapter 12**)
- polymeric single-ply (**Chapter 13**)
- copper sheet (**Chapter 14**)
- lead sheet (**Chapter 15**)
- other membranes (**Chapter 16**).

The next Chapter (**Chapter 17**) provides information for selecting thermal insulants.

Specification and contracts

Later parts of the Guide provide guidance to specifying and procurement:

- specifications (**Chapter 18**)
- contracts (**Chapter 19**)
- inspection (**Chapter 20**), which in this Guide is restricted to 'inspection of the works' and therefore is differentiated from 'supervision'
- maintenance (**Chapter 21**).

References

A comprehensive bibliography is provided at the end of the Guide (**Unit 22.1**), with a special bibliography on health and safety matters (**Unit 22.2**). These are complemented by including those same references, where appropriate, in each Unit. A technical glossary is also provided (**Unit 1.3**).

continued ▶

The typical Unit

The Unit includes special features, such as 'at a glance' summaries, and identifies the 'critical factors' for each subject covered. Cross-referencing within the Guide is achieved via **emboldened references** in the text, by guidance to further reading and by the visual index on every spread.

Figure 1.1.1 shows how the information is displayed in a typical Unit. A number of features can be noted:

A The **Unit reference number** is displayed in the top corner of each page and is repeated where a Unit extends to more than one spread. The first part of the number is the Chapter of which it is part; the second is its position in that Chapter.

B The **Unit title** is given at the top left-hand corner of the Unit and repeated there for further spreads.

C The guidance within each Unit is given at various levels of detail: first at the top of the page, the **strategic text**, which gives a headline summary of the principal information in that Unit. This shows what the reader needs to understand from that Unit. An initial scan of the strategic text for a Chapter, or group of related Units, can give the designer an overview of the likely implications of the main text before considering the issues in greater detail.

D The second level of information or guidance is the **main text** in each Unit, together with illustrations or tables. The main text is intended to provide information sufficient to design the majority of flat roofs.

Where a greater depth of information on a particular subject is required, either because of designer interest, or the particular nature of the roof, guidance is given to other sources (see below).

E Immediate **cross-references** are given in the text, either as publications (*italicised*) or to other Chapters or Units in the Guide (**in bold type**).

F Diagrams, drawings and photographs are used to **illustrate** the text and to provide graphic descriptions which may be faster summaries of crucial information. In certain detailed design Units, the diagrams are annotated to show the critical features to which the designer should give attention.

G The first 'further reading' block provides **references** to documents beyond this Guide. Sufficient information is provided here to know the nature of such documents and to find the full reference in the bibliography (**Unit 22.1**) or the special bibliography on health and safety (**Unit 22.2**).

H The second 'further reading' block gives **cross-references** to other related Units or Chapters.

I To enable quick recognition of the factors which may be **critical** for design, a 'critical factors' block is provided in each Unit – which must be addressed if the flat roof is to be properly designed and constructed. These are factors which, if ignored, may pose problems. Designers may also wish to use the 'further reading' and 'critical factors' blocks to record information and prompts of their own.

J The **end of the spread** is marked ■ (to indicate the end of the Unit) or with *continued* ▶ (to show that it continues overleaf).

K The sequence of Chapters – with numbers, titles and page reference – is shown at the bottom of each spread in graphical form, a **visual index**.

L The **highlighting** shows at which Chapter the reader has the Guide open. This should help the reader to find related Chapters or Units, whether called up in the text or in the 'further reading' block or raised as questions by the reader themselves. ■

Further reading:

Chapter	1	2	3	4	5	6	7	8	9	10	11
Contents	Introduction	History	Regulatory Methods	Principles	Surveys	Constraints & Targets	Design Selection	Calculations	Detail Design Principles	Evaluation of Design	Built-up Roofing
Page	*1*	*19*	*31*	*45*	*83*	*95*	*105*	*165*	*189*	*217*	*221*

© BFRC / CIRIA: *Flat Roofing: Design and Good Practice. 1993*

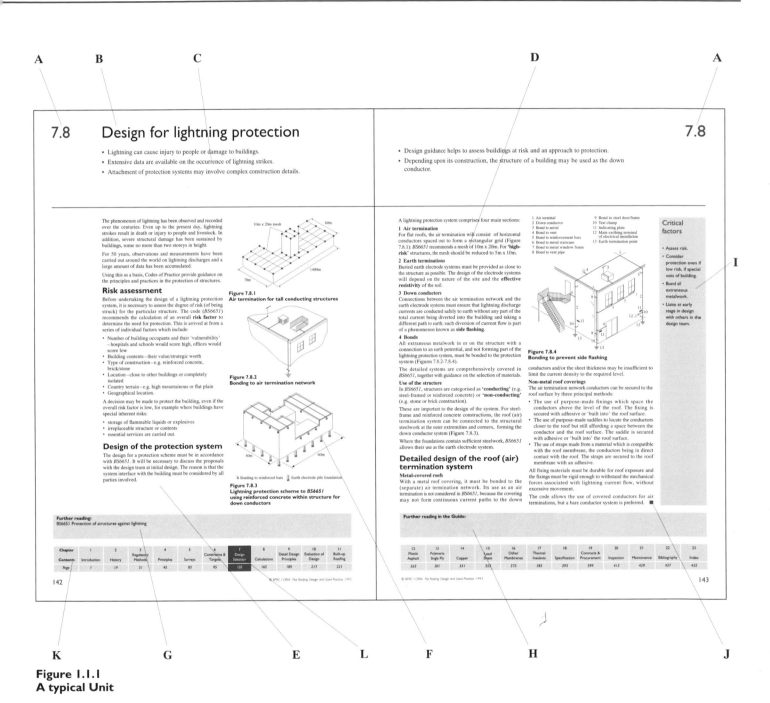

Figure 1.1.1
A typical Unit

Further reading in the Guide:											
12	13	14	15	16	17	18	19	20	21	22	23
Mastic Asphalt	Polymeric Single Ply	Copper	Lead Sheet	Other Membranes	Thermal Insulants	Specification	Contracts & Procurement	Inspection	Maintenance	Bibliography	Index
263	301	331	353	375	383	393	399	413	429	437	455

1.2   Contents

Chapter	1	2	3	4	5	6	7	8	9	10	11
Contents	Introduction	History	Regulatory Methods	Principles	Surveys	Constraints & Targets	Design Selection	Calculations	Detail Design Principles	Evaluation of Design	Built-up Roofing
Page	1	19	31	45	83	95	105	165	189	217	221

6

© BFRC / CIRIA: Flat Roofing: Design and Good Practice. 1993

1.3 Glossary

Throughout this Guide, definitions given in *BS6100 (Glossary of building and civil engineering terms) Sub-Section 1.3.2: 1989 'Roofs and roofing'* apply, except for terms defined below.

A

Access roof: A roof subject to regular pedestrian or vehicular traffic. (**Unit 7.11**)

Agrément Certificate: An appraisal certificate issued by the British Board of Agrément for a new product or technique which has been found, after test, to be satisfactory for a particular purpose. (**Unit 4.13**)

Angle fillet: See Fillet.

Annealing: Controlled heating of work hardened metal to soften it by causing recrystallization. (**Unit 14.1**)

Apron: Vertical asphalt on a fascia or overhang. Piece of sheet metal, plastic, etc., used to provide a watertight edge at the base of an inclined roof.

Apron eaves piece: A section formed by bending and folding an edge of fully-supported metal roofing sheet.

Asphalt: A mixture of asphaltic bitumen and inert mineral matter. (**Unit 12.1**)

Asphaltic cement: Bitumen or a mixture of refined lake asphalt and/or asphaltite having adhesive qualities suitable for the manufacture of mastic asphalt. (**Unit 12.1**)

Asphaltite: A naturally-occurring substance, allied to bitumen, characterised by a high softening point. (**Unit 12.1**)

B

Ballast: Loading applied to roof to resist wind uplift. (**Unit 7.10**)

Batten: Thin narrow strip of timber generally used to support other materials.

Batten roll: Rectangular or shaped timber strip between panels of sheet metal. (**Unit 14.3**)

Bay: (**1**) That part of a roof area to which mastic asphalt is applied in one continuous operation. (**Unit 12.3**)
(**2**) A unit of sheet metal covering as laid between rolls or standing seams. (**Unit 14.1**)

BBA: British Board of Agrément. See Agrément certificate.

Bitumen: A very viscous liquid or solid, essentially of hydrocarbons and their derivatives. It is substantially non-volatile and softens when heated. It is obtained principally by refining processes from petroleum and is also found as a natural deposit or in association with mineral matter, as a component of naturally occurring asphalt. (**Unit 11.1**)

Bitumen bonding compound: Oxidised bitumen melted and applied hot. (**Unit 11.1**)

Bitumen felt: Combination of fabric core of various types, typically glass or polyester, impregnated and coated with bitumen. In the Guide the term 'Built-up roofing' is used to describe membranes constructed from these materials. (**Unit 11.1**)

Bitumen primer: Bitumen cut back with volatile solvent. (**Unit 12.3**)

Bossing: The process of shaping malleable metal, especially sheet lead. The shaping of a sheet of metal to fit a roof or other surface. (**Unit 15.1**)

Brazing: The jointing together of materials with a film of copper-zinc alloy (hard solder) between the red hot contact surfaces.

BREEAM: Building Research Establishment & Environmental Assessment Method. A system of environmental assessment for buildings. (**Unit 4.15**)

Buildability: The extent to which the design of a building, or parts of a building, facilitates ease of construction, subject to the overall requirements for the completed building. It often involves criteria of simplicity, standardisation and clear communication. In some cases, it is taken to involve designing with a particular production unit in mind, utilising its specific resources and skills.

Built-up roofing: Two or more layers of bitumen sheeting continuously bonded and used as a roof finish, mainly to flat roofs. (**Unit 11.1**)

Buried roof: A 'warm deck' or 'inverted warm deck' roof with a substantial overlay of additional material such as concrete or soil. (**Units 4.2** and **9.2**)

C

Cap sheet: A bituminous sheeting suitable for use as a top layer in built-up roofing without additional surface protection. (**Unit 11.1**)

CAWS: Common Arrangement of Works Sections for building works. (**Unit 3.5**)

CE mark: Products which bear the CE mark shall be presumed to meet the essential requirements of the Construction Products Directive and therefore entitled to free circulation within the European Community, unless there are reasonable grounds for suspecting that such products do not satisfy these requirements. (**Unit 3.1**)

CEN: European Committee for Standardization (Comittée Européen de Normalisation). (**Unit 3.1**)

CFC: Chlorofluorocarbon. Gas with high molecular weight and low thermal conductivity used as a blowing agent in the production of some thermal insulation materials. (**Unit 4.15**)

Cleat: Copper strips, cut to lengths to suit roll or seam, placed at intervals and securely fixed to the roof base, the ends being welted in with the edges of the sheets to hold the sheet in position. (**Unit 14.3**)

Cold deck roof: One in which the principal thermal insulation is below the roof deck. (**Unit 4.2**)

Construction Products Directive: EC directive on construction products. (**Unit 3.1**)

Continuously-supported: Supported over its entire area.

Copper foil: Material of 0.15mm or less in thickness, of any width: either flat or in a coil form. (**Unit 14.1**)

Copper sheet: Material of exact length, over 450mm wide, more than 0.15mm, but less than 1mm thick. (**Unit 14.1**)

Copper strip: Material more than 0.15mm, but less than 1mm thick of any length. (**Unit 14.1**)

Core roll: Shaped section, usually of wood, around which sheet roofing is dressed. (**Unit 15.3**)

Corner block: A short triangular wooden fillet, tapered in its length, fixed against abutments, where sheets terminate at drips on roofs, walls and gutters.

COSHH: Control of Substances Hazardous to Health Regulations. These lay down essential requirements for the control of hazardous substances and an approach to the protection of people exposed to them.

Cover flashing: A flashing of organic material or metal built into the joint of a chimney or parapet wall and turned down over the top of an upstanding flashing or roof covering.

CPD: (1) Construction Products Directive. EC directive on construction products. (**Unit 3.1**)
(2) Continuing Professional Development.

Construction Products Regulations: UK legislation to enforce Construction Products Directive.

CPE: Chlorinated polyethylene. Polymeric material used for single-ply roofing. (**Unit 13.1**)

CPI: Co-ordinated Project Information. Methods of ensuring project specific information is arranged such that the various designer inputs are co-ordinated. (**Unit 3.5**)

Creep: The permanent distortion of a material which deforms under a low level sustained load including its self-weight. (**Unit 15.1**)

Critical layer: The air impermeable layer nearest to the building interior. (**Units 4.10 and 7.10**)

Cross-linking: The joining of long-chain molecules which is achieved by chemical process, including vulcanisation. (**Unit 4.13**)

Cross-welt: A seam between adjacent sheets of flexible metal roofing and at right angles to the length of the sheet. (**Unit 4.13**)

CSM/CSPE: Chlorosulphonated polyethylene. Polymeric material used for single-ply roofing. (**Unit 13.1**)

D

Day joint/daywork joint: The line between two areas of in situ-applied materials installed during different work periods, e.g. concrete, screed, mastic asphalt.

Dewpoint: The temperature at which the vapour pressure of a body of air equals its saturated vapour pressure. (**Units 4.7 and 8.3**)

Dog-ear: A box-like corner of three dimensions formed by folding a flat copper sheet without cutting. (**Unit 14.4**)

Double lock welt: Joint in metal sheet roofing, formed by folding the edge of one sheet over the edge of another, folding again and pressing them down flat. (**Unit 14.3**)

Drip: A step formed in a flat roof or gutter or roof edge across the direction of fall. (**Unit 14.3 and 15.3**)

Drop apron: Separate piece of copper fixed at the verges, eaves or gutters, to form a weathering and welted to the roof sheeting.

E

Eaves: The lower part of a roof which projects beyond the face of the wall.

Elastomer: A natural or synthetic material which may be distorted but will quickly return to its original shape when the distorting force is removed. This is the correct term for 'rubber'. 'Synthetic rubbers' are manufactured 'rubbers', as distinct from 'natural rubbers'. (**Unit 13.1**)

End lap (head lap): Joint formed at the end of a roll of sheet material.

EPDM: Ethylene propylene diene monomer. A 'synthetic rubber' used for single ply roofing. (**Unit 13.1**)

EVA: Ethylene vinyl acetate (a resin modifier). A polymeric material used to give flexibility to other polymers used for single-ply roofing. (**Unit 13.1**)

Expanded metal: A metal mesh made by cutting and pulling sheet metal into a mesh. (**Unit 12.3**)

Glossary *continued*

F

Fall: An inclination, given to a flat roof in order to convey rainwater to outlets. (**Unit 7.5**)

Fatigue: Failure of a material which has been repeatedly taken beyond a critical level of stress or strain.

Felt: See bitumen felt.

Fillet: (1) A strip of rigid material triangular in cross section used to ease the transition between horizontal and vertical work.
(2) For mastic asphalt, a triangular section formed in two coats with a minimum splayed face joining horizontal and vertical surfaces.

Flashing: A strip of thin impervious material used to weatherproof a joint between two materials (e.g. the joint between a roof covering and a vertical surface).

Flat roof: One with not more than 10° of slope to the horizontal.

Float: A flat faced wooden tool, with a handle, used for spreading and finishing the surface of mastic asphalt. (**Unit 12.3**)

Full bonding: The use of a layer of adhesive to adhere the underside of a flexible sheet to the underlying surface. (**Unit 11.3**)

G

Gauges: Wood or metal strips of required thickness, temporarily fixed as boundaries to bays or elsewhere, to assist the spreader in laying the asphalt. (**Unit 12.3**)

H

Heat welding: Welding two pieces of material using heat.

HCFC: Halogenated chlorofluorocarbon. Used in place of CFCs for some insulation materials because of their lower ozone depletion potential. (**Unit 17.2**)

Heavyweight: Construction of concrete with a roof slab of in situ or precast concrete. (**Unit 4.3**)

Hip: Inclined meeting line of two slopes in a roof forming a salient angle.

Hip roll: (1) An ornamental strip of metal, tile or wood for covering and finishing a hip.
(2) Round timber with a V cut in its underside to cover a hip or its flexible metal covering.

Hollow roll: A roll used in the direction of fall to join flexible metal-sheet roofing and in which the adjacent sheets are bent together to form a cylindrical roll without the use of a wood roll. (**Unit 15.4**)

Hot-air welding: A process of using hot air delivered by a machine to fuse two sheets of thermoplastic material together. (**Unit 13.3**)

Hot charge delivery: The supply of molten mastic asphalt to site in thermostatically-controlled agitated mobile mixers. (**Unit 12.3**)

Hybrid roof: One which at first assessment does not conform to the simplistic definitions of cold deck, warm deck or inverted roof. Often associated with refurbishment work. (**Units 4.1 and 4.2**)

I

Insulation: A material which, because of its properties, impedes the transmission of heat, fire, sound, electricity or vibration. In the context of this Guide it is a component included for the principle purpose of impeding such transmissions. (**Unit 17.1**)

Inverted warm deck roof: A warm deck roof in which the principal thermal insulation is placed above the waterproof covering. (**Unit 4.2**)

Isolating membrane: Material laid to separate materials which are incompatible for chemical or movement reasons. (**Unit12.3 and 14.3**)

L

Lake asphalt: A naturally occurring bitumen which contains 36% by weight finely divided clay. (**Unit 12.1**)

Layer (as in: first layer, intermediate layer and top layer): These terms are used to describe the various layers which go to make up built-up roofing. A top layer does not necessarily incorporate any self-weathering surface, it is intended for use where a separate protective finish – such as mineral chippings – is to be applied. (**Unit 11.3**)

Lightweight deck: Construction of purlins or beams with a roof deck of metal sheets, timber boarding or panels. (**Unit 4.3**)

Lining plate: A strip of copper of suitable width which is nailed to the eaves or verges of a roof and engaged with the lower edge of the drop apron to form a secure fixing. (**Unit 14.3**)

Liquid applied membrane: A roof membrane system where a thin membrane is formed *insitu* on the roof from liquid components. It refers to thin membranes less than 10mm to distinguish it from mastic asphalt. (**Unit 16.3**)

Lock joint: A single or double welted joint. (**Unit 14.3**)

M

Maintainability: A concept concerned with characteristics of design, manufacture and installation which affect an item's ability to conform to specified requirements of use and of maintenance. **(Unit 7.12)**

Mastic asphalt: A type of asphalt composed of suitably graded mineral matter and asphaltic cement in such proportions as to form a coherent, voidless, impermeable mass, solid or semi-solid under normal temperature conditions, but sufficiently fluid when brought to a suitable temperature to be spread by means of a hand float, or by mechanical means. **(Unit 12.1)**

Mechanical mixer: A mobile container fitted with heating and power units to provide mechanical agitation used for the purpose of re-melting asphalt. **(Unit 12.3)**

Membrane: A complete waterproofing system.

Membrane-faced metal: Sheet metal with a polymeric material bonded to it. **(Unit 13.3)**

Metal lathing: Bitumen-coated galvanised or stainless steel expanded metal used for keying asphalt to vertical or sloping surfaces. **(Unit 12.3)**

Mineral surfaced felt: A bituminous roofing felt which incorporates a factory-applied protective coating of fine mineral granules (usually slate). **(Unit 11.1)**

Mixerman: The operative responsible for melting the asphalt blocks and ensuring that there is sufficient for the work that has to be carried out that day. **(Unit 12.3)**

Modified bitumen: Bitumen to which polymers have been added. **(Unit 12.1)**

Movement joint: Wide joint deliberately formed in a vertical or horizontal plane intended to allow structural, thermal, moisture and other movements, whether linear or shear.

N

NDT: Non-destructive testing. The examination of an item to examine flaws, determine properties or assess quality. It is undertaken in such a way that the intended use of the item is not impaired.

Non-access roofs: A roof to which access is limited to inspection, maintenance or repair purposes only. **(Unit 7.11)**

O

Oxidised bitumen: A bitumen whose rheological properties have been substantially changed by reaction with air at high temperature: also referred to as 'blown'. **(Unit 11.1)**

P

Partial bonding: Using less than a full bond with the objective of allowing vapour diffusion beneath the waterproof covering and/or a certain amount of differential movement between the substrate and the covering. **(Unit 11.3)**

Patina: The thin stable insoluble film which forms on metal such as copper on exposure to air. **(Unit 14.1)**

PIB: Polyisobutylene. A 'synthetic rubber' used for single-ply roofing. **(Unit 13.1)**

Pitch: Dark coloured bituminous or resinous substance consisting of a fusible, viscous to solid, distillation residue of tars, especially coal tar. **(Unit 2.2)**

Plastic: Chemically-produced synthetic substance which may be moulded and shaped by heat or pressure or both.

Plasticiser: A chemical substance added to a plastic particularly PVC to increase its flexibility. **(Unit 13.1)**

Polymer: A material whose molecules are long chains formed from the combination of small molecules or 'monomers'.

Polymer-modified asphalt: An asphalt given enhanced properties by the use of polymer-modified bitumen during manufacture. **(Unit 11.1)**

Pour and roll: The term used describe the traditional method of attaching bituminous sheets to a substrate, that is pouring out hot bonding bitumen into which the roofing sheet is unrolled. **(Unit 11.3)**

PVC: Polyvinyl chloride. A plastic produced by the polymerisation of vinyl chloride and used for single-ply roofing. **(Unit 13.1)**

Q

QA: Quality Assurance. Systematic organisation to achieve the required standard consistently. (**Unit 3.3**)

QC: Quality Control. The checking which confirms that the required standard has been achieved. (**Unit 3.3**)

Quality Management: That aspect of the overall management function that determines and implements the quality policy. (**Unit 3.3**)

R

Refined copper: A metal with copper content not less than 97.5% and not more than 99.58% provided that the mass of all the other elements does not exceed the limits given in Table 1 of *BS6931: 1988*. (**Unit 14.1**)

Relative humidity: (RH). The ratio between the actual water vapour pressure of a sample of air at a particular temperature and the maximum vapour pressure the sample could contain at the same temperature, expressed as a percentage. (**Units 4.7** and **8.3**)

Rheology: Study of the deformation and flow characteristics of materials, particularly fluids.

Ridge: Intersection at the top of two slopes in a roof forming an apex.

Roll (common): A shaped core against the sides of which the copper bays are dressed or are turned up. (**Unit 14.3**)

Roll (ridge): A shaped core at ridge and hip against which the copper is dressed or turned up. (**Unit 14.3**)

Rolled copper: Rolled copper for roofing purposes must have a chemical composition that complies with that given in Table 8 of *BS2870: 1980 (BS6931)*. (**Unit 14.1**)

Roof deck: Parts of a flat roof which forms a principle support for the roof covering.

Rubber (natural): Natural rubber consists of the hydrocarbon ($C_{10}H_{16}$) 'Caoutchouc' with small amounts of proteins and resins. It occurs in certain tropical trees as latex which exudes when the bark is cut. (**Unit 13.1**)

Rubber (synthetic): Compound from the polymerisation of certain unsaturated hydrocarbons or mixtures of these monomers and other substances such as styrene or acrylonitrile which can be polymerised. (**Unit 13.1**)

S

Saddled end: The completion of a batten roll covering or a standing seam against an abutment. (**Unit 14.3**)

Seam: A joint between two sheets of flexible-metal roofing. Formed by bending up both sheets and doubling them over together. (**Unit 14.3** and **15.3**)

Separating membrane: Material laid to prevent bonding between subsequent layer and underlying surface.

Sheet (metal) A flat wrought product of exact length and of rectangular cross section, with uniform thickness over 0.15 mm up to and including 1.0 mm, supplied in straight lengths (i.e. flat) and usually with sheared or sawn edges. The thickness does not exceed one-tenth of the width.

Sheet (organic material): Individual pieces of material taken off a roll.

Side lap: Joint formed at the side of a roll of roofing material. (**Unit 11.3** and **13.3**)

Single lock welt: Joint in metal sheeting formed by folding the edge of one sheet over the edge of another. (**Unit 14.3**)

Single ply: A form of waterproofing laid in one layer. (**Unit 13.1**)

Solar reflective treatment: A light coloured finish applied to a flat roof covering (bitumen felt or asphalt) which reflects some of the solar radiation, thus reducing the temperature of the covering. (**Units 11.3** and **12.3**)

Solvent welding: Welding two pieces of material using a solvent, particularly used in some single ply roofing systems. (**Unit 13.3**)

Spreader: An operative (craftsman) skilled in the laying and finish of mastic asphalt. (**Unit 12.3**)

Spring: The bending of the substructure under load stress and recovery after removal. (**Unit 4.3**)

Standing seam: Joint in metal sheet roofing in which the adjoining edges are turned up perpendicular to the surface, welted together and left upstanding. (**Unit 15.3**)

Strain: The proportional change in a material's dimension due to an applied stress.

Stress: The internal force acting in a member resisting an externally applied force.

Stop end: The completion of a batten roll covering or standing seam at a drip or eaves. (**Units 14.3** and **15.3**)

Strip (metal): A product of rectangular cross section with a uniform thickness over 0.15mm, usually supplied in coils but may be flat or folded. The edges are usually slit to size but the length is not exact. The thickness does not exceed one-tenth of the width.

Substrate: Surface upon which the waterproof covering is laid.

T

Temper annealing: A process of carefully controlled heating to reduce hardness or tensile strength to within a specified range other than fully soft. (**Unit 14.1**)

Thermal capacity: That property of a material or element of structure which expresses both its ability to store heat and the rate at which the temperature of the material or construction will alter with changes in temperature of the adjacent air. (**Unit 4.6**)

Thermal conductivity: The quantity of heat in steady state conditions which is transmitted in unit time through unit area of unit thickness for unit temperature difference. (**Unit 4.5**)

Thermo-plastic: A material that softens when heated and hardens when cooled; the process is repeatable.

Thermo-set: A material which hardens or 'sets' irreversibly when heated.

Torch-on: A means of adhering membranes for built-up roofing which involves activating a factory applied layer of bitumen or modified bitumen using a gas torch. (**Unit 11.1**)

U

Undercloak: That part of the lower sheet of flexible metal roofing which is overlapped by the upper sheet at a drip, roll, seam or welt. (**Units 14.3, 15.3**)

Underlay: A layer of material used to isolate the roof covering from the substructure. Also a layer of roofing sheet intended to be covered by another layer in built-up roofing.

V

Vapour control layer (VCL): A layer of material intended to restrict the diffusion of moisture vapour through a construction.
The commonly used terms 'vapour barrier' and 'vapour check' are imprecise and should be avoided: rather, the designer should determine the degree of resistance required and then select a vapour control layer with a level of performance to meet that requirement. (**Unit 7.7**)

Verge: Sloping edge of a roof.

VET: Polyvinylchloride, made flexible by blending with ethylene vinyl acetate. (**Unit 13.1**)

Vulcanising: A process applied to a thermoplastic material which renders it a non-thermoplastic, increases its elasticity and reduces its deformation under load. It involves the application of heat and/or a chemical agent such as sulphur.

W

Waterproof covering: A layer of material which provides a complete waterproofing system in a flat roof (see also membrane).

Weatherproof covering: Discontinuous covering which prevents the ingress of water.

Welding: The joining together of two pieces of material by making their surfaces fluid which, when combined with pressure, fuses the two pieces.

Welting: Joining metal sheets at their edges by means of folding. Welting may be by single or double folds, such joints being termed single or double welts respectively. (**Units 15.3, 16.1** and **16.2**)

Wood-cored roll (Roll): A wooden membrane of more or less curved cross-section, used as an aid to the joint of adjacent sheets of flexible-metal roofing on their longer edges. (**Units 14.3, 15.3, 16.2** and **16.3**)

Work hardening: An increase in hardness caused by the mechanical plastic deformation of a metal or alloy. (**Unit 14.1**) ■

12 Mastic Asphalt	13 Polymeric Single Ply	14 Copper	15 Lead Sheet	16 Other Membranes	17 Thermal Insulants	18 Specification	19 Contracts & Procurement	20 Inspection	21 Maintenance	22 Bibliography	23 Index
263	301	331	353	375	383	393	399	413	429	437	455

1.4 Acknowledgements

The concept of this project was initiated by the British Flat Roofing Council in 1988. In September 1989, the Construction Industry Research and Information Association and BFRC agreed that collaboration would significantly enhance the Guide's utility and standing. The project was therefore run as a partnership between CIRIA and BFRC, under the direction of an Executive Management Group.

The project was managed and coordinated by Mrs Ann Alderson, Consultant Research Manager at CIRIA. The technical direction of the work was led by Mrs Ann Alderson and Mr Jim Hooker, Technical Officer at BFRC, with advice and guidance from Steering Groups. CIRIA and BFRC express their appreciation and thanks to all members of these Groups and Sub-groups.

EXECUTIVE MANAGEMENT COMMITTEE

Chairman
Mr Terry Cook
Permanite Ltd,
Chairman of BFRC 1989-91

Mrs Ann Alderson
Consultant Research Manager, CIRIA

Dr Peter Bransby
Director General, CIRIA

Mr Richard Grierson
RMJM Ltd

Mr John Moore
D Anderson & Son Ltd,
Chairman of BFRC 1991-1993

Mr Paul Newman
Director, BFRC

Mr Alan Willis
Director of Property Services,
Essex County Council

The work was largely funded by **BFRC** and the **Department of the Environment**, with additional contributions from:

SmithKline Beecham

Dumfries & Galloway Regional Council

West Sussex County Council

CIRIA and **BFRC** are grateful to them for their financial support.

STEERING GROUP

Chairman
Mr John Gammans
formerly of Northamptonshire County Council

Mrs Ann Alderson
CIRIA

Dr William Allen
Bickerdike Allen Partners*

Mr Brian Barnes
formerly of Higgs & Hill Construction Holdings Ltd

Mr John Beech
Building Research Establishment

Mr Ian Brown
Coolag Purlboard Ltd*

Professor Peter Clark
formerly of Trent Polytechnic

Professor Tim Clark
formerly of Institute of Advanced Architectural Studies, University of York

Mr Lawrence Cooper
Norfolk County Council

Mr Jim Hooker
BFRC

Mr John Jobson
J Sainsbury plc

Mr David Kimmins
CLASP Development Group

Mr Francis March
Briggs Amasco Ltd

Mr Richard Martin
Scott Brownrigg & Turner Advisory Services

Professor Charles Normand
London School of Hygiene & Tropical Medicine

Mr George Sinden
Marley Waterproofing Ltd

Dr Nick Wilson**
Rockwool Ltd

Mr Peter Woodhead
Department of the Environment

* for first part of project only
** replaced **Mr Ian Brown**

Other participants in **Steering sub-Groups:**

Mr John Blowers
Mastic Asphalt Technical Advisory Committee
Mr Roger Bonafont
Tarmac Industrial Products
Mr Brian Haymes
Permanite Asphalt Ltd
Mr Peter Maude
Chestertons Chartered Surveyors
Mr Denis Mills
Denis Mills Associates
Mr Richard Murdoch
Lead Sheet Association
Mr Len Prince
Colas Building Products Ltd
Mr Peter Rankin
HT (UK) Ltd
Mr Keith Rollinson/Mr Keith Roberts
Rollinson Glanville Consultants
Mr John Smith
Copper Development Association
Dr Alan Strong
Single Ply Roofing Association
Mr Alan Woollaston
Copper Development Association
Mr Richard Woolley
Derbyshire County Council

Contributors in-kind

Association of British Roofing Felt Manufacturers
Mr Roger Bonafont
Tarmac Industrial Products Ltd
Mr Len Prince
Colas Building Products Ltd
Mr Roy Milne
D. Anderson & Son Ltd

Mastic Asphalt Technical Advisory Centre
Mr John Blowers
Technical Director

Single Ply Roofing Association
Dr Alan Strong
Secretary
Mr Peter Rankin
HT (UK) Ltd

Copper Development Association
Mr Denis Mills
Denis Mills Associates
Mr Anthony Clark
Broderick Structures Ltd

Lead Sheet Association
Mr Richard Murdoch

Production of the Guide

The work to produce the present publication was undertaken by **Arup Research & Development.** Initial work on an earlier version of a guide was carried out by John Potter Associates.

Arup Research & Development were authors of the Guide with the exception of the membrane material specific chapters (Chapters 11-15). The information for Chapters 11-15, and other membrane material specific entries, were based on material provided by the industry as 'contributions in kind', with **Arup Research & Development** acting as coordinating editors. **CIRIA** and **BFRC** are most grateful to these in-kind contributors, and in particular for the cooperation of the **Copper Development Association** and the **Lead Sheet Association** who were not members of **BFRC.** The contributors in-kind are listed on the preceding page.

The overall graphic design, structure of the Guide, page design, setting and film layout was conceived, developed and produced by **Arup Research & Development** and the **Graphics Group** of **Ove Arup and Partners**; drawings and general illustrations were produced by the **Graphics Group.** The illustrations of the membrane details in Chapters 9 - 15 were co-ordinated, edited, and drawn by **Arup Research & Development** and the **Graphics Group** of **Ove Arup and Partners** from details supplied by the industry.

The Guide was written and produced by a team under the general direction of **Turlogh O'Brien.** The project supervisors, editors and principal authors were **Robert Cather** and **Steven Groák.** Many other members of **Arup Research & Development** and of the **Ove Arup Partnership** contributed, notably **David J. Brown, Paul Dickenson, Philip King, Gordon Puzey, Peter Ross, Kendrick White** and the **Library staff.** The Graphics Group work was coordinated by **Trevor Slydel** with key contributions from **Zelda Kifford** and **Peter Warren.**

The production and printing of the publication was managed by **Philippa Wright**, Publications Manager at **CIRIA.**

Copyright Acknowledgements

All text and illustrations in this Guide are copyright © BFRC and CIRIA, except where copyright permission has kindly been given, as follows.

Photographs
In some instances, these have been cropped from the original image.

Foreword: Roof of Willis Faber Dumas (Sir Norman Foster & Partners and © Tim Street-Porter); two sketches of Gomera Island (sketches by Birkin Haward; © Sir Norman Foster and Partners); Reliance Controls (photographer: Norman Foster; © Sir Norman Foster and Partners); Stansted Airport Terminal (Sir Norman Foster and Partners; © Dennis Gilbert).
Facing Chapter 1: Trafalgar Square, London (© Aerofilms Ltd).
Facing Chapter 2: Falling Water, USA (© Steven Groák).

Chapter 2:
Unit 2.1: Farnsworth House, USA (© David Dunster); Villa Savoie, Poissy, France - general view (Architectural Association, London, and © Bill Chaitkin); Villa Savoie, Poissy, France - courtyard view (© David Dunster); Staatsgalerie, Stuttgart, Germany (© Ove Arup Partnership); Broadgate Centre, London, UK (Ove Arup Partnership, and © Peter Cook); Gatehouse, Frankfurt-am-Main, Germany (Architectural Association, London, and © Andrew Higgott).
Unit 2.2: Franklin Court, Philadelphia, USA (© Steven Groák); Schroeder House, Utrecht, Holland (Architectural Association, London, and © Andrew Higgott); Oakland Museum, USA (Architectural Association, London, and © Roger Schluntz); Renault Centre, Swindon, UK (© Ove Arup Partnership).
Unit 2.3: Lloyd's, London, UK (Ove Arup Partnership, and © Roger Ridshill Smith); Willis Faber Dumas, Ipswich, UK (© John Donat Photography); Collezione Shop, Tokyo, Japan (Architectural Association, London, and © Bruno Murawiec).
Facing Chapter 3: Gateway 1, Basingstoke, UK (© Ove Arup Partnership).
Facing Chapter 4: IBM, Havant, UK (© Ove Arup Partnership).

Chapter 4:
Unit 4.3: two exoskeletal structures: Patscenter, Princeton, USA (Ove Arup Partnership, and © O. Baitz); Fleetguard Factory, Quimper, France (© Ove Arup Partnership); Chapel, Ronchamp, France (Architectural Association, London, and © R. Vickery).
Facing Chapter 5: Fort Regent Leisure Centre, Jersey (© ICB Ltd).

Chapter 5:
Unit 5.3: Aerial view of New York City, USA (© Steven Groák); Pyramid entrance to underground galleries, Louvre, Paris, France (© Steven Groák);
Unit 5.4: University of Sussex, Falmer, UK (© Steven Groák).
Facing Chapter 6: IBM, Cosham, UK (© Ove Arup Partnership).
Facing Chapter 7: University Centre, Cambridge, UK (© Construction PR Services).

Chapter 7:
Unit 7.1: University of East Anglia, Norwich, UK (© Ove Arup Partnership); Habitat, Montreal, Canada (Architectural Association, London, and © Rita de Pierro); Wolstonbury Court, UK (© Marley Waterproofing); Lloyd's, London, UK (© Ove Arup Partnership); La Grande Arche, Paris, France (© Steven Groák).
Unit 7.3: Lead membrane roof, UK (© Lead Sheet Association).
Unit 7.5: Roof ponding, USA (© Steven Groák).
Unit 7.6: Housing above refuse disposal unit, London, UK (© Ove Arup Partnership); spreading hot asphalt, UK (© Ove Arup Partnership); insulating cut to falls, UK (© Vencel Resil Ltd).
Unit 7.7: Hopkins House, London, UK (© Steven Groák).

Unit 7.10: Unité d'Habitation, Marseilles, France (© Steven Groák); National Theatre, London, UK (© Steven Groák); psp roof at Heathrow Airport, UK (© Robseal).

Unit 7.11: Bon Accord, Aberdeen, UK (© Briggs Amasco Ltd).

Unit 7.12: view from roof of Arab World Institute, Paris, France (© Steven Groák); Niemeyer House, Rio de Janiero, Brazil (Architectural Association, London, and © Peter Cook).

Facing Chapter 8: National Exhibition Centre, Birmingham, UK (© Ove Arup Partnership).

Unit 8.1: Town Hall, Seinäjoki, Finland (© Steven Groák)

Facing Chapter 9: Store, Sandhurst, UK (© Chorley and Handford).

Facing Chapter 10: Staatsgalerie, Stuttgart, Germany (© Ove Arup Partnership).

Facing Chapter 11: Fleetguard factory, Quimper, France (© Ove Arup Partnership).

Chapter 11:
Unit 11.1: psp roofs at Elephant and Castle, London, UK (© Robseal);

Unit 11.2: Lloyds, Bristol, UK (© Ove Arup Partnership); Basildon House, UK (© Warehouse Advertising and Publicity); Freeman's distribution centre, UK (© Airviews (M/c) Ltd).

Unit 11.3: Supermarket, UK (© Robseal Roofing); flexible walkway tiles, UK (© Tarmac Roofing Systems); loose-laid 3G felt, UK (© Axter Ltd); applying and spreading hot bitumen, UK (© Tarmac Roofing Systems); three views of fixing trim, UK (© Ove Arup Partnership); spreading bitumen to bond vapour control layer (© Tarmac Roofing Systems).

Facing Chapter 12: Royal College of Physicians, London, UK (© Ove Arup Partnership).

Chapter 12:
Unit 12.1: Pearl Assurance, Peterborough, UK (© Index).

Unit 12.2: Armada Centre, Plymouth, UK (© Briggs Amasco).

Unit 12.3: sequence of six views of mastic asphalt being laid (© Ove Arup Partnership).

Unit 12.4: International Conference Centre, Birmingham, UK (© R M Douglas); Dorchester Hotel, London, UK (© Cambridge Asphalt).

Facing Chapter 13: Stansted Airport, UK (© Ove Arup Partnership).

Chapter 13:
Unit 13.1: Elephant and Castle, London, UK (© Robseal).

Unit 13.3: hot air welding, UK (© Construction PR Services); solvent welding, UK (© Construction PR Services); laying the membrane, UK (© Goodyear); machine welding, UK (© Goodyear); upstand corner trim (© Mike Blissett); series of four views of fixing (© Ove Arup Partnership).

Facing Chapter 14: Royal Festival Hall, London, UK (Ove Arup Partnership and © Martin Charles).

Chapter 14:
Unit 14.3: Nani Nani offices, Tokyo, Japan (Architectural Association, London, and © Andrew Carton).

Facing Chapter 15: Offices, Guildford, UK (© Lead Sheet Association).

Chapter 15:
Unit 15.2: laying recast lead, UK (© Bartlett School, University College London).

Unit 15.3: four views of lead sheet work, UK (© Ove Arup Partnership).

Facing Chapter 16: Office, Perth, Australia (© Ove Arup Partnership).

Facing Chapter 17: Alban Gate, London, UK (© Ove Arup Partnership).

Chapter 17:
Unit 17.2: Bofill Office, Barcelona, Spain (Architectural Association, London, and © D. Tinero).

Facing Chapter 18: Bracken House, London, UK (© Ove Arup Partnership).

Facing Chapter 19: Hong Kong Shanghai Bank, Hong Kong (Ove Arup Partnership and © Ian Lambot).

Chapter 19:
Unit 19.2: St John's College, Oxford, UK (© Steven Groák).

Unit 19.3: Centre Pompidou, Paris France (© Ove Arup Partnership); Salzmann House, USA (© Steven Groák).

Facing Chapter 20: RMC Group headquarters, UK (© Martin Charles).

Facing Chapter 21: Inmos, Newport (© Ove Arup Partnership).

Unit 21.2: House, Ticino, Switzerland (© Steven Groák);

Facing Chapter 22: TWA Building, JFK Airport, USA (Architectural Association, London, and © Roy Summers).

Facing Chapter 23: Penguin Pool, London, UK (Architectural Association, London, and © Valerie Bennett).

Text and other illustrations
Foreword: Sir Norman Foster.

Unit 4.14: Figure 4.14.1 (© Ove Arup Partnership).

Unit 7.8: Figures 7.8.1-4 are redrawn with kind permission, based upon *Furse Consultants' Handbook 1992*, © W J Furse & Co.

Unit 7.11: Table 7.11.1 is an extract from *Advice Note BD 21/84* published by the Department of Transport, 1990 (© Crown Copyright).

Unit 8.1: Figure 8.1.5 is redrawn, based upon an earlier version, © Ove Arup Partnership.

Unit 8.4: Tables 8.4.3-6 are based upon *Flat roofing: a guide to good practice*, 1983, © Tarmac Ltd.

Unit 10.1: Evaluation Checklist is © Ove Arup Partnership
Chapters 14 and 15: The drawings in chapters 14 and 15 are derived from drawings, © the Copper Development Association and the Lead Sheet Association respectively.

British Standards:
The following extracts from British Standards are © Crown Copyright and are reproduced with kind permission of the British Standards Institution (BSI). Complete copies can be obtained by post from BSI Sales, Linford Wood, Milton Keynes MK14 6LE.

Unit 4.4: Figures 4.4.1 and 4.4.2 are redrawn, based upon *BS6367*.

Unit 4.10: Figure 4.10.1 is redrawn, based upon *BSCP3*.

Unit 8.1: Figures 8.1.1-2 are redrawn, based upon *BS6367*.

Unit 8.3: Figure 8.3.1 is from *BS5250* (BSI encourage the use of this chart and therefore permit its reproduction freely); Table 8.3.1 is an extract from *BS6229*; Table 8.3.3 contains extracts from *BS5250*.

Unit 8.4: Figure 8.4.1 is redrawn, based upon *BSCP3*; Tables 8.4.1-2 are based upon *BSCP3: Chapter V*.

HMSO Publications:
The following extracts are © Crown Copyright and are reproduced with the kind permission of the Controller of Her Majesty's Stationery Office:

Unit 3.2: *Technical Standards for Compliance with Building Standard (Scotland) Regulations*: Extract from Item 5 of Introduction to Part G: preparation of sites and resistance to moisture (Page 2G).

Unit 7.6: *The Building Regulations*: Extract from Part F2; Approved Document F to *The Building Regulations*: Extract from "Performance".

Unit 7.9: Approved Document B to *The Building Regulations*: Table 7.9.1 is based upon Paragraph 2.28; Tables 7.9.2-5 are extracts from Tables 17, 18 and A2, and part of Table A5. These draw upon Amendment 1992 to the Approved Documents and to Part B, 1992 edition, Second impression (with amendments) 1992 ■

History 2

2.1 General history

- The purposes and functions of buildings in society are extraordinarily complex. Buildings provide symbolic, practical, financial, aesthetic benefits and – occasionally – problems.
- One major requirement of many buildings in many societies is to provide shelter and security. The dominant element which achieves this function is usually the roof.

Historical development

The purposes and functions of buildings in society are extraordinarily complex. Buildings provide symbolic, practical, financial, aesthetic benefits and – occasionally – problems. One major requirement of many buildings in many societies is to provide shelter and security. The dominant element which achieves this function is usually the roof. The roof is the part of the building most exposed to the weather – wind, rain, snow, solar radiation, etc. The roof form – whether flat and/or of some other geometry – will often provide much of the character of a building.

The evolution of roof forms is intricately involved with the development of structural methods for spanning space – post-and-beam, arches, domes, vaults, trusses, slabs, warped membranes, etc. The development of a wide variety of flat roofing systems for many different types of building has been driven in part by the evolution, in the 19th century, of metal and concrete framing systems capable of spanning large distances without the 'space hungry' geometry of arches, domes, etc.

Today we have a significantly improved understanding of roofing as a total system.

The evolution of flat roof forms and technology both illustrate the complexity of technical developments, partly fuelled by the demands of designers, constructors and building users and partly by new ideas and products developed by manufacturers, etc. The reasons why flat roof technologies were introduced are often lost in history. However, many benefits were discovered in different countries through time. The principal reasons for using flat roofing technology today can be summarised:

- Minimises the enclosed volume.
- Maximises the planning envelope in volume terms.
- Frees the plan to allow variations in shape.
- Simplifies the structure.
- Provides access to the roof as a 'floor' for people, equipment, landscaping.
- Optimises the dimensions of the 'roof zone'.
- In the case of continuous membranes, allows the building to be 'sealed' against air, dust and noise infiltration (but with concomitant condensation problems).
- Allows economies of scale for large plan buildings, arising from large sheet materials, repetition and/or prefabricated details, etc.

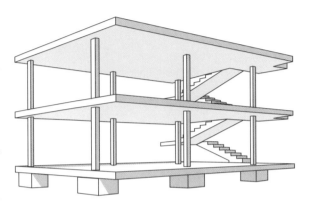

Le Corbusier - idealised structure and plan

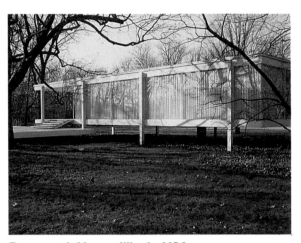

Farnsworth House, Illinois, USA

In some parts of the world, structural considerations for roofing have taken on a special emphasis because of local factors, such as earthquakes, typhoons, and other large dynamic loadings. A critical issue therefore has always been the relationship between the structural form, the structural material, and the means of dealing with the exclusion of the weather – in whatever part of the world the building is to be found. A related issue has been to deal satisfactorily with the need for the roof to be penetrated by chimneys, services, access ways, etc.

Further reading:
CLIFTON-TAYLOR, A. The pattern of English building • DAVEY, N. A history of building materials • GUEDES, P. (ed) The Macmillan encyclopedia of architecture and technological change

• The roof is the part of the building most exposed to the weather – wind, rain, snow, solar radiation, etc.

In the UK, these issues have to be seen in the context of the characteristics of the climate – the result of various systems intersecting (the warm-wet Atlantic system dominated by the Gulf Stream, cold weather from the north, and the hot/cold-dry system from continental Europe). Flat roofs in the UK have evolved to deal with the requirements of British society. By contrast, in certain societies with hot dry climates, the traditional flat roof has been used as an extra 'room', secure from the ground and enjoying greater air movement. The profusion of roof forms, materials, appearances and uses has been astonishing; flat roofing systems have provided important examples within this profusion.

The idea of the roof as the 'fifth façade', in the phrase of the Swiss-French architect Le Corbusier, has had an important influence on 20th century European and North American built forms, and their export around the world. The German-American architect, Mies van der Rohe, has also provided important examples of flat-roofed buildings, in housing and commerce.

Changing technology

The aftermath of World War 2 involved vast social, technical and economic changes. The building and building materials industries were not excluded from this upheaval, which involved significant restructuring of those industries, new ideas about building performance, changes in patterns of building use, and large-scale experiments in building products and systems. The building experiences of the 1950s and 1960s were a mixture of success and disappointment, often on a large scale because of the volume and pace of new building.

With the 1973 change in oil prices, and the responses in terms of seeking better thermal performance (especially from roofs), a number of the problems appeared to magnify (e.g. membrane splits) – or were certainly given closer attention. This was partly because the significant increase in thermal insulation of roofing systems changed the pattern of heat energy transfer between different 'heat sinks' in the total system and hence the differential hygrothermal behaviours.

Among the problems were widespread difficulties with certain flat roofing systems. Some of these difficulties for a time seemed so intractable that, in the UK, some clients insisted that their architects not specify flat roofs at all.

Villa Savoie, Poissy, France

Villa Savoie, Poissy, France

The flat roofing industry was faced with a crisis. Major research and development programmes grew up and the industry played a full role in this work. Although some early responses had 'teething troubles' with practical details for new product combinations, significant new systems and products began to emerge as reliable options.

continued ▶

Further reading in the Guide:
4.4 Precipitation: rain and snow

- The roof form – whether flat and/or of some other geometry – will often provide much of the character of a building.
- The evolution of roof forms is intricately involved with the development of structural methods for spanning space – post-and-beam, arches, domes, vaults, trusses, slabs, warped membranes, etc.

Staatsgalerie, Stuttgart, Germany

Broadgate Centre, London, UK

Further reading:

• In recent decades, we have significantly improved our understanding of roofing as total system.

New understanding

The effect of the R+D was to establish an extensive body of data and understanding of how flat roofing systems behave, why they had performed satisfactorily in earlier years, why the problems had arisen, and what would be a sound basis for improving both the products and the systems. Much of this transformation has been accomplished, and can be summarised:

• People realised why and how flat roofs have to be analysed as **systems,** and that these systems are a combination of elements and materials with different physical and chemical properties.

• The general **thermal behaviour** of roofing had always been understood in terms of basic physics, but in steady-state or even static terms. What had not been understood quite so clearly was how complex roofing systems behaved in relation to **dynamic** and **cyclic flows** of heat energy and water vapour, especially in transient conditions, and how this related to the 'heat history' of the materials used.

• Research improved understanding of mechanisms of thermal movement of decks of differing materials, heat storage, stress concentrations of board elements, shrinkage as well as expansion, material compatibility, and so on.

• Manufacturers became much more knowledgeable about the relation between their products and their performance in roofing assemblies.

• Designers and suppliers learnt a great deal about how the various elements of the roof had to be fixed (or not).

• Much more systematic information was collected on performance and durability.

It will be plain that many of the main membrane materials available today for flat roofing systems have been used in construction for some time – sometimes hundreds of years. The major change in recent years has been the improved understanding on which to design and construct. Much of this understanding rests in the specialist manufacturers and their research groups.

■ **Gatehouse, Frankfurt-am-Main, Germany**

Further reading in the Guide:
4.5 Thermal transmission

12 Mastic Asphalt	13 Polymeric Single Ply	14 Copper	15 Lead Sheet	16 Other Membranes	17 Thermal Insulants	18 Specification	19 Contracts & Procurement	20 Inspection	21 Maintenance	22 Bibliography	23 Index
263	301	331	353	375	383	393	399	413	429	437	455

2.2 Membrane materials

- 'Bitumen' covers a great variety of materials used to waterproof buildings. It includes the natural form, found in association with mineral matter, known as 'asphaltic bitumen' or 'asphalt'. It is also refined from petroleum, and further treated, to provide modern bitumens.

Bitumens and asphalts

As with many other well-established roofing materials, bitumen was found in the early civilisations. In Mesopotamia, for example, bitumen seeps into valleys, where it mixes with wind-blown sandstone dust. It is also available there as rock asphalt in the mountains. For some 5000 years, it has been used in that region in masonry and in waterproofing baths and tanks. In ancient Egypt, it was used as one of the ingredients for mummification!

Bitumen should be distinguished from coal tar pitch, which is a product extracted from coal and which also has waterproofing properties.

The bitumen seepages may occur at the bottom of lakes or the sea bed, as in the Dead Sea, where the material rises to the surface and was collected in lumps. Davey reports that the Dead Sea was known to classical writers as 'Lacus Asphaltites' and the bitumen thus obtained as 'Bitumen Judaicum'. Indeed, one of the first recorded uses of asphalt-type materials for waterproofing is quoted in *The Bible,* Genesis 6:14. We learn from the King James' Version that, in constructing his Ark, Noah was urged to:

Pitch it within, and without with pitch.

The mixing of bitumen with sand and fine filler to form an asphalt was an important development, because, without them, the material would have insufficient stability and 'body' to become a stable, waterproof membrane, or joining mortar, or to be used in any construction work.

Bituminous mixtures were also used in ancient road building, although some 2000 years were to pass before this application was rediscovered.

In 1595, Sir Walter Raleigh came upon Lake Trinidad, in Trinidad, which was to supply lake asphalt. This comprised a naturally-occurring mixture of bitumen and finely divided mineral matter, subsequently refined. But a further 200 years elapsed before asphalt was utilised in commercial use, in conjunction with Scottish shale grease (no longer used today). Sir Walter reported in his 'History of the discovery of Guiana':

From thence I rowed to another part, called by the naturals 'Piche'. . . we made trial of it in trimming our ships to be most excellent good, and melts not with the Sun as the pitch of Norway, and therefore for ships trading the South parts very profitable.

Franklin Court (underground gallery) Philadelphia, USA

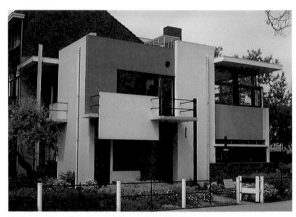

Schroeder House, Utrecht, Holland

The material became known as mastic asphalt, being an asphaltic substance laid hot without compaction. Its primary constituent was limestone rock naturally impregnated with bitumen, which occurred geologically throughout Europe. These consolidated calcareous deposits were known as 'natural rock asphalt'.

Further reading:
DAVEY, N. A history of building materials

Chapter	1	2	3	4	5	6	7	8	9	10	11
Contents	Introduction	History	Regulatory Methods	Principles	Surveys	Constraints & Targets	Design Selection	Calculations	Detail Design Principles	Evaluation of Design	Built-up Roofing
Page	1	19	31	45	83	95	105	165	189	217	221

- Bitumen should be distinguished from coal-tar pitch, which is a product extracted from coal. It too has waterproofing properties.
- The introduction of synthetic polymers has permitted the replacement of many naturally derived products. Improvements to the properties of asphalts and bitumens have also been achieved by the incorporation of polymers and synthetic rubbers.

The real commercial development of the material began in the 18th century. In 1712, one Eyrinus d'Eyrinus discovered rock asphalt near Neuchâtel. He developed a blend with hot pitch which was found very suitable for flooring. This led to the successful search for other deposits around Europe. In 1797, the Count de Sassenay developed material from a source near Seyssel in France, obtaining a much better product.

Mastic asphalt was extensively marketed in France in the early 19th century for surfacing floors, bridges and footways. Richard Tappin Claridge, a British visitor to Paris in 1837 to study the potential of this new material, returned home to establish a company, Claridge's Patent Asphalte, and to take out a patent:

> . . . a Mastic Cement or Composition applicable to Paving and Road making, covering buildings and the various purposes to which Cement, Mastic, Lead, Zinc or Composition are employed.

Isambard Kingdom Brunel extensively advocated the use of mastic asphalt, forecasting 'its adoption to many purposes not yet foreseen'. In 1860, it was portrayed as 'one of the indispensable materials in most building operations'.

In the late 19th century, felts made from a mixture of vegetable and animal fibres were impregnated with bitumens. In shingle form, they were used for pitched roofs; in roll form, they were used for both pitched and flat roofs. The modern versions of such products involve both newer versions of the bitumens (often polymer-modified) and more suitable fibre reinforcement (glass and polyester).

During the 1960s, modified bitumens were developed in Europe, finding a market in the USA in the 1970s. The term 'modified' refers to the addition of plastic or thermoplastic rubber-based polymeric binders to asphalt to improve its performance and durability, especially in relation to complex loadings. It led to multiple layers of modified bitumen being used in evolving built-up roofing systems.

The attraction of forming a membrane in situ by direct application of a liquid was recognised in mastic asphalt roofing. The development of polymer modified bitumens and synthetic resin systems has given greater possibilities for similar approaches but with thinner overall membranes.

Oakland Museum, California, USA

Polymeric single-ply

The introduction of synthetic polymers has permitted the replacement of many naturally derived products. Much of the initiative has come from outside the building or building materials industries. The superior chemical and environmental resistance of polymers in industrial applications became apparent. Chemical companies recognising positive features of some polymer types, such as flexibility over a wide temperature range and excellent resistance to oxidation and water, were clearly aware of the potential for waterproofing. *continued* ▶

Further reading in the Guide:
4.15 Environmental impact of materials • 11.1 Built-up roofing • 12.1 Mastic asphalt • 13.1 Polymeric single-ply

- Single-ply membranes, based upon synthetic polymers, were introduced in the 1950s.
- Early failures were attributed to a lack of understanding but improvements in both materials and installations have since taken place.
- Metal roofing has been used for centuries on roofs of many geometries. Its design is based on being water-shedding (or weatherproof) rather than waterproof.

The greater chemical inertness of polymeric sheeting enabled the use of membranes of reduced thickness, but made jointing more difficult. This resulted in reduced toughness and poor bonding, leading to local failures. It took time, and a variety of research approaches in different countries, before reliable waterproofing systems were established.

In the USA, in the 1950s, fabric impregnated with synthetic rubber solutions of polychloroprene and chlorosulphonated polyethylene were introduced for roofing. Partly as the result of surplus production, with the advent of tubeless tyres, butyl and subsequently EPDM (ethylene propylene diene monomer) in sheet form with appropriate adhesives were also used. Later, in Germany, PIB (polyisobutylene), a precursor of butyl, and PVC (polyvinyl chloride) were successfully developed for waterproofing.

Many companies were unaware of the critical role of installation; contractors unfamiliar with new products and systems often used traditional or modified techniques which were not directly applicable. This resulted in many failures. In the 1960s, a general retrenchment took place, leaving only a few companies who had developed chosen materials and complementary techniques for their respective applications. The need for an integrated material, design and installation approach was grasped in the USA, where a comprehensive service and guarantee achieved significant market penetration by the 1980s.

The fragmented nature of the European market, its industry and the national regulations, contributed to a diversity of responses to the initiative by European companies and the polymer materials they had chosen to supply. Germany, Switzerland and Scandinavia developed strong manufacturing bases with substantial penetration in their domestic market and also supplying other countries, including the UK, where there are only a few smaller manufacturers.

Copper

There is no clear agreement about the earliest use of copper in antiquity, but some authorities have suggested that it was available at least 3500 years ago in China and perhaps as long ago as 5000 BC in the civilisations of the region we now call 'the Middle East' – such as Sumeria and ancient Egypt – mostly for ornament, utensils and bells. It was later

Renault distribution centre, Swindon, UK

used in the classical civilisations of Greece and Rome (where it was used to cover domes). There are brass objects dating from 2000 BC (brass is an alloy of copper and zinc) and there is evidence of copper mining and smelting in England (in Cornwall) in prehistoric times.

The word copper comes from the Greek 'kyprios' – the island of Cyprus, where large quantities of copper were mined during ancient times. The Romans called copper 'aes Cyprium' but this was later changed to Cuprium, the first two letters of which are now universally used as the chemical symbol for copper. The Egyptians believed that copper, due to its exceptional resistance to corrosion, would last for ever and they gave it the Ankh symbol (a cross surmounted by a circle) that represented everlasting life.

During the Middle Ages, and into the 14th century, copper was used only occasionally for roofing. Bronze (an alloy of copper), was used extensively for bell casting and the manufacture of cannons and mortars. Towards the end of the 15th century, the demands for bronze for military weapons led to improved production methods for bronze (and necessarily copper). This fundamentally changed the scale of operations.

The greater availability of copper led to an extension of uses – sculpture, roofing, rainwater goods, etc. The Basilica in Vicenza, refurbished by Palladio (1549), is roofed in copper sheet. Copper roofing found particular favour in Northern and Eastern Europe.

Further reading:
ALEXANDER, W.O. & SWEET, A. Metals in the service of man • COPPER AND BRASS EXTENDED USES COUNCIL. Copper in architecture: a treatise for the information of architects, builders and lovers of good building • WEAVER, L. English leadwork: its art and history

- A number of different durable metals, i.e. copper, zinc, lead, have been used in sheet form.
- Lead roofing has enjoyed a particular vogue in English buildings, from the Saxons onwards.

In Britain, the *Mines Royal Act* of 1568 forbade the mining of copper by anyone other than agents of the Crown to prevent exploitation of the rich copper deposits found in Britain. (The Act was repealed in 1689.)

The 18th century Industrial Revolution in Britain included the expansion of engine and machine building in cities like Birmingham, with a surge of demand for brass. This induced a vast development of copper mining, quarrying and smelting. The metal continued to be used for a variety of uses and, of course, in the 20th century became an essential for electrical cabling. Its use for roofing was sustained.

Copper roofing used the standing seam joint exclusively up to the early 1870s, after which the batten roll was developed.

The conical batten roll was used for many years but, due to the difficulty of detailing at junctions and drips, and the frequent occurrence of cracking, it was replaced in the 1950s by the square batten roll (which is still in use today).

Longstrip copper for roofing has been in use in the UK since the late 1950s and in continental Europe, particularly in Switzerland, since the early 1900s. This form of construction, by material selection and fixing detail, allows much larger sheets to be used between cross joints.

The principal sources for copper today are USA, Chile, Canada, Zambia, Zaïre and the former USSR.

Lead

Lead is extracted from the ore galena – lead sulphide. Assyrian and Babylonian masons used molten lead for anchoring clamps and other fixings in masonry. Lead was used by the ancient Greeks and Romans as roofing sheets and for water services. Their working details often still form the basis for modern construction.

Lead mining has a long history in England. Lead has been used for centuries in buildings – roofing, rainwater goods, stained-glass window seals, ornament, etc. Its availability and suitability to the English climate were significant factors. The Romans exploited lead from the Mendips. By the 7th century, Saxon builders were using lead in their buildings. From medieval times on, it was often used in distinguished buildings (e.g. Hardwick Hall in the 16th century), although today the lead sheet to be found will usually have been renewed – probably during

the last 200 years. The common association now is with the long life requirements typified by church roofs. It is worth noting that the 19th century practice of laying much larger sheets than had been usual in previous centuries proved to be unsatisfactory. Modern practice is much more aware of the precautions necessary to ensure the best performance from the material.

Lead lent itself to the making of flat roofs, which was of special interest until the 18th century for military buildings. These needed high level systems for moving soldiers around for defence from the dominant points of the complex.

Lead was cast into sheets for roofing, with a resulting thickness and effect on its crystalline structure which contributed significantly to its durability. Rolling mills for lead were developed in the late 17th century. Before around 1850, most of the world's lead production came from Spain and England (especially Derbyshire). Since then, many other countries have developed lead mining: today, it comes from the former USSR, USA, Australia, Canada, Peru and Mexico.

Zinc

Zinc was first developed in its pure form in India in the 14th century, with parallel developments further west in the 16th century. Earlier developments may have involved less pure forms. Large-scale production in Europe built up during the 18th century, especially with the use of brass in mechanical engineering, but the real impetus came with the 19th century use of iron and the invention of galvanising.

Zinc roofing methods emerged in Europe in the 19th century – notably in Paris. The metal was used both in flat sheets laid on a continuous (usually boarded) base and in corrugated form.

The principal sources of zinc today are Canada, Australia, Peru, USA and the former USSR. ■

2.3 New developments

- Increased pan-European nature of the industry.
- Introduction of European standardisation.
- Increased understanding and computer modelling of roof behaviour.
- Continuing developments to refine and modify materials properties.

The significance of many developments in technology is not always appreciated at the outset. By retrospective analysis key developments can be clarified. Therefore presenting a clear narrative on 'new developments' has dangers. Some general trends are already apparent, but only in the future will their full significance be known. The continuing developments in flat roofing will ensure the continued appropriateness for the future. Some of these trends are:

- An increasing pan-European organisation of products and market.
- The development of harmonised European standards.
- Greater emphasis on training and certification of site activities.
- Warranties/ guarantees from product suppliers for the complete installation.
- The use of CAD for detail design of roofs, by manufacturers, contractors and consultants.
- Detailed attention to health and safety.
- Increased awareness of the environmental impact of materials in construction.
- Continuation of the move towards inverted or externally insulated roofs.

Trends in the ways that people use buildings may see more 'intermediate environments', as witnessed in the atrium buildings of the 1980s, and these may involve greater utilisation of the roof areas.

The impact of legislation and directives from the European Community will increase, either directly or through consequent national legislation.

Built-up roofing

The developments in built-up roofing now becoming established include:

- Improved understanding and production of bitumen/polymer blends, including the blending of different polymers.
- The development of composite bases (for example glass/polyester) with improved dimensional stability and mechanical properties.
- Flame free bonding techniques.
- Single-layer mechanically fixed bitumen membranes.
- Pre-formed and waterproofed roof panels and components.
- The development of mathematical models to predict membrane performance.

Lloyd's, London, UK

Mastic asphalt

In the mastic asphalt industries, it is anticipated that the following developments may prove to be important:

- The expansion in the use of polymer-modified mastic asphalts.
- An increase in 'hot charge' mastic asphalt supplies, leading to reduced programme durations.
- Greater use of the mastic asphalt flat roofing systems in the design of roofs for a variety of continuous activities (e.g. gardens, car parking, etc.).

Further reading:

Chapter	1	2	3	4	5	6	7	8	9	10	11
Contents	Introduction	History	Regulatory Methods	Principles	Surveys	Constraints & Targets	Design Selection	Calculations	Detail Design Principles	Evaluation of Design	Built-up Roofing
Page	1	19	31	45	83	95	105	165	189	217	221

© BFRC / CIRIA: Flat Roofing: Design and Good Practice. 1993

Willis Faber Dumas, Ipswich, UK

Polymeric single-ply

In the industries concerned with the manufacture of polymeric single-ply roofing systems, there are also a number of important ideas in prospect. These are suggested to be:

- Improvement in current polymers will continue rather than the introduction of new polymers. The emphasis may be more towards blending, compounding and laminating.
- Effort towards improved jointing capability; mechanical and dimensional stability; compatibility with building systems.
- Less distinction between 'polymer' and 'rubber' by modification of properties and performance, for installation and service life.
- Increased use of mechanically fixed systems, principally driven by cost and convenience. The number of fixings and the construction of the membrane will be required to accommodate the higher local membrane stresses. Thicker membranes may result.

Copper sheet

The copper roofing industry has identified a number of developments to watch out for:

- Wider use of proprietary systems with copper sheet as the weatherproofing.
- 'Panelled' copper bonded to a glass reinforced bitumen backing.
- Adoption of European dimensional discipline and detailing techniques.

Collezione Shop, Tokyo, Japan

With the growth of highly sophisticated electronic systems, and the integration of information technology systems and building management systems, copper sheet is likely also to have an important role in electro-magnetic screening of buildings.

Lead sheet

For future applications of lead sheet in roofing, three aspects of new developments are considered to be important:

- The extension of traditional dimensional disciplines to create special appearance attributes.
- The adoption of in situ monitoring of diurnal hygrothermal processes, to enable better detailed understanding of the behaviour of such roofs.
- A trend towards the increased use of direct cast lead sheet. ∎

Further reading in the Guide:
11 Built-up roofing • 12 Mastic asphalt • 13 Polymeric single-ply • 14 Copper • 15 Lead sheet • 16 Other membranes

Regulatory methods 3

3.1 Standards and certification: a framework

- Many national standards for roofing products and design exist.
- The advent of the Single European Market (SEM) is significantly changing the framework of certification for flat roofing.

Until recently, the position in the UK with regard to standards and certification was reasonably straightforward and clear. A few British Standards existed for specific materials and methods and for approaches to flat roof design and construction. The principal standards relating to membranes currently in force are shown in Table 3.1.1. Agrément Certificates could be obtained to give an independent opinion on the suitability of a product for a particular intended use where no national product standard was available. Large numbers of products on the roofing market, however, had no standard to relate to. Many companies did not perceive sufficient advantage in obtaining an Agrément Certificate. Products could be put on the market with little controlling framework of requirements.

With the advent of the Single European Market (SEM) and the associated legislation, the circumstances will be different. This section aims to provide some general guidance on the subject, to indicate a general framework. However, as there will be changes, or at least clarifications, as the SEM develops only the barest outline of this complex subject can be given here. It will be necessary to check the latest position on any issue.

Construction Products Directive (CPD)

Much EC law is issued in the form of Directives which are effectively instructions to the member states to incorporate the provisions of the Directive into their own domestic laws. The CPD had a very significant effect on products for use in construction. It was implemented by UK legislation in the *Construction Products Regulations (CPR)* with effect from 27 December 1991.

Under the CPD, products produced for incorporation in a permanent manner in buildings must enable the building to meet certain essential requirements. These cover:

- Mechanical resistance and stability.
- Safety in case of fire.
- Hygiene, health and environment.
- Safety in use.
- Protection against noise.
- Energy economy and heat retention.

Table 3.1.1
British Standards for roofing products and design

British Standard	Subject
CP143	Sheet roof and wall coverings
CP144: Part 3	Built-up roofing
CP144: Part 4	Mastic asphalt roofing
BS747	Roofing felts
BS2780	Copper sheet and strip
BS6577 & 6925	Mastic asphalt for building
BS6229	Flat roofs with continuously supported membrane
BS6915	Lead sheet roof and wall coverings

The details of the requirements under each of these headings are set out in the 'interpretive documents', published by the EC.

A product, of itself, does not comply with the essential requirements. It is the building that must comply. Products, when used in the way that is intended, must assist in achieving this aim. There will be two main ways in which a product can be shown to be satisfactory in this regard. Either it is be shown to meet the requirements of a 'harmonised' standard or it receives a 'European Technical Approval' (ETA). Products which conform with this European legislation will carry a 'CE' Mark (Figure 4.1.1).

Transitional arrangements will be in force during the period involved in developing the necessary standards. These will allow products to be marketed legally, but the benefits of unquestioned entry to other member countries will not necessarily be available. Existing national standards and regulations will play a key role in supporting the transitional system.

Not all European standards prepared by CEN, the European standards organisation, will support the CE Mark, and thus the CPD. To qualify, they need to be prepared under a mandate from the European Commission. Preparatory work for a 'harmonised' standard on factory-made flexible sheets for waterproofing is in progress. It is, however, expected to be some time before CE Marks can be obtained by this route. The CPD and CPR assume that these standards are in place.

Further reading:
EC Construction Projects Directive • Statutory Instrument: Construction Products Regulations • Health and Safety Executive: Construction (Design and Management) Regulations (Draft for comment)

Chapter	1	2	3	4	5	6	7	8	9	10	11
Contents	Introduction	History	Regulatory Methods	Principles	Surveys	Constraints & Targets	Design Selection	Calculations	Detail Design Principles	Evaluation of Design	Built-up Roofing
Page	1	19	31	45	83	95	105	165	189	217	221

- The *Construction Products Directive* implemented under the *Construction Products Regulations* are key documents.
- 'Harmonised' standards and 'European Technical Approval' will form the future basis for acceptance.

Figure 4.1.1
The European Community conformity mark.

The main alternative is the ETA. Akin to the Agrément system, it is being handled by similar bodies, such as the British Board of Agrément (BBA). ETAs may be granted on the basis of European Technical Guides, prepared following mandates from the Commission. In the absence of a guide, they may be granted on the basis of the interpretative documents, by agreement within the European Organisation for Technical Approvals (EOTA) which is charged with co-ordinating this activity. It is anticipated that liquid-applied waterproof membranes ('thin' film type) will proceed through the ETA route.

British and CEN Standards

As harmonised European standards are published, the relevant national standards will be withdrawn. In the UK they will be published through BSI, but will be clearly identified. They will cover the minimum necessary for compliance with the essential requirements of the CPD.

Existing British Standards often cover much wider areas, and it is likely that many CEN standards will also do so. It is possible that national standards which go beyond the CPD requirements will only be withdrawn in part. Careful checking will be needed when compiling specifications.

Agrément

Agrément Certificates assure the specifier/purchaser that a product has been independently assessed and found suitable for specific purposes, when used in accordance with the Certificate.

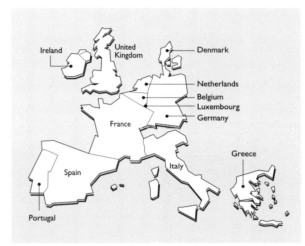

Figure 4.1.2
The European Community member countries

The existing Agrément system does not provide a direct way to achieve a CE Mark (Figure 4.1.1). It is expected that products having current Agrément Certificates will be able to achieve an ETA more quickly than products that have not been subject to this type of assessment. It is expected that the wider scope of appraisal given in the existing Agrément Certificates will have a place in the new scheme and that they will not be completely replaced by the more limited ETAs. However, this will depend on demand.

New Regulations

The *Construction (Design and Management) Regulations* (CONDAM) are out in draft for comment at the time of finalising this Guide. They may have major implications for all participants in the industry, in respect of health and safety, and should be checked once they are in force (see **Unit 3.4**). ∎

Further reading in the Guide:
3.4 Health and safety

12 Mastic Asphalt	13 Polymeric Single Ply	14 Copper	15 Lead Sheet	16 Other Membranes	17 Thermal Insulants	18 Specification	19 Contracts & Procurement	20 Inspection	21 Maintenance	22 Bibliography	23 Index
263	301	331	353	375	383	393	399	413	429	437	455

3.2   Building control

- If it is intended to erect a new building, or to extend or alter an existing building, or to put a building to a different use, *The Building Regulations* will probably apply.
- If the *Regulations* apply it will be necessary to notify the local authority and to comply with the *Regulations*.
- Separate regulations apply to Scotland and Northern Ireland.

The Building Regulations

The regulations for England and Wales considered here are *The Building Regulations 1991*, made under *The Building Act 1984*. Equivalent regulations in Scotland and Northern Ireland are *The Building Standards (Scotland) Regulations 1990* made under *The Building (Scotland) Act 1959* and *The Building Regulations (Northern Ireland)1990*.

The Building Regulations apply to:

- the erection or extension of a building
- the material alteration of a building
- the provision, extension or material alteration of a controlled service of fitting in or in connection with a building
- work required on a material change of use.

It may also be necessary to obtain planning permission. This is not directly linked to *The Building Regulations* and should be applied for separately.

There are two procedural options available under *The Building Regulations* for the inspection of the work.

- by the Local Authority
- by an Approved Inspector.

Fees are payable under both options. The fees charged by the local authority are prescribed, those of an approved inspector are negotiable.

Compliance

The manner of complying with the *Regulations* also falls under two methods.

One way of meeting the requirements is to follow the Approved Documents. These documents give guidance and technical solutions to achieve an acceptable level of performance required by the *Regulations*. Alternatively, it is possible to propose other solutions to the requirements of the *Regulations* that will still be adequate. Alternative proposals may have to be justified to the local authority or approved inspector. It is possible to ask the local authority for dispensation or relaxation of *Regulations*. There also is a right of appeal to the Secretary of State for the Environment:

- if the local authority refuse a request for dispensation
- if the local authority reject submitted plans.

Scottish *Regulations* follow a similar format, but the equivalents of the Approved Documents are described as 'Technical Standards'.

It should be noted that consultation with other bodies for consideration under other legislation may be required.

- The Fire Authority *(Fire Precautions Act 1971)*.
- The Local Authority (Public Health Acts).
- The Factory Inspector *(Offices, Shops and Railway Premises Act* and *The Factory Act)*.

Sections relevant to flat roofs

A brief summary of some relevant sections will give an indication of the scope of the *Regulations*. Reference to the full document and the additional standards and codes referred to *Regulations* should be made early in the design development (in this description, Section, Tables and Diagrams are those of the *Regulations*; Units are those of this Guide).

Section A – Loading and ground movement (see also **Units 4.3** and **7.11**).

A1/2 Section 3 – Re-covering of roofs:

- New roof coverings may impose higher or lower loads on the existing structure.
  - Compare loads.
  - Check existing structure capacity and means of controlling wind uplift.
  - Provide additional structure and restraint as necessary.

Section B – Fire safety (see also **Units 4.9** and **7.9**).

B1 Section 5 – Protection of escape routes (means of escape):

- Roofs that form part of a means of escape should have the appropriate performance given in Tables A1 and A2 of Appendix A.

B2 Section 6 – Rooflights (internal flame spread):

- The size and distribution of rooflights constructed of thermoplastic and plastic rooflights is limited. Table 11 and Diagram 21 illustrate the limitations.

B3 Section 8 – Junction of compartment wall with roof (internal fire spread):

- Compartment walls should be taken up to underside of roof covering and fire-stopped. Guidelines are given for combustibility of roof coverings either side of a compartment wall in Diagram 24.

Further reading:
The Building Regulations, 1991 • The Building Standards (Scotland) Regulations, 1990 • The Building Act, 1984 • The Building (Scotland) Act 1959 • The Fire Precautions Act, 1971 • BS5250: Code of basic data for the design of buildings

Chapter	1	2	3	4	5	6	7	8	9	10	11
Contents	Introduction	History	Regulatory Methods	Principles	Surveys	Constraints & Targets	Design Selection	Calculations	Detail Design Principles	Evaluation of Design	Built-up Roofing
Page	1	19	31	45	83	95	105	165	189	217	221

© BFRC / CIRIA: Flat Roofing: Design and Good Practice. 1993

- The main purpose of the *Regulations* is to ensure the health and safety of people in or about the buildings, through the soundness of the buildings themselves. They also consider heat loss.
- Planning permission is a separate requirement to *Building Regulations* approval.
- Cold roof deck systems are not deemed to satisfy Technical Standards to the *Building Standards* in Scotland; they can be used in exceptional circumstances when specifically approved by the local authority.

B3 Section 9 – Cavity barriers (internal fire spread):

- Regulations are given for cavity barriers in roof voids where ceilings contribute to fire resistance. See Diagrams 31 and 32.

B4 Section 14 – Roof coverings (external fire spread):

- This Section is principally concerned with performance of the roof when exposed to fire from the outside. The intention is to limit the use of roof coverings near a boundary which will not give adequate protection against fire spread over them.
  - The performance of a roof covering is designated by tests specified in *BS476: Part 3*. Constructions are designated by two letters A to D with AA being the best. The first letter is the time to penetration and the second the spread of flame.
  - Appendix A Table A5 gives notional designations of roof coverings.
  - Table 17 sets out the separation distances according to the type and size and use of the building. The separation distance is the minimum distance from the roof to the relevant boundary.
  - Table 18 sets out the limitations on the use of plastic rooflights, in conjunction with Diagram 42.

F2 Section 1 – Ventilating roof voids (Condensation) (see also **Units 4.7, 7.7** and **8.3**)

- This section is concerned with limiting condensation above insulated ceilings to ensure the thermal performance of the insulation and structural performance of the roof is not reduced. The requirements apply to cold deck roofs and not warm deck roofs.
- The requirements will be met by adequate ventilation of the roof void (Diagram 1 explains).
- An alternative approach can be met by following the recommendations of *BS5250: Code of basic data for the design of buildings. BS6229: Code of practice for flat roofs with continuously supported coverings* contains further information.

K2/3 Section 3 – Guards and Barriers (Pedestrian and Vehicle barriers).

- This section is concerned with guarding areas where people might otherwise fall:
  - The edges of a roof (including rooflights and other openings) should be guarded unless access to the roof is only for the purpose of maintenance or repair.

  - Diagram 11 gives the height required and the horizontal forces that the guarding should resist.

L2/3 Resistance to the passage of heat (see also **Units 4.5, 7.6** and **8.2**):

- L2 is concerned with dwellings, L3 is concerned with other buildings.
- Both sections are concerned with heat loss through the exposed fabric of the building.
  - Sections A and B show 4 methods of showing that the calculated heat loss will meet L2 and L3.

The Building Standards (Scotland) Regulations 1990

Technical Standards

Part G: (Preparation of sites and resistance to moisture) raises doubts about the suitability of the cold deck system in Scottish conditions.

The Introduction (item 5 of Introduction page 2G) to Part G states:

> For the control of condensation in roofs, the deemed to satisfy specification quotes *BS5250*, which provides guidance on the principal forms of construction, including cold deck roofs. There is evidence which suggests that condensation in this type of roof system is a problem. The Scottish Office considers that in the climatic conditions of Scotland ventilation of the roof void in flat roofs should not be endorsed as many instances of failure in cold deck systems have been recorded. Both the warm deck and warm deck inverted roof constructions, where the insulation is placed above the roof deck, are considered preferable. While the Regulations do not prevent the use of cold deck roof constructions, it is considered that much more reliable forms of construction are likely to result from over-roof insulation whenever this is possible.

Under G3.1 (vi), roofs with copper, lead, zinc and other sheet metal roof coverings require provision for expansion and contraction of the sheet material. In warm deck roofs, in order to reduce the risk of condensation and corrosion, it may be necessary to provide a ventilated air space on the cold side of the insulation and high performance vapour control layer between the insulation and the roof structure. It may also be necessary to consult the relevant manufacturers or trade associations. ■

Critical factors

- Compliance with *Regulations*.

Further reading in the Guide:
4.3 Structure and movement • 4.5 Thermal performance • 4.7 Condensation • 4.9 Fire behaviour • 7.6 Design for thermal performance • 7.7 Design for moisture vapour control • 7.9 Design for fire safety • 7.11 Design for traffic and load spreading • 8.2 Calculation of thermal performance • 8.3 Calculation of condensation

12 Mastic Asphalt	13 Polymeric Single Ply	14 Copper	15 Lead Sheet	16 Other Membranes	17 Thermal Insulants	18 Specification	19 Contracts & Procurement	20 Inspection	21 Maintenance	22 Bibliography	23 Index
263	301	331	353	375	383	393	399	413	429	437	455

3.3 Quality management

- Quality means achieving defined standards; the standards may be set by an authority, by specification, or by a company's description of its own product or service.
- Quality Assurance (QA) is systematic organisation to achieve the required standard consistently.
- Quality Control (QC) is the checking which confirms that the required standard has been achieved.

Quality objectives

Quality is an unarguable aim.Without reference to formal Quality Assurance, 'quality' is often used vaguely. Quality Assurance gives specific meaning to the term 'quality'.

The move towards QA has focused attention on quality, what it is and what exactly is expected. 'Quality' can be used to describe an unquantified scale of excellence or (as in 'quality level') to describe a company's quantified scale of product performance. However, for QA, it is related only to the product's (or service's) ability to satisfy a given need.

Quality is defined in *BS4778* specifically as:

> the totality of features and characteristics of a product or service that bear on its ability to satisfy stated or implied needs.

Once needs (requirements) are described, quality is unambiguous. Their description comes (singly or, more often, in some combination) from:

- legislation or legal precedent
- adoption of standards or codes of practice
- specification
- the contractor's or supplier's own description.

In many industries it is open to a supplier to define the 'quality level' or grade of his product. It is then their job to announce the specification and conform to it. The customer's decisions are whether that grade is worth the price and whether it meets their requirements.

In construction, requirements are set by reference to a contract specification, code of practice, a British Standard or an Agrément Certificate. Proprietary systems however, can still be offered on the basis of meeting the relevant Standards. The essential process is in three stages:

- Set and agree the standards.
- Achieve the standards.
- Demonstrate that the standards have been achieved.

Product standards

The benefit of product standards (such as British Standards and the Agrément system) is that they provide independent criteria for product characteristics. Designers, contractors and suppliers then all have a common understanding of what is available and achievable.

In established industries it becomes the exception for contractors and suppliers to offer products which do not conform to relevant Standards – although they may well offer products which go beyond the Standards' criteria, or have other attractive features.

The BSI Kitemark scheme provides independent assessment of suppliers' consistent output of products conforming to British Standards. The British Board of Agrément also considers the consistency of production in assessing a supplier for a Certificate.

Quality assurance

QA is not a substitute for satisfying the criteria of product Standards. QA is a parallel activity providing for organisation of effort towards consistent output of products meeting the criteria.

QA is defined in *BS4778* as:

> all those planned and systematic actions necessary to provide adequate confidence that a product or service will satisfy given requirements for quality.

QA is more than Quality Control (QC) although 'QA/QC' is a commonly used phrase. QC generally refers to inspections or tests of product, naturally following the process whose success they confirm (or in which they discover defects). While Quality Control is important, its limitation – and the reason for developing QA – is that it is retrospective. QA is aimed at the groundwork ahead of production, which minimises defects and maximises productivity.

QA embraces (in outline):

- the company's policy, organisation and system for achieving quality
- management of materials purchasing and identification
- management of the processes of design, specification, production and/or construction/installation
- inspection (quality control) and feedback of the results of inspection
- audits of the operation of the QA system
- training of the company's staff.

Further reading:
ASHFORD. J.L. CIRIA Special Publication 72 Quality management in construction • BS4778: Quality vocabulary • BS7229: Guide to quality system auditing • BS5750: Quality systems • CIRIA Technical Note 121 Sample quality assurance documents • CIRIA Special Publications 63 and 64 Quality assurance in construction

- Checking reveals problems after they arise; Quality Assurance aims to prevent the problems arising in the first place.
- All parties to a contract have a role in quality management.
- QA is about getting it 'Right First Time'.

The emphasis can be seen on organisation for, and management of, all of a company's work towards a product (installation) that satisfies the quality criteria. One of the catch phrases of QA is:

'Right First Time'

This needs planning, training, the proper plant, the proper materials and the ability to use inspection and feedback from clients to improve the whole system.

QA Standards

BSI issues a range of Standards in the field of QA. Many of them are also International (ISO) Standards and European (EN) Standards. The Standards most often quoted as requirements are:

BS5750: Quality systems; Part 1: Specification for design/development, production, installation and servicing. (Idcntical to ISO9001, EN29001.)

BS5750: Quality systems; Part 2: Specifications for production and installation. (Identical to ISO9002, EN29002.)

The whole of the scope of *BS5750: Part 2* is included in *BS5750: Part 1*. A company may choose, if setting up its own system, to adopt the wider or the more limited scope and a Certificate may be awarded covering the wider or the more limited scope.

BS5750: Quality systems; Part 3: Specification for final inspection and test (identical to *ISO9003, EN29003*) is of even more limited scope, included in both *BS5750: Parts 1 and 2*. *Part 3* will rarely be referred to, but some materials suppliers may adopt it where they wish to apply QA only to the pre-despatch Quality Control function.

Guidance is available from other Standards and Parts:

BS5750: Quality systems; Part 0: Section 0.1 Guide to selection and use. (Identical to ISO9000.)

BS5750: Quality systems; Part 0: Section 0.2 Guide to quality management and quality system elements. (Identical to ISO9004, EN29004.)

BS5750: Part 4: Guide to the use of BS5750: Parts 1-3.

BS4778: Quality vocabulary; Part 1: International terms. (Identical to ISO8402.)

BS4778: Quality vocabulary; Part 1: Quality concepts and related definitions.

BS4778: Part 3: Quality vocabulary; (Two sections) Availability, reliability and maintainability terms.

BS7229: Guide to quality systems auditing.

It is important to note that, of these documents, only *BS: 5750: Parts 1, 2 and 3* are 'specifications'. The remainder are guides which offer good or standard practice, but are not expressed as, and should not be used as, specifications.

Quality system

A Quality System is defined in *BS4778* as:

The organisational structure, responsibilities, procedures, processes and resources for implementing quality management.

and Quality Management is:

That aspect of the overall management function that determines and implements the quality policy.

Quality Systems are also referred to as QA systems and Quality Management Systems (QMS).

A QA system is a part of the company's operation – it may even be the whole operation – codified and documented. It is important that the system represents the assessment by the company's managers of the criteria they plan to satisfy, the means of doing so, and the organisation they have in place.

A QA system is not simply a set of documents. A system cannot be assessed, and cannot be used, on paper alone.

The British Standards provide a single independent benchmark by which a company's system may be assessed. However, it will be seen that the Standards contain few, if any, absolute criteria. They mainly require a company to determine what it considers to be the appropriate provision for the industry it works in and the requirements it is offering to meet.

The process of making the decisions and establishing the organisation to implement those decisions is itself a benefit to quality because the people involved are clearer about the company's objectives.

continued ▶

Critical factors

- Quality management status and system of consultant designers, contractors and suppliers.
- Proper identification of quality issues and quality management system.

Further reading in the Guide:
3.1 Standards and certification: a framework

- Certification can be by 'First Party' (the company), 'Second Party' (the client) or 'Third Party' (an independent authority).
- The National Accreditation Council for Certifying Bodies (NACCB) exists to certify the certifiers.
- QA has implications for all participants in the building process – including the client or employer.

The expressions Quality Management and QMS emphasise the contributions that management activities – planning, organising, deploying resources – make to success in achieving quality. Effective management is needed at all levels in the company, not just among 'managers'.

The expression 'Total Quality Management' (TQM) is also being used, as in *BS4778*:

> a management philosophy embracing all activities through which the needs and expectations of the customer and the community, and the objectives of the organisation, are satisfied in the most efficient and cost effective way by maximising the potential of all employees in a continuing drive for improvement.

Two points are clear:

- The approach of QA to mobilise management energy to the assurance of quality is extended to a broader perspective of the whole company.
- There is an implication of continuing improvement.

It is a feature of the movement to QA, although not included in the Specification Standards as such, that by adopting QA companies improve the quality of their product or service. This does not have to be better products for the sake of it, where they are adequate already. It may be greater consistency in achieving targets, such as delivery dates – more 'Right First Time' results.

Third Party certification

The First Party is the company. The Second Party is the customer or client. The Third Party is an independent authority who can do once what otherwise each Second Party would do separately for each contract (or could not afford to do at all).

The Third Party Certification (TPC) approach has been promoted in the UK by the Department of Trade and Industry (DTI) as a way for designers, contractors and suppliers to offer their QA systems with independent certificates that they meet the relevant Standard. TPC offers to QA the sort of independent check that the Kitemark and Agrément schemes offer for product performance (see also **Unit 3.1.**). TPC does not say anything about product performance. It says a lot about the certificate holder's organisation to achieve their quality targets.

The most respected authority for TPC is based on the DTI's National Accreditation Council for Certifying Bodies (NACCB). The NACCB exists to 'certify the certifiers'; it monitors the work of Certifying Bodies and – when content that they are properly assessing the QA Systems of companies – allows them to award certificates (including the NACCB logo). The NACCB is not itself a Certifying Body.

There are (as listed at June 1990) 17 Accredited Certifying Bodies for Certification of Quality Management Systems. Each body has a defined scope over which it is accredited to certify. Names and accredited scopes are available from NACCB.

Certification involves:

- a review of the company's system documents
- an assessment of the company's system in action
- award of the Certificate if the Certifying Body is content that the company meets the requirements of the Standard
- periodic monitoring visits
- reassessment after three years.

The benefit is partly internal – that the company subjects its system to independent scrutiny – and largely external in being able to offer customers/clients an independent authority's view that there is a system and it works.

One of the features of the periodic monitoring is that it demands that the company's own internal auditing is a continuing activity. The assurance to the customer comes from knowledge not just that the outsider is policing the system but mainly that the company itself is.

Implications

General

QA enhances confidence and reduces risk: internally, confidence in the company's achieving its objectives; externally, confidence in not being let down.

In construction all the parties involved depend on the others performing as agreed; construction is not unique in this. QA as a common approach encourages all involved to appreciate the same benefits from 'Right First Time'. The implications set out below will be of interest beyond the party identified.

Further reading:
OLIVER, G.B.H. CIRIA Special Publication 74 Quality management in construction - interpretation of BS 5750

Specific

The logic of 'assurance' giving benefit should be seen in improvements such as:

- fewer delays due to incorrect or defective materials
- few delays due to recovery from materials failures, workmanship shortcomings, or errors in general
- better programming and adherence to targets
- less time spent in supervision of contractors, sub-contractors, or suppliers and in resolution of disputes
- greater confidence in the end product being free of hidden defects.

QA offers three key benefits across the board:

- greater clarity in dealing with companies who respond to the company's orders or instructions
- more thorough matching of resources to demands
- more consistent meeting of commitments.

Applications

The principles of QA are the same across all sorts of company; however there are differences in application between a factory-based supplier, a site-based contractor, and an office-based designer.

Supplier

A works-based supplier is in the position most clearly covered by *BS5750*. Adoption of a QA system might start with vendor assessment purchasing and incoming goods inspection to confirm that the supplier's raw materials are of a standard consistent with their objectives. The system would run through the production process from planning to despatch, including inspection, and the matching of deliveries to orders.

Concepts such as the 'quality loop' encourage a company to use feedback to improve its system. The TQM approach extends to market research as part of the company's planning.

Sub-contractor

Implementing QA means documenting those practices which successful sub-contractors already recognise as important anyway. The programme and specification for each project need to be assessed individually and the resources brought in to match.

It is frequently a 'QA responsibility' to draft a comprehensive inspection and test plan for each project as part of the detailed technical supervision. A sub-

contractor particularly depends on workmanship to get it 'Right First Time': QA implies a managed approach to workforce training.

Main contractor

Where a main contractor has specialist work carried out by a sub-contractor, their exposure to the consequences of workmanship defects and delays are well recognised.

Adopting QA encourages clear communication of the programme and specification. It also encourages contractors to identify – and even formally 'rate' – sub-contractors, to identify reliable performers.

QA affects all areas of a contractor's management, made more demanding by the need to re-create a 'company' for each site. It is worth noting that legislative requirements are a part of the 'implied needs' of QA, so safety on site would be expected to appear in the QA provisions (see also **Units 3.4** and **3.1**).

Designer

The designer's application of QA to his or her own activity covers similar aspects to a contractor's or sub-contractor's, but under different names: assessment of the brief, programmed deployment of resources, a trained workforce, checking, and production to programme of the deliverables.

The designer, in drafting a specification and drawings, sets the detailed quality objectives of the contractors: the 'stated needs' of the definition of quality. The responsibility implied in this is eased by reference to British Standards and Agrément Certificates as independent authorities on technical criteria.

Client/employer

It may be worth recalling, for a client, what QA alone can not do. While it does encourage competent management, it cannot alone produce a 'high quality' product.

The 'quality level' of the product should derive from the agreement between client and designer on what is appropriate for the project.

With an approach which encourages clear and efficient communications, clients should benefit from it and play their part in it. ■

Critical factors

- Method of certification.
- Implications for each participant.

Further reading in the Guide:
3.1 Standards and certification: a framework • 3.4 Health and safety

3.4   Health and safety

- Health and safety are governed by legislation.
- The design of roofs – their procurement, implementation, use, maintenance and repair – requires the active consideration of safety issues at all stages.
- The designer should consider special construction aspects of the design and should seek to ensure that contract documents include provision for health and safety aspects to be priced.

General

Most people will associate the consideration of Health and Safety matters with the active site operations of construction work. Clearly, the operations necessary for the carrying out of roofing work constitute a particular problem, due to working at heights, exposure to the elements and the incomplete nature of the works.

Almost one in five of the deaths in the construction industry occur in roof work; others occur in inspection and surveys of roofs.

Roof work deaths could be significantly reduced by the provision and proper use of readily available equipment. However, health and safety is a much broader subject, encompassing all stages in the process, from design inception to final removal and disposal.

New requirements for the construction industry will be established, resulting from the new EC Directives and in particular from *Temporary and Mobile Work Sites Directive.* Regulations to implement this are due to be in place for 1 January 1994. At present the Health and Safety executive have presented a document for consultation before preparing proposals for regulations and a code of practice which may result in changes in the responsibility for site safety. This is known as CONDAM – Proposals for Construction (Design and Management) Regulations and Approved Code of Practice.

Design

Technically-qualified people may bear special responsibility to foresee and warn against potential dangers (in their fields of expertise) that would not be apparent to others less skilled. The designer should consider not only regulations applicable to roof design, but also, in special circumstances, health and safety in the sequence of construction implied by the designs, and in the implied amount and practicability of long-term maintenance and repair.

The designer should consider the safety issues of instructions issued to contractors and, where necessary, identify any possible hazards involved. Contract Documents should list items essential for health and safety and ensure that they have been included for by the tenderers.

Material protection and manufacture

Material production and manufacture is covered by extensive regulations. The manufacturer is required to prepare and maintain a Health and Safety Policy and to bring this to the attention of their employees. They are required to provide such information, instruction, training and supervision as is necessary to ensure, so far as is reasonably practicable, the health and safety at work of all their employees.

Significant recent legislation is *The Control of Substances Hazardous to Health Regulations 1988* (COSHH). These regulations lay down the essential requirements and an approach for the control of hazardous substances and protection of people exposed to them. The regulations do not cover lead or asbestos, which have their own regulations. Fire precautions in manufacturing plants, particularly where solvents and other flammable materials are used extensively, is another vital area of health and safety legislation.

Handling, application, installation and inspection

Three people are killed on UK building sites each week and 12 people are injured every day. Every person involved in the industry has a duty to help to prevent and reduce this level of accidents.

The installation of a roof clearly presents a number of health and safety issues, including:

- access to the workplace for operatives and materials
- handling of heavy, hot and awkward materials
- working on slopes, with possible wet or icy conditions
- unguarded edges to roofs and work fronts
- the use of mechanical fixings and implications for the user and those below: dropping of materials, tools, etc.
- exposure to hazardous substances by contact or inhalation
- hoisting and cranage
- scaffolding, ladders and access ways
- cutting and metal working tools
- exposure to asbestos products (in existing buildings)
- means of escape in case of fire
- correct use of safety harnesses and crawl boards.

The *Construction Regulations*, *The Offices, Shops and Railway Premises Act* and COSHH give extensive control and guidance to all of the above.

Further reading:

- Contractors should consider safety issues in the planning and execution of the work, ensuring protection is given to third parties.
- Building owners should have policy guidelines for the maintenance and other access to their roofs, whether this is by their own staff or employed contractors.
- New and proposed legislation (e.g. the *Construction Products Regulations*, *CONDAM Regulations*), gives greater emphasis to environmental aspects and to health and safety.

Protection of the public is a most important aspect of any safety regime. When work is being contemplated, it may be necessary to:

- Inform adjoining owners, tenants in the same building, people working nearby and the general public.
- Make sure that signs are posted and that diversions are in place (if necessary).
- Inform statutory authorities and give relevant notices.

Employers of operatives working on site must ensure that their Employer's Liability and Public Liability Insurance are adequate and in operation.

Safety in use

Once work is complete and in occupation, safety aspects will revolve around the occupier of the building, adjoining owners and members of the public. Those aspects where potential problems may occur are:

- fire performance (i.e. spread of flame, etc.)
- means of escape
- discharge of noxious or toxic fumes
- ease of access, guarding, lighting, etc.
- materials dislodged by wind uplift.

The employer/occupier has the same responsibilities under the *Health and Safety at Work etc. Act* as those summarised in the manufacture section. They will also have responsibilities under other regulations, e.g: *The Reporting of Injuries, Diseases and Dangerous Occurrences Regulations 1985*, and *The Health and Safety for Employers Regulations 1989*.

Surveys

Building surveys can occur at any time. They may take place prior to the installation of a new roof or the undertaking of repairs. They may take place during the life of the roof to assess its condition.

When undertaking survey work (see also **Unit 3.1**) the following should be ensured by the responsible parties prior to commencement:

- Identify any likely hazards.
- Commission protective work of dangerous premises, e.g. safe access and guarding, temporary support work, removal of rubbish, load testing.
- Check safety equipment.

- Inform people of the undertaking of any survey and leave the premises in a safe condition.

When carrying out surveys or maintenance of a roof, the following hazards may be present:

- possible collapse of structures, parapets, chimney stacks, walls, beams, floors and roofs
- defective staircases, floorboards, roof decking and joists
- roofs:
  - fragile coverings and rooflights
  - low parapets, unguarded edges, loose copings
  - slippery surfaces, crawling boards, ladders
  - defective ladders and hatches
  - insects, birds and bird droppings
  - contaminated atmospheres, asbestos, Legionella, fungicides
  - dangerous live services
  - high winds.

Disposal

During the life of a building, it may be necessary to remove all or part of the roof. This may be in order to carry out refurbishment, replacement or maintenance; or it may be part of the total demolition of the building.

A number of regulations cover demolition work:

- *BS6187 Code of Practice for Demolition*
- *Health and Safety in Demolition Work, Parts 1-4, Health and Safety Executives*
- *Safety in Demolition Work, Health and Safety Executive, HSE – HASAW Booklet 6E*
- *COSHH.*

Particular safety aspects should be borne in mind:

- removal and disposal of asbestos and lead
- pollution regulations
- fire regulations
- disposal of toxic materials
- environmental health and safety during demolition.

Under the Environmental Protection Act, new regulations will require the controlling person to know the ultimate destination of any removed materials and whether they are to be placed in a landfill site, incinerated or recycled.

Unit 4.15 provides more discussion of environmental considerations of materials. ■

Critical factors

- Contract documents to provide for health and safety issues.
- Construction planning.
- Safety provision for future maintenance and repair.

Further reading in the Guide:
3.1 Standards and certification: a framework • 3.3 Quality management • 4.15 Environmental impact of materials • 18 Specification • 19 Contract and procurement • 22.2 Health and safety bibliography

3.5 Organisation of technical information

- Project documentation falls generally under the three headings: specifications, drawings and bills of quantities.
- The Common Arrangement (CA) provides a co-ordinated reference system for all contract documentation.
- Several libraries of standard specification clauses are published.

Project information

The success of a project, whether new-build or repair, depends to a large extent upon the standard of the project information, which is generally issued in documentary form. For the majority of contracts, the documentation falls under three headings:

- The specification: which defines the quality or performance for the work. It is normally divided into a Preliminaries Section, giving general conditions and a framework for the project as a whole, followed by the various trade sections (see **Unit 18.1**).
- The drawings: which define the form and location of the various elements, and their relationship to each other.
- The bills of quantities: which, as the title implies, quantify the work – initially in terms of measure, and then, when priced, in terms of cost.

A standard format for the preparation of bills was agreed in 1922, with the publication of the first edition of the Standard Method of Measurement (SMM). Apart from this, however, presentation of specifications and drawings for tender purposes was, until recently, left largely to the initiative of individual practices. However, in 1987, a first attempt at providing a comprehensive referencing system for all contract documentation was published by the Building Project Information Committee under the title 'Co-ordinated Project Information' (CPI).

Co-ordinated Project Information

Information about a reference system which links specifications, drawings, and bills is contained within four separate books:

- **Common arrangement of work sections for building works** (the Purple Book). This volume describes the basic reference system, the Common Arrangement of Work Sections (CAWS). In simple terms, the Common Arrangement is a tiered reference system, which, at the third level, defines work sections, e.g:

Level 1	J	Waterproofing
Level 2	J2	Asphalt coatings
Level 3	J21	Mastic asphalt roofing/insulation/finishes

Table 3.5.1
Level 1 classes of the common arrangement

A	Prelims/general conditions
B	Complete buildings
C	Demolition/alteration/renovation
D	Groundwork
E	Insitu concrete/Large precast concrete
F	Masonry
G	Structural/carcassing metal/timber
H	Cladding/covering
J	Waterproofing
K	Linings/sheathing/dry partitioning
L	Windows/doors/stairs
M	Surface finishes
N	Furniture/equipment
P	Building fabric sundries
Q	Paving/planting/fencing/site furniture
R	Disposal systems
S	Piped supply systems
T	Mechanical heating/cooling/refrigeration
U	Ventilation/air conditioning
V	Electrical supply/power/lighting systems
W	Communications/security/control systems
X	Transport systems
Y	Services reference specification
Z	Building fabric reference specification

Further reading:
BPIC: Common arrangement; Project specification; Production drawings; SMM7 • National Building Specification • Specification

Chapter	1	2	3 Regulatory Methods	4	5	6 Constraints & Targets	7 Design Selection	8	9 Detail Design Principles	10 Evaluation of Design	11 Built-up Roofing
Contents	Introduction	History		Principles	Surveys			Calculations			
Page	1	19	31	45	83	95	105	165	189	217	221

© BFRC / CIRIA: Flat Roofing: Design and Good Practice. 1993

- Software is being developed for the production of co-ordinated documentation.

There are some 240 defined work sections, with scope for more. For each work section, a definition of the work content is given, together with included items, and items which would be described under alternative headings. It is already clear from the example that 'Flat Roofs' are not a first-level element, and the relevant work sections for the common flat roofing materials are divided between:

H Cladding/covering (where the assembled roof is composed of individual sheets or elements, and

J Waterproofing (where the final form of the covering is a monolithic membrane)

- **Project specification: a code of procedure for building works** (the Red Book). A checklist for each work section, defining the scope of the specification coverage. (see **Unit 18.1**).

- **Production drawings: a code of procedure for building works** (the Green Book). Describes a drawing reference system which is co-ordinated with CA.

- **Standard method of measurement of building works: Seventh edition** (SMM7 – the Blue Book). This edition is arranged in CA format, and the measurement rules have been transcribed from prose into classification tables.

Libraries of specification clauses

Several libraries of specification clauses are currently published, all in broadly the same format of 'standard' and optional clauses, and clauses requiring input, which can be edited to produce a project specification (relevant software is also being developed). The publishers are:

- **National Building Specification** (NBS). A multi-volume library of clauses covering the structural and architectural field. The text, with user notes, is in CA format and supplied in ring-binders. Software and an updating service are available.

In addition, NBS market 'Specification Manager', a software system linking specification clauses, standards and product information.

- **PSA General Specification.** A three-volume library of clauses covering the structural and architectural field. The text is in CA format and user notes are provided. Software is available, and the volumes are updated at intervals.

- **Specification.** The most established publication (first edition 1898) covering in three volumes technical matters, product information and model specification clauses. ■

Critical factors

- Consistency of approach and display of project information.
- Use of CAWS.

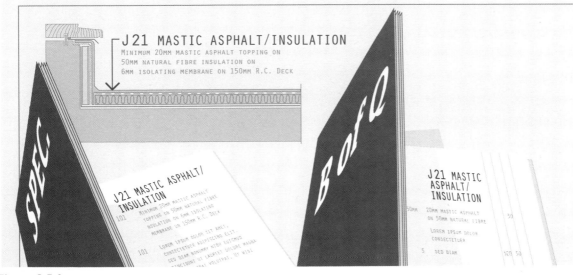

Figure 3.5.1
Relationship between drawings, specifications and bills of quantities

Further reading in the Guide:
Specification • 19 Contract and procurement

12 Mastic Asphalt	13 Polymeric Single Ply	14 Copper	15 Lead Sheet	16 Other Membranes	17 Thermal Insulants	18 Specification	19 Contracts & Procurement	20 Inspection	21 Maintenance	22 Bibliography	23 Index
263	301	331	353	375	383	393	399	413	429	437	455

Principles 4

Special Note: *The guidance provided in this Guide assumes that the roof will be exposed to typical UK climatic conditions. Care should be taken for other locations where different conditions may apply.*

4.1 Behaviour of assemblies

- Flat roof construction is a complex assembly of materials and components.
- The overall behaviour of the roof is governed by the response of the assembly to the environmental conditions.
- The performance of the assembly can be assessed for different degrees of localisation.

Modern buildings and particularly the external envelope, are a complicated arrangement of materials and components. The chemical and physical behaviour of the envelope will result from the interactive relationship between these components and materials, in response to the conditions imposed upon them. Flat roofs are one of the most important areas of the envelope for controlling the internal environment.

Designers will be able to exercise their design skill more effectively by understanding the fundamental physical behaviour of the roof rather than relying solely on rather rigid categories of previous solutions. It is thus important to develop an understanding of how such materials and components are likely to behave when in combination, rather than as individual elements. Many Units and Chapters in this Guide provide information on specific relationships. This Unit introduces the idea of interaction and the behaviour of an assembly.

Interactions

The performance of a roof and its interactions can be viewed at different levels. At one level, the whole roof has the essential function of keeping the weather out of the building. It is helpful if it is able to do this for some required period and cost.

At a more detailed level the roof contributes to the **thermal comfort conditions** within the building and the energy requirements to achieve them. At a similar level of importance is the overall **moisture vapour movement** characteristic – and **condensation risk** – which can affect the thermal and long-term durability performance of the roof.

The interactions between components also take place at local details such as upstands or penetrations. A specific example of this local interaction is that of mechanical fixings for the membrane, insulant, or both. It is clear that in principle a local cold bridge could cause condensation to form on the fixing surface and thus modify its long-term corrosion behaviour. The overall thermal and condensation risk analysis will not, normally, try to model such local conditions. It would, however, be very difficult to analyse numerically the transient conditions which might occur, with enough confidence to use the results in the design process. Indeed for most roofs such calculations are not attempted

and design is based largely upon experience of the possible extent of a real problem occurring.

The important point being made here, is that sufficient understanding of the likely interactions needs to be developed to know that these judgements can be made.

Flows

A second feature of the behaviour of assemblies is that of flow across the roof construction, usually in section, but the ideas have validity for flows across the plan of the roof. Such flows are the result of the differences in environmental conditions within and without the building and are permitted or resisted by the nature of the roof construction.

The principal sectional flows encountered in flat roof design are heat transfer and the movement of water in vapour form. More detailed guidance is given on the specific characteristics of these flows in other Units of this chapter and elsewhere in the Guide (see **Units 4.5, 4.7, 7.6 and 7.7**). The common point is that for both these it is usual to incorporate specific components into the roof construction – an insulant and vapour control layer – to modify the performance.

Other components in the roof build-up, such as the structural deck, can, however, strongly influence the overall performance – whether intended or not. A substantial concrete deck will have a significant contribution to the thermal resistance of the whole roof; a metal sheet, either as the structural deck or as the membrane may have a much greater vapour resistance than any deliberately incorporated vapour control layer.

Again the important point is that the roof will perform or react to environmental conditions in relation to those components, properties, and conditions that are actually present, not those designers hope might exist.

Categorisations

In flat roof design, as for many other aspects of buildings, there is a tendency to categorise types of construction and then make judgements based upon generalised ground rules. This approach can be useful to simplify the early stages of the design but designers should be extremely cautious of these categorisations becoming too dogmatic. The awareness of actual construction, as discussed in this

Further Reading:
GROAK S. The idea of building

Chapter	1	2	3	4	5	6	7	8	9	10	11
Contents	Introduction	History	Regulatory Methods	Principles	Surveys	Constraints & Targets	Design Selection	Calculations	Detail Design Principles	Evaluation of Design	Built-up Roofing
Page	1	19	31	45	83	95	105	165	189	217	221

• Categorisations of roof assemblies into pre-determined assemblies can be useful for initial conceptual design, but has dangers for the more detailed appraisals required for satisfactory performance.

Unit, is essential in any detailed appraisal of the design. Such categorisations are most obviously used in the terms 'cold deck roof', 'warm deck roof', etc. (see **Unit 4.2**).

These terms were originally derived from consideration of the thermal conditions of the roof components. However, the greatest significance is now for risk, location and the means of dealing with condensation. The configuration which is most commonly associated with the term 'cold deck roof' is where a void exists beneath the deck which must be ventilated to control condensation. The alternative arrangement, with insulation immediately below a structural deck, is also a 'cold deck roof,' but one in which condensation cannot be controlled by ventilation. In fact a vapour control layer is required, a solution most often associated with warm roofs.

These categorisations (e.g. 'warm deck roof') are based on particular configurations and are taken to imply particular physical behaviour. Designers might assume that as long as the configuration is the same, the behaviour is the same. In fact the configuration can remain constant but the behaviour can change significantly if the materials used and/or their dimensions are changed as, for example, in a roof garden, where substantial finishes are used over the roof surface.

A similar rigid categorisation, but perhaps less obvious, is applied to waterproof membranes. In this example there are properties of materials which may have advantages or disadvantages, and means of incorporating them into the roof also have a balance of advantages and disadvantages. For example, designers may consider that the use of modern polymers and synthetic rubbers give a good probability of long-term durability, but that the use of a single-ply membrane has too high a risk of defects at joints to be suitable. Similarly the majority of roofs using bituminous sheets are installed in several individual layers bonded together. Neither of these two combinations is implicit: bituminous sheets could, in principle, be laid as a single layer or a polymeric sheet laid as a multi-layer membrane. That 'normal' routes exist is because of a combination of technical, commercial, and historic factors.

Table 4.2 shows how a breakdown evaluation of conventional systems can highlight the essential characteristics, independent of the materials used.

It is useful, but perhaps not essential for each roof design process, to review and reflect upon some of the issues

Table 4.2
Advantages and disadvantages of various conceptual attributes of membranes

ATTRIBUTE	ADVANTAGES	DISADVANTAGES
Multi-layer	Greater security against defects in lapping joining of sheets.	Slower to lay. May be more difficult at details.
Single-ply	May be faster to lay than multi-layer. Possibility of pre-joining of sheets to achieve 'larger sheet'	Less barriers to water penetration than multi-layer. Some systems may be less robust.
Pre-formed sheets	Factory control of physical properties. Not dependent on site conditions for properties of membrane sheets.	Relies on site joining to achieve integrity. More difficult handling on site. May be more difficult to create details.
Liquid applied	Avoids joints as points of weakness. May be easier to form at details.	Relies more heavily on installation operative. Thinner systems may have less robustness than pre-formed membranes.
Fully bonded	Extra security to water ingress to building if membrane is breached, as no flow path under membrane. Can make tracing leaks easier because the point of ingress in the structure will be close to membrane defect.	More difficult to accommodate movements in substrate. May take longer for installation. More sensitive to substrate condition.
Partial/spot bonded	Movement accommodation in substrate may be more easily resolved. Installation may be faster.	Once membrane by-passed, water penetration into building easier. Tracing of leaks less easy than fully bonded membrane.

raised above so that the designer is led towards a fuller understanding of the way the complex behaviour of an assembly of components acts. It is essential, however, that the proposed roof design is properly evaluated for all the key performance issues – such as heat transfer or condensation – based on the actual arrangement of components and their real properties, as far as they can be assessed. ∎

Critical factors

• Interaction between components forming a whole.
• Real properties of components.
• Usefulness and dangers in categorisations.

Further reading in the Guide:
4.2 Behaviour of assemblies: flat roof configurations • 4.5 Thermal transmission • 4.7 Condensation • 7.6 Design for thermal performance
7.7 Design for moisture vapour control

4.2 Behaviour of assemblies: flat roof configurations

- A flat roof is a multi-layer construction comprising waterproof membrane, thermal insulation, and structural deck in some combination, with in some cases a vapour control layer, and protective covering.
- The arrangement of these components is a significant factor in the overall performance of a roof design.

Unit 4.1 described the initial benefits and dangers of categorising roof designs into strict 'types'. The most widely used categorisations are based originally upon a description of the thermal performance of the various options. This Unit explains in some greater detail this established approach and gives more information about the further real performance attributes which must also be considered by a designer. It must be stressed again that the categorisations are useful as an initial guide to design options. The developed design should be assessed comprehensively for real potential performance using the guidance and calculation procedures contained in this Guide.

Warm deck roof

The warm deck roof has the principal insulation above the structural deck but below the waterproof membrane. The principal significance is that the deck experiences temperatures throughout the year which are closer to that of the building interior than would be the case if the insulation was below the deck, i.e. a cold deck roof. The membrane will usually give a very high resistance to moisture vapour release from within the building. Therefore a vapour control layer will often be required beneath the principal insulant to control condensation build-up beneath the membrane. For most designs it is unlikely that the vapour control layer will have a higher vapour resistance than the membrane. The consequence of this is that some condensation is likely to be predicted during cold weather by calculation methods. An assessment is required of the significance of such predictions. (See **Units 7.7** and **8.3**). Figure 4.2.1 shows a typical arrangement of principal components. The warm deck roof is perhaps the most common type of roof constructed in the commercial sector over the last twenty or thirty years.

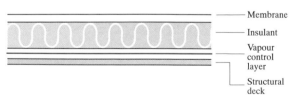

Figure 4.2.1
Warm deck roof

- Membrane
- Insulant
- Vapour control layer
- Structural deck

Inverted warm deck roof

This type of roof is also termed an upside down or protected membrane roof. All of these terms are an attempt to describe, simply, the essential difference between it and a warm deck roof. The inverted roof is also a warm deck roof with the insulation above the structural deck, but here the insulant is also above the waterproof membrane. The membranes used for this type of roof have good vapour resistance. The addition of a separate vapour control layer is therefore unlikely to change the inherent condensation performance.

For the majority of inverted roofs an additional heavy layer on top of the insulation to help with resisting wind uplift forces will be needed. This type of roof has become increasingly popular over the last twenty years but there are, however, some concerns about the suitability of some membrane types in regard to condensation risk. Further guidance is given in **Unit 7.1** and **Unit 7.3**. Figure 4.2.2 shows a typical arrangement of components.

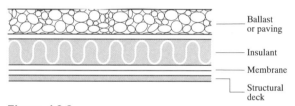

- Ballast or paving
- Insulant
- Membrane
- Structural deck

Figure 4.2.2
Inverted warm deck roof

Cold deck roof

In this configuration the principal insulation layer is placed below the structural deck. The deck therefore experiences temperatures considerably lower than those inside the building during the winter. This type of construction is normally associated with an independent ceiling beneath the deck, separated by an air gap. This air gap will normally be partially filled with an insulation layer, which serves to isolate further the deck and membrane from the building's internal environment. A principal concern with this roof configuration is that of controlling condensation. Although vapour control layers can in principle reduce the risk, the primary control is ventilation of the space beneath the deck. Whilst in some designs this approach can work, it is difficult to predict or

Further reading:
BS5250 Code of practice for the control of condensation in buildings • BRE Report 143 Thermal insulation: avoiding risks • BRE Digest 270 Condensation in insulated domestic roofs • BRE Digest 312

- It is important to design a roof with an understanding of how interactions between components occur. This understanding forms the basis for much of the guidance in the rest of this Guide.

- It has become convenient to categorise some of the confiigurations of components into general types of roof determined by the thermal behaviour of the relationship between insulation and structural deck. The confiigurations referred to in this Guide are: warm deck roof; inverted warm deck roof; and cold deck roof.

control with confidence. A particular factor is that the air movement required for ventilation can also bring in increased levels of moisture. The temperature behaviour of the underside of a deck which faces an open, cold night sky can create local environmental effects possibly leading to unacceptable condensation. Further discussion of these issues is contained in **Units 4.7, 4.8** and **7.7**. Figure 4.2.3 shows a general arrangement. This type of roof is most often encountered with small scale residential construction.

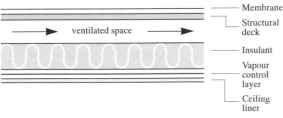

Figure 4.2.3
Cold deck roof

A second arrangement of components which on a thermal performance basis is a cold deck roof is where the insulation layer is fixed directly to the soffit of a structural deck - often of reinforced concrete. Such an arrangement might be designed where, say, a car park or other traffic deck is located over occupied spaces, e.g. over a shopping complex. The distinctions between these two cold deck roof arrangements become important when considering condensation control, as control of condensation risk can only be by vapour resistance not ventilation.

Roof variations
Many of the roof designs required for buildings will, because of other factors, not fall happily into one of the three 'categories' described above. The discussion in this Unit and in **Unit 4.1** has made the point, strongly, that designs should be assessed on the basis of the actual construction. Some of the variations on roof designs may occur sufficiently often for it to be reasonable to highlight the key implications of these variations.

The term '**buried roof**' is used by some designers to describe roofs with a significant layer of other construction over the membrane. This is in excess, say, of that for the inverted warm deck roof. Such designs may be found in roof gardens or car park/traffic decks. For the

hygrothermal performance of such roofs there is a considerable extra layer of material with insulating properties which must be taken into account in calculations of performance. In other aspects of the roof this extra layer may significantly modify the drainage performance and will severely restrict the scope for inspection and maintenance. The membrane is, however, given more protection from heat and UV radiation.

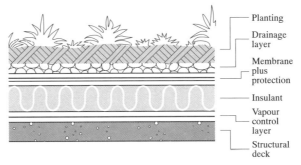

Figure 4.2.4
Roof garden

Another hybrid construction may occur where a roof component has a significant influence on properties other than that for which it was included. For example some roof deck systems can have a considerable thermal insulation performance.

Experience with some metal roof membrane installations has highlighted possible problems of condensation and corrosion in the typical cold and warm deck roof configuration described above. The development of approaches to avoid such problems is discussed in the relevant membrane Chapters of this Guide (**11-16**). ■

Critical factors

- The roof configuration is a significant factor in the overall performance behaviour of the roof.

- The actual behaviour of the roof should be designed and analysed with the construction and materials properties to be used.

Further reading in the Guide:
4.1 Behaviour of assemblies • 4.5 Thermal transmission • 4.7 Condensation • 4.8 Codensation pumping • 7.1 Design selection: general approach • 7.3 Design selection: membranes • 7.6 Design for thermal performance • 7.7 Design for moisture vapour control • 8.3 Calculation of condensation • 11 Built-up roofing • 12 Mastic asphalt • 13 Polymeric single-ply • 14 Copper • 15 Lead sheet • 16 Other membranes

4.3 Structure and movement

- The structure of a building can affect the design and detailing of the roof.
- Loads may be transmitted through all components of the roof, whether intended or not, unless deliberately designed not to do so.
- The structure must carry the loads imposed on it by the weight of the roof, wind load, snow load, equipment, planting, and any traffic on the roof.

Structural design

The design of the structure of a building will be influenced by many factors relating to its performance, assembly and use. For the majority of cases, the type and nature of the roof will not significantly affect the design of the structure beneath. The structure will, however, affect the design of the roof and will impose constraints on detail including: drainage, movement, acoustic and thermal performance, condensation control, fire performance.

Design of the structure is outside the scope of this Guide, and should be entrusted to a competent structural designer, but some brief comments may be helpful.

For the structural design of a building, the essential considerations are that, when subject to a variety of loads:

- It should not fall down – **strength**.
- It should not fall over – **stability**.
- It should deflect only as designed – **stiffness**.

In addition to the material-specific codes, data for dead, imposed, and snow loads are given in *BS6399*. *BSCP3: Chapter V: Part 2* gives basic data for design against wind (see **Unit 7.11**).

The size and capacity of the vertical supports will be determined by the total loads. Their location and size will not normally directly affect the selection or design of the membrane system (Figure 4.3.1). Indirectly, the horizontal structure may do so, because of movements and deflections.

Primary vertical structure on occasion may have a direct effect on membrane design, for example, with the use of masted exoskeletal structures to achieve greater internal free space (Figures 4.3.2, 4.3.3). Depending upon the detailed arrangement of the structural elements, greater numbers of roof penetrations might be created with such forms.

The forces which will act upon the roof, and thus the structure as a whole, are:

- **dead loads**: from the self-weight of the roof construction, and finishes, rooftop structures, planting, equipment.

- **imposed loads**: from use of the rooftop; environmental loads (snow, wind, water); plant, vehicle traffic, maintenance equipment and personnel.

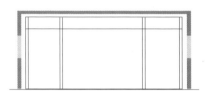

Figure 4.3.1
Internal columns:
no influence on membrane detail

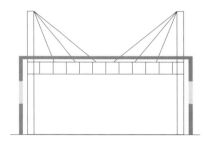

Figure 4.3.2
Exoskeletal (multiple connections)

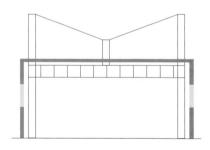

Figure 4.3.3
Exoskeletal (few connections)

Further reading:
BSCP3: Chapter V: Part 2 Wind loads • BS6399: Part 3 Code of practice for imposed roof loadings • BRE Digest 282 Structural appraisal of buildings with long open roofs

- The aspects of structural behaviour important to flat roof design are deflections, and response to dynamic and cyclic forces including traffic.
- The deck must be suitable for anchoring the roof membranes and insulation, and for transferring all loads to the structure.
- Structure and deck will contribute to the overall thermal performance. Structure in particular can be a source of cold bridges.

The aspects of structural behaviour of interest to the design of roofs are deflections, dynamic response and traffic. Traffic is dealt with in **Unit 4.11** and **7.11**.

Deflections

The arrangement and materials for structural elements are myriad. The most common materials are steel, timber and concrete, singly or in combination. The structure may be coherent, as in a monolithic concrete slab with concrete columns, or in discrete elements of flat deck areas on a supporting network of beams, purlins or joists. The means of creating falls for drainage will also have an impact (see **Unit 7.5**).

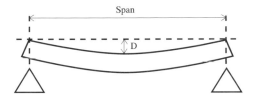

Span

D

Figure 4.3.4
Deflection under self-weight

Any horizontal element supported at discrete points will deflect (sag) under its own weight, towards the mid-point between supports, in a way which is reasonably calculable (Figure 4.3.4). The deflection (D) will depend upon the mechanical properties of the materials, the structural arrangement and the distance between the supports. Additional loads, from the roof build-up, imposed loads, snow, etc., increase the deflection. Structural design seeks to limit these deflections to acceptable levels.

Deflections of the deck and supporting structure may have an element of time dependency known as **'creep'** – the continued straining of some materials (e.g. concrete, timber subject to a sustained load). This will increase deflections.

Other movements resulting from the design, which may impinge upon the roof construction, include settlement of the building under its own weight and initial movements from the forming of the structure, e.g. shrinkage of concrete, which may cause cracks to form or joints to open up.

Dynamic response

A dynamic action is where the action varies – slowly or quickly – with time. Its magnitude, its rate of application and repeat time – or cycle – can vary. The sources of dynamic actions for roofs include traffic, direct environmental actions (wind and snow), or movements created indirectly (thermal and moisture changes). These may be localised and relatively rapid, as with traffic loads. Either the construction is capable of withstanding the load or it must be protected.

More evenly-spread loads – but still varying across a roof – are generated by environmental sources. For example, wind uplift will normally act across the whole roof but more at perimeter upstands. The rates of application may vary (gusting) and may affect the direction of the force (wind generates both negative and positive pressure).

Negative pressure can **uplift** the roofing if it lacks sufficient fixing (see **Unit 7.11**).

Indirect actions can occur because of solar radiation on the top surface of the roof, producing thermal movements in supporting layers. Changes in the internal environment of the building may generate temperature changes in the structure (see **Unit 4.5**). Virtually all materials will change their linear dimensions with temperature; the changes are proportional to a property of each particular material – its **coefficient of thermal expansion.** This must be accommodated within the design.

Many materials used in roof construction (e.g. concrete and timber) experience reversible volume changes with changes in moisture content. In concretes, this is absorption and loss of water from hydrated cement gel; in timber, water swells the cellulose fibres. *continued* ▶

Critical factors

- Deflection of deck for drainage.
- Membrane to accommodate movement of deck.
- Penetrations of membrane to provide structural connections.

Further reading in the Guide:
4.5 Thermal transmission • 4.11 Traffic on roofs • 4.13 Durability of materials • 7.5 Design for falls • 7.11 Design for traffic and load spreading • 8.1 Calculation of roof drainage

- The underlying structure and deck impose movements on the membrane, which must be able to accommodate them.
- Dynamic loadings must be considered.
- Permissible deflections may be given in structural codes of practice.

Roof response to structural actions

The response of the roof structure to the applied loadings and movements will be influenced by its nature. For example, a concrete deck and frame structure will be slower to respond and will produce less overall movement than a lightweight metal deck. The structure should be of such stiffness and strength that satisfactory performance is achieved: e.g. deflections are not unsightly; partition walls, doors and windows are not damaged; excessive vibration or fluctuation does not occur.

A deflection acceptable for serviceability and appearance within the building might be unacceptable for the roof design. The designed falls for a roof should allow for the effects of deflections on drainage (see **Units 7.5** and **8.1**). Deflections will depend upon the type of structure, finishes, nature of the membrane, the ability to form falls, etc. The structural design codes give normally permissible deflections as a proportion of span (e.g. concrete 1/250– for a 7.5m span this would give a maximum deflection of 30mm). The loads used in this deflection calculation should be dead load, imposed loads, and environmental loads (such as snow–but not wind).

The way the roof resists loads and movements may be influenced by the method of construction and joining.

A membrane mechanically spot-fixed to the deck will tend to lift between fixings under wind suction, putting the membrane into tension with localised forces at the fixings. This transmits the force to the deck to resist itself being pulled out. The deck will then be subject to an upward bending force, which it must resist, both by its inherent properties and by fixity to the vertical structure. A fully-bonded membrane will resist the same force by distributed fixity.

These different methods of fixing will have different consequences for loads arising from constrained movement, for example thermal or moisture. These can either be concentrated at specific points in a structure (e.g. a movement joint in a concrete structure) or at frequent, deliberate or unavoidable joints (e.g. board or panel joints in timber or metal deck roofs) (Figure 4.3.5).

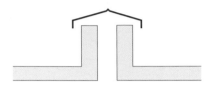

Designed movement joint

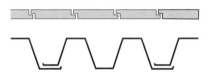

Non 'designed' movement joints

Figure 4.3.5
Movement joints

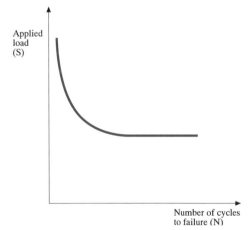

Figure 4.3.6
Typical fatigue S-N graph

- The method of fixing will affect the loading on the different components.
- Materials each have a tensile strain capacity beyond which damage will occur; temperature and strain rates may modify the strain capacity.

Exoskeletal structures

Chapel, Ronchamp, France

Each component or material will have a **tensile strain capacity** which it can experience without permanent damage or failure. If the strain experienced exceeds the tensile strain capacity, then damage or failure will result. There is some basis for checking this balance of imposed strain and material capacity. However, caution should be exercised, as the rheological properties of materials used in roofing are complex. Their properties are affected by temperature. They may show lower strain capacity at temperatures lower than those used for standard testing – often 20°C. Such lower temperatures will often occur when the joints or cracks in the substrate are widest. Similarly, strain rates will modify strain capacity. Standard tests are carried out at standard strain rates which may, or may not, correlate with those experienced on an installed roof (see **Unit 4.13**).

Of particular importance in long-term applications is the effect of fatigue. This involves repeated application of a load (stress or strain) above a critical value. The application of such a load for a small number of cycles would not cause distress, but, if repeated sufficiently, can lead to failure (Figure 4.3.6). Although a well-established phenomenon in mechanical or structural engineering, it has taken somewhat longer for it to reach prominence in roofing. Potentially all of the membrane systems likely to be used – metals, polymeric, and bituminous – could suffer fatigue failures in the wrong combination of conditions. The design of fixing systems and movement joints needs to allow for repeated movements because of this risk. ∎

Critical factors

- Movement joints designed or otherwise.
- Repeated loadings for risk of fatigue.
- Interaction of other design decisions on deflections, e.g. falls creation.

Further reading in the Guide:
4.13 Durability of materials

4.4 Precipitation: rain and snow

- Precipitation includes rain, snow and hailstones. Wind, microclimate and the building geometry will affect the way in which these are deposited and the extent to which they accumulate.
- Water should not accumulate on the roof. Falls must be provided for proper drainage.

Rainfall

A roof will be subject to precipitation, principally rain and snow. It is one of the primary design requirements that the roof satisfactorily resist water penetration from such precipitation. The fundamental point is that it rains, rather than how much rain occurs in the year. In the detailed design of a roof, of greater significance than the annual rainfall is the likely maximum rainfall at any given time (see Figures 4.4.1, 4.4.2). This is important for the design of drainage capacity and falls.

With the UK climate, precipitation varies within a single year and between the years. It is also variable around the country. The dominant climate in the UK means that winds from the west and south-west pick up moisture vapour from the ocean expanse. These air flows are interrupted and modified through the year by the incursion of weather patterns over the larger continental European land mass. Warmer, wetter, west and south-westerly winds rise over the higher land mass in western areas of the UK; the air cools and therefore deposits the excess moisture as rain. Study of rainfall patterns across the UK shows the west and north-west regions to have the highest overall rainfall per year. Perhaps surprisingly at first sight, it is the south and east of the UK which provide the more onerous instances because here the intensity of rainfall is higher.

Rainwater on roofs

Roofs can collect large volumes of rainwater and it is necessary to dispose of it safely. The retention of water on a roof is undesirable for several reasons:

- The weight of standing water will impose additional loads on the structure and might cause structural damage.
- In the event of damage or imperfection in the waterproof covering, the amount of water entering the roof will be increased.
- Freezing of ponded water may cause damage by expansion/contraction, or may produce a safety risk to traffic on the roof.
- Ponding of water will encourage the build-up of silt deposits which allow the growth of plants, moss and algae. These could damage some membranes but also detract from the appearance of the roof.
- The edges of ponded water may create local sharp temperature gradients, which could impose significant stresses on membrane materials.

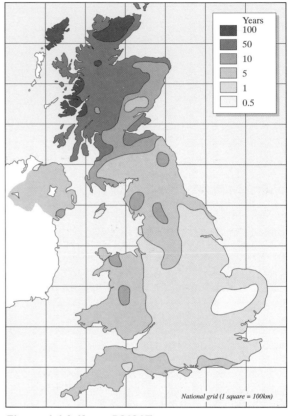

National grid (1 square = 100km)

Figure 4.4.1 (from *BS6367*)
Period in years between rainfall events of 75mm/hour for 2 minutes

Unit 4.6 gives data on surface temperature changes when rain falls. Such cooling, and the rate at which it occurs, will influence the mechanical performance of membranes, and moisture movement within the roof.

Design of a system of slopes (falls) on a roof, leading to a network of drainage gulleys and pipes, is the normal way of removing water from a flat roof; its behaviour on the roof is then governed by the science of fluid dynamics. The laws of flow in open channels govern the behaviour of water in a gutter.

Drainage design for roofs should not be such that large volumes of water flowing in gutters results. Hydraulic flow considerations thus are not appropriate, but it is still

Further reading:
BS6367 Code of practice for drainage of roofs and paved areas • BS6399: Part 3. Code of practice for imposed roof loads • BRE Digest 332. Loads on roofs from snow drifting against vertical obstructions and in valleys.

- With the UK climate, precipitation varies within a single year and between the years.
- The dominant climate in the UK means that winds from the west and south-west pick up moisture vapour from the ocean expanse.
- The north-west has the highest annual rainfall, but the intensity is greatest in the south and east.
- The build-up of snow has structured implications and can affect condensation risk.

prudent to incorporate their lessons, e.g. avoid sharp changes in direction, depth or width of flow path. Roof drainage uses the principle that water will normally flow downhill, although wind pressure can sometimes cause it to flow uphill. The ease with which the water flows downhill is governed by the positive force of the hydraulic head (the vertical distance between where the water is and the outlet) and by the resistance to flow (the distance to outlets and surface roughness). The surface roughness will be affected by the presence, or not, of mineral granules or stone chippings. Guidance on the design for drainage capacity is given in **Unit 7.4**.

In inverted warm deck roofs, the presence of the insulation and ballast/paving will also affect drainage of the roof. Buried roofs, being a more extreme case, may present significant resistance to water flow at membrane level and this will have to be catered for in design. Buried roofs under extensive soil/planting should have provision for free-draining layers to prevent excessive build-up of water, which may be undesirable for the planting and for structural loading.

Snow

Snow does not flow significantly under its own weight and therefore builds up. Structurally significant snow loads can build up on a roof, particularly where wind causes it to drift into deeper layers against obstructions on the roof. The freeze-thaw history is also significant. With the increased thermal insulation now incorporated in roofs, snow tends to remain longer. Recent experience of roof collapses under snow loading have led to a revision of the code of practice for imposed roof loads (*BS6399: Part 3: 1988*).

This revised guidance requires the structural designer to give attention to drifting on flat roofs against vertical obstructions such as parapets, plant rooms, and changes in level. This can affect condensation risks. However, this does not significantly alter the approach to the choice of roofing materials above the structural decking. It is also suggested by *BRE Digest 332* that a notional duration of one month be assumed. Because of its powdery nature, snow can penetrate crevices and junctions in roof details that would not be reached by rainwater. Particular problems of increased ponding can occur where snow partially melts to water, re-freezes at outlets and then blocks them.

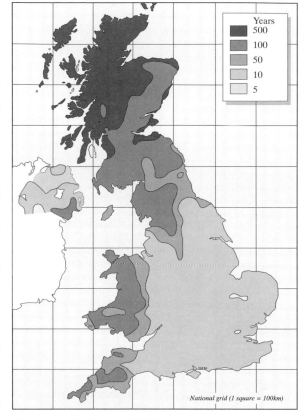

Figure 4.4.2 (from BS6367)
Period in years between rainfall events of 150mm/hour for 2 minutes

Acid rain

Acid rain – rainwater with significant content of pollutant gases such as carbon oxide or sulphur dioxide – has become a more serious issue in recent years. This can affect the durability of roofing materials (see **Unit 4.13**). ■

Critical factors

- Check both annual rainfall and likely maximum rainfall at any given time.
- Build-up/retention of precipitation.
- Build-up of snow can affect condensation risks.

Further reading in the Guide:
4.6 Solar radiation and thermal effects • 4.13 Durability of materials • 7.4 Design for drainage capacity.

12 Mastic Asphalt	13 Polymeric Single Ply	14 Copper	15 Lead Sheet	16 Other Membranes	17 Thermal Insulants	18 Specification	19 Contracts & Procurement	20 Inspection	21 Maintenance	22 Bibliography	23 Index
263	301	331	353	375	383	393	399	413	429	437	455

4.5 Thermal transmission

- Thermal comfort of occupants is a fundamental aim of building performance.
- Heat rises upwards within a building; solar radiation mostly acts downwards upon the roof surface.
- Thermal insulation performance is important: to control comfort within the building, to conserve energy, to control heat gain in the summer, to help control condensation.

Transfer of heat energy

Control of temperature is achieved by controlling the transfer of heat energy from one place to another. The transfer can take place in three ways: **radiation** – as in transfer of heat from the Sun to Earth; **convection** – as hot air up a chimney; **conduction** – as by heating a metal bar in a flame.

In considering the thermal performance of a flat roof, the primary mechanism is conduction through the build-up, together with convection. The main sources of heat energy arrive at the roof surfaces either by radiation (solar energy) on the top surface or by convection from within the building. Some materials are better conductors of heat than others – e.g. metals compared with plastics (in saucepan handles, or in teaspoons). Good conductors feel cold to touch on a cold day, as they quickly conduct body heat. The ability to conduct heat is a function of the microstructure of the material.

Heat flow through a body, under steady-state conditions, is proportional to the temperature difference between the two sides and their physical separation and the property of a material called **thermal conductivity.**
The rate of heat flow q is:

$$q = \lambda \frac{\Delta T}{t}$$

where ΔT is the temperature difference in degrees Kelvin over distance t metres.

λ is the thermal conductivity of the material and has units of watts per metre per degree Kelvin (W/mK). (The symbol **k** was used previously for thermal conductivity.)

The higher the thermal conductivity, the more heat is transferred. Table 4.5.1 shows the typical thermal conductivity of materials. Thermal conductivity (λ) is a material property, whereas thermal resistance (R) and its inverse (thermal conductance) are related to a specific thickness of material:

$$R = \frac{t}{\lambda}$$

For non-steady-state conditions, the heat flow is more complicated than for the steady-state described above. In such situations the concept of **thermal diffusivity** has to be introduced. This takes account of the ability of the material to store, or lose, heat energy rather than to transfer it. It is related to the thermal conductivity of the material, together with its density and specific heat, in the basic equation:

$$\text{Thermal diffusivity} = \frac{\lambda}{\rho c}$$

where ρ = density

c = specific heat

For the majority of thermal control calculations, and the thermal design of roofs, as required by statutory regulations, steady-state conditions are assumed, and thus thermal conductivity is the more relevant property (see **Unit 7.6**).

More complex equations can be used for checking corners, upstands, etc., if these are critical to the energy design.

All components in a roof have a thermal conductance. However, the structure and membrane system alone are unlikely to have sufficient resistance to heat transfer to meet most requirements for buildings. It is therefore necessary to incorporate materials to specifically resist heat transfer – insulants.

Table 4.5.1
Thermal conductivity of materials

Material	Typical thermal conductivity (W/mK)
Aluminium	230
Steel	50
Glass	1.05
Timber	0.15
Plastics (solid)	0.15 – 0.13
Water	0.6
Air	0.026
CFCs	0.008

Further reading:
CIBSE guide: Volume A, Section 3.

- Minimum requirements for insulation (to control energy use) are given by statutory regulations.
- Thermal insulation is a key component of a roof. It may also provide support or protection to the waterproofing membrane, depending on the roof system chosen.
- The insulating properties of some forms of insulation can change with time.

Insulating materials

The conductivity of an insulant is determined by its inherent material property and by the combination with other materials. For instance (Table 4.5.1), the thermal conductivity of a typical plastics material is 0.15W/mK. By creating a foam structure with cell walls of plastics and cells filled with air (λ = 0.026W/mK), a much lower overall heat transfer can be achieved. In such a structure, the air in the cells cannot freely move and convection transfer is restricted. Fibrous insulants are essentially similar in their mechanism, but may be less able to prevent air movement by convection.

If a material absorbs water into previously air-filled spaces, then the thermal conductivity will increase (this can be an issue for inverted roofs). This mechanism may also be important for condensation control, as the formation of condensation within the insulant, or any of the roof materials, will increase its conductivity – reduce its insulating properties – and may in turn lead to further condensation.

Beneficial substitution of air in cellular insulation can also be achieved. Many foamed plastics insulants are formed by using volatile fluids which then remain in the cells once formed. These enable a well-controlled cell structure to be created. Such gases may well have a thermal conductivity lower than that of air, giving a lower overall thermal conductivity. During the useful life of the insulant, some of the gas may diffuse from the cells; equally, as a separate process, some air or vapour may diffuse in. This process is called 'ageing'. A widely-used family of volatile materials for such applications are the chlorofluorocarbons (CFCs); in recent years, questions have been raised as to the environmental impact of these compounds.

Typically, a CFC-blown foam may have a thermal conductivity of 0.015W/mK when new, and be 0.025W/mK or higher after 10-20 years' full exposure. Encapsulated within the roof build-up, this release will be much slower and intermediate values of conductivity at 'middle age' may be more appropriate for thermal transmission calculations.

Other foamed materials used as insulants are manufactured using different gases; for example, carbon dioxide or water vapour. A knowledge of which gas is used will aid understanding of long-term performance and the environmental implications of the products.

Thermal insulation will also contribute to other aspects of roof performance. It can provide significant acoustic insulation dependent on the type of insulant used. It can provide reduction of impact sound (such as that from rain) and, with correct design, can contribute towards acoustic absorption within the building. It may also help to reduce impact sound transfer. Thermal insulation can be used to form the falls of a roof. If the insulation material has a sufficiently high vapour resistance, a separate vapour control layer may not be required; joints, however, must also be sealed if the effect is not to be lost. A number of different insulation materials are available: synthetic foam plastics, natural materials (e.g. cork), inorganic materials (e.g. glass fibre, cellular glass), mineral wool.

Other elements of a roof contribute to the thermal performance. Lightweight screeds, timber and air spaces may make a useful contribution to the overall thermal resistance achieved. Metal components, because of their ability to transmit heat readily, however, may cause cold bridging (see **Unit 4.7**).

Many aspects of thermal performance calculation or prediction are now available on computer programs accessible to the ordinary design office. ■

Critical factors

- Composition of material plus form of combination with other materials.
- Understanding the transmission of heat through building and building fabric.
- Insulant long-term performance.

Further reading in the Guide:
4.6 Solar radiation and thermal effects • 4.7 Condensation • 4.12 Acoustic behaviour • 7.6 Design for thermal performance
8.2 Calculation of thermal performance • 17.1 Insulants

12 Mastic Asphalt	13 Polymeric Single Ply	14 Copper	15 Lead Sheet	16 Other Membranes	17 Thermal Insulants	18 Specification	19 Contracts & Procurement	20 Inspection	21 Maintenance	22 Bibliography	23 Index
263	301	331	353	375	383	393	399	413	429	437	455

4.6 Solar radiation and thermal effects

- Significant levels of energy, and hence heat, from the Sun can impinge upon flat roofs.
- The quantities of energy incident on the roof are related to geographic location, season, weather, and roof orientation.
- The energy actually absorbed by and/or radiated from the roof surface is a function of its nature, exposed surface colour, and texture.

Absorption and radiation

The concepts of thermal conductivity, resistivity and diffusivity, which are important in matters of heat flow into and out of a building, were described in **Unit 4.5**. In this Unit, the effects of temperature change initiated by absorption, or reflection (re-radiation), of radiated solar energy are introduced.

Solar radiation is electromagnetic energy across a large spectrum of wavelengths (the shorter the wavelength the greater the energy transferred). The most obvious is the visible light spectrum, but heat gain and loss from roofs also occurs at other wavelengths (e.g. as in a greenhouse). Radiation with wavelengths just longer than those of visible light is called **infrared** and just shorter than visible light, **ultraviolet.**

The **absorptivity** of a surface will be a primary factor in determining the absorption of radiated energy in all parts of the spectrum. The colour gives a good guide to the balance between the absorption and reflection of solar radiation. In idealised terms, white surfaces reflect energy across a wide range (hence their colour, as all colours in the visible range are reflected); conversely, black surfaces absorb across a wide range and no colours are significantly reflected. A surface able to absorb or radiate all of the energy at the surface is termed a **'black body' radiator**. Other parameters affecting heat gain are the surface 'gloss/matt'; area; inclination; surface roughness; and air movement across the surface. As a rule, the whiter and shinier the surface, the better it performs as a radiation reflector. These surface effects are largely independent of the material's character or other thermal properties.

A flat roof is well placed to receive or emit radiated energy, irrespective of whether it is the membrane or other part of the roof construction which is directly exposed. The total roof system affects how energy is transferred between the building interior and the outside environment. For example, an inverted warm deck roof, with a substantial thickness of insulation, and paving or ballasting, will experience considerably less transfer of solar energy to the membrane, compared to a warm deck roof with the membrane exposed.

Solar radiation can transmit up to 700W/m^2 in the UK and measurements of the surface temperatures of black or dark bodies exposed to direct sunlight have recorded temperatures of 70°C or 80°C. A white surface under the same conditions might be 20°C cooler. Shade air temperatures coincident with these surface temperatures may however only be 30-35°C.

The actual energy taken up by a surface will vary with: the seasons; the location on the Earth's surface – latitude; climate and local weather patterns – clouds, smog, etc; and energy absorption characteristics of the surface.

Insulation can prevent heat absorption by the deck, but may lead to a greater temperature change in the membrane. As surfaces absorb energy during the day, so they lose energy by radiation at night, the **emissivity** being equal to the absorptivity. This loss is greatest with clear night skies. Such radiated losses can reduce surface temperatures to 5°C or more below adjoining air temperatures.

A further consideration is the rate of change of temperatures. Roofs will be expected to accommodate the change from summer to winter conditions. Rapid temperature changes impose significant stress upon a roof construction. They may increase risks of condensation (also see **Unit 4.8**). Surface temperature changes when clouds pass in front of the Sun have been recorded as fast as 5°C fall in 5 seconds, and 17°C fall in 60 seconds have been attributed to a roof subject to rainfall after sunshine.

Thermal capacity

A further thermal property of materials important to the overall performance of roofs is that of **thermal capacity**. This is the quantity of heat required to raise a body by one degree. The related term of **specific heat** is the quantity of heat required to raise the temperature of unit mass of a material by one degree. Hence, in simple situations where the object heats up uniformly (e.g. high conductivity or low mass, such as a metal sheet):

$$\text{Thermal capacity} = \text{Specific heat} \times \text{Mass}$$

A material with a low specific heat (e.g. most plastics) will require little external energy to raise its temperature; similarly, relatively little energy will need to be lost to reduce temperatures. A low specific heat or thermal capacity component in a roof construction will heat and cool more rapidly than materials or components with high specific heat or thermal capacity. It will tend to increase the number, extent and rate of thermal cycles in a roof. Changes in temperature of the roof interact with the component parts of the roof in several ways.

Further reading:
CIBSE guide: Volume A, Section 3.

- The energy absorbed can cause deterioration of the membrane or other exposed roof components.
- Total solar energy equals absorbed plus reflected plus re-emitted energy.
- The actual quantity of energy taken up by the surface depends on many factors, only some of which are within the designer's control. The resulting heat transfer has to be accommodated.

Thermal movements

All materials expand and contract by varying amounts, when subject to changes in temperature. The membrane itself and other components should be capable of accommodating these strains, either by inherent flexibility or by ensuring sufficient free length over which movements can take place (see **Unit 4.3**). Restraint from components such as penetrations or fixed traffic surfaces, can significantly reduce the ability of the roof components – particularly the membrane – to accommodate differential movements.

Most elastic or elastomeric materials are combinations of large organic molecules. Their rheological behaviour is complex. With time, because of the influence of heat and radiation, they can become less flexible, particularly at low temperatures and, if fully fixed to a moving substrate, may be less able to accommodate the induced movements. Conversely, at high temperatures, flow within materials might occur under self-weight of roof components – e.g. creep in bonding bitumens for built-up roofing, slumping on vertical asphalt work, creep in lead. These phenomena are widely recognised and can be avoided by appropriate material selection and detail design.

The term **strain** is defined as the proportional change in dimension of a material under stress. Cycling temperatures can induce fatigue failure in roof components, particularly the membrane. Long-chain-organic molecule materials, as in some membranes, may also show quite different strain accommodation with differing strain rates, such as with rapid temperature movements. In general, less strain accommodation is achieved at faster strain rates. Metal can also suffer fatigue failure when put through cycles of temperature change and where, through poor understanding of restraint, freedom to accommodate the strains is restricted.

The distribution of solar-radiated energy through a roof build-up will be determined by the balance between rate of energy absorption of the surface and the thermal characteristics of the combined array of materials beneath. A high conductivity substrate below a membrane will dissipate the heat build-up more rapidly than a low conductivity layer (see **Unit 4.5**). A high efficiency insulant can significantly increase the peak temperature and the rate of temperature change in the membrane when using a warm roof deck construction. Solar reflective surface treatments are used with some membranes to reduce the significance of the temperatures. With inverted warm deck surface and also buried roofs, the high thermal capacity of the finishes above the membrane will significantly reduce these thermally-induced changes at the membrane.

Chemical changes

The absorption of radiation energy by organic molecules can induce changes in the chemical structure of the materials themselves. For some rubber-based membrane materials, which derive their inherent elasticity from cross-linking between molecular chains, further cross-linking may occur. In time, this will lead to stiffening of the material, with loss of strain capacity and hence possible rupturing in service. **Unit 4.13** gives more information on the nature of these changes.

Bitumens and some polymers will suffer some reduction in flexibility by oxidation. These chemical reactions take place at faster rates with increased temperature. Reduced flexibility can occur when volatile materials are lost from the surface as the result of the high surface temperatures generated by solar radiation.

Water vapour

Moisture beneath a membrane will be heated by absorbed radiant energy and may be converted to vapour in voids or porous materials. The consequent increase in volume and pressure on the membrane can generate blisters and – in extreme cases – cause failure of the membrane. The extent of the risk is a balance between the quantity or availability of moisture (from trapped water or condensation), the ease with which the vapour can disperse, and the quantity of heat energy at the membrane surface.

There is also a balance to be struck between outward vapour pressure 'relief', to avoid blistering, and the reverse path that may allow condensation to occur on the underside of a membrane. The exact material and fixing method will be the principal determinants. This raises a more general consideration of transfers throughout the roof system of vapour and thermal energy – their interactions can cause local condensation problems although a simple analysis may not reveal this. ■

Critical factors

- Solar energy can degrade building materials through heat gain and ultraviolet radiation.
- Solar heat gain can induce significant thermal movement; it can also be abruptly interrupted (e.g. by clouds).

Further reading in the Guide:
4.3 Structure and movement • 4.5 Thermal transmission • 4.8 Condensation: pumping • 4.13 Durability of materials

4.7 Condensation

- Occupants of buildings and their activities generate moisture and raise air temperatures within buildings.
- For much of the year in the UK, external temperatures are lower and relative humidities are generally higher than those inside buildings. But this is not always true for absolute moisture contents.
- The warmer the air, the more water vapour it can contain.
- When moisture-laden air is brought below its dewpoint temperature water condenses.

Vapour

Water can exist in all three physical phases: solid (ice), liquid (water), gas (vapour or steam). The latter two are of interest here. To turn a liquid into a vapour, the molecules require increased energy to escape from the attraction forces of neighbouring molecules. When boiling a kettle we are providing such energy input. At any steady-state energy condition, even at room temperature or below, some of the molecules will already have sufficient energy to escape and hence will evaporate, while other molecules will condense – returning to the liquid state. When the two rates are aligned, an equilibrium or steady-state will be achieved.

The presence of the water molecules in the gaseous state will create a vapour pressure in the system above the liquid/gas interface. This system will achieve equilibrium and thereafter the air cannot hold any more water and thus the term **saturated vapour pressure** (SVP) is used to describe this vapour pressure. Increasing the temperature of the air/vapour system increases its ability to hold water molecules and thus the saturated vapour pressure will also be increased. 'Boiling' occurs when the saturated vapour pressure is equal to atmospheric pressure. It should also be apparent that reducing the temperature of the air/vapour system will reduce its capacity to hold moisture and a net condensation will have to occur to re-establish equilibrium.

Relative humidity

Various terminology is used in discussion of condensation which can be defined against the essentials of physical behaviour described above. **Relative humidity** (RH) is used to describe the quantity of water in the air compared to the maximum it could hold at that temperature. It can either be defined as:

$$\%RH = \frac{M_v}{M_{vs}} \times 100$$

where M_v = mass of water vapour in a given volume of atmosphere

and M_{vs} = mass of an equal volume of saturated water vapour at the same temperature

or, perhaps more commonly

$$RH\,(\%) = \frac{\text{actual vapour pressure}}{\text{saturated vapour pressure}} \times 100$$

When the relative humidity of a given volume of air reaches 100%, i.e. the air has as much water vapour as it can hold, it is said to be at the **dewpoint** (a temperature). Any further water vapour arriving will condense out. Similarly, reducing the air temperature will cause the dewpoint to be passed and water molecules will condense (the lower temperature is a dewpoint for a smaller mass of vapour at 100% RH).

The saturated vapour pressure for any temperature can normally be found in psychrometric tables or calculated from formulae. The relationship between RH, temperature, moisture content of the air and vapour pressure can be plotted on psychrometric charts (see **Unit 8.3** and Project Notebook).

These changes also affect the outside of the roof, as the same physical principles are involved on a larger scale in cloud and rainfall formation.

The relative humidity of air outside a building envelope may be similar or higher to that inside. However, because of the generally higher temperatures indoors, it is probable, for most buildings, that the air on the inside will contain more water vapour and hence have a higher vapour pressure. The sources of water within a building will be primarily people – through perspiration and breathing – the domestic/industrial processes taking place – cooking, washing, combustion of fuels, etc. – or moisture released from the construction. One estimate suggests that a typical UK 4-person household may generate the vapour equivalent of 20-30 litres a day of liquid water, dispersed through the building. Occupancy rates and room volumes thus have a major effect, closely associated with the desirable level of air changes.

A few specialised building types may not create higher internal vapour pressures than outside – e.g. storage buildings. Some might even be lower than outside – e.g. cold stores. Conversely, indoor swimming pools may have very much higher vapour pressures, but this will depend upon the airflow management design used within the building envelope.

Further reading:
BRE Report 143 Thermal Insulation: avoiding risks, HMSO • BS5250 Code of practice for control of condensation in buildings • CIBSE guide Volume A, Section 10

- Condensation can occur on cold surfaces when in contact with moisture-laden air. The quantities, temperatures and location of this potential condition can be predicted by calculations.
- Computer programs exist for condensation risk analysis.

Vapour movement

Wherever there is an imbalance of vapour pressure, other physical laws show that the systems will tend to establish equilibrium via a flow of water vapour. This could be by convection through continuous routes – doors, windows, penetrations – or by diffusion through 'solid' semi-permeable membranes. These movements can be seen as either direct flows or as more complicated interactions (see **Unit 4.8**). Many materials used in construction will be porous and may be permeable. **Permeability** is a widely used – and sometimes misused – term, but has a specific physical meaning. It is a measure of the ability of a solid to allow a fluid (gas or liquid) to pass through when subjected to a pressure differential.

Diffusion is a similar process of fluid flow through a solid, but is related to a concentration differential. For moisture vapour, having a concentration difference also creates a partial pressure difference and thus similar movements may occur.

All materials, even still air, will have some resistance to the movement of vapour. Their relative performance in restricting its movement is an important part of the prediction and control of condensation.

Forms of condensation

As the flow of water vapour occurs through the construction, it may reach zones where the temperature is sufficiently low that the dewpoint (RH = 100%) has been reached and hence condensation will occur within the construction. This is called **interstitial condensation** and is one of the most perplexing conditions to identify, which can cause considerable damage if not avoided. These conditions are most likely to occur in the UK during winter months. In summer months, the dewpoint may not be reached and condensation is less likely. Some condensate formed during winter months may now also evaporate, either inwards or outwards, depending upon the relative vapour pressures and resistances to vapour flow.

Surface condensation is a second form, or manifestation, of condensation which can also be important for roof design. If a surface in contact with vapour-laden air is at a temperature below the dewpoint, then it will cause local condensation from the air onto the surface. More general condensation (e.g. fog) does not form because the air above is warm enough to be above the dewpoint.

Unit 4.6 described the radiation of heat energy from a surface towards a dark night sky. For roof surfaces, particularly metals this can cause surface condensation on the underside of the membrane.

A surface may also be at a lower temperature because it is part of, or connected to, a good heat conductor which exists elsewhere, in part, at a much lower temperature. The conductor is thus called a **cold bridge**. Cold bridges in a roof could be service penetrations, fixings, local changes in construction, or gaps in insulation.

Assessing risk

The thermal capacity (see **Unit 4.6**) of the various roof elements in combination will also be an influence in condensation risk. A construction of high thermal capacity will heat up or cool down more slowly than one with a low thermal capacity. In rapidly-changing environmental conditions, either externally through the weather or internally through deliberate comfort control, the temperature of surfaces of a high thermal capacity construction may not change as quickly as the surrounding air. Thus, surface condensation may be created in cold weather, particularly so if the heating is intermittent.

With an inverted warm deck roof system using a membrane and/or deck with a low thermal capacity, short term condensation can occur inside the roof because the temperature of these low thermal capacity elements is chilled by cold water (from rain or snow melt) running beneath the thermal insulation.

Computer programs exist for calculating/predicting condensation conditions.

Although diffusion can be calculated, many critical issues of condensation risk arise at cold bridges and constructional discontinuities. These are best explored through thorough drawing of the three-dimensional arrangement of the construction. ∎

Critical factors

- Air can contain water vapour to a level determined by its dewpoint.
- Water vapour will try to diffuse through a roof construction to balance vapour pressure differences.
- Although steady-state conditions may be acceptable, local changes in temperature and/or construction can induce condensation.

Further reading in the Guide:
4.6 Solar radiation and thermal effects • 4.8 Condensation: pumping • 7.7 Design for moisture vapour control • 8.3 Calculation of condensation

4.8 Condensation: pumping

- Roofing assemblies invariably incorporate voids. The transient changes in the pressure of such voids can create 'pumping', a process which relies on significant pressure differentials between the void and its surroundings.
- Two forms of 'pumping' can arise. One is induced by changes in the external atmospheric pressure. The other is induced by changes in the temperature of the roof, e.g. as a result of cooling by sudden rain, followed by heating via solar gain.

Differential pressures

In recent years, considerable attention has been given to the effects of local pressure and temperature differences across the often narrow zone of the building enclosure, in walls and roofing. The precise physics of the mechanisms, and their long-term significance, are still a matter of debate.

Roofing assemblies invariably incorporate voids, whether deliberately (as in cold deck roof systems) or as a characteristic of materials (as some insulants) or inadvertently between components which are not correctly bonded. Many such voids will be 'enclosed', and their pressure may differ from the surrounding air pressures. They do not readily re-establish equilibrium because of relatively slow changes of the enclosed air volume. Two manifestations are identified – 'atmospheric pumping' and 'thermal pumping'.

Atmospheric pumping

As the external air pressure varies, perhaps because of local wind effects, there will be fluctuating pressure potentials between the exterior, the enclosed voids and the building interior (see **Unit 4.10**). For cold deck roofs, the pressure differential is required to provide the intended ventilation and thus expel the vapour-laden air from the roof space.

The concern is that venting of the roof void can mean that the relative humidity of the internal void air will roughly match that of the immediate exterior. If the external surface temperature (e.g. of a metal sheet membrane) is at the dewpoint for that relative humidity (see **Unit 4.7**), so will be the underside of that same membrane. Condensation can equally occur on both the outside and inside surfaces. For this reason, some authorities now question the venting of cold deck roofs.

Thermal pumping

The second type of action, termed 'thermal pumping' by Bickerdike Allen Partners of London, who have elucidated the mechanism, relies on a cyclic pattern of positive and negative pressure differentials arising from changes in temperature of the enclosed void.

The void may have fine gaps or hairline cracks or minor penetrations of its enclosure (e.g. fixings of the VCL, or gaps at metal seams), any of which allow passage of significant volumes of warm humid air provided there is a suitable pressure differential. Differentials can arise because of temperature changes, induced by sudden rainstorms, external air temperature, solar gain, and night sky radiation.

If the temperature drops, the pressure will reduce if the volume of air in the void cannot change rapidly and in step. This is governed by the ideal gas law. The product of the pressure (P) and the volume (V) of a given mass of gas are directly proportional to the Absolute Temperature (T), expressed as: $PV = RT$, where R is a constant. Similarly, if the temperature rises and the volume and mass of enclosed air cannot change in step, the pressure increases.

Rather more slowly, and under the driving force of the pressure differential, air will either be sucked in or blown out. Because of the time lags induced by constriction of flow at fine cracks, etc., the transient behaviour of the total gas in the enclosed void differs from what would be expected if the volume of air could change immediately with the changes of surrounding temperature and/or pressure.

Combined pumping

A particular problem which has involved both forms of pumping has arisen in recent years with some lead sheet roofing. The microclimate has induced pressure differentials across the metal-metal folded seams with sub-atmospheric pressures generated between the vapour control layer and the covering. Because the joints can 'breathe', as rainwater runs across the roof surface, it can be sucked into the joint. This partly seals the joint, increasing the restriction of ventilation under the lead sheet and hence exacerbating the differentials, which may then suck in water from the joint.

The condensate may evaporate before recondensing in other areas where it may cause damage or water penetration. It may condense on the underside of the lead sheet and, as pure water, induce corrosion. The water may enter the building, either through soaking and capillarity or through pressure-assisted capillarity. The Lead Sheet Association has proposed construction details to overcome this potential problem.

Further reading:
ANDERSON, J.M. & GILL, J.R. Rainscreen cladding, • LDA/LSA Leadwork Technical Note 3.

- Such mechanisms can arise in forms of roof assembly involving previously acceptable standards of design and construction. Their recognition or detection can be extremely complex.

- The incidence has increased with conditions in today's buildings with higher thermal insulation performance, warmer interiors, and greater airtightness.

- 'Pumping' can cause interstitial condensation which may create the appearance of a leak into the building.

Condensation through pumping

Particular problems of condensation can arise from these mechanisms. This is outlined in a sequence:

Consider a notional roof space (Figure 4.8.1), where the external pressures (P1, P2, P3) vary because of wind, etc. They also vary from the pressures in the roof space (P4) and the building interior (P5). If P5 is sufficiently higher than P4, warm vapour-laden air can be driven from the interior to the roof space, via imperfect joints, fine cracks, etc. in the construction–even if a vapour control layer (VCL) has been installed. The humid air has been 'pumped' into the roof space.

This air raises the relative humidity of the air in the roof space (RH4), as it is now at the lower temperature T4 compared to temperature T5 and relative humidity RH5, when below the ceiling (Figure 4.8.2). However, because of cooling effects from the outdoor environment next to the roof surface (e.g. recent rain), there may be surfaces in the roof space which are at a lower temperature (T6).

If T6 is at or below the dewpoint for air at relative humidity RH4, vapour will condense on that surface (Figure 4.8.3). If the roof space is effectively enclosed (i.e. poorly ventilated), that condensate can collect on the VCL or in absorbent materials. It may not leak back through the ceiling to the interior. Depending on the atmospheric conditions, it may slowly evaporate to the outside, but the roof space may remain damp–or even wet–for prolonged periods.

If the roof space then heats up, perhaps from solar gain (Figure 4.8.4), P4 may then exceed P5.

If the differential between P4 and P5 is great enough (Figure 4.8.5), the earlier 'pumping action' is reversed. Provided that the water reaches those same fine cracks, etc., through which it entered the roof space as vapour, it can be driven back into the building by pressure-assisted capillary action. The effect on the ceiling is liquid water, possibly maintained over a period by the capillary action. This can give the initial impression of a roof leak, when in fact the waterproof membrane is still intact. The true mechanism of failure can require considerable skill and analysis before detection. In examining apparent leaks, it is therefore important to establish whether their occurrence is closely associated with rainstorms: if so, their origins are more likely leakage than pumping, but will still need careful study. ■

Note: These diagrams are not to scale. They are intended to illustrate general behaviour in a void but do not apply to cold deck roofs.

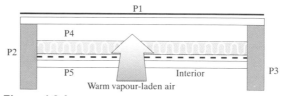

Figure 4.8.1

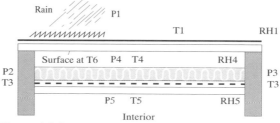

Figure 4.8.2

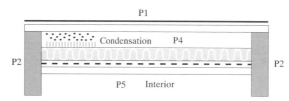

Figure 4.8.3

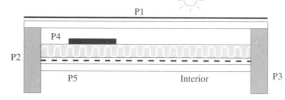

Figure 4.8.4

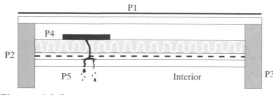

Figure 4.8.5

Critical factors

- Rate of ventilation of roof voids.
- Fluctuating weather conditions coincident with 'leaks'.
- Increased levels of thermal insulation separating void from building interior.

Further reading in the Guide:
4.7 Condensation • 4.10 Wind

12 Mastic Asphalt	13 Polymeric Single Ply	14 Copper	15 Lead Sheet	16 Other Membranes	17 Thermal Insulants	18 Specification	19 Contracts & Procurement	20 Inspection	21 Maintenance	22 Bibliography	23 Index
263	301	331	353	375	383	393	399	413	429	437	455

4.9 Fire behaviour

- Fire can directly affect building users by heat or smoke. It can also affect the stability of the structure and the safety of adjacent buildings.
- Materials selection is the key to fire performance. It is not always appropriate to select non-combustible materials, so knowledge of an individual material's behaviour is essential.

Fire and buildings

Fires generate heat and smoke. Building designers, constructors, owners and users need to know how the performance of their structure in fire is affected by design and by the selection of materials.

If a building structure, fabric or contents start to burn, two key functions have to be achieved to prevent loss of life. First, the structure must remain stable for long enough for the occupants to reach safety or be rescued. Second, the fabric must contain the fire for long enough to prevent it spreading to adjacent properties. The ability of the elements of a building to survive exposure to fire is known as the period of fire resistance. To protect both building occupants and the emergency rescue services, minimum periods of fire resistance are given in guidance to meet *The Building Regulations*. These are presented in Approved Document B, Fire Safety.

Fire and resistance to it involves energy and energy transfer. Safety in fire is heavily dependent on peoples' behavioural response to, and perception of a fire.

The chemistry of fire

Most materials are chemically stable in the atmosphere and at room temperature, but there are a few exceptions (such as phosphorus) that can ignite spontaneously. The majority of combustible materials need heat energy before they can ignite. All fires need an ignition source; this need not be a flame, it can be radiant heat source (such as an electric element). Eventually, depending upon the material, the surface may start to decompose and volatile gases will be evolved. This process does not occur for most inorganic materials unless they incorporate organic additives such as resin binders.

During heating, organic materials (e.g. paper or wood) eventually produce volatile, short-chain hydrocarbons (e.g. methane). Often, these will not burn by themselves. They need to be mixed with oxygen before they chemically react during combustion to form water and carbon dioxide (CO_2). The amount of oxygen required to produce a given amount of heat is approximately the same for all materials. If oxygen is absent, decomposition occurs without flame. Some heat is evolved, but no flames are evolved. An example is the production of charcoal (almost pure carbon) from wood at relatively low temperatures in conditions of restricted air supply. Charcoal is later used as a fuel that burns at a relatively high temperature – in a plentiful supply of oxygen (such as the bellows-assisted blacksmith's furnace).

Flames are therefore not produced if oxygen is not present during heating. However, within buildings, a critical fuel/oxygen mix is likely to form and a fire hazard can exist. Flames will also be inhibited if other more reactive elements are present. Useful flame inhibitors include the reactive halides (such as chlorine) which react with volatile gases during heating to form non-flammable stable compounds, such as hydrogen chloride (HCl). Flame extinguishing systems often include halons (halogenated hydrocarbons – usually bromine) as '**reactive flame inhibitors**' or CO_2 as an '**inert flame inhibitor**' (oxygen suppressant). The use of halons is now discouraged because of concerns over the effects on the atmosphere.

The characteristics of materials in combustion are complex. PVC, for example, forms HCl rather than CO_2 and water (H_2O) and therefore has inherently lower flammability. Other plastics (e.g. polyethylene) are only capable of producing more reactive short-chain hydrocarbons, and are therefore highly flammable if heated above a critical temperature.

Rate of fire spread

If a fire develops within a building, the danger to occupants is both direct and indirect. Heat and smoke are immediate hazards, but building collapse could occur some time later. Peoples' perception of risk from fire is often determined by their experience of it. Burning rubbish outside gives little idea of the movement of smoke and heat inside a room or building. Outside, smoke and heat rise to safety; inside they spread and may quickly affect and trap people. Media presentation of fire is often unrealistic: effects of radiation are difficult to convey; smoke inside buildings is not photogenic. Peoples' concept of fire and its effects on them inside buildings is therefore unrealistic. The dangers are perceived to be less than they actually are. The rapid rate of development and spread of real fires usually takes observers by surprise.

Fire tests

Heat energy from a fire is transmitted by conduction, convection and radiation; and these processes occur simultaneously during flame spread. The British Standard tests have been designed to investigate the performance of

Further reading:
Approved Document B of the Building Regulations, as amended 1992 • BS476 Fire tests on building materials and structures

© BFRC / CIRIA: Flat Roofing: Design and Good Practice. 1993

- Most materials decompose when heated, but only some evolve flammable gases. Materials only catch fire when, on heating, they evolve a flammable gas.

a combination of materials or components with or without a test load. Laboratory tests alone are rarely truly representative of the scale, complexity and diversity of situations in real building fires, but they provide crucial reference data for the design and development of materials to be used in buildings.

To evaluate the likely fire performance, standardised test procedures have been established within *BS476*. This standard describes fire tests for both materials and systems.

Whether a material is inside, outside or part of the structure of a building, its performance in a fire may affect the performance of the whole building, and therefore the safety of the occupants and adjacent property.

Parts 4, 6 and 7 of *BS476* are most commonly used to describe the performance of materials in terms of reaction to the tests. Part 4 is the non-combustibility test which demonstrates whether the test material significantly adds to the fuel load during a fire. Only inorganic materials pass this test. Part 6 measures the same property, but under both radiant heat and naked flames. It is called ' Method of test for fire propagation'. This test can be useful for comparing different materials, but has most significance when it is required alongside the Part 7 'Surface spread of flame' test.

Part 7 presents a means of categorising materials into 4 classes depending upon their 'spread of flame' characteristics. Class 1 demonstrates least spread of flame and Class 4 the worst. Class 0 is not part of the Standard, but is defined in the *Approved Document*. Class 0 sometimes needs to be specified (e.g. exterior cladding for flats), and can only be achieved if the material achieves the best performance category for both Parts 6 and 7 of the Standard.

Structures or systems of components depend upon the materials from which they are made and the interaction between those materials during a fire. Standard tests are available to record and categorise systems, in terms of their period of fire resistance and load bearing capacity during exposure.

Specific tests are also available for evaluating roof structures. These tests demonstrate how well a roof protects the building from, say, burning debris falling from other buildings.

Table 4.9
Summary of *BS476* fire tests relevant to roofs

BS476 part	Title
3	External fire exposure test.
4	Non-combustibility tests for materials.
6	Method of test for fire propagation for products.
7	Method of classification of the surface spread of flame of products.
20	Method for the determination of the fire resistance of elements of construction (general principles).
21	Method for the determination of the fire resistance of loadbearing elements of construction.
22	Method for the determination of the fire resistance of non-loadbearing elements of construction.

Building cavities can play a major role in spreading fire. Cavities need to be interrupted with appropriate materials to prevent flame or smoke spread.

An external fire exposure roof test is described in *BS476: Part 3: 1958*. Although this test method is in an obsolete standard it is still referred to in the *Approved Document* (see **Unit 7.9**). This test is the standardised procedure for monitoring the integrity and flame propagation of a panel representing the roof construction. It should always be carried out on the total roofing system and not just the 'outermost layer'. The performance of materials and systems in the fire tests determines their location in relation to a boundary and on the type of occupancies in which they may be used.

Further *BS476* tests have been developed to categorise the performance of structural elements (Part 21) and non-load bearing components (Part 22) during a period of exposure to a standardised test fire.

Further information on the use of these tests in the design of roofs is given in **Unit 7.9**. ∎

Critical factors

- Understanding the chemistry of fire.
- Speed of fire spread.
- Nature of tests.

Further reading in the Guide:
7.9 Design for fire safety • 17.1 Selection of insulants

4.10 Wind

- Wind can generate positive and negative forces on roofs. These must be resisted by the roof system to prevent damage.
- The magnitude of wind forces depends upon the height and shape of the building, together with the local terrain and climate.
- The security of a multiple component roof exposed to wind depends upon the negative pressure (or suction) above the system and the positive pressures that develop within the building, or within the roof composite itself.

Air movement

Wind is generated as air flows from regions of high pressure to regions where the pressure is lower. Just as a convector heater generates a gentle though discernible air flow, so 'energised' hot air expands and causes movement to disperse its energy to cooler areas. When this process occurs on a global scale, and air movements are caused by temperature and pressure gradients across seas and land masses, air movements can become rapid and destructive.

Different countries experience different climates and this is often a result of local wind patterns or prevailing wind directions. In the same way, but on a different scale, buildings can experience their own local micro-climate. Generally, the climatic changes around individual buildings are not noticed by building users. However, they can be significant if they induce high wind forces at street level. These wind forces occur at a microclimatic level and scale upon the whole roof structure, where they affect the integrity of roofing details and individual roofing components.

Wind forces

The principles

The varying effects of simpler wind forces can be illustrated by the following examples. When wind hits a flat upright panel, such as a fencing panel, atmospheric pressure exists on one side; but higher pressure develops on the windward side. Eventually, if wind pressure is enough to overcome the resistance of the fence posts, and there is no equal and opposite force on the other side of the panel, it will be pushed down where its wind resistance – and therefore the pressure differential – are both minimal. But different shapes experience or induce different forces, as another example makes plain.

As air moves at different rates over the upper and lower surfaces of an aircraft wing, resulting from forward motion created by the engines, the negative pressure (suction) formed above the wing, and the relatively higher pressures developing underneath the wing, together develop enough forces to overcome gravity acting on the mass of the aircraft and thus enable it to fly.

Buildings experience a mixture of wind forces. When wind strikes the face of a flat-roofed building, it causes positive pressure on that face. The wind is deflected around and over the building, and it causes a reduction in

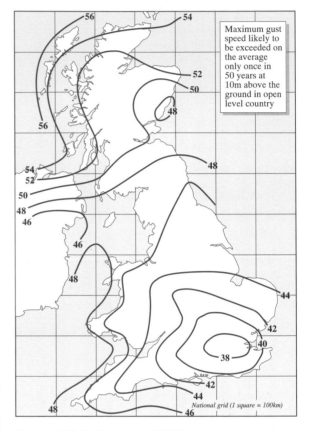

Maximum gust speed likely to be exceeded on the average only once in 50 years at 10m above the ground in open level country

National grid (1 square = 100km)

Figure 4.10.1 - based on *BSCP3*
Basic wind speed (m/s)

pressure (suction) on the top surface of the roof and on the end walls of the building (Figure 4.10.2). Openings, such as doors and windows on the windward side of the building, will allow a positive internal pressure build-up. This pressure may act on the underside of the roof, in addition to any negative pressure above, and could increase the likelihood of roof failure. This 'push and pull' mechanism can also occur as a result of local impact damage or component failure on the windward side of the building. Furthermore, the integrity of roofing systems can be affected by the permeability of the various layers in a roof system.

The walls of a building are designed to resist lateral – as well as vertical – loads imposed by the roof and floor

---

Further reading:
SPRA (BFRC) Guide for the assessment of wind loads acting in roofs • BSCP3 : Chapter V: Part 2 Wind loads

---

- The air permeability of different layers, significantly affected by care in design and installation, can affect the likelihood and mode of failure.

- Wind forces can cause secondary hazards, such as displacement of components, gravel or pebble ballast. This could affect both the performance of the roof and the safety of people.

structures, the building user, and wind forces. The roof largely relies upon gravitational forces to keep it in position, with strapping down as well. Should sufficient extreme wind pressures be generated, roofs may be lifted off before walls are blown down.

With all these effects, the greater the wind speed the greater will be the pressures generated. Roof structures must therefore be designed to overcome the various forces that are developed in high winds.

Basic data

Meteorological records provide information on basic wind speeds in the UK (Figure 4.10.1). However, the wind speed experienced by a particular building will be influenced by:

- nearby topography (hills, valleys, cliffs, escarpments or ridges) and ground cover, which may accelerate or decelerate the wind
- the degree of exposure – a high building on flat open moorland will be subjected to greater wind speeds than a low building in a town centre
- the life of the building (the longer a building stands, the greater the statistical probability it will experience extreme wind speeds).

Local effects

Wind forces not only affect the stability of the roof as a whole, but also develop local zones of high and low pressure of different locations around the roof, especially at edges and other discontinuities. Local zones can develop enough fluctuating forces to compromise the integrity of roofing components, the fixings through to the roof structure, the security of gravel ballast layers, and even the structure itself. This is especially likely if wind blows obliquely onto the building. As most sites can experience wind from any direction, not just the direction of the prevailing wind (as shown on wind rose maps), roofing details need special considerations, taking account of context and topography.

Unit 7.10 shows how the various wind forces described here are considered in flat roof design.

The critical layer

In any flat roof construction subjected to the 'push and pull' wind forces, there will be a **critical layer** where these forces will be at a maximum. This usually occurs at the

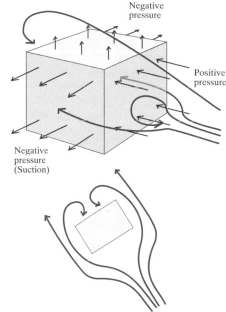

**Figure 4.10.2
Positive and negative pressures induced by wind**

most air impermeable layer, nearest to the building interior and can cause this layer to act like a diaphragm. If the diaphragm is too weak, or is inadequately bonded, the critical layer will be the weak link and delamination or rupture can occur.

The roof above the critical layer will generally not be vulnerable to wind uplift if the critical layer, and all layers above it, are adequately sealed against air beneath that layer. This favourable effect arises from the presence of a small but finite quantity of air trapped between layers. As wind uplift acts on such a layer, the upward pressure creates a counterbalancing (but not necessarily equal) downward suction in the trapped air below the layer, which helps to hold it in place. This does however require that the construction below the layer is airtight, or at least effectively so, to prevent the suction being destroyed by the inflow of more air while uplift is acting. Hence thorough sealing is essential.

The impact of the critical layer and its identification are described in **Unit 7.10**. ■

Critical factors

- Complexity of wind-induced stresses on complete roof assembly.
- Wind action from any direction not just prevailing wind.
- Identification of critical layer.
- Resistance to uplift.

Further reading in the Guide:
7.10 Design for wind resistance • 8.4 Calculation of wind uplift

4.11   Traffic on roofs

- All roofs will bear some traffic during their life.
- The extent, frequency and types of loading will vary, from limited access (for maintenance only), to roofs trafficked by heavy wheeled vehicles.
- Loads may be static or dynamic. They can cause abrasion as well as deflection and, hence, if not properly considered, may damage components by indentation, fatigue, surface abrasion, tearing, etc.

Occurrence of traffic

All roofs will receive some traffic during their life, and a roof design should try to anticipate that which is likely to occur, from consideration of the projected building use. The nature and frequency will vary greatly. Consideration needs to be given to the effects of traffic on the roof and what extra protection, if any, should be provided. This should include the construction phase as traffic may occur during installation; other site works may also impose unpredicted loads and traffic upon the roofing already installed (partially or completely).

Roofs with least amount of traffic will be where the roof is designed not to be accessed, possibly without roof-mounted equipment or facilities. Such roofs will, however, still need access several times a year for maintenance – details, gullies, etc. Often, roofs will have plantrooms or facade access cradles, to which regular/ frequent access for monitoring, use, or maintenance is required. Other roofs may be used as part of the external space of a project, for example terraces for recreation or for safety refuge in commercial developments. Access decks in retail developments may be similar in nature. The most severe load conditions for roofs are those where vehicles (cars, lorries, fire engines, etc.) have access.

Patterns of traffic

General roof maintenance routes will follow few, if any, predetermined traffic patterns. Other than the point of access to the roof, the route thereafter is likely to be random and not repeated from one visit to another. The actual loadings encountered will be light. Roofs accessed for maintenance of plant, or parts of the building, will often have predetermined routes to and from the entry point. Some routes may be designed, although the tendency is to use the most obvious or direct routes.

Machinery, plant or tools essential to maintenance are likely to traffic the roof and may be carried or require wheeled trolleys. Pedestrian access terraces will be regularly trafficked by larger numbers of people than for the non-general access. It is likely they can also bring hazards to the roof as well as increased local loadings. Such hazards could be cigarettes, sharp implements, glasses, rubbish, umbrellas, etc. Some liquids (e.g. oils, even milk!) can affect some roofing materials if spilt.

Characteristics of loads

The loads resulting from trafficking of the roof will be static or dynamic, the latter sometimes producing abrasion. **Static loads** are the easiest to visualise and to design against. *BS6399: Part 3* gives design-imposed loads for the roof and roof covering for two categories of roof: those with no access except for cleaning and repair; those with access in addition to cleaning and repair.

Dynamic loads, such as those from wheeled vehicles, are sometimes more difficult to define and design for. They produce a different rate of loading to static loads, may be more concentrated, variable (depending upon compression in the wheel itself), and produce lifting forces after passage of the wheel. Direct effects of loadings might be evaluated by assessing the load compression character-istics of the various components – for example the insulation in a sandwich warm deck roof. In a cold deck roof, the critical capacity is that of the deck spanning between supports with sufficiently little deflection to prevent damage to the membrane. Stiffness under static or dynamic loads is often the more important criterion than resistance against load to complete failure.

Where materials of different stiffness are incorporated within the roof and the load moves across them, the differing axial stiffness may be sufficient to cause membrane rupture. This might occur with a mechanically spot-fixed membrane, because of the axial stiffness of the fixing, compared to the surrounding insulation, or the use of a locally stiffer underlay to the membrane (e.g. insulant) in walkway areas.

Abrasion comes either from scrubbing actions of wheels, when turning, or from scuffing from pedestrian traffic; these are two-dimensional movements, in the plane of the roof. They are very difficult to determine or measure in a meaningful way. Some laboratory test methods exist, but their mimicking of real abrasion is not good. They are therefore difficult to design against on a codified basis, and previous experience is the best guidance available.

Resistance and protection

The primary requirement in consideration of traffic is that the roof itself should not suffer permanent damage. This applies to all the component parts of the roof. The overall roof structure should be capable of withstanding the

Further reading:
BS6399: Part 3. Code of practice for imposed roof loads • GLC Materials and Development Bulletin No.43 (2nd series) 1971

- Standardised loads and methods of calculation are available only for some aspects of traffic loadings.
- Roof components may be able inherently to withstand the traffic loads, but the design has always to be assessed to see whether specific measures need to be taken.

imposed loads without undue deflection or damage (see **Unit 4.3**). The significance of the way in which the roof can withstand loads will be different for different roof types. In a warm deck roof, the insulant must be able to resist the compressive forces so that the membrane above does not rupture. In an inverted warm deck roof, the membrane is beneath the insulation so this is less relevant. Different membrane materials will also have different requirements. For abrasion resistance, some membranes will have more inherent resistance than others: advice should be sought from individual manufacturers.

In resisting imposed loads, it is essential to assess whether the basic roof construction will be satisfactory or whether extra measures may be required. Extra measures could include:

- **Increasing the thickness** of some of the roof components, e.g. of mastic asphalt.
- Placing **extra layers** of the same components, e.g. for built-up roofing .
- **Overlaying** the roof – locally or generally – with other systems designed specifically to provide protection e.g walkway mats (Figures 4.11.1 and 4.11.2), concrete overlays.
- Special **raised walk/railways** fixed directly to primary structure.

Levels and tripping

Where localised extra protection layers are provided, the free edges provide the opportunity for pedestrians to trip, as do areas with discrete paviors. There are no codified rules for what size of step will generate a **tripping** hazard.

Slip resistance

Slip and skid resistance for pedestrians and vehicles are related issues. They are governed essentially by the coefficient of friction between the surface and the shoe/wheel concerned. However, marked differences in values of resistance will be found for dry and wet conditions. Smooth sheet materials will often have adequate slip resistance when dry but will be extremely slippery when wet. Vehicular traffic will normally be running on asphalt or concrete surfaces and existing guidance can be followed.

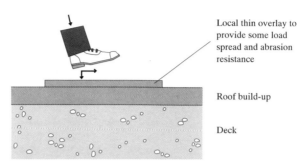

Local thin overlay to provide some load spread and abrasion resistance

Roof build-up

Deck

Figure 4.11.1
Thin overlay and resolution of force into vertical and slipping components

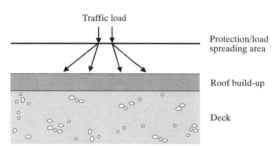

Traffic load

Protection/load spreading area

Roof build-up

Deck

Figure 4.11.2
Load spreading through an overlay

Some scientific principles can be applied to the slip resistance of surfaces for pedestrians (Figure 4.11.1). When walking, a person will come into contact with the roof generally via a small contact area of heel. The leg will usually be at an angle to the roof surface. The direction of force can be resolved into a vertical component (the load on the roof) and a horizontal component. The horizontal component is resisted, or not, by friction with the roof. It has been proposed that, if the coefficient of friction is greater than 0.4, slipping is unlikely to occur.

Slip resistance is important for the safety of public access roofs and for limited access. Some measurements of slip resistance are possible using the swinging foot pendulum device used for roads and other surfaces. ■

Further reading in the Guide:
4.3 Structure and movement • 7.11 Design for traffic and load spreading • 17.1 Selection of insulants

4.12   Acoustic behaviour

- Sound is a form of vibration energy, transmitted in a medium (e.g. air, concrete structure). Its control is important to comfort and even to health.
- Sound can be transmitted along continuous paths through air or solid structures. Blocking air paths or breaking the continuity of structures can reduce unwanted sound transmission.
- Roofs can transmit exterior noise, such as drumming rain or aircraft noise, into buildings.

Sound as vibration

The term **acoustics** encompasses all forms of sound and noise vibration. Hearing and vibration-awareness is one of the most influential senses that humans possess. The acoustics of a building, or part of the building, can determine how successfully the building meets the occupants' needs. Too many sounds, or too much sound of a particular type, leads to noise (harmful and/or unwanted sound). Building users often need protection from noise, so it is important to understand the fundamentals of sound and how building design can affect what the occupant hears.

Motion can create vibration, which may be sensed as sound. There is motion all around and within buildings and the design of the roof can influence how much external sound, such as traffic noise, enters the building. It affects how much the occupant can hear external influences on the building, such as rainwater drumming on the roof. It can affect the dispersal or transmission of interior sounds, such as machines or voices, within and across the building.

Sound travels as vibration waves, which we can hear because energy is transmitted via the air to sensitive organs within our ears. Audible vibration can be continuous (the constant drone of motorway traffic), intermittent (the sounds from a television), or discrete (the sound of a door slamming).

Sound transmission

Someone speaking close by can usually be heard without much difficulty. This is because there is an uninterrupted path, via the air, between their mouth and our ear. However, if they speak quietly, the listener's ears might not receive enough sound energy to make sense of this signal. Consider a simple telephone made from a piece of string stretched between two empty tin cans. The listener can hear a quiet voice, transmitted from the speaker's mouth, via the air, to the speaker's tin can, then via the string to the listener's tin can, then via the listener's tin can to the listener's ear via the air. In this example, sound energy is transmitted by three media – fluid (air) and solid (string and can).

Within buildings, sound transmission occurs in the same way. Sound can be transmitted directly via the air (through an open door) or indirectly (through the

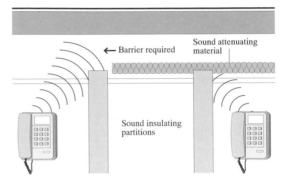

Figure 4.12.1
Direct airborne sound

structure). So two types of sound transmission need to be considered; **direct airborne** (Figure 4.12.1) – from one room to another via an open door, via the cracks around the door, or via a continuous void (e.g. ceiling vents adjoining roof voids, or rooflights); **indirect airborne** (Figure 4.12.2) – from a source (e.g. a radio or an aeroplane) to the structure (e.g. a downstairs wall), then via the structure to another part of the structure (e.g. upstairs or the neighbour's wall), then from the structure to the listener's ear.

Both examples involve sounds created in the air. Impact on solid materials also generates sound and this can also be transmitted via the structure. Examples of impact sounds include rainwater drumming on the roof or foot traffic on terraced roofing.

To reduce the amount of sound energy transmitted by air or by the structure, the energy must be reflected away or absorbed.

Sound reflections

We can generate an echo by speaking into a pipe, whistling down a tunnel, or shouting in a quarry. An echo is airborne sound, reflected back to us from a solid surface. Generally, hard surfaces (like steel sheet) reflect sound more efficiently than soft, irregular surfaces like softboard. Use of reflective materials can be advantageous if sound is reflected away from the listener, or disruptive if sound is reflected towards the listener. Similarly, non-reflective materials, e.g. carpet which diffuses airborne sounds, can reduce the amount of sound energy dispersed.

Further reading:
BS8233: Sound insulation and noise reduction for buildings • FORSYTH, M. Buildings for music • PARKIN, P. & HUMPREYS, H. Acoustics, noise and buildings • CIRIA Report 127 Sound control for homes • BRE Digest 337 Sound insulation: basic principles; Digest 338 Insulation against external noise

4.12

Sound absorption

Just as motion generates sound, so sound generates motion.

In acoustic terms, sound exerts an oscillating force upon a mass, and it produces an oscillating acceleration. If this occurs over a period of time, work is done and energy transformed from sound energy (air movement) to kinetic energy (small movements of the mass). If the mass is a wall, or a roof, the amount of energy absorbed in transmission – the insulating effect – will depend on the mass of the wall or roof. The heavier the mass, the greater the absorption.

Sound insulation is measured in decibels (dB). This is an expression of energy attenuation (the ratio of emitted energy to received energy) and is arranged on a logarithmic scale. Table 4.12.1 shows how the mass or density of a material affects its sound insulation. Note also, the effect of rooflights at only 10% of the roof area.

Table 4.12.1
Sound reduction for various constructions based on their mass

Roof construction	Approximate sound reduction
a) Concrete of mass not less than 200kg/m³.	45
b) Metal trough deck and insulating board, no ceiling.	34
c) Timber and boarding, with ceiling.	30 – 35
d) Timber and boarding, without ceiling.	20 – 25
e) as a, b or c with rooflights	25

Materials can therefore be used to absorb sound energy. However, they will only be effective if they 'intercept' the sound (direct, indirect, or reflected) along its various possible transmission routes (via air or structure).

Impact sound can be absorbed at source (e.g. place carpet on the floor to neutralise footsteps). Airborne transmission can be absorbed by dense materials (e.g. block cavities with dense metal shielding). In certain critical cases, transmission through the structure may have to be disrupted by introducing an acoustic isolator – such as a flexible rubber pad – between elements of the structure.

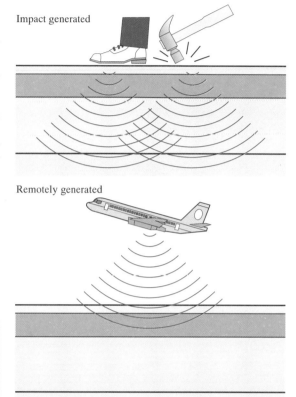

Impact generated

Remotely generated

Figure 4.12.2
Indirect airborne sound

A combination of dense absorptive materials, shaped reflective materials and perforated or soft diffusive materials, may be necessary to reduce sound transmission to permissible levels. They could be used as part of the roof structure, additional to the roof covering, or placed within the roof void to prevent transmission from one room ceiling to another, or from one building via a common roof to an adjacent building.

General control

BS8233: 1987 contains advice on the special measures required for controlling sound transmission. This Standard includes advice on ventilation or air-conditioning ducts which penetrate roof spaces or transfer noise from room to room. ∎

Critical factors

- Sound sensitivity of building functions.
- Consider how artificial is acoustic environment.
- Noise intrusion from outside.
- Noise escape from building.
- Noise reflection and attenuation inside building.

4.13 Durability of materials

- Durability is an important consideration for the long-term performance of a roof. Materials and components should be selected which resist the natural degradation processes.
- Materials in a roof system are affected by exposure to environmental conditions and by interaction with other materials. The most important environmental agencies are solar radiation, water, oxygen, biological organisms.

Concepts

Durability of materials and buildings is a subject which can generate much debate and even emotion. There are widely-expressed views that the materials used in construction are not durable enough and that they should be better. Although some materials have performed below expectations, there are a number of factors which have exaggerated this for flat roofs. The most clear cut are: the high degree of exposure to harsh environmental conditions, the relatively long expectations for life of a roof, and changes in other facets of building design (e.g. energy conservation) (Figure 4.13.1).

The term 'durable' is difficult to define and its description may lead people to use various concepts and phraseology. A broadly-based definition could be taken as 'the property of achieving performance for the required service life'. This definition then requires that both **'adequate performance'** and **'required service life'** are defined. These two criteria are at the heart of the durability debate.

Performance

Modern manufacturing methods are capable of producing highly technical products to a consistent and appropriately high quality. In-house quality control, conformance with standards, and certification by third parties: all can give

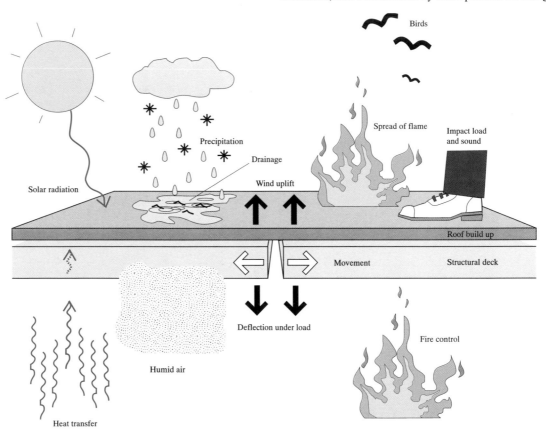

Figure 4.13.1
Performance of the roof

Further reading:
DAVIS, G. & VENTRE, F. Performance of buildings and serviceability of facilities • MASTERS, L.W. Service life prediction: a state of the art • BS7543: Guide to durability of buildings and building elements.

- The ability of roof components to resist mechanical loadings are determined by the size and frequency of the loads and by the change in material properties.
- In accelerated testing, it is not usually possible to simulate fully the complexities of weathering regimes on real buildings.

confidence that the required consistency of production is achieved. The majority of products will have been produced by companies with specialist knowledge of the materials and end-use requirements. Testing will have been carried out to show compatibility of performance and requirements. However, the generally long-term nature of the required service life and the complex options for component combinations make it very difficult for testing by manufacturers at the time of production accurately to reflect the likely real performance of roof components in a system. Accelerated testing is very unlikely to be able to simulate the complexity of conditions that will alter the properties of materials with time.

The physics and chemistry of material degradation

There are four aspects of degradation which are important for flat roofs. These are: chemical; biological; mechanical; those associated with water. Some of the underlying principles are discussed below.

All atoms, molecules, compounds and materials exist in an 'energy state'. That is, by virtue of their composition and structure, they have energy trapped within them. There is an inherent physical trend for materials to tend to the lowest energy state that they can. For example, a volume of water will, if free from outside influences (e.g. gravity), tend to form a spherical drop, as this reduces its surface energy for any given volume to a minimum. In other situations, two elements or compounds may find it energetically beneficial to combine, by reaction, to form a new compound. The most obvious example in construction is that of metals.

Most elemental metals, with the exception of the noble metals (gold, silver, etc.), exist in their natural state in the ground as compounds—especially as ores (oxides and sulphides). The essential feature of the extraction and separation of the useful metal form is the input of significant energy. In service, the tendency is for the metal to revert back to its more stable form of oxides, etc. Different metals do so to different extents, but the conditions which affect these processes are outside the scope of this Guide.

Bitumen and asphalt materials degrade—become more brittle—by reaction with oxygen when exposed (as in a roof membrane). Some oxidation is beneficial during the

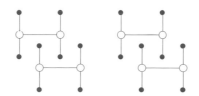

Elasticity from chain interaction

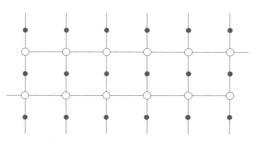

Interaction reduced after chain scission

Increased strength and reduced elasticity with full cross-linking

Figure 4.13.2
Schematic representation of polymer degradation

manufacture of bitumens, giving a degree of hardness and toughness.

With polymeric materials, significant energy is introduced into the system during the extraction of raw materials from oil and their conversion into materials based on long-chain complex molecules. In service the tendency is for these compounds (Figure 4.13.2) to break down into shorter chains (**'chain scission'**), or to undergo cross-linking between chains—both of which would tend to give less flexible materials. These degradation reactions usually require an energy input to activate the overall process. This degradation is notably different in concept from that of metals as the resulting materials do not revert to compounds resembling the original oil source.

continued ▶

Critical factors

- Materials in combination.
- Simulation of weathering.
- Replication of degradation mechanisms.
- Service life and performance requirements.

Further reading in the Guide:
4.3 Structure and movement • 4.14 Life-cycle costing

- Biological degradation is critical for organic materials, although typical modern roofing materials are not usually very susceptible.
- Water and oxygen are often key elements in degradation of construction materials.
- Various forms of testing exist for construction materials, although there are limits to their predictive power for installed performance.

The degradation mechanism for polymeric materials is, however, not simply one of chain scission; other chemicals, particularly oxygen, have a role to play. By deliberately incorporating molecules which are more reactive than oxygen (e.g. chlorine) onto the polymer chain, the overall degradation of the polymer chains can be retarded – examples in roof membrane materials are polyvinyl chloride (PVC) or chlorosulphonated polyethylene. Other materials may specifically incorporate stabilising compounds to limit the rate and extent of degradation.

The energy input for the activation of these various degradation processes comes from ambient temperatures and ultra-violet radiation (see **Unit 4.6**). A general estimate is that in the UK up to $700W/m^2$ of radiation/energy can impinge upon flat roofs on a summer day.

For some polymeric materials, degradation of properties occurs by other processes, for example loss of plasticising components when these are used to provide optimum flexibility. The migration of such materials – by molecular diffusion, water leaching, or other mechanisms – may lead to the loss of useful properties or even, in extreme cases, failure of the membrane.

Accurate prediction of long-term service from accelerated testing has to mimic, as far as possible, the type, nature and severity of the various influences on the material. Merely increasing temperature often does not mimic the degradation process in a way that cycling temperatures might do.

Biological degradation

Biological degradation is particularly relevant to organic materials (polymeric, bituminous, and others). Virtually all organic materials can be subject to biodegradation, given the appropriate organisms and environment (usually involving the presence of water and perhaps oxygen). The majority of membrane materials and other components in a roof construction will not be expected to suffer such problems; but some can, and it is necessary to be aware of the essential points.

Whether a material is attacked by an organism will depend upon the chemical nature and structure of the material and whether the organism has evolved a method of digesting it – the organism (e.g. insect or fungus) is feeding on the material as a food. The example most frequently encountered is that of cellulose materials, such

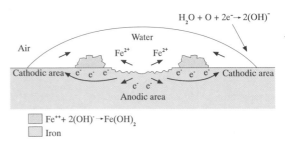

Figure 4.13.3
Basic corrosion mechanism of iron in water

as wood or fibre boards. The cellulose fibres in wood are relatively easily digested, but the resinous binder that holds the cellulose together (lignin) is much less easily digested. The way in which these two are combined in the cellulose-based product will significantly influence the resistance to biodegradation. Where this cannot be assured by the natural properties of the material, further protection against attack might be necessary by using preservatives, which poison the cells against the predatory organisms. Today, we are more conscious of the dilemmas of the environmental impact of preservative chemicals.

Effects of water

Water is a substantial influence on the durability and degradation of materials and, with solar radiation, is very significant for the performance of roof components. Water is a key part of the corrosion of metals (Figure 4.13.3), either directly in the reaction, conveying corrosive elements to the metal, or forming part of the conducting path in any corrosion cell. As noted above, biodegradation usually requires the presence of moisture. Some materials can undergo a change in properties as the result of chemical reaction with water (usually called a hydrolysis reaction). Other properties may be changed by a physical interaction. Two quite different examples of this physical interaction are the swelling of timber or wood fibre boards and freeze-thaw damage to concretes or ballasting gravels.

Mechanical degradation

Materials have both strength (stress resistance) and elasticity (strain accommodation), properties which are essential in fulfilling their requirements in a roof build-up. Materials will have been designed to withstand the foreseeable attack when new, but must have sufficient

Further reading:
BS7543: 1992 Guide to the durability of buildings and building elements, products and components • ICE Design life of buildings

- It is important to clarify and define the intended or anticipated 'service life' of the roof system, and to link this to planned maintenance programmes.
- Durability can be expressed in economic, functional, and aesthetic terms.

'reserve' of performance to withstand similar conditions when aged by one of the processes discussed above. Changes such as reduced flexibility may be relatively unimportant when the membrane is subject to no, or little, movement. But at joints – either deliberately designed movement joints or 'non-designed' joints (such as at insulation board junctions) – the changes might result in failure (see **Unit 4.3**).

Testing

All of the factors introduced above will, in concert, determine whether the materials will have adequate performance for the required service life. Appraisal and testing for performance over time should be broader than consideration of a material in isolation. A material will usually form part of a component or system of materials. It is the performance in combination and interaction with the other materials that is crucial. In a specific set of environmental exposure conditions it is quite possible for a material in isolation to perform well but when combined with other materials, exhibit poorer performance. Examples of such behaviour are bimetallic corrosion of metals and the interaction of some rubber components with bitumens.

It is usual for an assessment of likely adequacy to be based upon a combination of experience and testing – short-term, accelerated, and long-term. For well-established materials, used in familiar ways, experience will often give most confidence. However, care is needed to ensure that the prior experience is directly relevant to the new situation, that subtle but significant changes in the situation have not been introduced. For newer materials, real exposure testing is a good way of generating confidence in long-term behaviour, but the time to reach conclusions is great and the exposure conditions cannot be controlled. Laboratory testing alone is rarely adequate for reliably predicting long-term performance, and accelerated testing or intensified environment testing needs to be correlated with real life exposure to ensure satisfactory interpretation.

Required service life

The durable 'life' of a material or component in a roof is not as easy to define as might be expected. An initial question might be: How is the end of life determined? Is it outright failure, or insufficient reserve of performance to allow confident retention? Reviews of past experience

with particular materials can give some measure of performance. Independent testing and assessment of products (e.g. Agrément) may give predictions of life expectancy, but perhaps without the basis for the prediction being clearly stated. Some uncertainty is reasonable, as the same product incorporated into two different roofs with quite different exposure conditions is likely to have different life expectancies.

Similarly, guarantees from manufacturers or contractors may be available but for different time-scales than an independent assessment. The apparent inconsistencies are a reflection of perceived risk. Manufacturers guarantee a product for a period of years because they are confident that, properly installed, the risk of a failure is sufficiently small that the commercial consequences are sustainable. The same manufacturer may have a reasonable expectation that the product will last much longer – perhaps two or three times – but fears that an unusual occurrence outside their experience or control might increase the commercial risk to an unacceptable level. As experience of a particular material increases, then the gap – between guaranteed life and expected life – might decrease.

A further 'life' definition might be that time after which planned replacement should be allowed for. This term may be defined at the outset of a project, or during the useful life of a building. A building owner might reasonably expect the planned life to be greater than the guaranteed life, but would probably choose for it to be shorter than expected life. However, a decision whether to implement replacement might be taken only after a rigorous assessment of performance at the time.

A further issue in the service life is that of maintenance. If appropriately maintained, some materials may have virtually indefinite life. In other cases, maintenance might not be adopted and wholesale replacement preferred. Thus, durability – the performance of materials and components over time – leads firmly into the concept of life-cycle costing or whole life cost. Assessment of service life and performance is a complex interaction of decisions, and methods such as accelerated testing give only part of the story.

BS7543 gives an approach to a framework in which such assessments of the life cycle of a building, or components, may be made. **Unit 4.14** discusses the concept of life-cycle costings in greater detail. ■

Critical factors

- Service performance over the whole life of the building.

Further reading in the Guide:
4.3 Structure and movement • 4.6 Solar radiation and temperature effects • 4.14 Life-cycle costing

4.14 Life-cycle costing

- True economic evaluation must take all costs incurred over the life of the item being evaluated.
- Changes in the value of money over time must be taken into account by amortisation.
- Risk and uncertainty must also be considered.

General

The purpose of life-cycle costing is to provide an economic input when making decisions on available design options. All costs incurred over a given time span including maintenance, part and full replacements are summated for each design option under consideration so that whole life cost comparisons can be made.

Because interest return on investment and inflation affect the value of money over time, a real discount rate combining both these factors is used to amortise or 'discount' the expenditure.

The summation of all discounted costs over the life of any element (including first cost and final disposal value) is termed the **Present Value** (PV). The annual expend-itures discounted year by year form the **Discounted Cash flow** (DCF).

Life expectancy of materials

BS7543: 1992 gives guidance on taking considerations of durability, failure mechanisms, and effect of failure into account during the design process.

To convert this approach into information on which life-cycle costs can be calculated, the various materials in the complete roof element must have their life expectancies defined. In making comparisons and explaining them to clients, it can help to construct a simple life performance profile for each roof as shown in Table 4.14.

In fixing a specific life expectancy of a material so that a financial capital re-investment plan can be prepared, the risk of premature failure must be assessed.

Life expectancy of exposed materials will generally be based on the assumption that inspections and maintenance will be carried out to the manufacturer's recommendations.

Life-cycle costing procedure

Step 1: Identify the basic assumptions and determine the exact life-cycle costing exercise.
The client should be involved in setting the period for the study (often termed the period of client interest–the table of building durability in *BS7543* is useful for this) and should be consulted about the relevant discount rate. As a general guide HM Treasury publish figures which aim to reflect the value of money over time.

Table 4.14.1
Indicative performance profile for notional construction

Construction	Years						Maintenance
	5	10	15	20	25	30	
Solar reflection layer (paint)	▬						Repair every x years
Waterproof membrane		▬▬▬▬▬▬▬▬▬▬▬					Replace every 20 or so years
Insulation		▬▬▬▬▬▬▬▬▬▬▬					
Vapour control layer	▬▬▬▬▬▬▬▬▬▬▬▬▬						
Deck	▬▬▬▬▬▬▬▬▬▬▬▬▬▬▬▬▬▬▬▬▬▬▬▬▬▬▬						Permanent
Inspection and cleaning	▪▪▪▪▪▪▪▪▪▪▪▪▪▪▪▪▪▪▪▪▪▪▪▪▪▪						Annual Inspection
Gutters and other goods	▪▪▪▪▪▪▪▪▪▪▪▪▪▪▪▪▪▪▪▪▪▪▪▪▪▪						Annually cleaning gutters

The physical extent of the choices of roofing system to be evaluated needs careful consideration so that like is compared with like.

Step 2: Establish the basic assumptions and determine the exact life-cycle costing procedure to be adopted.
The design team should be involved in establishing the assumptions necessary to provide a basis for costing. In the more complex roofing designs, provisions for access, cleaning and repair, and traffic may have an impact on parts of the building other than the roof itself.

Step 3: Compile the data.
It is best for this to be done methodically for each design option and circulated to the design team for comment before calculations are commenced.

Further reading:
BS7543: 1992 Guide to the durability of buildings, products and components • READING UNIVERSITY Life-cycle costs for architects • FLANAGAN, R. et al Life-cycle costing, theory and practice • SOCIETY OF CHIEF QS IN LOCAL GOVERNMENT Life-Cycle Cost Planning • DoE/PSA Costs in Use: elemental tables VENMORE-ROWLAND, P. et al Investment, procurement and performance in construction • SOMERVILLE, G. Design life of structures.

Step 4: Compute and discount the life cycle costings for each alternative.

The following discounting formula is applied

$$PV \text{ of } S = \frac{S}{(1 + r)^t}$$

where

PV = Present Value

S = Sum expended

r = real discount percentage rate

t = number of years until expenses incurred

e.g. PV of £100 expended in 10 years time with 5% real discount rate

$$\frac{100}{(1 + 0.05)^{10}} = £61.39$$

Step 5: Compare the results.

The results can be compared in total £PV terms and in terms of discounted cash flows, the lowest PV being the best investment. An example of how this may result is shown for two notional design options in Figure 4.14.1.

Step 6: Evaluate the results for uncertainty and risk.

Allowing for risk and uncertainty in any forecast is difficult. Strictly, risk is the name given to outcomes whose probability of occurrence is known, whereas uncertainty refers to events whose probability of occurrence is unknown.

The cash flow forecast should reflect the forecaster's view of the most likely events, timings and costs. This can be straddled by a 'best/worst' forecast to give some idea of the possible spread of outcomes.

Sensitivity analysis is the most frequently used technique to cope with uncertainty. The basic approach is to try to identify the critical assumptions which underpin the cash flow forecast. The sensitivity of the forecast to variations in these assumptions can then be tested. For example, how would the outcome be affected if the actual cost of capital was 3% higher or 3% lower than expected? The effects of variations in the critical assumptions can be tested either independently (single variate analysis) or in conjunction with each other (multi-variate analysis).

As an example of the implications of including essential considerations of risk, consider accidental damage. A key risk in flat roof construction is the susceptibility of one

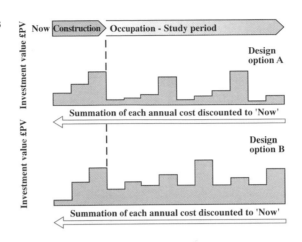

Figure 4.14.1
Investment appraisal/expenditure profile at feasibility/design stages

type of construction to damage by traffic as opposed to a different type. An allowance for the likely risk of damage and associated repair cost for each option can be included in the respective performance profile for comparative purposes, but the assessment can only be done on a subjective basis.

Step 7: Report on the findings and conclusions.

Clients or other readers of the report may not be as familiar with the techniques or complexity of the processes of life-cycle costing as the compiler. It is therefore preferable to write the main report in simple narrative statements, rather than present the information as a series of large tables.

Life-cycle cost – application

The calculation of comparative Present Values and Discounted Cash flows is a simple arithmetical task, once the basic performance data on life expectancies and maintenance work has been defined.

At the present time, very little independently validated data on these matters is available to those having to choose between roofing options on an economic basis.

However references can be made to manufacturers' technical data and reasonable assumptions can be made and the results tested by sensitivity analyses. ■

Critical factors

- Assessment of design options by design team.
- Assumptions for discount rate of money value.
- Clear reporting of conclusions.

Further reading in the Guide:
4.13 Durability of materials • 6.1 Design requirements: constraints and targets • 7.1 Design selection: general approach • 7.12 Design for maintenance

4.15 Environmental impact of materials

- Everything we do has environmental impact of one sort or another and the key is to minimise this impact to an acceptable level.
- When environmental impact is deleterious, there is a strong pressure to review policy, practice and procedure.
- Any action that can show an overall saving in energy use is of positive benefit.

Material selection to minimise environmental impact

Everything that we do has an effect on the environment in some way, and often this effect might be considered to be detrimental. The process of constructing buildings involves the use of materials that need to be manufactured and assembled, and these processes require the use of raw materials and the consumption of energy. The extraction of raw materials will in most cases cause irreversible changes to the environment, and even when steps are taken to ensure some form of rehabilitation of, say, a spent quarry, the end result will always be different from the original one. The vast majority of raw materials are obtained from finite resources, and even some potentially renewable resources such as timber can be cleared far faster than their ability to regenerate. All activities will require the expenditure of energy, and currently the majority of this is generated from finite resources of fossil fuels.

The fundamental concept in attempting to minimise impact on the environment to acceptable levels is to **use less** of everything. However, at present, legislation is slow to define and therefore limit what should be done and, as there is not always a short-term financial benefit, it is often difficult to define and implement changes that could benefit the environment. There is a clear benefit to be gained by consuming the minimum possible. This can be achieved by thoughtful design, and also by the adoption of strict site control procedures to minimise wastage. Secondly, materials, buildings and commodities should be **re-used** wherever possible, thus saving the material and energy cost of new manufacture. Thirdly, if re-use is not possible, **recycling** or **refurbishment** should be considered in preference to disposal.

The energy expended in recycling is often far less than that required for production of the virgin material, and there is again a direct benefit from the avoidance of further material extraction for new construction. Recycling also avoids problems created by **material disposal.** Lastly, if disposal cannot be avoided, it should be done in a way that creates the minimum possible impact on the environment.

Environments

There are various levels of environmental concern and these need to be addressed by the specifier, the supplier (or manufacturer), the product user and the building user.

- **Global effects** are those that affect the earth as a whole, or at least are able to cross continental boundaries. The greenhouse effect, for example, is created principally by the developed world, whose energy use is centred around industrial production, space conditioning, and the use of vehicles. The detrimental effects of the phenomenon, however, are also likely to affect developing countries.

- **Regional issues** are those where the environmental effect is felt within the region, but not necessarily at source. Pollution is a good example of this, whereby industrial processes create both liquid and gaseous discharges which can affect the air quality of the region, and the river system.

- **Local issues** are those related to the immediate environment, and would cover aspects such as internal air quality, lighting levels, etc. Health and safety of building fabricators and building users can also be a local effect determined directly by product specification and use.

The majority of materials can affect the environment in all these three areas, although the global and regional effects may often be 'hidden' for a variety of reasons. A typical manufacturing process will involve the use of energy, depletion of raw materials, the creation of pollution, and, in many cases, the production of a material or by-product which could create environmental concerns on health grounds.

Environmental impact assessment

There is a need to focus attention upon the most significant materials or processes in order to minimise irreversible detrimental changes to the environment and hazard to health. This is often difficult to achieve as there are so many conflicting interests. Two approaches are to evaluate **life-cycle** considerations and **priority by scale** of effect:

- **The life-cycle** approach looks at a material from extraction to disposal, recognising that environmental

Further reading:
CURWELL, S et al. Buildings and Health: The Rosehaugh guide to the design, construction, use and management of buildings. • CURWELL, S. & MARCH, C. Hazardous building materials: A guide to the selection of alternatives. • The COSHH Regulations. • SAX, N.I. & LEWIS, R.J. Hazardous chemicals desk reference. • BRE Report BREEAM an environmental assessment.

© BFRC / CIRIA: Flat Roofing: Design and Good Practice. 1993

- Re-use and recycling should be encouraged, disposal avoided.
- The use of renewable materials and renewable energy resources is to be encouraged.
- Materials that are known to be hazardous to health, such as asbestos, should be avoided whenever possible.

---

effects will be present at each stage of a product's life and could include: extraction, transport, manufacture, erection, use, maintenance, demolition and disposal. Each of these activities will involve the use of energy, and create local or regional pollution. Some involve a degree of health hazard either to operatives or building users, and could create waste disposal problems. Extraction will normally involve the depletion of a finite resource. Demolition and disposal could create possibilitics for re-use or recycling, or could give rise to concerns over safe disposal of waste.

- **The scale of effect** refers to the fact that certain materials have a much more significant effect than others because of the volumes used. The building fabric, walls, floors and roof contain the majority of the mass of building products, and consequently careful selection of, say, walling materials can produce a far greater environmental benefit than the selection of ceramic tiles in toilets. It follows from this that efforts should be concentrated into those areas that can show the most significant improvements.

Environmental issues are a minefield of argument and counter argument, and cover such a complex series of subjects that clear guidance on specific subjects is often difficult to give. Some information (such as pollution and pollutants) is often readily available but others (including embodied energy within different materials) are more difficult to define on a comparative basis.

Schemes which attempt to formalise environmental assessments have been established (e.g. BREEAM). Because of the complexity of interactions of environmental considerations, such assessment schemes inevitably have to simplify the arguments and balance of conflicts required to arrive at a decision. Different clients, users, specifiers, etc., may also place varying priorities on data whose scale is agreed. Even arguments which at first derivation appear clear-cut can, after further debate, become more complex. Such an argument is that of relative atmospheric **ozone depletion potential** of various chlorofluorocarbons (CFCs). Some people now claim that the rate of depletion is more important than the overall value more normally quoted. This is because the effects in the first few years are thought to be more significant for the atmosphere than the overall depletion.

Impact of materials

There are a great many materials which can be incorporated in a flat roof. A comprehensive environmental assessment of these is outside the scope of this Guide. Some of the key materials commonly encountered in flat roofing are, however, briefly discussed below.

Asbestos

Asbestos is a naturally-occurring fibrous silicate mineral previously widely used in buildings. Inhalation of asbestos fibres is a major health risk and strict precautions must be observed for operatives, particularly those involved in the demolition of post-war buildings. Asbestos use is still permitted in this country, but the products made are all of the type in which the asbestos is contained in a binding matrix where fibre loss is marginal, and are used in very specialist situations. Environmentally, asbestos must be seen as an undesirable material, although its incorporation into modern building materials is highly unlikely, and the most significant risk relates to work on existing buildings. Asbestos is, therefore, most frequently encountered in repair and refurbishment work and specific regulations are applicable and should be followed.

- COSHH and asbestos regulations should be strictly observed.
- Asbestos products should be avoided where possible.
- Major health hazard during demolition and refurbishment.
- Extraction is environmentally damaging.

Asphalt and bitumen

This range of products, generally referred to as asphalts, can either be produced synthetically as a by-product of petroleum distillation (bitumens) or can occur naturally as 'asphalt lakes'. Asphalts and bitumens are therefore derived from non-renewable resources. Where derived from petroleum distillations the bitumens may be regarded as a by-product and therefore less disadvantageous. Bituminous materials used for road surfacing can, to some extent, be recycled. However, because of irreversible chemical changes during manufacture, and the way in which they may be incorporated with other materials, it is not currently economical to employ the same principles

continued ▶

Critical factors

- Everything we do has an environmental impact of one sort or another; the key is to minimise this impact to an acceptable level.
- Re-use and recycling should be encouraged, disposal avoided.
- Relevant health and safety regulations, and the COSHH Regulations should be strictly observed for all activities.
- Materials sold for recycling may attract revenue.
- Re-use of materials in remedial work may reduce material costs but increase labour costs.

Further reading in the Guide:
3.4 Health and safety • 4.14 Life-cycle costing • 17.1 Selection of insulants

12 Mastic Asphalt	13 Polymeric Single Ply	14 Copper	15 Lead Sheet	16 Other Membranes	17 Thermal Insulants	18 Specification	19 Contracts & Procurement	20 Inspection	21 Maintenance	22 Bibliography	23 Index
263	301	331	353	375	383	393	399	413	429	437	455

- Environmental assessments of the materials used in roofing are complex if rigorously carried through. More often simplified 'rules' are applied.
- For insulation materials the benefits in lower energy use for the building will normally be considered to outweigh the impact of manufacture.

---

for the recovery of roofing materials. The disposal of most built-up roofing materials presents no special environmental hazard. Mastic asphalt is non-toxic and odourless after installation.

- These are waterproofing, thermoplastic materials with adhesive properties.
- Bitumens are naturally occurring or waste by-product of petroleum industry, but non-renewable.
- There is limited scope for recycling, but some embodied energy could be re-gained if used as heating fuel.
- Observe COSHH Regulations on application, particularly when heated.

Copper

Copper is a naturally-occurring element that is extracted during the refinement of sulphide ores or occasionally from native copper. Extraction is heavily polluting unless thorough fume recovery is carried out. Though copper is a non-renewable resource, its longevity in service gives rise to considerable life-cycle benefit. Recycling is commonplace and energy-efficient in comparison with extraction from ore.

- Mining and extraction is environmentally damaging.
- Recycling is financially and environmentally beneficial.
- Longevity in service yields life-cycle benefits.

Insulation

Good insulation is vital in reducing heating demand, with all the associated benefits for reducing the burden upon non-renewable fossil fuels and reducing the emission of combustion gases. All buildings should therefore be insulated to the highest affordable standard, balanced with overall energy use. Insulation materials are available in many forms, of which foamed plastics and man made mineral fibres are the most commonly specified. Though the manufacture of all insulation materials involves considerable energy, there are long-term benefits from the use of insulation to reduce subsequent energy use in buildings.

Foamed plastics are derived from petroleum and some utilise CFCs in the manufacturing process. Manufacturers are making considerable progress in producing more environmentally friendly products by substitution with less environmentally damaging CFCs in place of those

previously used. Some 'CFC-free' materials are available but are not appropriate for all applications. This is a rapidly changing field and it is essential to obtain up-to-date information from manufacturer's technical departments.

Man-made mineral fibres are generally considered to be a 'green' material in use, although they involve considerable energy demand during production and require resin binders. Problems might be created during installation with inhalation of airborne fibres, and in this respect, COSHH regulations should be strictly adhered to.

Other specific information on materials can be found in **Chapter 17**.

Insulation products are not easily recyclable but are normally expected to have a long life. It is generally accepted that the advantage of good insulation, such as lower energy usage in service, outweighs the detrimental effects, such as energy demand during production, potential ozone depletion, and/or need for safety precautions during installations, of some of the materials. It is nevertheless important to minimise those effects as far as is possible, for example, by the selection of 'CFC-free' material.

- Good insulation is a positive benefit in reducing energy demand of buildings.
- Specify to avoid use of CFCs.
- Observe COSHH Regulations particularly with fibre products.

Lead

Lead is a material whose physical qualities of durability, softness and density, have made it a well-used building material in specialised applications. It is known to be a cumulative poison and no lower limit of acceptable exposure has been established. The potential hazards of lead to health very much depend upon the way it is used. For example, lead plumbing used for hot water supplies present more of a health risk to building users than when it is used with cold water supplies. Although there is legislation to prevent the use of lead in plumbing systems, there are no such restrictions when lead is used in locations such as roofing and flashings that are unrelated to the food chain. However, when lead is used, or encountered in existing buildings, COSHH Regulations should be observed, particularly with regard to inhalation of dust or fumes.

Further reading:
HENSTOCK, M F Design for recyclability • FOX, and MURRELL, Green design: A guide to the environmental impact of building materials.
VALE, B and R. Towards a green architecture • BRE Reports: BREEAM: an environmental assessment.

- The use of materials or processes that are known to affect the environment in a deleterious way, such as CFCs and halons, should be avoided.
- Relevant health and safety regulations, and the COSHH Regulations should be strictly observed for all activities.

With a properly detailed roof where all rainwater is collected in gutters and taken to the drainage system, there is no risk to building occupants or passers-by. The rate of dissolution from the surface is extremely low and thus the risk, compared to other potential sources of lead contamination, is insignificant.

As for most metals, the extraction of lead is locally damaging and the refining process both energy-intensive and polluting. However, there are life-cycle benefits of using a durable material and recycling is commonplace. Recycling of lead is energy-efficient in comparison to extraction from sulphide or carbonate ores.

- There is health risk associated with inhalation or ingestion.
- There is possible health risk from skin contact.
- Ensure application of COSHH Regulations.
- Extraction has an environmental impact.
- Recycling is commonplace.

Plastics

Plastics are a complex and varied family that find extensive use in the construction industry. High performance, lightweight (sometimes reinforced) polymers have been developed for use as roofing membranes and their advantages relate to high strength-to-weight ratio, low toxicity and good chemical resistance. Their high performance may create overall energy savings over alternative materials. No authoritive data yet exists on the energy consumed in manufacture although work in this field is progressing. All commercial plastics are currently derived from non-renewable resources, although there is scope for development of renewable resources. Re-use is virtually impossible and recycling is restricted. Some material can be used, in small proportion, in the production of new roof sheets and some into different products. Some manufacturers have recycling schemes set up. Plastics are currently disposed of to waste tips but there is scope for use of plastics in heat-recovery incineration if technical problems of flue emissions can be solved. The complex technology and wide variety of materials and processes give significant scope for development of more environmentally friendly materials in terms of resources and recycling.

Concern has been expressed about polymers containing chlorine, particularly in respect to their incineration. Regulations now require minimum operating temperatures and flue scrubbers to control the problem.

- Plastics have good performance/weight ratio.
- Plastics have good chemical and thermal resistance.
- Plastics are derived from non-renewable resources.
- Recycling is possible but difficult: much scope for technological improvement.

Rubber

Rubber can be natural or synthetic, or a combination of the two. Membranes made from products such as chlorosulphonated polyethylene, EPDM, and butyl, are all synthetic materials and therefore derived from non-renewable resources. There are a variety of formulations available that, with careful selection and detailing, make them suitable for exterior applications such as roofing membranes. It is not usual to specify natural rubber when durability is required in service. There are alternative fixing methods for all polymer membrane systems, whether plastic or rubber. Installation may involve mechanical or adhesive fixings and the appropriate health and safety precautions must be followed, especially if large areas of solvent-based adhesives are to be used.

- Synthetic rubbers are derived from non-renewable resources.
- Synthetic rubbers generally have properties which overcome the technical limitations of natural rubber.
- Rubber-based adhesives may incorporate solvents that will have implications under the COSHH Regulations.

Summary

The materials presented in this Unit represent only a few of those encountered in the roofing applications. Other ancillary components that have not been covered in this brief review include: the roof deck, fixings and adhesives, sealants, trims, solar finishes, etc. As described earlier, where there is significant concern for the environment, an evaluation based on the scale of use, life-cycle benefit, environmental impact and potential health hazard can be helpful. ∎

Critical factors

- Minimise waste to reduce costs, optimise global resources and reduce pollutants.
- Remedial work involving hazardous materials may be costly.
- The long-term benefit to the environment may result from short term costs to individual projects.

Further reading in the Guide:
3.4 Health and safety • 4.14 Life-cycle costing • 17.1 Selection of insulants

Surveys 5

Special Note: *The provision of detailed guidance is intended to assist Architects, Clerks of Works, Superintending Officers, Surveyors, or other agents of the Employer or building client/owner, who may have a duty to inspect the works, in identifying which matters require attention in the particular circumstances. Any duties of 'survey or inspect' will be governed in each case by the terms of appointment and this guidance should not be interpreted as a description or definition of such duties.*

5.1 Types of survey and inspection

- The terminology of surveys, inspections, examinations, appraisals, and inspections is inconsistent. A particular usage is proposed for this Guide.
- 'Survey' is defined as an examination to establish a factual description of what exists at the time of the survey.
- 'Inspection' is defined as inspection of the construction works by someone acting as agent on behalf of the employer.

Types of survey and inspection

The terms 'survey' and 'inspection' and 'supervision' are used in many different ways in the building industry, referring both to works under construction (typically to check the quality of work) and to examination of existing buildings in place (typically to establish the existing condition). The terms overlap at times and this can lead to confusion.

In this Guide, the terms are deliberately used in a restricted form, described below after a brief discussion of the range of terms available. The key issue in any survey or inspection is that the scope of work must be clearly defined so that there is a proper understanding between the person carrying out the work and the person commissioning it.

Surveys

A 'survey' is taken to refer to the different forms of examination (or inspection) of a site or of a building or part of a building, where the purpose is to establish a factual description of what exists – the condition at the time of survey. It may also include an evaluation – a technical opinion – of that condition (e.g. the immediate or likely future need for repairs).

The initiative may come from a prospective purchaser of the site and/or building; it may come from a building owner, as part of a maintenance programme or in considering possible upgrading of the building's performance; it may come from a building leaseholder, seeking to establish the level of dilapidations – the state of disrepair in a property where there is a covenant to repair.

Inspection

The term 'inspection' as a distinct activity is here restricted to 'inspection of the works'. That is, it is the inspection of current construction works, on or off site, by someone acting as Agent for the client or Employer – such as an architect or other Superintending Officer or a Clerk of Works. It may form a basis for certification.

The task is strictly to determine whether or not the works are being carried out in accordance with the requirements of the Contract. It may result in an instruction being given to the contractor, but does not involve instructions directly to the workforce.

In this sense, 'inspection' is different from 'supervision'. This Guide offers some guidance on inspection, but not explicitly on supervision.

Supervision

The term 'supervision' is here restricted to the role of the contractor or sub-contractor in ensuring that their workforce carry out the works properly, with the implication that, where appropriate, instructions will be given to the workforce – by the contractor or sub-contractor concerned.

Checking the works as part of supervision will often involve attention to the same matters as those for inspection. The guidance here on inspection may be helpful to those responsible for supervision; but the two activities are usually carried out by parties with different contractual responsibilities.

Scope of surveys, inspections, etc.

Some examples of different types of survey, inspection, examination, investigation, etc. – and variations of terminology – are included here.

Site survey

The dimensional and topographic description of the site up to and including all legal, administrative and physical boundaries and existing works and infrastructure. It should where possible identify relevant titles and ownerships. It may identify special legal requirements (e.g. for planning applications). It may include information beyond the site – e.g. to clarify location, services connections, etc. It may also refer to items such as trees and special features (e.g. listed buildings, easements, rights of way etc.), microclimate or pollution levels.

Site investigation

The three-dimensional geotechnical description of the site, including soil types and strata, underground waterways, etc. It will often include assessments such as the loadbearing capacity of the ground. It has sometimes included assessments of pollutants and other environmental factors.

Building survey

The general term – preferred in this Guide – for surveys (as defined above) referring to the whole building, or specified parts of the building (such as the roof). It deals with the material of the building, its general physical condition, including factual evidence of any deterioration or performance failure. It may often include assessments of need for repair or other attention. (Such surveys have often been termed 'structural surveys' or 'condition surveys' – these terms can be misunderstood and 'building survey' appears to be a less ambiguous term.)

Further reading:

HOLLIS, M. Surveying for dilapidations.

- The advice in this Guide concentrates on surveys and inspections. It does not explicitly deal with supervision, although some of the advice on surveys and inspections may be useful there.
- It is imperative that the scope of work any survey or inspection be clearly defined. This will ensure the person commissioning the work and the person carrying it out have a clear understanding of what is expected.

Structural survey
This is usually taken to cover the physical condition of the loadbearing elements of the building, but sometimes is thought to cover all the fabric. It is sometimes taken only to cover matters described by 'structural inspection' (see below), but in general the term 'building survey' is preferred.

Condition survey
Another term for 'building survey' (see above).

Structural inspection
This is an established term, which is therefore used in this Guide. Despite its name, it refers to a limited form of building survey (see above). It establishes as far as possible the main arrangement of the loadbearing structure and its constituent materials. It may comment on the current serviceability, capacity for extra load, stability, the condition of the materials. It may also assess whether any repair work is necessary – immediately or in the foreseeable future.

Inspection for a Schedule of Condition
This examination describes the condition of the building in cases where a lease is held on a property and places upon the tenant a covenant to repair ('repairing leases'), as the landlord or superior lessee or the tenant may require a record of the condition of the building. This may even be bound into the lease. It may also be required at any time during the lease. The coverage is as for a building survey, but may be limited to those items of relevance to the lease.

Inspection for a Schedule of Dilapidations
This examination identifies disrepair in cases where a lease is held on a property and places upon the tenant a covenant to repair ('repairing leases'). Typically it is required where there is a dispute or initiative concerning defects to be remedied, for instance as covered by Section 146(1) of the *Law of Property Act 1925* (under which a Notice of Repair may be issued). The assessment may be compared with a Schedule of Condition at the start of the lease, to establish work needed. The Schedule may be served as an Interim Schedule (e.g. during the currency of the lease, accompanying a Notice of Repair, because the landlord is concerned about deterioration of the fabric). It may be served as a Terminal Schedule, typically within the last three years of the lease.

Inspection of the works
This deals with 'inspection' as defined above, the examination of whether or not the construction in progress is being or has been carried out in accordance with the requirements of the Contract. This may also form the basis for certification.

Site inspection
Another version of 'inspection of the works', for on-site works only.

Inspection of works off site
This covers 'inspection of the works' insofar as these are carried out off site, for example in a factory, and are delivered to site in a partially or wholly complete form for installation. It may include prototypes or samples, against which the manufacturer tests the quality of production output.

Site supervision
A version of 'supervision', as defined above, which covers the examination of construction works by the contractor or sub-contractor responsible.

Maintenance survey
This is a form of 'building survey' (see above), as part of an assessment of maintenance needs. It may be restricted to specific items identified in a maintenance programme, which may identify some items as needing more frequent survey than others. It may also arise where a tenant requires an inspection for a Schedule of Condition or a Schedule of Dilapidations (see above).

Remedial work survey
A limited building survey, initiated where a known defect or failure requires attention. The task is largely dictated by the urgency of the problem (see also **Unit 21.2**).

Survey as a condition of a guarantee or warranty
This is a restricted building survey, perhaps carried out as part of a more general maintenance survey, where a guarantee or warranty is only available or its continuance maintained on condition that such a survey is carried out on a defined and regular basis.

General
Other forms of survey, inspection, examination and supervision exist. The principal guidance is that in any of these circumstances the parties concerned should be clear and in agreement on:

- what is the extent and limits of the work to be carried out (e.g. it is preferable to entitle the work by an exact description, rather than a general title)
- what will be covered by any formal report
- for what purpose the results are to be used
- what are the responsibilities of those concerned. ■

Critical factors
- Extent and limits of the work required.
- Clarity for all parties on what are agreed as the surveyor's instructions.

Further reading in the Guide:
5.2 Surveying buildings: scope • 20.1 Inspection of the works • 21.1 Planned maintenance • 21.2 Diagnosing effects and remedies

12 Mastic Asphalt	13 Polymeric Single Ply	14 Copper	15 Lead Sheet	16 Other Membranes	17 Thermal Insulants	18 Specification	19 Contracts & Procurement	20 Inspection	21 Maintenance	22 Bibliography	23 Index
263	301	331	353	375	383	393	399	413	429	437	455

5.2   Surveying buildings: scope

- This Guide concentrates on advice to those people acting normally as Agent for the client or Employer. The Employer may be:
  - a prospective purchaser of the building
  - the current owner of the building wishing to assess possible upgrading or other maintenance programmes
  - the current tenant of the building, with a 'repairing lease' wishing to ascertain liabilities, etc.

Surveys covered by this Guide

In **Unit 5.1**, various forms of survey and inspection are identified and compared. For the purposes of this Guide, two main types of survey of buildings are of particular significance – 'building surveys' and 'structural inspections'.

Building surveys

The building survey (as defined in **Unit 5.1**) refers to the whole building, or specified parts of the building (such as the roof), and deals with the material of the building. This refers to its general physical condition, including evidence of any deterioration or performance failure.

A survey will often not be able to cover those parts which are concealed, or inaccessible even with the use of special equipment. In some cases, a limited amount of moving or even opening up may be permissible and the inspection extended accordingly.

A considerable range of non-destructive testing equipment now exists. In some cases, the equipment is available only via special services.

If desired, the survey can be extended to cover the testing of the mechanical and electrical services, although not usually relevant to consideration of a flat roofing system.

Structural inspections

A structural inspection (as defined in **Unit 5.1**) establishes as far as possible the main arrangement of the loadbearing structure and its constituent materials, and may comment on its current serviceability, capacity for extra load, stability, the condition of the materials, whether any repair work is necessary – immediately or in the foreseeable future. Instructions may also be given to evaluate the implications for refurbishment.

Reasons for survey

There are a number of possible reasons for carrying out a survey of the roof, for example:

- as part of a maintenance programme (see **Unit 21.1**), whether regular or occasional, preventative or responsive
- as part of a review of the development of a building/site, which may involve significant building works or refurbishment, or the owner wishing to take advantage of a builder's presence for other work

- to help to establish the asset value of the building (e.g. for purchase or sale of the property)
- as part of repair cost budgeting, to assess the likely repair budgets needed over a defined period (e.g. 10 years)
- because of reported building problems (see **Unit 5.4**), such as water penetration, assess whether the cause is failure of the roofing system
- as part of a claim under dilapidations, assess whether a loss has occurred for which there is a remedy
- as part of work to be carried out under insurance, e.g. arising from a fire in the building as a whole, to arrive at an estimate of the repair costs involved
- to obtain necessary information if a general decision has been made to refurbish the roof
- as part of more general building works to the roof and/or other parts of the building, to help the designer check any factors which may affect those other works

The surveyor

A survey or inspection should be carried out only by a competent person. Surveys by others may be helpful in giving early warnings, but these should always be followed up properly. In some cases, the owner or responsible tenant organisation may employ permanent staff (e.g. building managers) competent to conduct an initial inspection. However, if an extensive survey is required, then a professional surveyor, engineer or architect – as appropriate – should be engaged.

Manufacturers and suppliers will sometimes undertake limited forms of building survey, as part of the technical services they offer designers and clients. It may be appropriate to explore such services as soon as possible, for example where the client has decided early on that a particular roof system – or even a particular supplier – is to be used.

In all cases, it is essential to define clearly what is to be examined and on what aspects of the building a report is required. Establishing the basic condition at a point in time – including where it is not possible to know – is essential before building works are initiated.

Further reading:

HOLLIS, M. Surveying buildings • HOLLAND, R., MONTGOMERY-SMITH, B.E. & MOORE, J.F.A. Appraisal and repair of building structures.

- A survey may be seen in four stages: preparation, visiting the building, reaching a conclusion, writing a report.
- Surveys and inspections should be carried out by people competent to do so.
- Standard formats for recording and reporting can be helpful to all concerned.
- Safety of those surveying is always a critical matter.

Coverage of a survey

There are a number of typical and optional tasks involved, subject to instructions, and regular procedures to follow.

Initial appraisals

It can be useful for the surveyor to conduct an initial appraisal–to define the nature and extent of a suitable survey and to help the client to finalise their brief and instructions.

Typical tasks

In general, an inspection or survey should:

- Clearly identify the extent of the building which is to be inspected and those aspects which are to be inspected and/or tested.
- Discover what facts can be established. These may include relevant documentary evidence (e.g. previous surveys, original drawings and specifications, the building history, etc.) as well as those established by direct inspection of the fabric.
- Identify the elements or aspects which could not be identified or inspected and indicate why (e.g. because of inaccessibility).
- Observe the building as instructed and evaluate its condition, where possible. Where earlier surveys are available (perhaps on a regular basis), evaluate the current condition in relation to the earlier evaluations. This should take account of the internal and external environments–a special issue for roofing systems (e.g. as with indoor swimming pool enclosures).

Optional tasks

The surveyor may also be instructed to:

- Establish recommendations for further enquiry or investigation, where appropriate. (Normally, a survey is only a description and evaluation. Unless specifically instructed, it will not entail diagnosing or remedying any problems which may be discovered.)
- Evaluate the general condition, any defects or disadvantages in relation to contemporary standards and to those applicable to the period of construction (if possible noting where these may imply different performance standards), that is taking account of what would appear to be reasonable estimates of the 'working life' of the components, materials and systems.
- Evaluate recommendations for necessary immediate repair or improvement and advise on long-term implications.

Formats for surveys

It is helpful to establish early on a standard format for regular roof inspections, (e.g. in a maintenance manual) so that comparisons can be made easily over a period. This should include reference plans and sections to a suitable scale, in multiple copies, on which information can be recorded. Any areas of special concern or known defects should be located unambiguously–e.g. by reference to distances from particular features or from facades (defined by compass points). A note should be made of the weather at the time of the survey.

Photographic records

It is also desirable that a record be made with colour photographs, if possible using a camera with databack to print the date on the photograph. The photographs should be numbered (e.g. frame number) and their position located on the roof plan. A table of the photographs should also be made, recording any specific comments against the number.

If possible, information on the general context should be established. For instance, it may be possible to take a general photograph of the building (with its roofs clearly shown) from a nearby higher building.

Inclusions and exclusions

Special care should be taken when surveying to ensure that the survey brief is not exceeded. Where descriptions are included of elements outside the brief, but no comment of concern has been made, the reader may (perhaps mistakenly) assume that those elements have been surveyed but no problems exist.

Safety of those surveying

Surveys and inspections can involve dangerous work. Where it is on an active building site, those involved will often be alerted to potential dangers by the fact of site works, advice from the contractors, etc. In any event, the contractor concerned will have a responsibility for ensuring the health and safety of anyone entitled to enter the site and for those within potential danger.

It is not always sufficiently recognised that surveys or inspections of existing buildings, especially where they are unoccupied, may involve considerable danger. Proper precautions should always be taken to ensure the safety of those making a survey, in particular that it is known by others (e.g. in their office) that they are in the building and how long they expect to be there. It is generally recommended that an empty building should not be surveyed –in whole or in part–by anyone on their own. ■

Critical factors

- What information is essential?
- Is it available? How often has it been gathered?
- What is to be done as a result of the survey?
- Ensure safety of those conducting the survey.
- Define standard survey procedure, including safety aspects.
- Obtain report and evidence that procedure has been followed.
- Ensure reports are stored available for future comparisons.

Further reading in the Guide:

5.3　Surveying buildings: roofs

- Time spent on reconnaissance is never wasted: always try to discover as much information as possible from previous surveys, records, etc.
- Testing of materials to be used in the construction should be carried out at time when the results will be of most use. Early testing should be undertaken, to try to ensure that no materials are incorporated in the works that are subsequently found to be unsatisfactory. Similar tests sometimes arise after a period of service.

This Unit identifies particular issues in building surveys or structural inspections (for general definitions, **see Unit 5.1**) which relate to roof construction and flat roof systems.

Preliminary investigations

What is the information on the original drawings and specifications (e.g. held by the owner, original designer), on the specialist roofing sub-contractor, details of manufacturers' products, etc? These will help to clarify the details of the roofing system, for example:

- dates of design and construction of original building and of any major repairs or refurbishment, including clarification of building control requirements and other legislation which was satisfied at the time
- structural support and design loads (including load capacity of existing structure)
- assumed wind loading, connection design and methods of attachment
- other decking materials and substrates
- vapour control layer (VCL)
- insulation
- nature and detail of the waterproofing membrane
- surface finishes
- designed falls
- rainwater disposal
- aspect and orientation, shading
- assumptions about special conditions, etc.

NB: Such drawings may be 'final design' drawings, not 'as built' drawings.

Previous works and information

There may have been other repairs or other works (including installation of additional services for the building) to the original roofing system. It is therefore important to check:

- Are there records of that work?
- Have there been works or treatment of parts of the building which may have implications for the roofing system?

There may be other documented information which is useful for comparisons, for example:

- Does the owner or building manager hold a maintenance manual for the building?
- Is there any information on regular or occasional maintenance inspections?
- Are there any reports from previous surveys available?

Patterns of use and scrutiny

In examining the condition of the roof, it may be relevant to discover how it has been used, managed, and scrutinised. For example:

- Might the uses of the building have particular implications (e.g. laundries, swimming pools, food manufacturing, etc.)?
- Is the roof used regularly?
- Is maintenance of the vertical envelope organised from the roof?
- Are there any discharges from plant or equipment directly onto the roof?
- Do the local statutory officers have information about the local air quality?
- Are there any records or oral reports of problems which might be associated with the roofing system?
- Is there any information on the general history of the building and of the roof in particular?
- Have there been any significant changes in use which might affect the internal environment?
- Are any parts of the roofs overlooked from the building itself?
- Are there any informal observations from the occupants which might be helpful in assessing the performance of the roof?

Leak detection

A variety of methods exist. All require interpretation of their results, as they may not be conclusive. Flood testing can be used to test a roofing system at installation, even if no leaks are apparent; it can also be used later, if leaks are detected.

Non-destructive testing

Leak – or moisture – detection methods, such as infra-red thermography, capacitance meters or neutron absorption gauges, can be used to show differences in moisture content across the roof.

The cause may not be failure in the roofing system – for example, it may be caused by soaking during the construction process or condensation. Remote sensing using infra-red thermography may also be used to show the overall thermal performance of the roof and to highlight areas of poor insulation and cold bridging (of which leaks may be a cause).

Further reading:
HOLLIS, M. Surveying buildings • HOLLAND, R., MONTGOMERY-SMITH, B.E. & MOORE, J.F.A. Appraisal and repair of building structures • GRIFFIN, C.W. Manual of built-up roof systems.

- Testing on materials is only worth instigating if action will be taken as a result of the tests. Therefore, the methods and criteria for testing should be clearly established and agreed in good time.
- Guidance here covers a range of advice, from which the surveyor may select according to need and their terms of appointment.
- Testing of the complete roof system can be by non-destructive or flood testing.

Pyramid entrance to galleries under courtyard, Louvre, Paris, France

New York City, USA

However, it depends on a particular differential between external and internal temperature, and therefore may not be effective in the case of unoccupied buildings.

Endoscopes or fibre-optic probes may be used to examine zones which are otherwise difficult to reach without substantial opening up of the fabric. They may be rigid or flexible and can be inserted for instance into the roof voids to look at the condition of the structural decking.

Flood testing
The following is a typical flood test procedure for completed flat roofs with a continuous waterproof (organic) – not water-shedding (metal) – membrane:

- Check that the test (and any defects revealed) throughout the necessary period will not interfere with programmed works or, in the case of a building in occupation, with that occupation.
- Confirm that the superimposed load of the test is structurally acceptable.
- Check that the intended flood level does not come above kerbs, flashings, etc.
- Prior to flooding, check that all relevant work is complete and inspect for damage. Remedy any damage as necessary.
- Externally cover and seal all outlets and protect from water pressure.
- Flood for 48 hours to an agreed level and continually inspect for leaks.
- Drain slowly: it is unlikely that all bends and couplings will be sufficiently braced for unrestricted flow under the head created by the test.
- Carry out any necessary remedial work and retest, incorporating a dye (if necessary) to distinguish from entrapped water from a previous test.

Other methods
An alternative, non-destructive method is available: electronic leak detection. This involves creating a weak electrical field on the dampened roof surface. Any current that leaks through the waterproofing and 'earths' into the building changes the nature of the field locally. This can be located and can pin-point the penetration. Importantly, the system is also capable of showing when water penetration does not originate from a roof leak. ■

Critical factors

- Check existing information available.
- Allow sufficient time for testing
- Apply protection at all stages of testing.
- Establish testing methods and criteria.
- Establish protection proposals.
- Monitor protection installation.
- Record the results of testing.

5.4 Surveying buildings: roof materials and details

- Roof surveys will be dominated by material performance.
- The typical materials used in roof systems, whether for the waterproof membrane or elsewhere, will have a number of typical problems and hence symptoms.

This Unit deals, specifically, with the material performance issues in surveys or inspections of flat roofs.

A number of the points listed are included as useful indicators or warning signs: they may not conclusively mean that a failure has occurred or is about to occur, but they are helpful as a sign of possible problems.

In particular, they may be of assistance to an initial maintenance check, where the question is raised as to the desirability of paying for a comprehensive building survey.

Material durability

The long-term performance of the roof system depends on the durability of the different components and fixings, in the specific environment and micro-climate of the roof.

Some materials may expand in a predictable manner with changes in temperature, but their shrinkage on cooling may not be a simple reversal of that movement to their previous position or configuration. This 'ratchet effect', with a permanent realignment of the material over a period of time, can sometimes lead to changes in the thickness or other characteristics. The surveyor should watch for signs of this kind of change, which might be beneficial, where materials such as mastic asphalt have been used, to ensure that no such problem has arisen.

In general, it is important to watch for signs of degradation, to pre-empt potential failure, for example:

- Are there signs of distress in any flashings or mastic sealants, especially where there are changes in material and/or geometry (e.g. roof penetrations, skylights, etc.)?
- Are there signs of distress near flues, service exhausts or overflows?
- Are there any membrane distortions, blisters, ridges, splits (e.g. at changes from chippings finishes, at changes in type of structural deck, at changes in level)?
- Are there any signs of distress in the membrane at laps or joints?

Geometrical complexity

In a flat roof, considerable geometrical complexity can develop, especially at movement joints, penetrations and upstands, and areas which have been modified after the original construction. This can have particular consequences for the performance of the materials involved, whether as principal materials or as fixings or fastenings.

Parapets and abutments should be scrutinised with particular care. They have proved to be a frequent source of maintenance problems, because of the complex geometries, the multitude of materials involved and the tendency to locate rainwater outlets at their junctions with the flat roof.

In older buildings, even where the principal waterproofing membrane has been refurbished, in some parts of the construction it is not unusual for there to be no dpc, or other impervious barrier to water penetration, where today it would be expected.

If repair is needed, consider:

- Are there factors which affect ease of access for the new construction (e.g. proximity to equipment housings or penetrations of the membrane)?
- Are there special factors which might affect the location of contractor's equipment in the event of extensive repair work or refurbishment?

Roof surfaces and boundaries

There should always be suitable protection to the roofing surface (e.g. maintenance walkways) and any examination can be assisted by attention to any signs of their absence.

It is also important to watch for general indirect evidence of possible problems, for example:

- Are there signs of damage from impact or point loads (e.g. near access ways or gantries for cleaning cradles, outdoor furniture, etc.)?
- Are any parts of the roof surface 'spongy' to walk on? (NB this test should be made with special care if the roof is designed only for maintenance access.) If apparent, this could be due to inadequate mechanical properties or loss of mechanical properties resulting from water absorption.
- Are there signs of distress because of severe exposure to wind? If so, does this appear to have been considered in earlier construction?
- Is there evidence of the prevailing direction of the wind and/or intense rain as it affects this building? (NB inspection of the building exterior more generally may also be helpful here.)
- Are there signs of some parts of the roof weathering very differently from others? Does this appear to be related to the prevailing microclimate or might it signify something requiring attention?

Further reading:
GRIFFIN, C.W. Manual of built-up roof systems.

Chapter	1	2	3	4	5	6	7	8	9	10	11
Contents	Introduction	History	Regulatory Methods	Principles	Surveys	Constraints & Targets	Design Selection	Calculations	Detail Design Principles	Evaluation of Design	Built-up Roofing
Page	1	19	31	45	83	95	105	165	189	217	221

- The geometry of roofs–even flat roofs–at a level of detail invariably presents problems of site installations. These can sometimes translate over time into durability or performance problems for the assembly, as the roof experiences changes of weather, temperature, etc.
- The real behaviour of rainwater disposal can be a useful indicator of problems.
- It is always important to examine the structure, as performance problems there may be critical.

Because of the need to interrupt the membrane, penetrations are a particular location for leakage problems and close attention should be given to them. Likewise any boundary, upstand or other detail involves a more complex geometry, which increases the likelihood that it will be a leak location.

Rainwater disposal

There can be obvious evidence that rainwater disposal is not happening as intended; in general, it then needs to be checked in case the unintended route is leading to actual or potential damage or failure.

It is important to remember that, if rainwater lays on the roof surface without disposal, it can contribute to a general degradation of performance of some materials–e.g. through mechanisms such as 'thermal shock' (where there can be surprisingly large temperature gradient at the edge of a puddle, following a flash rainstorm onto a sun-warmed roof surface).

Typical indications include:

- Are there general signs of ponding (ponds, sedimentary deposition, etc.)? These may indicate either an original construction fault, or subsequent permanent deformation of the continuous support, including the insulation layer.
- Are there signs of ponding at:
  - parapet walls?
  - abutments?
  - edge details?
  - edges of penetrations through the roof membrane?
  - plant rooms or small support structures for external service runs?
  - flashings?
  - handrail supports?
- Are the flashings generally at a suitable height above the waterproofing membrane? do they appear to connect correctly to the dpc?
- Are there any signs of distress at or near service penetrations, drainage outlets or other rainwater disposal elements?
- Are there signs of movement at rainwater goods?
- Are there protective devices (e.g. gratings) to gutters or outlets in place and in good order?
- Are they blocked with dead leaves or other debris?
- Are there any other signs in parts of the flat roof which might prevent rainwater running off as intended?

Structural deck

The principal structure of the roof is a prime element for examination. It is usually a very serious and urgent matter if there are signs of serious performance failure in the structural deck. Different issues can predominate, for example:

Steel decking:
- Are there signs of rusting?
- Is there evidence of differential deflections at side or end laps or excessive deformations?
- Are any penetrations (e.g. HVAC ducts, access hatches, etc.) showing signs of distortion or relative movement?
- Can one observe loosened fixings?

Timber decking:
- Are there signs of biological attack (e.g. insect, fungus)?
- Are there signs of moisture-based distortions?
- Are there excessive gaps between sections?
- Is there breaking away of fixings?

Strawboard/chipboard deck:
- Are there signs of failure of attachment of the deck to its supporting structure or of other elements to the deck?
- Are there signs of water damage or water-based movement?
- Are there signs of biological attack (e.g. fungus, insect)?

Reinforced concrete deck:
- Can one observe any cracks (especially if wider than 0.3mm)?
- Is there evidence of excessive deflections?
- Are there signs of spalling, softening or reinforcement corrosion?
- Is there evidence of excessive horizontal movement?

Precast concrete deck:
- Are there excessive joint gaps, especially mid-span?
- Can one observe differential deflection at adjacent units?
- Are there signs that the above might be due to deflection, poor site tolerance or mixtures of pre-cambers?

Woodwool slabs:
- Is there evidence of excessive deflections?
- Are there excessive joint gaps?
- Is there disengagement of reinforced edges?
- Is there breaking away of fixings?
- Is there evidence of dampness or rot?   *continued* ▶

Critical factors

- Understand the roof system and its performance in the specific micro-environment.
- Check early warning signs.
- Check for signs of inappropriate use of the roof.

Further reading In the Guide:
4.6 Solar radiation and thermal effects • 4.7 Condensation • 4.11 Traffic on roofs • 4.13 Durability • 5.1 Types of survey and inspection

12 Mastic Asphalt	13 Polymeric Single Ply	14 Copper	15 Lead Sheet	16 Other Membranes	17 Thermal Insulants	18 Specification	19 Contracts & Procurement	20 Inspection	21 Maintenance	22 Bibliography	23 Index
263	301	331	353	375	383	393	399	413	429	437	455

- The membrane material is often the only real 'line of defence' against water penetration. It is essential to check its well-being.
- Different types of roof assembly present different problems of access in checking their elements.

Other structural information:

More general matters which may be helpful to the survey generally include:

- evidence of foundation movement (cracks in structural or non-structural elements)
- identifying changes in the type of structural deck (e.g. part in reinforced concrete, part in metal decking), as these may move differently with temperature or moisture-based change and set up unexpected and damaging stresses.
- changes in span direction of structural deck
- signs of distress through constrained movement
- location of rainwater outlets (may have complicated original site works if inconveniently located)
- location of penetrations (e.g. services).

Membrane materials

There are various warning signs associated with specific membrane materials which, although not an infallible method of detection of actual or potential problems, can often draw attention to matters for further investigation.

Built-up roofing:
- A principal sign of distress is the presence of blisters in the membrane.
- Inadequate detailing for thermal conditions may be revealed by signs of movement of the membrane.
- There may be tearing or cracking due to:
  - differential movement
  - perforation of blisters or unsupported felt
  - sharp bends being formed during the original laying.
- Blisters between layers of felt, or between felt and the deck, may be caused by entrapped air or water.
- Cockling and rippling may be caused by movement, for which inadequate provision has been made, or by insufficient bonding of the layers, or by expansion of the materials.
- Lifting of laps may be because they are inadequately bonded.
- Breaking down of surface can be caused by expansion of volatile fractions of bitumen.
- General deterioration or embrittlement can sometimes be observed, indicating possible incorrect choice of material, falls or method of laying.

Mastic asphalt:
- These membranes may display surface crazing. Some minor surface crazing is not necessarily a problem, but may indicate inadequate solar reflective treatment, which should be remedied. It can also be due to ponding caused by inadequate falls or blocked drainage.
- Blisters may indicate that the membrane is not on sheathing felt, or other isolating membrane.
- Cracking can be due to drying shrinkage of unsuitable solar paint or by movement.
- Cracks more than 3mm deep or splits may indicate inadequate consideration of thermal movement.
- Creep can occur in mastic asphalt, especially on steeply inclined surfaces and not reinforced (e.g. with expanded metal). This can change thickness.
- Patch area repairs to mastic asphalt can be carried out satisfactorily, but are sometimes carried out with inappropriate materials. Any areas of previous repair should be inspected carefully.
- Repeated repairs, by adding layers on top, may have significantly increased the dead load on the structural deck.
- Mastic asphalt membranes are usually dressed up (to upstands, etc.) from the principal horizontal surface: such junctions should be paid particular attention to ensure that thermal movement is able to take place without difficulty.

Polymeric single-ply:
- Lifting of laps may be caused by unsatisfactory bonding.
- Excessive ballooning of sheets – beyond design tolerances – in windy weather can be caused by wind uplift, where the restraint is inadequate.
- Softening of the membrane can be caused by ponding or chemical effects.
- Delamination of the membrane may give indication of possible faults in manufacture.
- Punctures may be due to debris being trodden into the surface of the membrane.
- Visible evidence of substrate fixings on the membrane surface may indicate that these fixings have been pulled out by the effect of the wind.

Metal sheet:
- The principal signs of distress are splits and ripples in the metal sheet.
- These are often used also for the guttering to the flat roof. Particular attention should be paid to the seams and points of tight curvature.

Further reading:

Chapter	1	2	3	4	5	6	7	8	9	10	11
Contents	Introduction	History	Regulatory Methods	Principles	Surveys	Constraints & Targets	Design Selection	Calculations	Detail Design Principles	Evaluation of Design	Built-up Roofing
Page	1	19	31	45	83	95	105	165	189	217	221

University of Sussex, Falmer, UK

- Metal sheet coverings can have small local patch repairs done satisfactorily, but these should be given particular attention on subsequent survey.
- The presence of any areas of moss or lichen above metal sheet roofing should be noted, as their acid secretions can accelerate degradation for several metals (e.g. lead) used in roofing.
- Corrosion or deterioration of the sheet (e.g. copper) can arise due to the action of sulphur-based chemicals in concentrated flue gases, leaching from cedar shingles and acidic water run-off from roofs covered with lichens and mosses.
- Mechanical damage of the roof sheeting can come by natural causes, such as wind uplift or thermal movement.
- Accidental damage can be caused by:
  - falling masonry
  - scaffolding poles
  - scaffold planks- loose nails and screws
  - persons walking on the roof without soft-soled shoes
  - the storage of materials on the roof.
- Failure of the roof substructure (i.e. not the principal structure – which is described above) can arise from:
  - condensation
  - mechanical subsidence
  - deformation due to excessive loading
  - natural damage caused by wood-boring insects.
- Leaking may be due to defective joints.
- Where there is evidence of water penetration into the roof substructure, the seams of the roofing should be opened carefully and trays lifted for more detailed inspection.
- 'Drumming' of the sheets in windy conditions may be a warning of potential displacement of roofing sheets.
- Star cracks, caused by repeated bending and flexing of the roofing sheet, are visual evidence of potential localised fatigue failure of the roof. If left untreated, star cracks can develop into splits in the sheet, allowing the entry of rain and wind.
- Adverse bowing of the sheets between seams is often a precursor of damage caused by wind uplift.

Roof types

Warm deck roofs and cold deck roofs:
- Because the waterproofing membrane is either at or close to the top of the system, it is prone to more attack by weather and activities. This location also means that it is relatively easy to inspect.

Inverted warm deck roofs:
- As the waterproofing membrane is placed in a protected position, it is not subject to the attack and temperature variation of other systems. This also means that it is less accessible for inspection.

Thermal insulation

Insulation layers will not normally be directly visible but the effects on them of water, trafficking, or lack of adequate fixing may be detected by indirect means. In some instances, more direct inspection is possible. Other examinations mentioned above may also give helpful clues.

Ballasting layers

Where ballasting is used, particularly for inverted warm deck roofs, it is important that it is retained in an even layer. Wind movements can cause ballast to move on the roof surface (scour) and can, in extreme circumstances, blow it from the roof.

If unchecked, loss of loose laid insulation boards could occur. The health and safety implications of potential ballast loss from the the roof must be considered. ∎

Critical factors

- Check signs of material change or movement which suggest that it is not adequately placed or secured.
- Do not be deterred from checking elements because of difficulty of access.

Further reading in the Guide:
Chapters 11-15, 20 Inspection, 21 Maintenance.

Design requirements 6

6.1 Design requirements: constraints and targets

- The design brief will be specific to the job, but can be based upon the constraints and targets identified in this Chapter.
- A Project Notebook is provided, which includes a blank pro forma with the main headings described here.

Introduction

It is assumed that the designer/specifier (on behalf of the client) must always make the design decisions specific to the contract. This Unit provides notes which the designer may wish to consider. The development of the client's brief, the **design requirements**, and their detailed description in what is termed here **constraints** and **targets**, rest on judgements by the designer in discussion with the client, users and others. For a given contract, there may be other factors which cannot be foreseen here and the designer will need to incorporate them into this analysis.

Development of the brief
In some cases, this will be highly specified early on; in others it will emerge – for a while remaining undefined in critical respects. It is not always possible to consider all requirements at the early stages of design, but these notes attempt to highlight those which may be – even surprisingly – critical. There are bound to be several cycles of design analysis, if only because some requirements also arise as a consequence of other provisional design decisions: their resolution may affect that previous decision.

The Project Notebook

A separate pro forma is provided, as part of a project notebook, in which the **requirement headings** are provided for both **constraints** and **targets**, and later for **assessments**, so that the designer can quickly judge and summarise what is being sought in the design at any stage. The pro forma does not include all the possible sub-headings listed here, as many may not be relevant for a specific project.

Two descriptions of design requirements

Designers will have their own ways of describing and initiating design requirements. In this Unit, two distinct descriptions of requirements arising from the brief – constraints and targets – use the same headings. Some can be expressed numerically for/by the designer; many can only be expressed qualitatively – but nevertheless should be as explicit as possible. It is against these descriptions that the intermediate and eventual design proposals should be assessed (see **Unit 10.1**).

Constraints
By this is meant those externally-imposed limitations or requirements which – at least in the short term – the designer cannot modify. The most obvious are those imposed by *The Building Regulations* and other legislation.

Targets
These are the requirements set by the designer – either in response to the constraints or even where constraints have not been defined. They may exceed the constraints – for example where the client seeks a better thermal performance than that required under *The Building Regulations*. Targets may change – and certainly more often than constraints.

The requirement headings
The headings used are:

- Client programme/budget
- Form/function
- Context
- Structure
- Climate control
- Internal environmental control
- Durability/working life
- Health and safety
- Environmental impact
- Security
- Construction method
- Design process
- Site processes
- Contract administration.

The headings and sub-headings for both constraints and targets, and their more detailed possibilities, are given below. A sub-heading sometimes occurs more than once, as a check, in case its significance is only apparent in a particular context.

Client programme/budget

This heading covers those considerations which are entirely a consequence of the specific client requirements of the project. Examples include:

Type of work
Four main types of construction work to flat roof can be identified, all involving design decisions:

- new build
- repairs and maintenance
- refurbishment
- replacement.

Further reading:
The Building Regulations

Chapter	1	2	3	4	5	6	7	8	9	10	11
Contents	Introduction	History	Regulatory Methods	Principles	Surveys	Constraints & Targets	Design Selection	Calculations	Detail Design Principles	Evaluation of Design	Built-up Roofing
Page	1	19	31	45	83	95	105	165	189	217	221

- The design requirements are identified in terms of constraints (which cannot easily be changed) and targets (over which the designer has some discretion).
- The client programme/budget is the first set of requirements to consider.
- The implications of form and function, including appearance, may impose constraints and affect requirements.

Each has distinct implications for design choices and the organisation of the design and construction process.

Contract programme

For the whole project, or for the roof element alone, the contract programme is likely to be an important constraint on the designer's choices, sometimes even dominating the choice of technology. Its significance to the design therefore should be assessed as soon as possible.

Programming of roof element

The sequencing of the roof element may be an important factor, whether all or part is on the critical path. For example, watertightness in areas of the building may be necessary while still accepting the presence of following trades on the roof – which could result in damage to completed work. A two-stage waterproofing, or even an initial sacrificial membrane, might be appropriate.

Budget

There will be several possible ways in which budget constraints may be placed on the roof system:

- proportionately from the total building budget (e.g. elemental cost plan)
- a specific budget limit
- constraints on particular parts of the roof system
- via value engineering trade-offs between the roof and other elements
- part of a life-cycle costing exercise, with maintenance predictions taking a significant role (see **Unit 4.14**)
- part of a general policy for maintenance budgeting (see **Chapter 21**).

Existing design decisions

Even for new build, at the time that the roof design is approached in detail there may already be other design decisions which limit the designer's choice of roof system or membrane material. For example, if an early decision has been to use a structural steel frame with lightweight metal decking, this may discourage the use of certain membrane materials. In refurbishment or replacement, there may be a preference for restoring an existing system to its previously satisfactory state.

Preferred systems

Some clients have strong views about particular systems, perhaps where they employ maintenance or facilities management staff with considerable experience of different roof systems. Some insist upon particular

systems or materials, even preferring an early nomination. The designer may anyway recommend this action for a particular contract. There is no inherent problem (with design proposals to, rather than by, the client's designer/specifier), provided that the implications are recognised and the responsibilities (for checking and reviewing) carried out systematically.

Restrictions on materials or methods

Some clients may wish to avoid using certain materials or building methods because of their ethical implications (e.g. for global resources or for possible health risks) or because of implications for neighbours, etc.

Building occupied during construction

This arises as more building types are subject to rapid change during their working lives. Phasing and decanting may constrain the site processes – and in some cases the preferred design solution. Where the works have to be carried out over an unavoidably occupied volume of the building, this problem is even more complex.

Quality Management regime

If used in all or part of the project, the effects may impinge significantly on the type of information required, the procedures for checking etc. This may be a client requirement – in some cases a pre-condition of tendering at all.

Form/function

This covers general issues related to the shape of the roof and its relationship to the purpose the building is intended to serve. Detailed performance requirements are covered under subsequent headings.

Appearance

This is perhaps the most general issue in resolving design constraints and design targets. Whether the building is prestigious or mundane, the client – and others – will reasonably expect it to be designed attractively. This affects the roof treatment. The designer cannot assume that much of the roof will be invisible and therefore need not receive careful attention to its appearance; nor can the designer assume that only the roof edge matters visually – its appearance from the ground level.

Clients and users may not be aware of the eventual visual impact of all the services penetrations and plant, attachments, communications hardware, gantries, rainwater disposal, and lightning protection which *continued* ▶

continued ▶

Critical factors

- Undertake an overall review of the likely project requirements early in the design process.
- Identify any extra factors or headings not covered by pro forma and notes.
- Consider early involvement of supplier or sub-contractor – e.g. for specialist design.

Further reading in the Guide:
4.14 Life-cycle costing • 10.1 Evaluation checklist • 21 Maintenance

12 Mastic Asphalt	13 Polymeric Single Ply	14 Copper	15 Lead Sheet	16 Other Membranes	17 Thermal Insulants	18 Specification	19 Contracts & Procurement	20 Inspection	21 Maintenance	22 Bibliography	23 Index
263	301	331	353	375	383	393	399	413	429	437	455

- Roof geometry is amongst the most complex of design issues.
- The roof zone – especially its depth – will have major implications for design.

---

may have to be arranged above the general level of a flat roof: it may be helpful to raise such issues with them early in the briefing process.

The total appearance of the flat roof system – complete with all its attachments, penetrations and embellishments – should be incorporated into the total design concept for the whole building from the earliest possible stage. This applies as much to work on existing buildings as to new build. The concern arises in many ways:

- conformity with a corporate identity established for broader commercial reasons
- roof overlooked by other buildings (immediately or potentially) or by higher parts of the building itself
- provision of terraces, roof gardens, etc., thus making the roof an important part of the building's amenity, its useful space, as well as its external appearance
- flat roof technologies associated with forms such as large barrel roofs
- visible penetrations (e.g. services outlets): wherever possible, these should be arranged not only for functional efficiency, safe discharge, ease of maintenance and cost effectiveness, but also as attractive features of the building's engineering. A number of notable buildings have made special features of the external servicing, but this approach has to be judged carefully.
- planning limitations on roof materials because of their appearance, or to match those of existing buildings. In buildings for conservation areas, this may be a dominant issue.

Roof geometry/configuration
Constraints may arise from considerations such as:

- planning requirements
- depth of plan of the building (especially if rainwater must be drained to the perimeter)
- overhead restrictions
- perimeter conditions (e.g. party walls, relative movement)
- corporate image for the client (e.g. maintaining a particular visual identity)
- for re-roofing, location of points of potential structural support or connection
- for refurbishment, the type of roof (warm deck, cold deck, etc.) and the potential re-use of existing components
- location of service entries or connections to infrastructure

- avoiding intrusion on protected views (e.g. of cathedral domes)
- rights of light or other easements
- arrangement of lightning protection systems (e.g. to avoid electric arcing across air spaces)
- security of the building against intruders.

Targets will have to be set against any constraints which have been stipulated, either to satisfy those constraints directly or possibly to seek higher performance (whether suggested by client or designer). Examples might include:

- response to local or site features (e.g. skyline)
- consequences of internal functional or spatial requirements (e.g. auditoria in large buildings for public performances)
- easing of site operations and buildability (e.g. location of cranes)
- implications for total energy efficiency of the building, including heat gain consequences of orientation
- achieving a more sheltered environment for roof-level terraces
- consequences at ground level of roof-level winds
- control of sunlight or daylight penetration to the interior (e.g. to achieve desired lighting levels in schools)
- control of rainwater run off to prevent undesirable material interactions either with other construction or with landscaping.

Roof zone and penetrations
The depth of the roof zone has to be defined:

- in terms of the principal elements or components of the build-up – from ceiling to the highest point of construction
- initially in schematic form
- dimensionally as soon as possible (note: the roof zone depth may vary across the plan area – and critically so)
- with some tolerance for later adjustment in the design process.

Various penetrations (service inlets and outlets, structure, access, etc.) will need to be considered in terms of:

- number of penetrations of waterproofing membrane
- consequential problems (e.g. creation of cold bridges)
- discharges from services (e.g. chemical compatibility with roof finishes, health and safety, environmental impact)
- complicating the constructional method and/or sequence (at each element of the roof zone)

Further reading:

- The broader context of the building introduces those local factors which are not a consequence of the client's brief.
- Early clarification of the structure, and the structural behaviour of other elements, is required.

- location of movement joints (consider this as soon as possible)
- potential for standardising the details at the penetrations.

Access/traffic

The significance here is principally for:

- structure (assumed loadings for primary structure; but also structural performance of elements such as insulation, under both static and dynamic loads)
- durability (especially those materials directly bearing the traffic)
- safety of people
- safe control of any equipment used on the roof.

The above will depend on whether the roof is intended to be a 'non-access roof' or an 'access roof', in terms of:

- terrace for assembly of people
- means of escape
- vehicles/mechanical plant
- tanked planters (or a planted roof – which presents different constructional problems)
- repairs and maintenance, including related equipment, of building fabric and of roof-accessed services plant
- allowance for change of use or enhancement/replacement of services.

Context

The context covers local factors (i.e. not a consequence of the client's brief) within and around the site which may impinge upon roof design decisions, such as:

Local climate

This is set within the general issues of climate (below). In the UK, the critical issues defining constraints and targets will be:

- rainfall (annual amount and maximum severity)
- wind
- exposure (and allowing for changes, such as demolition of adjacent buildings).

Nature of the site

This covers characteristics such as:

- ground conditions which may affect the type of primary structure and hence, indirectly, the choice of membrane.
- views to surroundings
- flora (e.g. overhanging deciduous trees, with critical significance for drainage systems)
- adjacent buildings.

Appearance

There may be planning local requirements based upon prevailing vernacular forms in terms of roof geometry, materials, etc.

There may be consequences of local planning requirements, such as density of development or acceptable visual bulk of the building, e.g. thus affecting plan forms.

Special planning contextual factors can arise:

- historic buildings, especially where these are listed, in terms of materials, methods of construction, options for improving the almost invariably low standards of existing thermal insulation
- height restrictions, whether to maintain the general character of the area or to protect views or to restrict the density of development of the site.

Local environment

This may include a range of chemical, physical and biological factors, such as:

- air pollution (e.g. chemical and/or dust discharges from nearby factories, pollens), which can affect material choices
- ground pollution (e.g. gases such as methane or radon)
- fauna (e.g. birds – which have been known to attack some membrane materials).

Administrative systems

This includes the effects of various factors:

- legal constraints, such as easements, party wall arrangements, rights of light
- land ownership, such as limitations imposed by freeholders, special considerations when on Crown land, etc.

Structure

This covers all aspects of structural performance, both by the primary structure and by other components and elements, such as:

Loadings

These include:

- dead loads
- imposed loads (including snow)
- wind loads. continued ▶

Critical factors

- Check legal aspects – easements, etc.
- Establish roof zone depth across whole plan.
- Check liveliness of roof structure.
- Check location and arrangement of movement joints.
- Use of the roof.

- The control of the effects of climate on the building may have wider design implications.
- The internal environmental requirements of the building will affect roof design; in some special cases, these may impose severe constraints.

The dead loads arise from the self-weight of the structure and other fixed elements of the roof construction. Basic data are provided in *BS6399*. The constraints arising from loads for new build are defined in *The Building Regulations*, Approved Document A, which in turn refers the designer to *BSCP3: Chapter V: Part 2* for data for design against wind (see **Units 4.3, 4.10, 7.10** and **8.4**).

Deflections

Limits to the deflection of the primary structure will be set by relevant codes. The change in deflection under imposed load, or flexibility, will be a factor in the choice of a roofing system (see **Units 4.3** and **7.11**). For existing structures, the loadbearing capacity and the liveliness of the existing substrate will have to be assessed.

Movement

System design details (see **Units 4.3** and **9.1**) will be influenced by movement of large structural elements, and particularly the relative movement at discontinuities (e.g. movement joints in the structural deck). Movement joints are not determined solely by structural factors and may have to be considered at a surprisingly early stage in design in terms of types of movement (linear, shear, etc.), extent of movement, and location.

Climate control

This heading includes the general implications of climate, as distinct from the description of the local climate (above).

Sun

Solar radiation control – especially heat absorption – is significant in flat roof design, for both heat balance control of the internal environment and the durability of roofing materials (see **Units 4.6** and **4.13**). The protection system has to be maintainable. Refurbishment works offer particular opportunities for upgrading in this respect.

Wind

Wind generates both positive and negative forces on roofs (see **Units 4.10** and **7.10**) and is complex to control. The negative (uplift) forces are particularly significant for lightweight roofing systems. These negative forces also affect the method of fixing the roof elements to the structure. In some cases, the wind effects at ground level of particular roof forms may be a significant issue. The building's degree of airtightness affects energy efficiency.

Precipitation

One of the dominant issues in the design of roof systems (see also **Unit 4.4**) is the exclusion and disposal of water as rain, snow or hail. Constraints for new build are defined by Approved Documents C and H of *The Building Regulations*. A principal concern will be the choice of flat roof membrane to exclude water – whether waterproof (organic materials) or watershedding/weatherproof (metals). The strategy for rainwater disposal and arrangement of outlets should also be considered as soon as possible. For some special building uses, drumming vibration from precipitation may be an issue in selecting roof finishes. Snow loads affect the design of the primary structure.

Internal environmental control

This deals with the principal parameters of the internal environment of the building and their relationship to the design of the roof system:

Thermal control

The general energy performance of the building may be dominated by the thermal insulation performance of the roof, especially if it is a deep plan building and/or single-storey. Constraints are defined in Approved Document L of *The Building Regulations* (see **Units 7.6** and **8.2**).

Humidity/condensation control

Unless the building is air-conditioned, the internal relative humidity will be determined largely by external conditions, the internal temperatures, and any internal functions which generate large amounts of water vapour (e.g. swimming pools). Constraints are defined in Approved Document F of *The Building Regulations* (see **Units 7.6** and **8.2**).

Acoustic control

The acoustic environment will be determined mostly by the arrangement of internal volumes, their surface absorptions, and the insulation of internal divisions. The roof assembly contributes sometimes by allowing or preventing flanking transmission of sound or other vibration (see **Unit 4.12**). It may also be a significant element in the acoustic insulation between the internal and the external environments. Where the flat roof is used as a terrace, consideration may be needed to control structure-borne impact sound.

Lighting control

The requirement for natural light via rooflights has to be considered in terms of its coordination with the artificial

---

Further reading:
Health and Safety at Work Act • Approved documents A, C, F, H, L of The Building Regulations • The Construction (Design and Management) Regulations• BS6399: Loading for buildings • BS6651: Code of practice for protection of structures against lightning • BSCP3: Chapter V: Part 2. Wind loads

Chapter	1	2	3	4	5	6	7	8	9	10	11
Contents	Introduction	History	Regulatory Methods	Principles	Surveys	Constraints & Targets	Design Selection	Calculations	Detail Design Principles	Evaluation of Design	Built-up Roofing
Page	1	19	31	45	83	95	105	165	189	217	221

- Durability covers quality performance over building life, including its relationship to maintenance.
- Health and safety considerations arise both for the construction and the use of the building.

---

lighting systems (and hence sometimes with other ceiling services) and with the structure. It has major implications for detailing the penetrations through the roof zone – especially of the waterproofing membrane – and the general energy efficiency of the building.

Special internal environments
In certain cases, the internal environment required may imply severe constraints:

- unusual levels of internal relative humidity (e.g. indoor swimming pools, laundries, large amounts of internal fountains and planting)
- unexpected condensation problems (e.g. cold storage warehouses)
- intolerance of noise intrusion (airborne or structure-borne) or other vibration (e.g. buildings for public performance, such as for music)
- particular control of ventilation intakes – affecting services and the air-tightness of the building (e.g. some manufacturing processes, special medical facilities, art galleries)
- natural light (general or from a particular orientation) required across a deep plan (e.g. offices).

Durability and working life

This heading deals with quality performance over building life. It deals with the behaviour over time of materials and the more complex matter of whole roof systems. It has to take account of maintenance and repairs within a life-cycle costing framework (see **Units 4.13, 4.14, 7.12** and **21.1**). Particular considerations include:

'Maintainability'
This is the concept that the designer (whether for new build or for work to existing buildings) can take some account of the subsequent maintenance and repair (see **Unit 7.12**) at the early design stage; it may also affect **'buildability'**. Where possible, for flat roofs this includes:

- Does the roof arrangement allow safe access, including fixing points for safety equipment?
- Is detailed inspection straightforward – preferably by eye (e.g. outlets, flashings)?
- Is any problem of pattern-staining likely?
- Does the detailing allow for component replacement without wholesale reconstruction of the surrounding fabric?
- Resistance to vandalism.

Planned maintenance
This has always to be seen within a life-cycle costing framework and may affect the choice of suppliers, in terms of guarantees and warranties.

Material compatibility
This is often a matter for detailed design, but can be a general issue with metal membrane roofs. It also arises when considering certain combinations of membrane, insulation, and substrate, and overlaying new membranes on old roofs.

Recycling of materials
Some clients may prefer to use materials which can be recycled after demolition. In refurbishment, this may also be an issue for existing components.

Demolition
Some initial design choices will simplify eventual demolition. Where demolition is required before new construction is carried out, attention should be paid to health, safety and environmental considerations for the intermediate construction phases and for disposal of discarded materials.

Health and safety

Designers should remember their statutory responsibilities, such as those under the *Health & Safety at Work etc. Act* and forthcoming UK and EC legislation (e.g. *The Construction (Design and Management) Regulations* – CONDAM). Particular sub-headings are:

Fire
The principal aspects (see **Unit 7.9**) are:

- fire resistance, where this affects the protection of means of escape over the roof, where the roof acts also as a floor (e.g. car parks), and where the roof helps to support elevations
- flame spread and fire penetration, which affect the choice of materials
- other matters, principally preventing the roof bypassing other fire controls.

Lightning protection
Systems may have awkward implications for the design if not considered as early as possible (see **Unit 7.8**). The critical consideration is the calculation of the overall **risk factor**, in accordance with *BS6651*, taking account of any special vulnerabilities or inherent risks. *continued* ▶

Critical factors

- Check special internal environments.
- Establish strategy for rainwater disposal.
- Consider 'maintainability'.
- Check health and safety, especially risk factor for lightning protection.

Further reading in the Guide:
4.3 Structure and movement • 4.4 Precipitation: rain and snow • 4.6 Solar radiation and thermal effects • 4.10 Wind • 4.12 Acoustic behaviour • 4.13 Durability of materials • 4.14 Life-cycle costing • 7.6 Design for thermal performance • 7.8 Design for lightning protection • 7.9 Design for fire safety • 7.10 Design for wind resistance • 7.11 Design for traffic and load spreading • 8.4 Calculation of wind uplift • 9.1 Key diagram • 21.1 Planned maintenance.

12	13	14	15	16	17	18	19	20	21	22	23
Mastic Asphalt	Polymeric Single Ply	Copper	Lead Sheet	Other Membranes	Thermal Insulants	Specification	Contracts & Procurement	Inspection	Maintenance	Bibliography	Index
263	301	331	353	375	383	393	399	413	429	437	455

- Environmental impact considerations have to be made, often with limited reliable information.
- Roofs have to be secure against forced entry and, sometimes, against theft of their constituent materials.
- Construction method should be considered in initial design analyses.
- The organisation of the design process itself can affect design choices.

Environmental impact

Greater attention is being given to the much broader implications of materials used in buildings (see **Unit 4.14**): those which remain part of the installation; those (e.g. solvent-based adhesives) used in its creation. At present, there is only a small amount of reliable information which is of use in design selection, although this may well improve quickly under the demands of legislation such as the *Construction Products Regulations* (see **Unit 3.1**). Potential constraints or targets include:

Excluded materials
Apart from client stipulations, the designer may wish to check whether proposed materials (or those to be retained in an existing roof) are regarded as possibly harmful to the environment – even if not prohibited by existing legislation.

Non-renewable materials
Many materials used in construction are non-renewable. Some clients and/or designers seek actively to minimise the demands on known reserves.

Embodied energy
This refers to the total energy consumed in transforming a material or component to its final installed form from its original natural sources.

Security

Control of entry
This includes not only obvious aspects (e.g. windows and access doors to the roof), but in special cases can also have implications for methods of construction.

Value of materials
The resale value of construction materials (e.g. lead) can be a factor in the roof design, to deter its theft.

Resistance to vandalism
The design of the roof, and particularly edge details (e.g. gutters and downpipes) can strongly influence the accessibility to vandals.

Construction method

The methods of constructing the flat roof, and their detailed implications, should be considered as soon as possible. This becomes more feasible as the design proceeds and decisions converge. Particular issues include:

Reference to suppliers and manufacturers
These have considerable experience and feedback on the performance of their products in roof systems. Many offer a comprehensive service on roof design generally and the detailed use of their own products and systems. This may also be linked to the use of specialist sub-contractors.

Dimensions
This means identifying the critical dimensions (e.g. roof zone depth across the whole plan, heights of upstands, or flashings above roof membrane), some of which may be specific to the contract. It also includes:

- dimensional coordination, particularly if the project is planned on a three-dimensional grid or other modular arrangement
- tolerance and fit, taking account of the needs of manufacturing, assembly, future movement (e.g. thermal) once installed, and maintenance replacement
- general movement and designed movement joints (see also above), considering the size of components and elements (e.g. ex-factory, or maximum possible for the contract) and their behaviour under structural load, or thermal or hygrothermal change.

Discontinuity of materials and/or geometry
Most detailing problems arise at joints or junctions. The designer can control the complexity of detailing by strategic design choices early in the roof design process, if their significance – in the particular contract – is recognised and considered. These conditions include:

- discontinuities in a material, such as bonding or butt-jointing the material to itself
- changes of material, vertically or horizontally
- geometric complexity, notably where a material has to change direction in more than one dimension (e.g. internal corners at abutments), with consequences at movement joints and other very complex locations
- interfaces with other elements, where the performance requirements may alter
- perimeter or boundary conditions, whether free air or adjacent buildings
- penetrations by services, safety attachments, etc.
- flexibility for change, either during the design process (keeping options open) or in the constructed roof (e.g. upgrading services which penetrate the roof).

Buildability
This means taking account of site factors (e.g. access for handling equipment) and **site processes** (see below). In some cases, the designer can take account of the special skills and resources of the specialist sub-contractor and/or the main contractor.

Further reading:
EC Construction Products Directive

- The site characteristics affect design directly; they also affect it indirectly because of their constraints upon potential ways of organising site production and assembly.
- The administration of the contract and the form of contract have to be considered for their implications on design.

Design process

The organisation of the design process, whether a standard office practice or developed for the specific contract, can affect the design choices. This is for three main reasons:

Division of design responsibilities
The crucial issue will usually be whether sub-contractor design is used. Using of work packages also has implications, especially if linked with performance (rather than materials and workmanship) specifications, as certain decisions are critical earlier and are less easily modified.

Extent of research
The design data and feedback available for new build may differ from that for works to existing buildings—the latter may be dominated by the existing fabric and/or survey results. The extent to which designers research roof systems depends on the particular contract and their familiarity with appropriate systems.

Translation of the contract programme
The designer has to allocate time for developing the brief (constraints and targets), strategic and detailed design, building control applications, specification writing, reviewing design proposals, etc. This judgement is made in the context of early assessments of potential solutions. The use of quality management systems will also impinge upon this process, in researching, checking and documenting such activities.

Site processes

The particular characteristics of the site directly affect design choices and the organisation for production (e.g. work to existing buildings, limited use of roads for unloading). Design choices may be indirectly affected by necessary constraints upon the organisation of production on site; site production is significantly determined by design decisions. Particular attention may be needed for:

Access
This may affect deliveries, demolition and removal, the kind of cranes and handling equipment that can be used on site, etc. In turn, these may affect the designer's preferred choices. Consideration should also be given to the need for protection from following trades.

Storage
The potential and provision for adequate storage, and its location in relation to the installed work, will affect the quality of construction.

Off-site work
The potential of particular systems for prefabricated components and preformed flashings, etc., can relieve certain site difficulties.

Workmanship and supervision
Site features may ease or complicate the task of achieving good workmanship and/or supervision, which in turn may affect design choices.

Availability
The availability of labour and/or materials (e.g. reliable delivery horizons, use of imported products) may affect design choices, especially if the contract programme requires fast speed of construction of the whole building or of the roof element (e.g. to provide protection for following trades). Such questions may arise in reference to suppliers and manufacturers (see above).

Health and safety
Site safety of the workforce and others must be considered. Design choices may be affected by the need of some materials or methods for particular equipment which present a safety hazard in a particular situation (e.g. use of hot-poured materials may be a fire risk in listed buildings).

Contract administration

The administration of the contract can affect the balance of decision between design choices, for example:

Procurement
The organisation of buying in the work can affect design choices, directly or indirectly (by virtue of its implications for site processes), for example:

- the use of nominated suppliers, perhaps to speed up design selection
- tendering procedures and criteria for acceptance
- the requirement of warranties and guarantees
- the stipulation of site labour of a particular quality
- the form of specification (performance or materials and workmanship).

Type of contract
There are significant consequences of choosing, for example, a design/build contract as against a management contract. Each has its own merits and implications for the organisation of work. The use of sub-contractors will usually be an important matter, especially if they offer a design service as well. ∎

Critical factors

- Consider early involvement of supplier or sub-contractor.
- Clarify design responsibilities.
- Identify constraints arising from site restrictions on contractor.
- Check that all headings and sub-headings have been considered and document this for quality management.
- Significance of detailing in design choice.
- Choice of contract.

Further reading in the Guide:
3.1 Standards and certification: a framework • 4.14 Life-cycle costing

Design selection 7

Special Note: *The guidance provided in this Guide assumes that the roof will be exposed to typical UK climatic conditions. Care should be taken for other locations where different conditions may apply.*

7.1   Design selection: general approach

- The process design selection for a complete roof relies on a series of interacting decisions. It is possible to address the questions involved in varying orders and from different starting points.

- This Unit attempts to show, through the flow diagram and the narrative in the following pages, how such a design selection may be attempted and recorded. Chapters are referenced in red in relevant boxes.

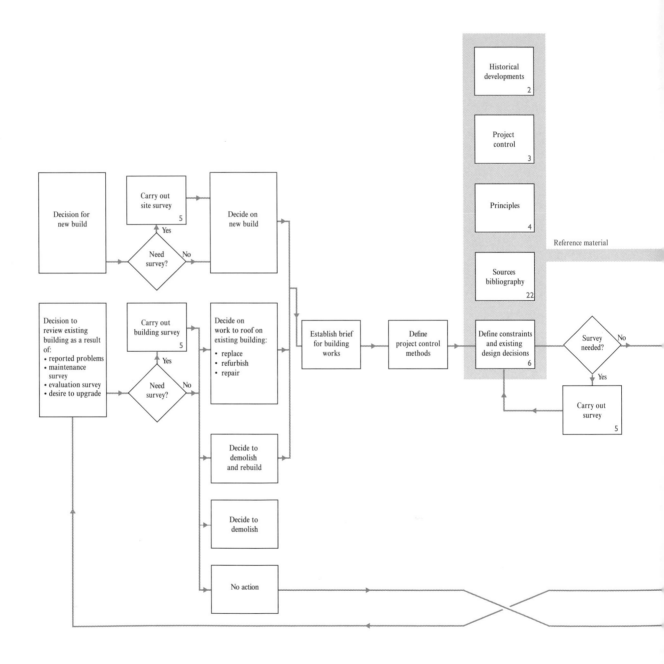

© BFRC / CIRIA: Flat Roofing: Design and Good Practice. 1993

- The flow diagram provides a complete description of the main activities which have to take place in order that a flat roof be designed, constructed, inspected, surveyed, repaired, replaced, refurbished, or demolished (as part of the building).
- The flow diagram and the following narrative are a recommended sequence for these activities. Some of these activities may, if designers prefer, occur in parallel or in a different sequence.

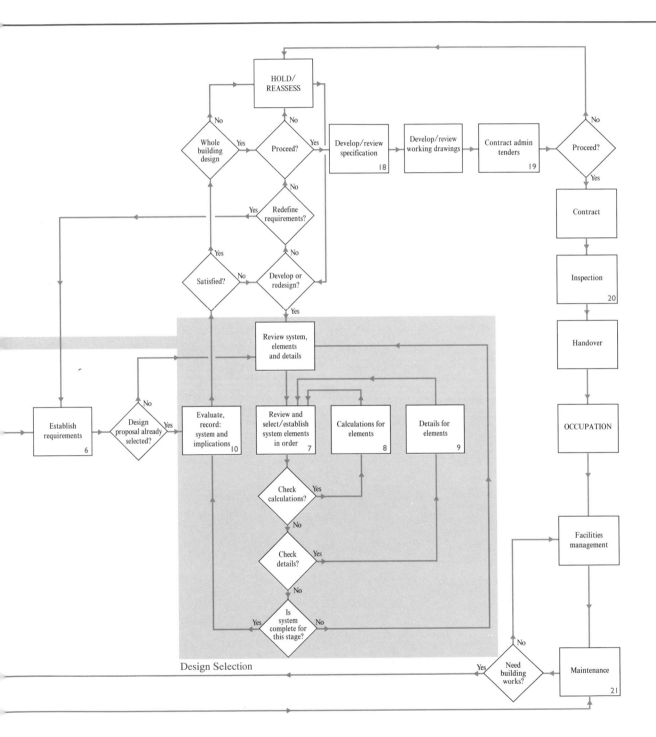

Design Selection

12 Mastic Asphalt	13 Polymeric Single Ply	14 Copper	15 Lead Sheet	16 Other Membranes	17 Thermal Insulants	18 Specification	19 Contracts & Procurement	20 Inspection	21 Maintenance	22 Bibliography	23 Index
263	301	331	353	375	383	393	399	413	429	437	455

- Provision is made for designers to start at any point in the chart and to be taken through a sequence of stages which will help them make any checks they consider relevant. It is important to note that, where designers have already dealt with an aspect, they can 'jump' to the next stage.

- The purpose of design selection is to arrive at a description of the roof system, either as a performance specification or in terms of materials, workmanship and details.

Design selection

The purpose of design selection is to arrive at a description of the roof system, whether as a **performance specification** or in terms of **materials, workmanship and details**. In the latter case there are two broad types of materials specification: nomination of material or by reference to standards or certification. This Chapter concentrates on the design issues relevant to both these material's workmanship and details approaches although the decision process is still relevant to performance specifications.

This Unit takes the designer through all the steps of the design selection procedure at a preliminary level so that the interaction of the decisions can be seen. The following Units then address each of the aspects in greater detail.

There may be benefit in developing descriptions of a few roof options, prior to final selection. Although in principle it is preferable to keep all design options open, in practice this may not be appropriate. Whether for new build or for work to existing buildings, design decisions about the system or its elements may in effect have already been taken, directly or indirectly, for one or more of the following reasons:

- Client preference, including their own experiences from previous contracts or from maintenance and facilities management.
- Location of responsibility for design/specification.
- Designer/specifier recommendation, perhaps based on previous experience(but subject to review here).
- Prior commitments to a particular supplier or contracto with proprietary methods or materials.
- Prior commitment to a particular form of procurement.
- Project-specific technical factors, such as:
  - planning requirements
  - matching an existing roof
  - the need to obtain a consistent external appearance on flat and adjoining pitched roofs
  - refurbishing an existing building with existing systems
  - a particular appearance (e.g. in terms of colour).

The roof is defined in terms of the following items (developed in greater detail in Table 7.1.1), whose sequence is based on a recommended sequence of design decisions:

- Dimensions and geometry.
- Structure and falls.
- Roof configuration type.
- Waterproof/weatherproof membrane.
- Drainage system.
- Thermal insulation.
- Vapour control.
- Finishes.
- Health & safety.
- Details, joints and junctions.

These are the features or aspects of the roof which will have to be designed at some point using the following Units of the Guide. It is probable that several different design solutions exist for the same overall requirement. Some post-design selection process of evaluation may be appropriate to make a single selection. This Chapter of the Guide suggests a way of carrying out a design selection process with some ongoing evaluation checks. It may be appropriate however to take the alternative solutions through to a tendering process.

The design selection procedure proposed here is supported by checklists which helps designers – if they wish – to record the myriad decisions and judgements which are involved in the design and construction of a satisfactory modern flat roof system.

During the design selection process it may become apparent that solutions for particular aspects of the roof are in conflict with the requirements. In such an event these conflicts may be resolved when encountered or it may be preferable to leave them unresolved until all the issues become clearer and which may lead to modification of the requirements.   *continued* ▶

Further reading:
The Building Regulations

© BFRC / CIRIA: *Flat Roofing: Design and Good Practice.* 1993

- The following Units concentrate on a materials, workmanship and details approach although the decision process is still relevant to performance specifications.
- The design process outlined here is supported by checklists which help with evaluation of the selections and recording of the decisions.

Table 7.1.1
Design selection

- **Dimensions and geometry:**
  - Arrangement in three dimensions
  - Depth of roof zone(s)
  - Plan areas

- **Structure and falls:**
  - Materials
  - Form
  - Load-bearing capacity
  - Movement in all three dimensions
  - Deflections

- **Roof configuration type:**
  - Cold deck roof
  - Warm deck roof
  - Inverted warm deck roof
  - Variants

- **Waterproof/weatherproof membrane:**
  - Material:
    - Organic materials:
      - Built-up roofing
      - Mastic asphalt
      - Polymeric sheet
      - Thin liquid applied
    - Metal sheets:
      - Copper
      - Lead
      - Aluminium
      - Stainless steel
      - Zinc
  - Reinforcement:
  - Assembly:
    - Single layer
    - Multi-layer
  - Dimensions:
    - Thickness
    - Sheet size
  - Manufacture:
    - Pre-formed off-site
    - Formed insitu
  - Fixing and jointing:
    - Membrane to itself
    - Membrane to other elements:
      - Full bonding
      - Partial or spot bonding
      - Isolating membranes

- **Drainage system:**
  - Direction of run-off, falls, etc
  - Arrangement of gutters, outlets, etc

- **Thermal insulation:**
  - Materials
  - Dimensions
  - Location
  - Methods of attachment

- **Vapour control:**
  - Materials
  - Dimensions
  - Location
  - Methods of jointing
  - Methods of attachment

- **Finishes:**
  - General appearance
  - Solar reflective treatment
  - Trafficking surfaces
  - Ballast

- **Health & safety:**
  - General considerations
  - Fire protection
  - Lightning protection
  - Excluded materials

- **Details, joints and junctions:**
  - Typical conditions
  - Changes of roof geometry and/or material
  - Penetrations and upstands
  - Movement joints
  - Handrails, etc
  - Gantries, etc

Further reading in the Guide:
6.1 Design requirements: constraints and targets • 10.1 Evaluation checklist

- This unit takes the designer through all the steps of the design selection procedure at a preliminary level so that the interaction of the decisions can be seen. The following units then address each of the aspects in greater detail.

- It is feasible and in some cases desirable, to take more than one design selection forward to the next stages of evaluation.

Design selection for flat roof design

A designer will need to be clear about the requirements and organisation of project co-ordination, any formal procedures and their implications for recording of design decisions, and the effects of *The Building Regulations* and any other legislation. Further guidance about these aspects in relation to the specific project, is given in **Chapter 3**.

To commence design, a designer should first establish dimensions and the structure. Then consider system and membrane selection, in either order, in terms of the project constraints (what has to be provided) and the project targets (including performance requirements and other desired attributes). To do this, a designer will have to make judgments about the significance to the particular project of the various characteristics described in the following Units for systems and membrane materials. After that, selection of the other elements of the roof system is required.

Recording of information

Designers may wish to formally record individual design decisions as they are made. These can be useful for record purposes or for a further evaluation of the design. A design selection checklist proforma, with suggested headings, is included in the project notebook which designers may use if they wish. The same major headings, combined with those described earlier in this Unit for the design decisions, form the basis for the evaluation checklist used in **Unit 10.1**.

Constraints and targets

Constraints and targets are described in **Unit 6.1**. The constraints are those conditions imposed upon the project; the targets are defined by the designer/client – whether in terms of simply meeting the constraints (e.g. structural performance) or of exceeding their requirements to provide higher standards or by defining a target where there are no constraints. They arise from the brief and the specific circumstances of the project. These constraints may for example be very different for new build or refurbishment projects. They are covered by the following general headings :

- Client programme/budget
- Form/function.
- Context.
- Structure.
- Climate control.
- Internal environment control.
- Durability/working life.
- Health and safety.
- Environmental impact.
- Security.
- Construction method.
- Design process.
- Site processes.
- Contract administration.

If not already established, these constraints and requirements, at least provisionally, should be so before proceeding with the design selection.

University of East Anglia, Norwich, UK.

Further reading:
The Building Regulations

- The headings for the checklists are the same as those used in Unit 6.1 and Unit 10.1. A full list of main headings is also included in the Project Notebook.
- It is important for following design decisions to set out a spatial framework for the roof. This framework will need to recognise the likely requirements of the roof design (e.g. depth of roof zone for falls).
- Some decisions, such as the nature of the building structure may already have been decided.

Principal dimensions and spatial geometry

After defining the requirements and targets for the roof design, it is helpful to identify the principal **controlling dimensions** and **spatial geometry** of the roof or roofs involved. A basic plan and any information on controlling vertical dimensions are important to establish – especially if there are any critical controls on the overall depth of the **roof zone(s)**. This zone includes the structural deck, the rest of the build-up to its top surface, the minimum 150mm to the top of the membrane upstand from the highest point of the roof, and any necessary construction above that line. Such dimensions may be dictated by external factors such as planning consents or the requirement to match with existing adjacent roofs. Each project will have its own combination of factors which will determine the controlling dimensions. It is therefore not possible to provide detailed guidance here.

Design selection sequence

With the basic design requirements for the roof laid out, the design selection sequence can begin. As with many design processes where separate decisions influence others, there are many ways, or routes, a designer can take to complete the design. In the following units of the guide a particular sequence is recommended, based on experience and the knowledge that the earlier selection decisions will simplify those later on. Designers may, if they wish, choose an alternative route.

If possible first establish the design of the structural deck. The Guide does not cover structural design, so this will in any case have to be handled elsewhere.

Influence of roof structure

The design of the structure of the roof, and the building, may have significant influence on the design of the roof build up. It is therefore important to establish the likely significance early. There are three likely situations:

A The structure has already been determined, whether earlier in the design of a new building, or because the job is work to an existing building.
B The structure has not been determined, but could be now – in part or completely.
C The structure cannot yet be decided.

If A, obtain the following details from the structural designer:

- Materials.
- Form.
- Load-bearing capacity.
- Movement in all three dimensions.
- Deflections and 'liveliness'.

For existing buildings the overall suitability of the deck will have to be evaluated for the new roof requirements.

If B, ask the structural designer to make a provisional strategic decision on the same aspects of the roof deck, so far as is possible. Some decisions may have to be reconsidered when the structure is more fully designed.

If C, proceed, but recognise that some provisional design options on the roof as a whole are likely to be aborted when the structure design is finalised.

The structure selection will obviously relate to the function of the roof e.g. plant, car park, gardens, but will also affect other design selections in this chapter, for example selection of the method of creating falls (see **Unit 7.5**).

Other considerations relating to structure

In addition to the functional aspects of the roof deck there may be other considerations for the particular design which influence the selection of the roof deck. This could be, for example, building form.

Further information on the influence of structural design on roof design is given in **Unit 4.3**.

If acoustic insulation performance is critical to the project, the mass of the structural deck (and sometimes that of the membrane where it is heavy metal sheet) will be the dominant factor.

If the minimisation of impact sound transfer is critical, then this will be determined by the resilience of the material(s) between the surface of impact and the structural deck.

Design for acoustic performance is not included in this Guide, but the principles are set out in **Unit 4.12.**

continued ▶

Critical factors

Further reading in the Guide:
3 Regulatory methods • 4.3 Structure and movement • 6.1 Design requirements: constraints and targets • 7.5 Design for falls for drainage • 10.1 Evaluation checklist

- The sequence of deciding on membrane and roof configuration may be interchanged without great significance for the remainder of the selection procedure of many roofs.

Roof configuration type and membrane

The next stage for design is to choose the system and then the principal waterproof/weatherproof membrane. Alternatively, select the membrane first and then determine the system. At this stage of the design process, it makes little difference which is done first. Some designers argue that you should choose the system first, on the grounds that this is the more general consideration, but others regard the membrane as the key. In some cases, as indicated earlier in this unit, client preferences or project-specific factors will mean that in reality the membrane or the system has already been chosen.

Roof configuration options

It may be convenient for initial design selection to consider broad categories of configuration of roof components. The developed roof design must, however, be assessed for actual performance using specific properties of the components. To achieve this it is necessary to understand some of the principles of the physical and chemical behaviour of the different systems. It is crucial to understand that a modern flat roof system is a complex assembly of materials and components. Some of these components arrive on site in small elements which then have to be joined together. The overall behaviour is affected by this process.

Manufacturers have devoted much research and practice to establishing reliable methods of making their roofing systems.

In this Guide, three principal types of roof configuration are dealt with:

- cold deck roofs. Note that these are not recommended for use in Scotland and can only be used there with the specific approval of the local authority (See **Unit 3.2**)
- warm deck roofs with variants for metal membranes and others.
- inverted warm deck roofs (also known as upside-down roofs or as protected membrane roofs)

The Guide concentrates on two families of membrane material:

- organic materials
- metal sheet.

The principles of the behaviour of these configurations of roof components are discussed in **Unit 4.2**.

The principal characteristics of the three roof configurations should be considered. They can be related to the headings from the checklist of constraints and targets in **Unit 6.1**. Notes can be made against this checklist of which characteristics are of particular importance: whether a given characteristic is an overriding or determining factor usually depends upon the specifics of the project.

It is important to recognise that, in this Guide, only certain combinations of system and membrane are positively recommended for consideration and for which detailed guidance is given. Others may not be recommended although might be satisfactory after detailed consideration and design. These various recommendations are displayed in Table 7.1.2. In some applications these other combinations may be unavoidable, for example, in refurbishment.

Table 7.1.2
Options for combinations of membrane and roof system

Roof configuration	Cold deck roof	Warm deck roof	Inverted warm deck roof	'Buried roof'
Membrane material				
Built up roofing	B	A	A	A
Mastic asphalt	B	B	A	A
Polymeric sheet	B	A	B	C
Thin liquid applied	C	B	C	C
Copper	B*	B*	E	E
Lead	B*	B*	E	E
Zinc, aluminium, Stainless steel	B*	B*	E	E

Key to table:

A - Generally recommended in this Guide.

B - Recommended for specific conditions or configurations only (see relevant materials chapters of this Guide).

C - Requires the specific endorsement of the material supplier.

D - Combination to be avoided if possible.

E - This combination should not be used.

* - There are particular concerns with the performance of metal sheet roofs, resolution of which requires particular attention to the component configuration. The current best advice from these sections of the industry are discussed in the relevant materials chapters (**Chapters 14** and **15**).

Further reading:

- Not all of the possible combinations of roof configuration and membrane are the subject of further guidance in this Guide.
- Roof configuration types may be helpful in initial design selection, but the developed design must be checked for potential performance using specific properties of the components.

Fuller guidance on the essential characteristics and selection features of the roof system types is given in **Unit 7.2**.

Standard solutions: roof configuration

The Guide provides critical information on the behaviour of roof systems, not 'standard solutions', as these depend on the specifics of the project. The designer will then have to make a judgement about which roof system is most suitable. It may be preferred – at least on an initial circuit of the design process – to keep more than one option of roof system. Initial decisions can be recorded on the design selection checklist.

Membrane selection

The paragraphs below on membrane selection can be used for initial guidance on membrane selection.

The designer should understand the particular characteristics, advantages and disadvantages of the principal materials covered in this Guide.

The essential characteristics of the membrane types are given in summary form in **Unit 7.3**.

Fuller information is given in the material specific chapters of the Guide as follows:

Organic materials:

Built-up roofing	Chapter 11
Mastic asphalt	Chapter 12
Polymeric single-ply	Chapter 13
Thin liquid applied	Chapter 16

Metal sheet:

Copper	Chapter 14
Lead	Chapter 15
Zinc, aluminium and stainless steel	Chapter 16

These material specific chapters together with the information in **Unit 7.3** on membrane selection can provide sufficient information on the likely performance of the membrane types. A fuller evaluation and understanding of potential performance is often very useful. Aspects of the general considerations of durability and environmental impact are covered in **Units 4.13, 4.14** and **4.15**.

Habitat, Montreal, Canada

Standard solutions: membrane types

Again, as with roof configurations, crucial attributes are given in the Guide, but their significance depends upon what is important in the context of the particular project. The designer will have to make a judgement about which membrane is most suitable. It may be preferred – at least on an initial circuit of the design process – to keep more than one option of membrane type.

That decision will define the material and – where possible at this stage – whether it is a reinforced version, single or multi-layer, critical dimensions, how it is jointed and how it is connected to other elements.

Review of the design so far

At this stage several key aspects of the roof will have been decided; the dimensions, structural deck, membrane and roof system. For some of these more than one option may have been kept open. If a formal process of recording project information is being followed, these decisions may have been entered into a design selection checklist.

It will often be useful to review these decisions before proceeding further with the remainder of the detail design.

continued ▶

Critical factors

- Roof configuration categories for initial design selection only.

Further reading in the Guide:
4.2 Behaviour of assemblies: flat roof configurations • 6.1 Design requirements: constraints and targets • 7.2 Design selection: roof configuration
7.3 Design selection: membranes

12 Mastic Asphalt	13 Polymeric Single Ply	14 Copper	15 Lead Sheet	16 Other Membranes	17 Thermal Insulants	18 Specification	19 Contracts & Procurement	20 Inspection	21 Maintenance	22 Bibliography	23 Index
263	301	331	353	375	383	393	399	413	429	437	455

- A sequence of design decisions is shown which allow subsequent decisions to be made with fewer returns to earlier decisions. Designers may prefer to work with an alternative sequence.
- Selection and design of thermal performance depends upon the overall requirements and other properties of insulants such as fire and mechanical performance.
- Design for drainage considers falls, total roof zone depth, gutter and outlet capacities.

Design for roof drainage

The next stage of design is to consider the design of the roof drainage system. A summary of the procedure is given here and more detail guidance is given in **Units 7.4** and **7.5**. Where designers have sufficient confidence in their understanding of the geography of rainfall and the principles of incidence on, and removal from roofs, they can start the detail design. Where such understanding is not developed, further explanation is given in **Unit 4.4**.

Scope of design

Design of the roof drainage requires resolution of a number of issues connected with the build up of the complete roof system including the structural deck arrangement to ensure that rainwater is drained correctly to the outlets. This means designing the direction of flows and the falls (and where necessary the build-up to achieve them). It also means designing the arrangement and size of outlets to get rid of that rainwater. To determine these capacities, a calculation has to be made to determine the rate of water discharge from the roof and the flow capacities of rainwater goods. The choice of proprietary rainwater goods is made from manufacturers' literature and is not covered in this Guide.

Design approach

To design the drainage system, refer to **Unit 7.4** for the general design approach and considerations, and to **Unit 8.1** for the related calculations of rate of discharge, flow capacities of outlets, etc (including a worked example). The flow chart in **Unit 7.5** shows how to develop the design decisions for the drainage in relation to the creation of falls. It can be seen here that the designer needs to know the structure, its likely deflection and construction tolerances, and the limit, if any, of its roof zone depth, to calculate the fall arrangements – which may then be achieved by a variety of methods including tapering the insulant, using separate screeds, or creating a slope in the deck.

At the end of this stage of the design there may still be questions to be resolved (e.g. the solutions contradict the design requirements already agreed). The designer may choose to try to resolve them immediately, or to wait until the end of this circuit of design. The design calculations for drainage may be required for submissions or design records.

Thermal insulation

The designer should now consider the thermal performance of the whole roof and, hence, the requirements for thermal insulation. This requires that the designer knows – or can make a sensible assumption for – the structural deck and the roof system.

To carry out such design it is helpful to understand the basic principles of thermal behaviour of roofs, which although straightforward in many respects, is in detail a complex set of interactions. If designers think that they have sufficient understanding of this stage of design, they should proceed with the detail design. If further understanding about the principles of thermal behaviour is required these are set out in **Units 4.5.** and **4.6** (It also overlaps with the water vapour behaviour, covered in **Unit 4.7 and Unit 4.8**.)

Design for thermal performance

The sequence of decisions and considerations for thermal design and selection of thermal insulant are set out in **Unit 7.6**. The flow chart in that Unit describes a design selection process for thermal performance, starting from the overall thermal performance of the roof including the structural deck. From this base the selection of the thermal insulant can proceed taking account of the other important properties such as fire performance, mechanical properties, durability or environmental considerations. The calculations for thermal performance are described in **Unit 8.2**.

The particular insulation product, whether to be specified by name or type, will normally be selected from manufacturers literature. **Chapter 17** of this Guide gives general information on the key properties and features of the different types of insulant without specific reference to manufacturers.

Design for moisture vapour control

The designer should now consider the design for the control of water vapour in the roof which is important for avoidance of condensation and possible reduction in the long term performance of roof components. Explanation

Further reading:

© BFRC / CIRIA: Flat Roofing: Design and Good Practice. 1993

- The method of vapour control must be based upon assessment of condensation risk.
- Roof surface finish selection will depend upon the requirements of roof configuration, proposed traffic, wind uplift resistance, solar reflectance and appearance.

---

of the principles of water vapour behaviour, in terms of vapour pressures, flows of vapour, condensation is given in **Unit 4.7**. The overall approach to this is given in **Unit 7.7**, where the flow chart shows the series of decisions to be made. The crucial issue is the evaluation of **condensation risk** which is done by calculation. This calculation method is shown in **Unit 8.3**. Some aspects of condensation, such as that of **pumping,** can only be done at present on a qualitative basis. That is, designers have to make a judgement based on their understanding of the construction, the environment and the ways in which this phenomenon can occur. The particular phenomenon of 'pumping' is covered in **Unit 4.8**.

The designer should, by this stage of the design, have checked the condensation risk and will have identified any problems. If they contradict the design requirements, it may be necessary to modify the overall design or to proceed to the end of this circuit of the whole design and then evaluate the whole design.

The outputs from these decisions are a decision on the nature and location of any vapour control layer (VCL) or other methods of vapour control, and a condensation risk analysis (including calculations).

Design for surface finishes

Scope of design

Various design decisions concerning roof finishes are necessary. The surfaces concerned will depend upon what roof configurations have been (provisionally) selected.

The main considerations will be any surface finish requirements for trafficking, fire performance, and solar control. It is important to understand the broad issues involved as well as the obvious design decisions. If sufficient is understood, proceed with the design selection. If further information is needed on the principles involved in each of these they are covered respectively in **Unit 4.11, Unit 4.9,** and **Unit 4.6**. The more general concern of durability is covered in **Unit 4.13**.

There are a number of options for which both the type and sequence will vary for different projects. Those discussed below are the more likely considerations but may be decided in a different sequence to that listed.

Traffic resistance
It should be assessed whether the roof requires a surface treatment or protection layer for the particular traffic. If it is to have access as a roof terrace, for example, then particular paving finishes or even separate walkways will normally be essential. Guidance on how to design for load spreading is given in **Unit 7.11**.

Wind uplift
The designer needs to decide whether added resistance is needed against wind uplift, for example by providing a layer of ballast or paving. For inverted roofs this may be essential. This decision will be taken by consideration of the wind uplift forces (calculated in **Unit 8.4**) and how the components of the roof are otherwise fixed down. Guidance on this design decision is given in **Unit 7.10**.

Solar reflection
Depending on the roof system and the membrane type there may have to be a separate solar control treatment. This will depend whether the membrane is itself exposed and, if so, whether solar gain or degradation are significant. The design selections already made for other reasons may provide sufficient solar control.

Appearance
The designer will have to decide what appearance is required for the roof finish. In some cases, there may be strong preferences from the client or requirements from others, such as planning authorities (e.g. because the building is in a conservation area). The context (e.g. adjoining roofs) may also imply a preference for one sort of appearance or colour. The form and configuration of the roof and its edges, etc. may feature significantly here. The appearance of course has to be judged in terms of the building design as a whole.

continued ▶

> ## Critical factors
>
> - Building Regulations requirements.
> - Early design of drainage for roof.
> - Evaluation of condensation risk.

Further reading in the Guide:
4 Principles • 7.4 Design for drainage capacity • 7.5 Design of falls for drainage • 7.6 Design for thermal performance • 7.7 Design for moisture capacity • 7.10 Design for wind resistance • 7.11 Design for traffic and load spreading.

- Health and safety of building users may impose constraints on the roof design.
- The principal aspects of health and safety that affect flat roof design are fire and lightning protection.

Design for health and safety

In this context health and safety refers to the performance of the completed roof, rather than the–equally important–construction phase.

At this stage of the design the designers should have a good idea of the basic roof system which is suitable for the project. However, there is still a need to develop the design in terms of health and safety, which means lightning protection and fire precautions.

The general issues for health and safety are described in **Unit 3.4** and the related bibliography is in **Unit 22.2**. There are related issues for inspection in **Chapter 20** and for maintenance in **Chapter 21**.

Design for lightning protection

This aspect of design is described in **Unit 7.8.** There is often a significant amount of work in a protection system and there may be complications of details where the protection system is connected to the building. Some buildings (e.g. for storage of flammable liquids) may present special risks.

La Grande Arche, Paris, France

Design for fire performance

In practice, the fire performance of the roof is likely to be considered as part of the fire protection strategy for the whole building. If sufficient is understood at this stage, proceed with the design selection, however, the designer may find it helpful to gain a better understanding of the basic principles of fire behaviour, which are described in **Unit 4.9.** Design for fire safety in relation to the roof is described in **Unit 7.9**, which is based on the assumption that the designer is following Approved Document B, as amended 1992, of *The Building Regulations*. The design work here will involve a mixture of evaluation or checking of earlier design decisions and detailed material selections if not already made.

Design of details

Roof design will require examination of the various details, at joints and junctions, to ensure that the general roof design does not present difficult or insuperable problems when it comes to consider the design of such details. A review should assess both the typical and the special details, giving particular attention to any places where there is a change or discontinuity in geometry and/or material in the roof construction.

The general approach to the design of details is described in **Chapter 9.** Designers must judge how far at this stage of the design process they wish to examine the detail, but it is worth examining complex details–such as movement joints–as early as possible.

Wolstonbury Court, Burgess Hill, UK.

Further reading:
Approved Document B, as amended 1992, of the Building Regulations

- Cost and time estimates are an important part of successful roof design.
- Although final design of details may occur late in the design process, consideration of their likely strategic significance is preferable early in design.
- The proposed roof design should be evaluated against target requirements.

Lloyd's, London, UK.

Other requirements

Some clients may seek to make general or specific requirements for the materials to be used in the roof. For example they may wish to carry out an **environmental review** or to maintain a list of **'excluded materials'**, i.e. a list of materials they consider might affect the long term performance or commercial viability, but about which there is no general agreement in the industry.

The practical effects for the designer will depend on the attitudes of the client, users and the designer. Its implication will be principally in the selection of materials and, sometimes, on processes involved in manufacture or assembly. The critical thing is to try and establish early on to what extent it is an issue.

Cost and time estimate

The designer should now have a complete design proposal for the structural deck and roof system, with some idea of system performance under all the necessary headings. They should also have some idea of its dimensions and details. The extent of design development will depend on which circuit of the design sequence is to be followed. However, the designer should have sufficient information to obtain a cost estimate and, perhaps, an estimate of the time involved in roof construction.

Detail guidance on this subject is outside the scope of this guide. There are many different approaches to these and the designer should arrange with whoever has the responsibility for them, e.g. the Quantity Surveyor, to obtain information.

Data collection and evaluation

The designer should carry out an evaluation of the roof design proposal against the target requirements set earlier. A pro forma is shown in **Unit 10.1** and a further copy is in the Project Notebook. These allow the designer to summarise how the proposed design meets the requirements. A decision should then be taken whether to proceed with that design or whether to redesign or even rethink the target requirements.

Further guidance on design

The following Units of this Chapter provide more guidance on the design decisions which have to be made. The Units are set out in the same general sequence used in this Unit.

Critical factors

- Health and safety.
- Cost and time requirements.
- Design of details considered as early as possible, perhaps at a strategic level.
- Evaluation of design.

Further reading in the Guide:
3.4 Health and safety • 4.15 Environmental impact of materials • 7.8 Design for lightning protection • 7.9 Design for fire safety • 10.1 Evaluation checklist.

12 Mastic Asphalt	13 Polymeric Single Ply	14 Copper	15 Lead Sheet	16 Other Membranes	17 Thermal Insulants	18 Specification	19 Contracts & Procurement	20 Inspection	21 Maintenance	22 Bibliography	23 Index
263	301	331	353	375	383	393	399	413	429	437	455

- The selection of the type of roof configuration is a fundamental decision in the preliminary design.
- The three types of roof considered in this Guide are described in principle in **Units 4.1** and **4.2**.

Many of the design decisions covered in this Chapter give a decision flowchart which aids the selection procedure. The selection of roof type is however more difficult and will often be less definitive. This Unit describes the essential characteristics of the basic roof configurations – positive and negative – which are likely to influence performance and thus selection.

Designers should use their judgement to decide which combination and balance of the characteristics are important for the particular project.

Designers may wish to devise their own approach to apportioning this balance, either formally through a 'points score' or by a more informal consensus. The Guide does not attempt to devise such systems. Further information on the characteristics is provided in other Units in the Guide. The further reading in the Guide references help to identify these.

The designer may find it helpful to enter design decisions into the design selection and evaluation checklists provided in the Project Notebook.

Units 4.1 and **4.2** introduce the idea of the roof configuration types and some of the benefits, and dangers, of such categorisation. The point is repeated here that, although such an approach can be useful for initial design selection, the developed design should be properly assessed for real performance, based upon actual configuration and material properties.

Some general considerations can apply, such as the examples which follow. The more exposed the membrane, the greater its need to be resistant to the extremes of the external environment. Conversely, the greater the build-up of finishes on top of the membrane, the more difficult it becomes to achieve drainage and maintenance access. This may lead to a requirement for enhanced membrane specification with a lower risk of failure and enhanced requirements for testing, on completion of the membrane. Predominantly because of the effects of any overlaying components, the roof configuration can place significant requirements on the loadings the building structure has to resist.

Warm deck roof

- **Weight of system** is low if components are bonded and/or mechanically fixed
- **Roof zone depth** is the sum of all component thicknesses including insulation
- **Deck movement** is not directly transmitted to the waterproofing and can be modified or eliminated by the insulation
- **Imposed loads** on the roof will be transmitted through membrane and the supporting insulation to the structural support
- **Drainage design** is straightforward, enabling the use of lightweight outlets
- **Solar UV radiation** at the membrane is high and may necessitate additional protection of roof field and details
- **Membrane temperature** range and rate of change is greater than for other configurations and will be largely determined by external conditions
- **Condensation** is controlled by selection of a vapour control layer appropriate for the building function
- **Ventilation of roof voids** is not required or desirable, allowing a wide choice of plan shapes and abutment conditions
- **Insulation** can be provided continuously across the roof and details
- **Resistance to external fire** may be affected by the insulation, requiring additional surface protection
- **Wind uplift force** may be transmitted to the deck through the insulation where a fully bonded membrane acts as the critical layer. Interlaminar strength of the insulation is then an important criterion.
- **Acoustic insulation** performance may be improved by appropriate selection of thermal insulation
- **Service penetrations** are more easily constructed than for other roofs
- **Additional protection** from following trades or traffic in service may be required
- **Testing, inspection and maintenance** is facilitated by exposed membrane (unless ballasted)
- **Refurbishment with thermal upgrading** is straightforward.

Further reading:
Approved document B, as amended 1992, of the Building Regulations

Chapter	1	2	3	4	5	6	7	8	9	10	11
Contents	Introduction	History	Regulatory Methods	Principles	Surveys	Constraints & Targets	Design Selection	Calculations	Detail Design Principles	Evaluation of Design	Built-up Roofing
Page	1	19	31	45	83	95	105	165	189	217	221

- The combination of roof configurations and membranes for which guidance is given in this Guide are shown in Table 7.1.2.
- The characteristics of each roof configuration have to be balanced against specific design requirements.

Inverted warm deck roof

- **Weight of system** is high, due to ballasting of insulation and may have implications for structural support
- **Roof zone depth** is generally greater than for other configurations for a given 'U' value
- **Deck movement** may be transmitted directly to the membrane unless appropriate separation layers are interposed
- **Insulation movement** will generally not be transferred to the membrane
- **Imposed loads** on the roof may be spread by the ballast and insulation
- **Drainage design** is constrained by the need for two-level outlets and avoidance of gutters or exposed eaves. Water flow, at membrane level, is more difficult.
- **Solar UV radiation** at the membrane can be eliminated
- **Membrane temperature** range and rate of change is the lowest of all configurations and may be largely determined by internal conditions
- **Condensation** can be effectively controlled by appropriate design of the structural deck. A separate vapour control layer is not required
- **Ventilation of roof voids** is not required or desirable
- **Insulation** can be provided continuously across the roof and details but allowance must be made for thermal losses due to drainage
- **Resistance to external fire** may be dominated by the material used for ballast
- **Wind uplift force** is overcome by appropriate selection of ballast, and by restraint of insulation at details
- **Acoustic insulation performance** may be improved by thermal insulation and the mass of the ballast
- **Service penetrations** may be more difficult to detail
- **Additional protection** from following trades or traffic in service may not be necessary if suitable ballasting is used
- **Testing inspection and maintenance** of the membrane is more difficult because other components are placed over it
- **Waterproofing of the roof** may be completed more rapidly than for a warm deck roof
- **Refurbishment** with thermal upgrading is straight-forward.

Cold deck roof

- **Weight of system** is low if membrane is bonded or mechanically fixed
- **Roof zone depth** is the sum of all component thicknesses excluding the insulation if the latter is placed between the structural support
- **Deck movement** may be transmitted directly to the membrane
- **Imposed loads** on the roof will be transmitted directly through the membrane to the structural support
- **Drainage design** may be constrained by the requirement for ventilation of roof voids
- **Solar UV radiation** at the membrane is high and may necessitate additional protection of roof field and details
- **Membrane temperature** range and rate of change will generally be lower than for a warm deck roof but higher than an inverted warm deck roof
- **Condensation** is difficult to control
- **Ventilation of roof voids** is essential, thereby restricting the choice of plan shapes and abutments
- **Insulation** may be interrupted or reduced by structural support, with the risk of cold bridging
- **Resistance to external fire** will be largely determined by the membrane and any additional surface protection
- **Wind uplift force** may be transferred directly to the deck where the membrane acts as the critical layer
- **Acoustic insulation performance** may benefit less from thermal insulation than for other roof types
- **Service penetrations** are difficult to detail through total roof construction
- **Additional protection** from following trades or traffic in service may be required
- **Testing, inspection and maintenance** is facilitated by exposed membrane (unless ballasted)
- **Waterproofing of the roof** may be completed more rapidly than for warm deck roof
- **Refurbishment** with thermal upgrading is very difficult. ∎

Critical factors

- Use configuration for initial design selection only.
- Assess design for real performance.
- Compare balance of design, essential characteristics and roof requirements.

Further reading in the Guide:
4.1 Behaviour of assemblies • 4.2 Behaviour of assemblies: flat roof configurations • 4.3 Structure and movement • 4.8 Condensation: pumping
7.4 Design for drainage capacity • 7.7 Design for moisture vapour control • 7.9 Design for fire safety • 7.11 Design for traffic and load spreading
17.1 Selection of Insulants

12 Mastic Asphalt	13 Polymeric Single Ply	14 Copper	15 Lead Sheet	16 Other Membranes	17 Thermal Insulants	18 Specification	19 Contracts & Procurement	20 Inspection	21 Maintenance	22 Bibliography	23 Index
263	301	331	353	375	383	393	399	413	429	437	455

7.3 Design selection: membranes

- The waterproof membrane will normally be considered the most important component of a flat roofing system.
- This Unit does not attempt to list which membranes should be used in which locations, as the interaction of conditions encountered are too numerous to give specific recommendations.

For many designers the selection of the roof membrane type will be the fundamental design issue. For other cases, e.g. using a pure performance specification, the designer might invite a contractor to propose the most suitable combination. Designers may have firm views about which type of membrane they believe to be the best. This might be based on previous experience or on guidance documents (such as this Guide). There are difficulties in producing hard rules for which type of membrane is the most appropriate in particular circumstances. To some extent, most membranes 'can be made to work' in most of the situations most of the time; the question is which is most likely to be most appropriate for the particular project at hand.

This Unit does not attempt to produce a list or chart of which membrane should be used in which situation, as the number of conditions facing the designer is too great. It sets out below the **essential characteristics** and **implications** for the four broad types in this Guide: built-up roofing; polymeric single-ply; mastic asphalt; and metal membranes. Some factors will be common to many of the membranes and are therefore not specifically raised. Examples include: life expectancy – all are greater than 25 years; health and safety; repairability.

Designers should use their judgement and knowledge of the particular project to consider the balance of factors and make appropriate selection(s) of membrane.

Table 7.3.1
Options for combinations of organic membrane and roof system

Roof configuration	Cold deck roof	Warm deck roof	Inverted warm deck roof	Buried roof
Membrane material				
Built-up roofing	B	A	A	A
Mastic asphalt	B	B	A	A
Polymeric sheet	B	A	B	C

Key to table:
A - Generally recommended in this Guide.
B - Recommended for specific conditions or configurations only (see relevant materials chapters of this Guide).
C - Requires the specific endorsement of the material supplier.

Built-up roofing

Built-up roofing normally comprises layers of sheets of bitumen-impregnated and coated fabric core, laid in hot bitumen. Some homogeneous bitumen or pitch-modified polymer materials without a fabric core are also made for built-up roofing.

- **Multi-layer systems** give more levels of defence against water ingress.
- **Full bonding** restricts water passage beneath membrane, partial bonding does not.
- **Tough membranes,** based on polyester core, provide good robustness against damage when installed. Combined with bitumen adhesives as interlayer, they can provide some movement accommodation.
- **British Standards** classifications exist for some materials.
- **Speed of installation** can be slower than other membranes but pre-planning reduces the difference. Staged installation of an initial layer can, under careful site control, be useful to give temporary waterproofing.
- **Design of details** and junctions requires care to minimise difficulty in installation, particularly if sheets become stiff in cold weather. Some pre-forming of detail pieces may be available. This needs pre-ordering.
- **Protection** to exposed membranes can be achieved with self-finish sheets, using minerals or metal foils. Extra protection may be required for fire spread and for some access traffic (particularly wheeled).
- **Spillage of hot materials** during installation can damage other building components. Flames from bitumen heaters or gas torches present a fire hazard. The temperatures of hot bitumen can be sufficient to damage other roof components, e.g. some insulants. Care is needed in selection.
- **Environmental impact** of bitumen useful as it is the by-product of oil distilled for other purposes.
- **Chemical resistance** of membranes can be selected from manufacturers' data. Better performance possible from use of modified polymer/elastomer sheets.
- **Movement** accommodated better by partial bonding.

Further reading:
BSCP144: Part 3 Built-up bitumen felt • BSCP144: Part 4 Mastic asphalt • BS747 Specification for roofing felts • BS6925 Mastic asphalt for building • BSPD6484 Commentary on bimetallic corrosion • BRE Digest 372 Flat roof design: waterproof membranes • BRE Information Paper IP 8/91 Mastic asphalt for flat roofs.

Chapter	1	2	3	4	5	6	7	8	9	10	11
Contents	Introduction	History	Regulatory Methods	Principles	Surveys	Constraints & Targets	Design Selection	Calculations	Detail Design Principles	Evaluation of Design	Built-up Roofing
Page	1	19	31	45	83	95	105	165	189	217	221

120

© BFRC / CIRIA: Flat Roofing: Design and Good Practice. 1993

- By consideration of the essential characteristics of the membrane types and project factors, a design selection consensus can be reached.

Mastic asphalt

Mastic asphalt normally comprises an asphaltic cement combined with suitably graded mineral materials. It is laid as a hot liquid to form an in-situ membrane without joints.

- **Multi-coat application** gives better defence against water ingress. This is further enhanced by 'seamless' application.

- **Strength** of the membrane gives resistance to damage.

- **Movement accommodation** and crack resistance are dependent on design of membrane and substrate; some accommodation by isolation from substrate with a sheathing felt. Substrate roughness or other restraint may affect ability to accommodate movements. Stable deck (e.g. concrete) preferred. Polymer modified asphalt has greater flexibility

- **Conventional mastic asphalt** is vulnerable to damage if exposed to prolonged sub-zero temperatures. Polymeric modified mastic asphalt is therefore preferred.

- **Partial bonding** allows water passage beneath membrane.

- **British Standards** classifications exist for many materials, but not for polymer modified materials. Agrément certification possible.

- **Site forming of details** by liquid application can ease complexity, but the design of the details must consider long-term performance, particularly for movement. Preforming of asphalt is not possible.

- **Wind uplift** resistance can be achieved for many roofs by dead weight of membrane alone.

- **Protection** to membrane not required for foot traffic; wheeled traffic can be resisted using paving grade in combination. Support beneath asphalt to resist loadings is important.

- **Protection** against solar radiation is required but not for fire resistance on many substrates. Protection layers can be used to enhance appearance.

- **Spillage of hot materials** during installation can damage other building components. The temperatures of asphalt during installation can damage substrates, e.g. some insulants.

- **Environmental impact** of asphalts is useful as it uses the by-product of oil distilled for other purposes.

Polymeric single-ply

These membranes are normally pre-formed sheet manufactured from synthetic polymers or rubber. Products may or may not be reinforced with a fabric core. Joints are formed on or off site by a variety of gluing or welding techniques.

- **Single-ply** application requires a good level of membrane integrity.

- **Fixing** can be by adhesive or ballasting, but more commonly mechanically point fixed. Point fixing allows water passage beneath the membrane. Such fixing gives greater ability to accommodate movements of the substrate.

- **Long-term performance** of the point fixings into the substrate is essential to ensure retention of wind uplift resistance.

- **British Standards** generally not available but many products have Agrément certificates. Proprietary products, used with success, vary more widely in nature and properties than other membrane types. Comparison between products can be difficult.

- **Speed of installation** enhanced by single application together with the ability to pre-form many roof details. Speed of initial waterproofing may be balanced by confidence in integrity.

- **Protection** may not be required for light foot traffic but will be required for most other roofs.

- **Protection** against solar radiation is inherent in many of the membrane materials. A range of finish colours can be used to improve appearance where needed.

- **Chemical resistance** can be achieved for most situations by appropriate material selection.

- **Spillage of materials** during installation is less of a hazard than for other membrane systems.

- **Environmental impact** of many single-ply materials is more difficult to assess. To ensure durability, specially-manufactured polymers are used but in smaller quantities overall than for other membrane types.

- **Solvents** used for installation have health and safety and fire risk considerations. *continued* ▶

Critical factors

- Selection of membrane type may be the key design choice.

- Most membrane types may be capable of satisfactory performance in a particular roof; which is likely to be the most appropriate?

- Relate membrane attribute to the project constraints and targets.

Further reading in the Guide:

- More than one membrane type may be appropriate for a particular roof design.
- Designers have to use their judgement to make a final selection of membrane type.
- Metal roofs require different design treatment and site skills from organic membranes.

Metal roofs

A number of different metals are available for use in fully supported sheet roofing. Copper and lead are the most used and are covered in greater detail in **Chapters 14** and **15** of this Guide. Alternative metals used in roofing are zinc, aluminium and stainless steel. Most of these are laid with standing seams, rolls, drips and welted joints to connect the sheets together. Rapid heat gain of such materials in response to sunlight makes it unwise to form a rigid blanket by, for example, welding the sheets together. In this context some designers, and sources of advice on metal sheet roofing, suggest that the term 'waterproof membrane' is inappropriate. A preferred term may be 'weatherproof membrane', which is taken to imply joints and junctions which are not fully sealed (unlike the organic membrane roofs). A consequence of non-sealed joints is the need to drain water away from the area of the joint and possibly to raise the joint above the general membrane level, e.g. as with standing seam roofs.

Metal roofs, particularly those in copper or lead, are most often associated with buildings of a monumental or civic nature. This image is drawn from the generally good inherent durability of the metals and the way in which the patination of the metal in service changes and mellows the appearance of the roofscape. Such a generalised view of the applications of metal roofing obscures the wider potential for such roofs. They have been used for many more innovative projects and buildings, not only where the appearance of the roof is the high priority.

The design principles and applicability to roof configurations are notably different from those for the organic family of membranes. Table 7.3.2 lists the combinations for which further help is given in this Guide.

The following paragraphs discuss some of the **essential characteristics** to be taken into account when designing for a metal roof and which may, therefore, influence selection.

- **Joining methods** for these materials are generally traditional, practical, aesthetically pleasing and suitable for working with typical sheet sizes. They require, however, the special skills of a sheet metal worker, experienced in roofing, for their successful installation.

Table 7.3.2
Options for combinations of metal membrane and roof system

Roof configuration	Cold deck roof	Warm deck roof	Inverted warm deck roof	Buried roof
Membrane material				
Copper	B*	B*	E	E
Lead	B*	B*	E	E
Zinc, Aluminium Stainless steel	B*	B*	E	E

Key to table:
B - Recommended for specific conditions or configurations only (see relevant materials Chapters of this Guide).
D - Combination to be avoided if possible.
E - This combination should not be used.
* - There are particular concerns with the performance of metal roofs in relation to condensation and corrosion. The current advice for detailing for vapour control is given in the relevant materials Chapters (**Chapters 14** and **15**).

- **Movement accommodation**, arising from the structural deck is tolerated to some extent by the membrane because of the use of separating layers. Care is needed in the detailing to allow this movement to take place. Thermal movements of the membranes are themselves more significant than for organic membranes and require attention in detail.
- **Traffic resistance** of the membranes is not as good, particularly in regard to local damage or interference with patination. Metal membranes should not be used on roofs with regular foot traffic without special walkways, but occasional maintenance traffic is usually acceptable. Care is needed with access to a standing seam roof because of the trip hazard of the seam.
- **Condensation** is a particular concern with metal membranes because the possibility of rapid temperature changes, combined with good heat conduction, can lead to the membrane quickly becoming colder than the rest of the roof construction. This may occur with cold night skies or sudden rain showers. **Units 4.6 - 4.8** of the Guide give further explanation of the principles involved, particularly of the effect called 'pumping'. Condensation on the underside of the membrane is of concern because it may lead to corrosion. For copper roofing, a separate weatherproof membrane is used

Further reading:

Chapter	1	2	3	4	5	6	7	8	9	10	11
Contents	Introduction	History	Regulatory Methods	Principles	Surveys	Constraints & Targets	Design Selection	Calculations	Detail Design Principles	Evaluation of Design	Built-up Roofing
Page	1	19	31	45	83	95	105	165	189	217	221

© BFRC / CIRIA: Flat Roofing: Design and Good Practice. 1993

- The characteristics of the membrane classifications used in the Guide are the result of materials characteristics and the way in which they are combined in the roof.
- Local environments may affect the durable life of metal roofs.

Lead roof

beneath the copper sheet to prevent condensate reaching the membrane. This layer is normally sealed in 'warm deck roof' configurations and just lapped for 'cold deck roofs' (see **Chapter 14**). For lead roofs, a two-deck 'ventilated warm roof' approach proposed by the suppliers is described in **Chapter 15**.

- **Corrosion** is a considerable concern for metal roofs even where condensation is not occurring. The nature of run off from other parts of the building(s) such as higher level roofs or gutters must be properly considered. Dissolved salts (e.g. from concrete) can accelerate attack, and other materials may cause localised pitting. It should be remembered that some metals – zinc and aluminium – are amphoteric, that is they can be attacked by both acids and alkalis. Bimetallic corrosion can arise where two dissimilar metals are in contact with water, or another conducting path, and should be avoided by good design. It is possible for materials to leach out of timber preservatives and initiate corrosion where the timber is in contact with the metal. Atmospheric pollution (e.g. soot deposits landing on the metal) have been known to cause pitting corrosion. A further consideration may be

the potential effects of water run off from the metals on to other areas. These could possibly affect building materials by staining, or poisonously interact with plants or animals.
- **Fixings** of metal roofs have many common features for the different metals; they are usually by mechanical clips and cleats fixed to the (commonly timber) substrate.
- **Forming to complex geometry** is possible, but to varying extents for the different metals. Specific guidance may be necessary from the suppliers.
- **Costs** of the membrane materials will usually be higher than for the organic membranes, on initial cost, but the differential may be less for the life-cycle cost of the complete roof system.
- **Health and safety** for metal roofs will have specific requirements connected with the working of the metals, particularly lead.
- **Environmental impact** may be rather more obvious for metals compared with other roof materials, by virtue of their mining and extraction from ore. This impact can, however, be counterbalanced by the long life expectancy of a well-designed roof. ■

Further reading in the Guide:
4.6 Solar radiation and thermal effects • 4.7 Condensation • 4.8 Condensation: pumping • 14 Copper • 15 Lead sheet

7.4   Design for drainage capacity

- Falls should generally be at least 1:80 installed, after allowing for tolerances of construction, deflections, etc. In the absence of detailed calculations this can mean designing to 1:40.
- There are three ways of disposing of rainwater:
  - into outlets within the main roof area
  - to the perimeter and into external hopper heads (via chutes)
  - to the perimeter and into eaves gutters.

General

The layout of drainage falls and the layout and disposition of outlets will have a profound effect on the total depth of the roof zone, which includes structure, falls and protection layer. When deciding the floor level of any construction above the flat roof – such as an upper storey or a plant room – the designer must make due allowance for the full roof zone including the necessary 150mm upstand above finished roof level (Figure 7.4.1).

Rainwater disposal and layout of falls

There are three ways of disposing of rainwater from a flat roof:

- Collect it into outlets set within the main roof area.
- Drain it to the perimeter and discharge it through chutes to external hopper heads.
- Drain it to the perimeter and discharge it over the edge into eaves gutters.

The first and second methods imply a roof contained within parapets; in the third method the roof oversails and protects the external wall. When roofs are contained behind parapets, there is always a risk of surcharging should outlets become restricted or blocked; allowance should be made for loss in outlet capacity and provision made for more than one outlet on an enclosed roof. The design should be such that some overflow of the roof or increased water depth can occur without permanent damage.

The designer must decide which method – or combination of methods – to adopt before planning the arrangement of falls and the location of outlets, taking account of the risk of blockage and any damage that might ensue.

Falls to the perimeter can be simply formed by sloping the structure or by adding material to provide falls (see **Unit 7.5**). The use of internal outlets and chutes both involve consideration of falls in two directions. Internal gutters are normally assumed to be level for the purpose of calculation, (i.e. working on a hydraulic gradient) but should be constructed to a fall. All calculations in *BS6367* are based on level gutters. Figures 7.4.2-7.4.5 show alternative ways of draining to eaves gutters, to chutes, and to internal outlets.

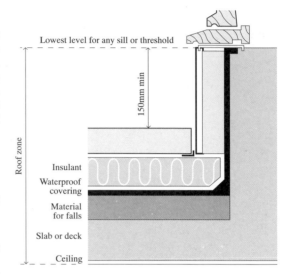

Figure 7.4.1
Roof zone

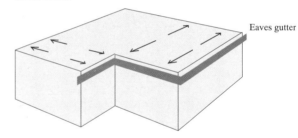

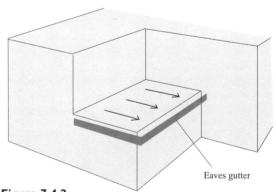

Figure 7.4.2
Draining to eaves gutters

Further reading:
BS6367 Drainage of roofs and paved areas

- Drainage design should allow for overflow without damage in extreme weather conditions.
- Drainage design will have a significant impact on the total roof zone depth.
- Contained roofs should be designed with multiple outlets.

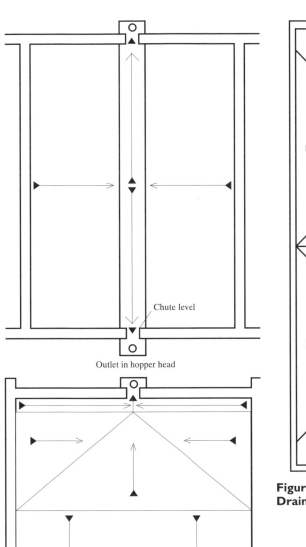

Chute level

Outlet in hopper head

Figure 7.4.3
Draining to chutes (shows two alternatives)

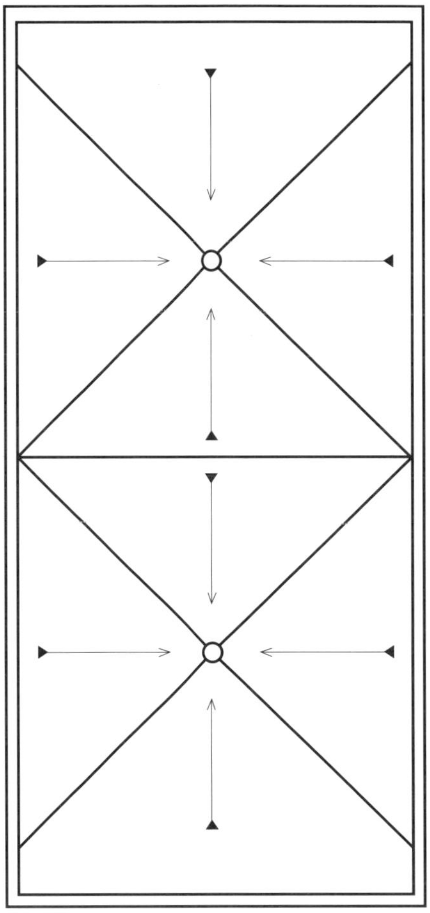

Figure 7.4.4
Draining to internal outlets

continued ▶

Further reading in the Guide:
4.4 Precipitation • 7.5 Design for falls for drainage • 8.1 Calculation of roof drainage capacity

- Allow sufficient space around outlets to enable membrane detailing.
- Traffic roofs can increase difficulty of drainage of membrane level.
- Syphonic drainage systems can increase capacity of downpipes and outlets.
- The efficiency of outlets can be increased by setting them in sumps.

Table 7.4.1
British Standards for rainwater pipes and fitting

Material	British Standard
Aluminium	BS2997
Asbestos cement	BS569
Cast iron	BS460
PVC, unplasticised	BS4576
Galvanized	BS1091
Wrought copper, wrought zinc	BS1431

Pre-formed rainwater gutters, pipes and accessories should comply with the requirements and recommendations of British Standards, as in Table 7.4.1.

When draining to external gutters, the size, number and position of outlets will not affect the layout of roof falls.

With a roof contained by parapets, the designer must make an initial estimate of the size and number of outlet points required before planning a pattern of falls. A useful rule-of-thumb is that 700mm^2 of cross-sectional area of downpipe will drain approximately 10m^2 of roof area (1in^2 of cross section drains 100ft^2). The area drained will vary according to the chosen rainfall intensity (see *BS6367*).

The efficiency of internal outlets can be greatly increased by setting them into sumps or internal gutters.

To achieve their design discharge rates, outlets must be sited at the centre of the area they drain, so that water run-off is evenly distributed around their perimeter. If at all possible, outlets should not be located close to parapets or to penetrations, otherwise their efficiency will be reduced and it may be difficult or even impossible to form a watertight seal between the waterproof covering and the outlet. An all-round clearance of at least 200mm is suggested.

It may be useful to site outlets at points of maximum deflection rather than at column heads. This means some horizontal pipework will be necessary; it must be designed to accommodate movement of the roof deck.

Large roofs and those of irregular plan form must be broken down into discrete areas, each area being considered in relation to its neighbours. Falls should intersect on a true 45° mitre. This is particularly important when using rigid materials such as plywood deck or taper-cut insulation; it also facilitates setting out and laying of screeds and the formation of rolls and drips in sheet metal work.

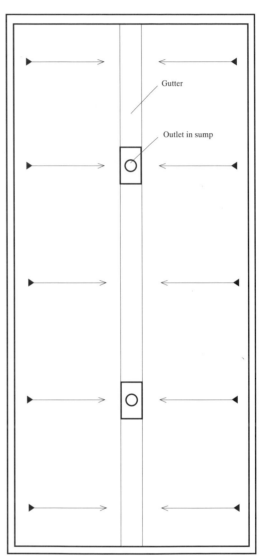

Outlets should be located midway between columns to allow for roof deflection

Figure 7.4.5
Draining to gutter

A suggested design sequence for creation of falls is given in **Unit 7.5**.

Further reading:
BS6367 Drainage of roofs and paved areas

• Some inverted warm deck roofs may need to have drainage at two levels – at paving and membrane.

Access roofs

In situations where paving and screed are laid above the waterproof membrane, it is possible for calcium hydroxide to leach out of the screed. This then forms an insoluble deposit around the inside of rainwater pipes, considerably reducing the bore in just a few years.

Draining vehicle access roofs

Vehicles bring onto the roof road salt, mud, silt and snow as well as oil and petrol: the design of drainage falls and outlets should take account of those factors. Standing water should be avoided because of the risk of freezing/skidding and it may be necessary to provide silt traps or mud gullies at outlets (see *BS6367* for recommendations on the drainage of paved areas).

Particular problems may also arise if the roof has to be drained at two levels, e.g. with an inverted warm deck roof, where the insulation and paving restrict flow at membrane level. There are no preferred methods for achieving this, but it is essential that proper drainage occurs at both levels.

Drainage of roof gardens

Roof gardens should be designed with drainage falls in the same way as other flat roofs. To aid the removal of excess water from the roof, a drainage layer – commonly of expanded clay or lightweight aggregate – is placed over the waterproof covering before laying vegetable soil. The drainage layer is in turn overlaid by a geotextile layer, usually a proprietary non-woven durable plastic material, which allows water but not soil to pass through to drain. Outlets should be set in access chambers to allow ready access for cleaning (Figure 7.4.6). An upstand should be detailed to retain approximately 50mm depth of water in the drainage layer for plant growth.

Syphonic drainage

This method of drainage is only applicable to internal roof outlets which are best located in a gutter or sump. All previous text relating to roof and gutter design are still applicable, as the system differs only from the roof outlet down.

Traditional gravity systems are inefficient, in that pipework operates at a maximum of a third to a quarter full, even at the design storm intensity. This is due generally to the vortex at the outlet and the core of air in the centre of the vertical pipework.

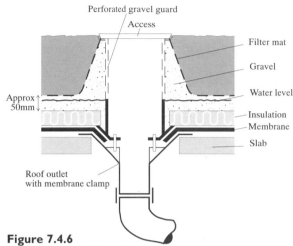

Figure 7.4.6
Draining of roof gardens

A **syphonic** roof outlet incorporates a sump and baffle which excludes air at the design rainfall intensity and allows pipework to run full. The difference in height between the roof outlets and the discharge point at ground level can be used to design the system operating under a head, at full bore, with considerably smaller pipework.

Horizontal pipework at high level can be laid level, as it is operating under a head, with drops at the building perimeter. This system is particularly useful for large areas of roof, where there is a requirement to reduce the number of stacks and eliminate underground drainage within the building. Lower areas of roof must be drained separately as connecting them to a main roof stack would interfere with the operating head.

Flow capacity of the outlet is not calculated by establishing a depth of water over a weir (perimeter of outlet or sump), as in a gravity system. The rate of flow from the outlet is determined by the exclusion of air and the operating head of the system.

Typical outlet flow rates are 3.5 litres/sec. for a 60mm diameter outlet and 7.5 litres/sec. for a 75mm diameter outlet. For particular flow rates, reference should be made to manufacturers' literature, as outlet design is critical to the flow rate.

The majority of specialist contractors in this field provide a design service. ∎

Critical factors

• Particular drainage requirements for roof gardens

Further reading in the Guide:
4.4 Precipitation: rain and snow • 7.5 Design of falls for drainage • 8.1 Calculation of roof drainage capacity

7.5 Design of falls for drainage

- Design of falls in a roof are an essential element in the overall drainage of the roof.
- Minimum falls are required to direct precipitation to drainage outlets.
- Provision of falls can be determined by assumption or by calculation.
- There are various options for creating the fall at the membrane level.
- The minimum finished of 1:80 fall should apply to cross falls.

The creation of falls on a roof are essential to allow rainfall and water from other precipitation to be directed to roof outlets. There are two primary considerations in designing for falls: First, the **magnitude** and arrangement of the falls and second, the **method of construction** of the falls. For the majority of roofs it should be the intention to end up with an **effective fall** of at least 1:80. There may be special cases where this cannot be achieved or is unacceptable. In such cases it will be necessary to reassess the probability of achieving reliable waterproofing, to consider the likely long-term performance of the roof finishes with prolonged periods of being wet, and perhaps to decide to upgrade the membrane system.

Design of falls arrangements is essentially the creation of a **three-dimensional surface geometry**. Figures 7.4.2–7.4.5 in **Unit 7.4** show some typical arrangements. In roof drainage calculations (**Unit 8.1**) it is usual to assume that gutters are laid flat, with any benefit from a fall not counted in design. However, it is preferable to provide a fall in gutters, particularly those formed in the roof finishes.

The nature of the roof structure (including the deck), together with the construction process, will tend to reduce the effectiveness of an assumed or notional fall, either by **deflection** or by the effects of construction **tolerances**.

These consequential effects and, in particular, any loss in drainage effectiveness, may be exacerbated when, for convenience, downpipes are fixed to vertical structural elements, as these will tend to be high points in the deflected roof shape. It is therefore important that, to achieve the minimum requirement of a finished fall of 1:80, allowance should be made, by calculation, of the likely reduction in effective fall from such influences. This minimum finished fall of 1:80 should also apply to crossfalls. Alternatively, a conservative estimate of the likely effects may be appropriate and a design produced on, say, an initial 1:40 fall.

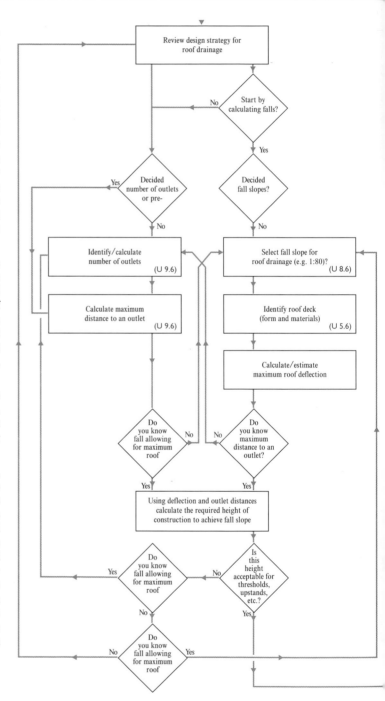

Further reading:

• These options interact with other design decisions and should be considered with reference to them.
• Figure 7.5.1 shows how the interaction of decisions may be addressed to select a method of creating satisfactory falls.

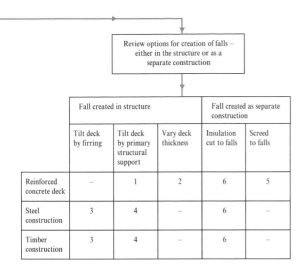

Review options for creation of falls – either in the structure or as a separate construction

	Fall created in structure			Fall created as separate construction	
	Tilt deck by firring	Tilt deck by primary structural support	Vary deck thickness	Insulation cut to falls	Screed to falls
Reinforced concrete deck	–	1	2	6	5
Steel construction	3	4	–	6	–
Timber construction	3	4	–	6	–

Figure 7.5.1
Selection of method for creating falls

Roof ponding

Notes to options 1-6 in Figure 7.5.1

1 • Lower roof dead load than 2.
 • More complicated formwork, especially on roofs of irregular plan or many penetrations.
 • Acceptable appearance of variable height soffit?
 • High workability concrete (e.g. lightweight aggregate) on metal deck difficult to control.
 • Preplanning of falls needed early in design.

2 • Higher roof dead load than 1.
 • Simpler formwork setting out and construction.
 • Level soffit.
 • Increased risk of cracking if reinforcement does not follow top surface of slab.

3 • Arrangement of supports simplified.
 • Adjustment for tolerances during construction.
 • Difficulty of firring retention if the rise and fall of the deck is great.
 • Possible difficulty for structural connection between deck and support.

4 • Structural support arrangement more complex and with limitations on choice.
 • Changes to falls subsequent to construction difficult.
 • Construction tolerances need to be more controlled.
 • Deck/structure connection easier.

5 • Cement-based screeds have greater weight than other options.
 • Possible separate trades for deck and screed.
 • Possible concern about introduction of wet construction into roof build-up. Concrete deck also contributes to this.
 • No-fines screeds can be used to reduce weight, but significantly increase the risks of trapped water.
 • Good flexibility in falls arrangements achievable, even after deck is decided.
 • Minimum thickness for conventional screeds high – 40mm. Proprietary products can achieve lower thicknesses.

6 • Dry, lightweight construction may be beneficial.
 • More expensive than screeded option.
 • Improved thermal resistance to construction, but may be more than required.
 • Preplanning of falls required to ensure availability.
 • Less amenable to design changes.
 • Good for regular plan roofs with few penetrations.
 • Available product range not as large as constant thickness insulants. ■

Critical factors

• Falls are essential to move water to drainage outlets.
• Roof fall must aim for effective fall allowing for deflections and tolerances.
• The creation of falls has an impact on the overall depth of the roof zone.
• Constraints imposed by methods of creating falls.

Further reading in the Guide:
4.4 Precipitation: rain and snow • 7.4 Design for drainage capacity • 8.1 Calculation of roof drainage capacity

7.6　Design for thermal performance

- Thermal insulation is important to provide comfort inside the building, to reduce energy consumption and to help control condensation.
- *The Building Regulations* have requirements for thermal performance of buildings.

The thermal performance of a roof is important for the building and its occupants because of the desire to provide comfort inside the building, to help reduce energy consumption in achieving comfort, and to help control condensation. Thermal performance is usually identified in Northern Europe as important for retaining heat within a building against the generally lower external temperatures. It is however also important for the reduction in heat gain from outside when warmer conditions persist. *The Building Regulations* have requirements for the thermal resistance of constructions which are shown in more detail in **Unit 8.2**.

The thermal performance of a roof will be determined by the cumulative effects of all the constituent materials or components of it. Although all of the component parts of a roof contribute to the thermal performance, the specifically included thermal insulant will normally be the most significant component. The contributions from other components should not be ignored and can even influence other design selections. For example, a reinforced concrete deck will have a greater contribution than a lightweight wood or metal deck. Using a lightweight aggregate concrete deck will further increase thermal resistance. **Units 4.5** and **4.6** give information on the principles of heat transfer.

Insulant selection

The selection of insulant type is unlikely to be a primary input to the selection of either the roof or membrane type. The selection of insulant will normally be driven by other design decisions. As with all the roof components there will be a degree of interdependence with other elements. This Unit gives information on the design selection for thermal performance, on the selection of insulants, and how this choice might affect and be affected by other design considerations. A decision flow chart, Figure 7.6.1, shows how such a selection process might be organised.

A wide range of insulant materials are available, most often in board form. These proprietary products may be either single manufacturer specific or may be proprietary variants of a similar technical origin. The diversity of proprietary products can create difficulties when giving generalised guidance on performance and selection. Material specific information on available types of insulant is given in **Chapter 17**.

Insulants in roof configurations

The various configurations of roofs will impose different requirements on the insulant. Some of these requirements may appear obvious but are essential to a proper understanding of interactions.

For warm deck roofs the insulation directly supports the membrane, and therefore needs to resist imposed loads either in compression – for, say, access – or in tension if the insulant is used to provide directly resistance to wind uplift. The insulant also interacts with the membrane when fully adhered by transmitting the thermal and moisture movements of the deck and insulant to the membrane.

For inverted warm deck roofs the insulant will be fully exposed to surface water. The effective thermal performance of the insulant will usually be reduced by the presence of water around the insulant and this should be taken into account in calculations. The original concept of the inverted roof needed an insulation of closed cell construction which limited the effects of water ingress. Fibrous insulants are now manufactured for incorporation into inverted roofs and require different ways of maintaining performance when wet, compared to the closed cell foam approach.

Interactions between insulants and other roof components can occur in the short and long term. During installation the use of hot materials or solvents can damage some insulants. In the longer term, unless suitable isolation layers are incorporated, chemical interactions can occur by the migration of minor constituents affecting roof components by changes in volume, elasticity or durability. Further general guidance on selection of insulant materials and on the assessment of compatibility between membrane and insulant is given in **Chapter 17**.

Further reading:
Approved Document L to The Building Regulations • BRE Report 143 Thermal insulation: avoiding risks • CIBSE Guide, Volume A, Section A3.

- There are many factors which influence insulant selection other than thermal resistance.
- Selection of insulant type is unlikely to be a primary input into the selection of roof configuration type or membrane type: it will normally follow from other decisions.
- The different roof configurations will impose different performance requirements for the insulant.

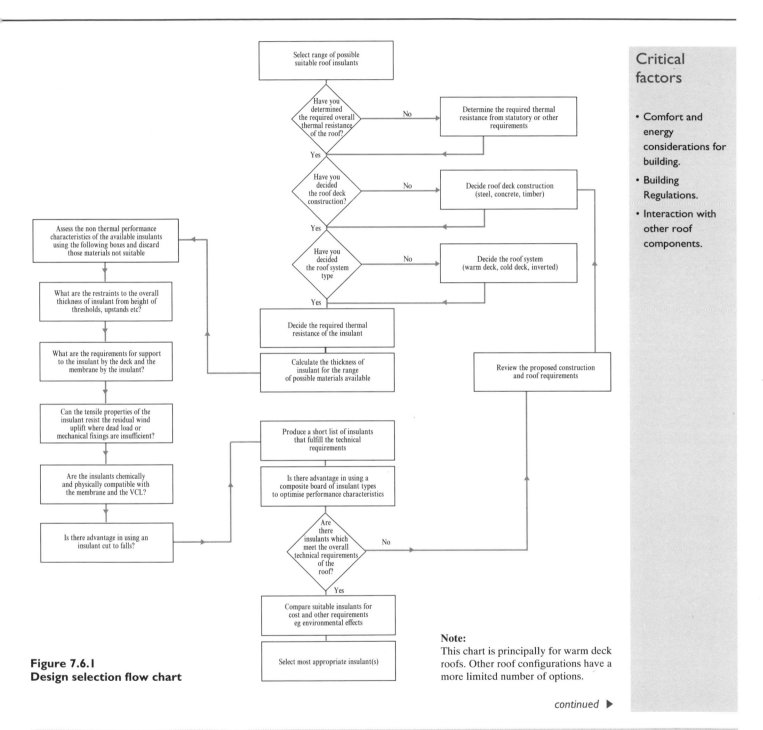

Figure 7.6.1
Design selection flow chart

Critical factors

- Comfort and energy considerations for building.
- Building Regulations.
- Interaction with other roof components.

Note:
This chart is principally for warm deck roofs. Other roof configurations have a more limited number of options.

continued ▶

Further reading in the Guide:
4.5 Thermal transmission • 4.6 Solar radiation and thermal effects • 8.2 Calculation of thermal performance • 17.1 Selection of insulants

- Mechanical properties, fire performance, moisture susceptibility, environmental considerations, cost effectiveness have significant importance in selection in addition to the thermal performance.
- The thermal performance of a roof arises from the combined overall performance of the component parts.
- A specifically incorporated thermal insulant will normally be the most significant component for the thermal performance of the roof. Other components can make useful contributions.

Thermal performance

The thermal performance of the roof construction is determined by the summation of the thermal transmission resistance of each of the components in the roof construction.

The essential starting point in considering thermal performance requirements of the whole roof is the required thermal transmittance (U value) or its inverse, thermal resistance (R value). For a particular roof design the U value may be determined by statutory requirements such as the Building Regulations or by the detailed consideration of the energy/heat requirements of the building. In the latter case there may be overall financial and environmental benefits in achieving higher standards of thermal resistance, or conversely there may be a risk of excessive heat build-up from some process industries. **Unit 8.2** shows, by worked examples, how the calculation of thermal resistance, to meet specific targets, can be carried out.

Insulants

The thermal performance of an insulant is determined by the physical properties of the materials within the product and the method of combining them. The objective with most thermal insulants is to trap pockets of gas – air or others – within a 'solid' such that convection and conduction is restricted. This trapping of gas is achieved either by creating a foam – the gas-filled cells are discrete with only minimal interconnection – or by creating a network of closely spaced fibres – of glass or spun mineral held by a resinous binder. Using a gas of lower thermal conductivity than air provides a better overall thermal performance, although the subsequent inwards migration of air can result in the insulant having a reduced performance in this 'aged' condition. See **Unit 4.5** for further information.

The thermal performance – sometimes termed the thermal efficiency of the insulant – will influence the design and performance of the complete roof in aspects other than heat flow. Because of the varying thermal efficiency, different insulants will require different thicknesses to achieve the same overall thermal transmittance. This has an effect on the total depth required for the roof zone and has particular influence on the required heights for upstands, thresholds and parapets. A less efficient insulant increases these depths but may have an advantage of producing less thermal shock on the waterproof membrane in warm deck roofs.

The use of insulants which consist of two layers of differing thermal performance – a **composite insulant** – can be an effective way of achieving good combination of thermal properties.

Other roof components

It may be appropriate to deliberately use other roof components or materials to provide all or part of the required thermal performance. Most significant of these are **insulating screeds.** They are broadly of two types: bitumen-bound lightweight aggregates or lightweight concrete – the latter either lightweight aggregate or directly foamed concrete. The primary disadvantage of these materials is their relative inefficiency compared to board insulants. In addition the cement-based screeds may introduce excess water into the roof build-up if trapped between the vapour control layer and the membrane. Bitumen-bound lightweight aggregate products have shown a significantly increased risk of allowing water (from rainfall) into the build-up during construction, after which it is very difficult to remove. Because of these considerations it is unlikely that insulating screeds will often be an appropriate design selection as the sole means of providing thermal resistance.

Moisture vapour properties

Condensation control is an important part of the thermal design of the roof. For warm deck roofs, although vapour control layers may be seen as the front line defence, selection of the insulant, in terms of its thermal and moisture resistance, is also important. The thermal resistance may influence the position of any dewpoint.

The absorption of moisture by the insulant will modify its thermal performance, and might in some cases give reduced mechanical properties. The moisture vapour resistance of the insulant, and its method of fixing, may have a noticeable effect on the overall movement of moisture vapour. For example, compare an open-textured insulant with mechanical fixings through the vapour control layer with a closed cell foam insulant fixed by bedding in hot bitumen.

Further reading:
Approved Document L to The Building Regulations • BRE report 143 Thermal insulation: avoiding risks • CIBSE Guide, Volume A Section A3.

- Insulants and other components will also influence moisture vapour movement, which is an important consideration for condensation control.
- For warm deck roofs the insulant provides mechanical support to the membrane.

Mechanical properties

The majority of flat roofs will have requirements for load-carrying capacity, ranging from a 'non-access roof' with occasional foot traffic, through access terraces, to more heavily loaded roofs for vehicular access. These loads will, for warm deck and inverted warm deck roofs, need to be transmitted through the insulant. Similarly where the insulant and the membrane are fixed solely by adhesive, the wind uplift forces experienced by the roof build-up will be resisted by the adhesive strength between the various layers and the cohesive strength of the insulant.

Assessment of the likely loadings and whether they are short-term or sustained or fast or slow rates of application, can be important. For compression loads, a sustained load of similar magnitude to an occasional load is likely to be more onerous especially for foamed plastics—because of creep. See **Units 7.11, 8.4** and **7.10** for guidance on design and calculation of these effects.

Compression strain

Compression loads on foamed plastics give varying modes of deformation with increasing load. These variations make it inappropriate to quote a 'compression strength' of foamed plastics. Instead it is more common to quote a load for a given compression strain, usually 10%. **Chapter 17** gives a fuller description of the compression behaviour of foamed plastics thermal insulants. Other compressible insulants, although perhaps having different modes of compression strain, generally use a similar approach to quoting compression resistance.

For the various design loads the compression experienced should not be such that permanent set or damage will occur to the insulant or to the membrane when this is supported by the insulant. In selecting insulants it is normally appropriate to assess what compression would occur when subject to the design loadings and to compare the % compression to the 10% figure with a factor of safety.

Housing over refuse depot, London, UK

Overlays

Where an insulant preferred for, say, fire or environmental considerations is not alone adequate to support the imposed loads, overlays of other materials can be considered to distribute the load over an acceptable area of the insulant. For heavily trafficked roofs this may require a substantial thickness of concrete. **Unit 7.10** gives an approach to calculating the required load spreading.

Partial support

In some roof constructions, typically on trough metal decks, the insulant may not be fully supported and the insulant board will be required to span between troughs without undue sagging or collapse. Appropriate performance may be designed by calculation from basic flexural strength data but is more commonly derived from experience and development of approximate rules for specific products, e.g. 'span = 2.5 × thickness'. **Chapter 17** gives more specific guidance for various insulation materials.   *continued* ▶

Critical factors

- Thermal transmission behaviour.
- Contribution to resistance of all roof components.
- Moisture vapour resistance.
- Mechanical support to membrane.

Further reading in the Guide:
4.5 Thermal transmission • 4.6 Solar radiation and thermal effects • 4.7 Condensation • 7.10 Design for wind resistance • 7.11 Design for traffic and load spreading • 8.2 Calculation of thermal performance • 8.4 Calculation of wind uplift • 17 Thermal insulants

- The thermal insulant can affect the performance of the membrane system and therefore they must be physically and chemically compatible.
- Fire performance is normally assessed by standard tests which can only give broad indications of how a complete roof construction might behave in a fire.

Fire performance

With the trend towards highly insulated warm deck roof construction, the fire performance of the insulation has a significant effect on the fire performance of the roof system - resistance to both external and internal fire. The approach to design for fire safety of the whole roof given in **Unit 7.9** and the background to the principles of fire behaviour are given in **Unit 4.9**.

Fires within buildings

A variety of standard test methods exist for comparing the fire properties of building materials. These normally give a comparative indication of how materials will behave in a particular test rather than the performance of a roof construction. Where the possible fire hazard is by breakthrough from inside the building, an insulant over a concrete deck, for example, would be less critical than the same insulant over a wood or trough metal deck. Consideration should therefore be given to the roof build-up including the influence of other combustible materials used, and the likely performance of the complete roof under fire conditions, before accepting or rejecting an insulant on its fire properties. Some insurance companies providing cover for commercial buildings utilise this whole roof approach by approving only specific combinations of materials and build-up.

External fires

Fire from an external source is discussed in detail in **Unit 7.9**. That Unit particularly comments upon the effects of the insulant on the notional fire rating of the roof surface, from the Approved Document to *The Building Regulations*. Although foamed plastics have been most closely examined for fire performance, there is considerable variability in performance between the materials available. Phenolic foams are now recognised as having the better fire performance for this general type of insulant, although formulation improvements and fire retardants can be helpful for other foam plastics. Further considerations in the behaviour of all insulants in a fire are the quantity and possible toxicity of smoke released. These may be of less concern for a roof than the same materials within a building. However a project specific judgement should be made by designers.

Non-plastics insulants

Other insulants, not based on foam plastics, are generally considered to have better fire properties but, although not contributing as greatly to fire load, can sustain damage in a fire. Man-made mineral fibre boards have a resin binder content which is combustible; similarly cork would suffer damage. Even those materials with no combustible content, such as cellular glass, would melt at sufficiently high temperatures.

Membrane compatibility

Compatibility of an insulant with the membrane covers a number of issues chemical, physical and mechanical. A cross comparison should be made for the effects on the membrane by the insulant and vice versa.

Mechanical

Where a membrane will be in firm contact but not bonded to the insulant, as might occur, say, with mastic asphalt, the surface smoothness of the insulant may be important for the membrane to accommodate relative movements.

Dimensional instability of insulants has caused failures of fully bonded membranes. This should not now be a common problem as the effects are now better researched and recommendations from manufacturers reflect the potential risk.

Temperature

Temperature compatibility is often important during the installation phase when using hot applied systems such as mastic asphalt. Materials that would soften or suffer damage unduly such as polystyrene foams are not recommended for such situations. In less onerous but still hot conditions, such as when using pour and roll bitumen, it is often sufficient to interpose a layer of less temperature sensitive insulation board between polystyrene and the membrane. Fibre board or other non-plastics can be used for this and may be

Spreading hot asphalt

Further reading:
Approved Document B to The Building Regulations • Approved Document L to The Building Regulations • BRE Report 143 Thermal insulation: avoiding risks
CIBSE Guide, Volume A, Section A3

- Approved Documents to *The Building Regulations* give 'notional' fire ratings for flat roof constructions which do not include many of the commonly used insulants.
- Insulants used to improve the thermal performance of roofs are prominent in discussion of environmental impact.
- The cost of an insulant should be adressed as a whole life cost.

incorporated either as a separate board or pre-laminated. Although bringing benefits during installation the use of these second boards will increase the overall thickness requirements compared to the primary board alone as they are generally of higher thermal conductivity. An alternative, available for some products, is to factory pre-bond a first layer of membrane using cold adhesives.

Chemical

With some membrane systems chemical compatibility with the insulant may be a consideration. Volatile or mobile solvent or plasticiser constituents could migrate from the membrane to the insulant. This might be possible, for example, with warm deck roofs comprising a PVC membrane with expanded polystyrene insulation where inappropriate grades of materials were selected.

Falls

A further consideration in the insulant selection for warm deck roofs may be the ability to provide falls by using cut preformed board insulants. Although in its early development this concept was linked closely with expanded bead polystyrene, it is now more widely available. Rigid urethane foam, mineral wool, cellular glass, cork, extruded polystyrene have all been made available in cut to falls versions.

It is probable that using such systems will be less economic where only minimum insulation standards are required because of the inherently higher cost of the boards compared to forming falls by screeding. In situations such as refurbishment where changes to the underlying construction

Insulation cut to falls

may not be feasible, then adopting an insulant board which can be used to create (extra) falls can be beneficial. The boards have to be precut off-site to a predetermined pattern. Some manufacturers offer a comprehensive design service which can accommodate most roof geometries.

Environmental considerations

Insulation and energy conservation are foremost in environmental discussions and in general it is perhaps less contentious than for many environmental topics to conclude that the benefits of higher insulation standards outweigh the disadvantages of materials consumption and energy consumption during manufacture. Design of the overall thermal performance can take account of both the energy conservation implications and the wider environmental issues from manufacture of the insulants. Plastics foams are widely used for insulation because of their generally good insulation properties.

Further information on the environmental aspects of insulants is given in **Unit 4.15** and **Chapter 17**. Because insulants are so prominent in the environmental discussions there is much opportunity to promote the credentials of particular materials. Where such considerations are important for a particular project, close scrutiny of the available information may be necessary to evaluate a true balance of information. As an example, the interpretation of 'ozone friendly' needs care as some substitute materials will still have measurable influence on ozone depletion.

Cost

The cost of the insulant should be assessed on an 'as incorporated in the roof' basis, not just per square metre of board. The cost comparisons should be made only where the technical requirements have already been assessed and found satisfactory. Cost per unit of insulation value per square metre is a better starting point but the cost implications of the effects of insulation on other details – in relation to thickness or load spreading for example – cannot be ignored. Some claims are made for incorporating the overall life of the insulant into the costs. At present it would be very difficult to predict safely varying lifespans of most of the commonly used insulants.

Project commercial considerations make it impossible to give a comparison of value for money for insulants. ∎

Critical factors

- Fire behaviour of total system in building.
- Interaction between roof components.
- Close scrutiny of environmental attributes.
- Whole life cost.
- Physical and chemical compatibility.

7.7 Design for moisture vapour control

- Many activities within a building generate moisture; some roof construction materials will release it into the roof build-up.
- Moisture can condense within the construction materials, in voids or in building spaces.
- Control of condensation is required for health and safety of occupants and to prevent damage to the building.

The control of condensation risks in flat roofing is a statutory requirement in *The Building Regulations*. It is also sought because of the poor performance and even failure of buildings and components when the phenomenon is not controlled. This poor performance can manifest itself as: ineffective thermal insulation resulting from higher moisture content; the degradation of materials within the roof – e.g. rotting of timber and similar materials or corrosion of metal decking, fixings or membranes; manifestation of liquid water inside the building which might be misinterpreted as leakage through the membrane.

The Building Regulations (Part F2) require that:

'Adequate provision shall be made to prevent excessive condensation:

(a) in a roof; or

(b) in a roof void above an insulated ceiling'.

The Approved Document F2 goes on to say that:

'... the requirement of F2 will be met if condensation in a roof and in the spaces above insulated ceilings is limited so that, under normal conditions:

(a) the thermal performance of the insulating materials and

(b) the structural performance of the roof construction

will not be substantially and permanently reduced.'

Condensation formation

Condensation in roofs, its occurrence and control, is concerned with flows of moisture vapour through the construction and how they are affected by the thermal and vapour transmission resistance of the components within a roof.

The scientific principles of the behaviour of moisture in air, and how this changes with temperature, are discussed in **Unit 4.7**.

The principles of the methods of calculation for condensation risk are well established. They are particularly sensitive to the quality of the assumptions which have to be made and to how the input data is selected (see **Unit 8.3**). Calculations are, however, only concerned with diffusion through the roofing and assume a steady state. Air leakage through gaps and discontinuities can be more significant for overall performance.

Condensation control: principles

Control of condensation can be achieved by the incorporation, at an appropriate location within the build-up, of layers or membranes designed to control transmission of moisture vapour. It may also be achieved by the provision of adequate ventilation or modification of the thermal performance of the roof build-up.

Consideration of the need for and specification of, vapour control layers in flat roofing is essential to avoid the deleterious effects of moisture build-up. All materials, even still air, have some resistance to the diffusion of moisture vapour.

Condensation control: materials properties

Sources of data for the moisture vapour resistance (or transmittance) of the materials in isolation are readily to hand, although the values quoted may vary from source to source. It is more difficult to make an estimate of the real resistance of components as incorporated in a roof build-up. For example a metal deck with good seals at sheet laps will be a very effective barrier to moisture vapour and may have more effect than a deliberately incorporated 'vapour control layer' if the latter is installed badly or subsequently damaged. Moreover, as shown by research at BRE (*BRE Digest 270*), for domestic buildings the great majority of the moisture vapour that accumulates in a roof space enters via penetrations through the ceiling, e.g ceiling roses or loft hatch, even where foil-backed plasterboard has been used in an attempt to control vapour transmission.

Other roof components, (e.g. insulation materials such as foamed glass) have high vapour resistance when fully bonded in bitumen. Table 7.7.1 gives values for water vapour resistivity of a range of materials likely to be incorporated within a flat roof. These values are derived from *BS5250* and flat roof industry sources.

Within the preferred overall description 'vapour control layer' it has become common to use two categorisations 'vapour check' and 'vapour barrier'. These categories of performance are imprecise and should be avoided. Designers should determine the degree of resistance required and select a vapour control layer with such performance.

The requirement for vapour control should be determined for each project, taking into account the probable internal and external environments through the year, the thermal characteristics and design of the roof, the potential effects of intermittent or accumulated moisture within the roof on the components, e.g. on the insulation or fixings.

Further reading:
BRE Digest 270 Condensation in insulated domestic roofs • Approved Document F to The Building Regulations • BS5250 Control of condensation in buildings • BS6229 Flat roofs with continuously supported coverings

- Condensation control by design involves considering likely internal and external environments; thermal performance of the construction; provision of specific vapour control layers (VCL); ventilation.
- *The Building Regulations* include requirements for the control of condensation.
- Assessment of condensation risk is essential.

The potential for condensation to occur can be calculated for assumed diffusion behaviour. These calculations should use, where possible, real data from previous experience for materials and the air environments. The likely vapour control layers and ventilation can then also be assessed (see **Unit 8.3**).

Guidance on an approach is given in Approved Document F2:

- The requirement will be met by ventilation of cold deck roofs.
- It is not necessary to ventilate warm deck roofs or inverted roofs.
- It is not necessary for the purposes of health and safety to ventilate small roofs such as those for porches and bay windows.

The Approved Document approach of ventilating cold deck roofs, and by implication, using other methods of control for warm deck and inverted warm deck roofs is one which will be most appropriate for the majority of situations. Some special considerations may require a more onerous or limiting approach. For example the weather conditions in Scotland are such that in cold deck roofs are strongly discouraged by the *Building Standards (Scotland) Regulations* (see **Unit 3.2**). There are also special considerations for metal sheet roofs which increase the risk of condensation in a cold roof, even when ventilated (see **Chapters 14** and **15**). Some installations, such as a reinforced concrete slab with insulation applied directly to the soffit, are in effect cold deck roofs, but here condensation cannot be controlled by ventilation.

Entrapped moisture

Water trapped in the roof build-up, either as the result of expected construction activities (e.g. in concrete slabs or screeds) or inadvertently (e.g. during rainfall), can contribute to the nature of the control of moisture vapour. Designers should consider the likely volumes of water entrapped, the local vapour pressures which might result, i.e. depending upon the temperatures to be experienced, and the provision/potential for water vapour pressure to dissipate without harm. This may concern the bonding of components, vents, formwork for concrete slabs. *continued* ▶

Table 7.7.1
Vapour resistivity for roof construction materials[a]

Material	Resistivity (MN.s/g.m)
Plywood	2000
Chipboard	500
Dense concrete (2200kg/m³ dry density)	200
Lightweight concrete (aerated)[b]	50
Metal deck with unsealed laps	10[c]
Vapour control layers	see table 7.7.2
Asphalt	100 000[d]
Built up roofing	10 000[d]
Metal sheet membranes (sealed laps)	10 000[d]
Polymeric single ply membrane	refer to manufacturer
Lightweight cement screed	100
Rigid urethane foam (closed cell)	650
Extruded polystyrene	1000
Expanded polystyrene	250
Cellular glass	100 000
Cork board	100
Mineral or glass fibre board	5

Notes:

(a) Because of the range of materials available within each type and the effects of construction processes, these values can only be taken as notional for calculation purposes. Where necessary specific values may be able to be determined from manufacturers or independent tests.

(b) Lightweight concrete, used for structural purposes, made with lightweight aggregate will be influenced by the nature of the aggregates and the mix design. In the absence of specific data from manufacturers, values similar to those of dense concrete of a similar strength may be used.

(c) Overall vapour resistance of the construction in MNs/g.

(d) The values are notional values for the purposes of calculation.

Critical factors

- Building Regulations requirements.
- Control by ventilation or vapour control layer.
- Effective vapour resistance of construction.
- Condensation risk assessment

Design for moisture vapour control *continued*

- Design selection involves a number of interactive decision steps.
- Selection is influenced by the internal and external environments, the nature of materials used, and their means of incorporation into the roof.
- Ventilation to control condensation in cold deck roofs is normally only effective for small, simple roof plans.

Figure 7.7.1
Design selection decision flow diagram

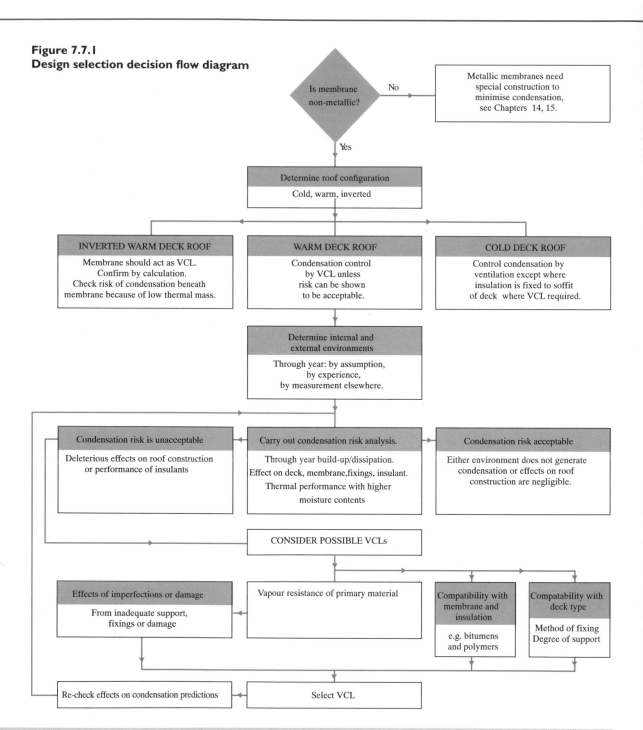

Further reading:
Approved Document F to The Building Regulations • BS5250 Control of condensation in buildings

Chapter	1	2	3	4	5	6	7	8	9	10	11
Contents	Introduction	History	Regulatory Methods	Principles	Surveys	Constraints & Targets	Design Selection	Calculations	Detail Design Principles	Evaluation of Design	Built-up Roofing
Page	1	19	31	45	83	95	105	165	189	217	221

- Design for ventilation uses approximate rules to calculate the amount of ventilation.
- Cold, moist air coming into the ventilation space can increase condensation risk.
- Vents on the surface of a cold deck roof should be avoided as they can increase condensation risk.

Design selection

Figure 7.7.1 shows the way in which the various considerations in condensation control can interact in the design solution.

Ventilation of cold roofs

The calculation of the ventilation required to deal with condensation in a cold deck roof is based upon Approved Document F2 and *BS5250*. Although control of condensation by the use of a vapour control layer is not normally the primary method recommended for cold deck roofs, the incorporation of such a layer beneath the insulation may have some benefit in restricting the quantity of moisture vapour which needs to be vented to avoid unacceptable condensation. Materials which might be used for such purposes are polyethylene sheet, foil-backed plasterboard, or surface coatings applied to the soffit of a ceiling liner. Such layers are, however, likely to have reduced efficiency over the parent material, because of penetrations by fixings or fittings.

Ventilation, to be effective, requires a sufficiently large air path and a means of inducing air flow without creating dead spaces. For these reasons, it is normally only appropriate with roofs of relatively simple plan and small span. More complicated roofs might achieve this with extensive mechanically-forced ventilation, but such measures are outside the scope of this Guide.

For simple square or rectangular roofs, provision of slots in the edges of opposite sides of the roof can provide a ventilation route. Both Approved Document F2 and *BS5250* suggest the equivalent of a 25mm continuous slot along the complete length of two opposite sides (see Figure 7.7.2). In addition, a 50mm clear space between the top surface of the insulation and the underside of the deck is required. F2 suggests this is sufficient for roofs up to 10m span. For larger roofs an increase in roof edge opening to 0.6% of the total roof area is suggested (equivalent to a 30mm slot for a 10m span roof). *BS5250* differs from F2, in that it suggests that effective ventilation may be difficult to achieve with the 25mm equivalent slot for roofs over 5m span and that, therefore, increased slots and clear space should be provided. No guidance on the desired increase is given. Because of the difficulty in predicting the effectiveness of ventilation, serious consideration should be given to changing to an alternative roof construction for roofs over 10m span. Increases in the amount of slot ventilation can be considered for roofs 5-10m span.

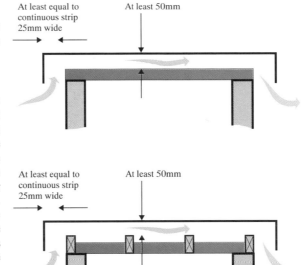

At least equal to continuous strip 25mm wide   At least 50mm

At least equal to continuous strip 25mm wide   At least 50mm

Figure 7.7.2
Ventilation requirements for a cold roof

Where, because of the arrangement of the roof in relation to other structures, free air paths and effective ventilation are unlikely to be achieved, alternative roof construction to a cold deck roof should be selected.

Roof vents

Vents in the surface of the roofs, rather than at the eaves, should not be used. Due to the negative pressure on the roof surface caused by wind, air will be drawn out of the cavity thus reducing the pressure within. This may cause moist warm air to be drawn in from the room below, and thus increase condensation risk.   *continued* ▶

continued ▶

Further reading in the Guide:
4.7 Condensation • 4.8 Condensation: pumping • 8.3 Calculation of condensation • 14 Copper • 15 Lead sheet

- Design for condensation control must consider the actual properties of materials.
- In refurbishment, the existing construction has vapour control properties.
- A separate vapour control layer is normally required for warm deck roof configurations.

Control of condensation using a vapour control layer (VCL)

Design approach

For warm deck and inverted warm deck roofs, the control of condensation is normally achieved by prediction of the likely risk and modifying the construction until the risk is considered acceptable. The predictions are made by considering the moisture vapour flow in and out of the roof construction and the risk of the vapour pressure reaching saturated vapour pressure. The influence of specific vapour control layers can be assessed by these calculation methods and a decision taken on whether to include one.

Some references on the design of flat roofs give categories of buildings which should or should not have a specific vapour control layer installed. This type of guidance can be helpful in giving an impression of the sensitivity of building types to condensation problems. However, calculations for the specific build-up should always be carried out.

The essential performance requirement of the VCL is that it should limit the quantity of moisture vapour passing through it, to a level which can be dissipated by lateral pathways under the waterproofing or through the membrane, or where the condensate occurring is acceptable for that construction. Some predicted collection of condensate may be acceptable during peak conditions if it can be shown that:

- it will re-evaporate subsequently
- the construction will not be permanently damaged by the occurrence.

VCL incorporation

Whether to include a VCL specifically to control unacceptable condensation can be a complex argument, but a VCL should be included for warm deck roofs unless it can be positively shown to be unnecessary. The VCL is normally placed on the warm side of the primary insulation component. Reasons sometimes given against the incorporation of a separate VCL are: the time for installation, cost, and the care needed to ensure continuity and damage-free installation. Most of these issues are avoided with an inverted warm deck roof where, generally, the waterproofing membrane will act as a VCL as well as primary waterproofing. Some concern has been expressed that, particularly with polymeric single-ply membranes, in an inverted roof, a risk of condensation can arise on the underside of the membrane. This condensation has, on occasion, been mistaken for leakage through the membrane. This is believed to be the result of the relatively low thermal mass of the deck and membrane compared to that of rain or melted snow which has percolated down between the membrane and the insulation. There is less concern with thicker membrane systems which it is currently believed have sufficient thermal mass to avoid the problem. Specific guidance should be sought from individual membrane manufacturers.

Table 7.7.2
Approximate vapour resistance values of typical vapour control layers[A].

Material/Construction	Vapour Resistance (MN.s/g)
Bitumen felt[B] – single layer on trough metal deck	100
Bitumen felt[B] – single layer, fully supported, lapped but loose laid	300
Bitumen felt[B] – two layers, fully supported, fully lapped and fully bonded	500
Bitumen felt with aluminium foil[C] – single layer fully bonded	>1000
Polyethylene sheet (0.12mm) – loose laid on trough metal deck	100
Polyethylene sheet (0.12mm)[D] – loose laid, all joints fully lapped and taped	300

Notes:

[A] These values are approximations for the materials/ constructions listed, taken from published guidance. They may be appropriate for many condensation control calculations. Where necessary more specific information may be available from manufacturers or direct tests.

[B] The vapour resistance of the felts is not substantially affected by the nature of the carrier/base. However, the better robustness of the higher performance (polyester) membranes will normally result in reduced damage where movement or reduced support is likely (e.g. timber boarded or trough metal decks).

[C] Aluminium foil thickness greater than 0.05mm and typically 0.075mm.

[D] On non-continuous decks, the use of a rigid board beneath the VCL during taping enables better sealing.

Further reading:
BS747 Specification for roofing felt • BS5250 Control of condensation in buildings

- The two main types of material used for vapour control layers are bitumen sheet and polythene sheets.
- Special consideration is needed to control condensation by pumping

Hopkins House, London, UK

Materials for vapour control layers

New construction
Although many materials could be used as VCL, practical aspects mean that, primarily, two families of materials will dominate – bitumen sheets (generally for BUR and asphalt roofs) and polythene sheet (generally for polymeric single-ply roofs). Many other guides on flat roofing design and condensation control give values of the vapour resistance of materials used as VCLs. Comparison of the information reveals that the guidance is not entirely consistent or easy to relate.

Some general data on the vapour resistance of materials used as VCLs may be found in Table 7.7.2, or more specific information can be obtained from manufacturers.

Roof refurbishment
When upgrading or refurbishing existing flat roofs, a design approach is to consider the existing membrane as the VCL. This prompts a general point that any calculation of condensation risk should recognise the potential effectiveness of existing constructions as a VCL. Typical values for vapour resistivity of membrane materials are given in Table 7.7.2.

VCL performance
The effectiveness of a vapour control layer is dependent upon the inherent properties of the materials, the effectiveness at discontinuities. Any joints or laps should be continuous throughout the roof and sealed at perimeters. The extent and nature of any damage incurred during the installation will also determine the actual VCL performance. The inherent properties can be measured in laboratory tests but the other effects can only be very broadly estimated. The calculation methods for control of condensation needs to make allowance, as far as possible, for these effects. Some indications of the extent of these effects are given in Table 7.7.2.

Many roofs in the past will have used bitumen sheeting to types 1B or 1F of *BS747* as a VCL. These materials have a vapour resistance which is useful but which will be reduced by incomplete support or mechanical damage. More recent products for vapour control layers have incorporated an aluminium foil with the bitumen-impregnated sheet. Where sufficiently thick (0.7 mm in UK) this aluminium layer significantly increases the overall vapour resistance of the VCL. With these higher vapour resistances the effect of any lap and puncture defects becomes proportionately greater. High mechanical performance polyester-based felts are also available in combination with aluminium foils which give much greater resistance to mechanical damage, particularly where support is discontinuous. The sheets in combination with aluminium foils do not have performance requirements laid down in British Standards in respect to their use as VCLs, however manufacturers can usually supply data on vapour resistance and mechanical properties such as tear and bursting strength which are helpful in comparing likely installed performance.

When considering the merits of using polyester or other high performance felts, with or without aluminium foil incorporated, it is more appropriate to compare the benefits against the total installed cost of the VCL rather than simply against the price per m² of material.

Unit 8.3 gives guidance on, and shows worked examples of, the methods of calculation of risks and on the assumptions of environmental conditions and effects which may be used in the calculations.

Condensation pumping
Special considerations might be needed to avoid the consequences of condensation formed by pumping. The principles of the phenomenon are described in **Unit 4.8**. Ensuring the design does not incorporate poorly ventilated voids is important. Furthermore for some metal roofs the incorporation of other membranes, beneath the metal sheet, is proposed to prevent condensate collecting on the metal. Guidance on design for this issue in relation to metal roofs is given in **Chapters 14 and 15**. ■

Further reading in the Guide:
4.7 Condensation • 4.8 Condensation: pumping • 8.2 Calculation of thermal performance • 8.3 Calculation of condensation • 14 Copper • 15 Lead sheet

7.8 Design for lightning protection

- Lightning can cause injury to people or damage to buildings.
- Extensive data are available on the occurrence of lightning strikes.
- Attachment of protection systems may involve complex construction details.

The phenomenon of lightning has been observed and recorded over the centuries. Even up to the present day, lightning strokes result in death or injury to people and livestock. In addition, severe structural damage has been sustained by buildings, some no more than two storeys in height.

For 50 years, observations and measurements have been carried out around the world on lightning discharges and a large amount of data has been accumulated.

Using this as a basis, Codes of Practice provide guidance on the principles and practices in the protection of structures.

Risk assessment

Before undertaking the design of a lightning protection system, it is necessary to assess the degree of risk (of being struck) for the particular structure. The code (*BS6651*) recommends the calculation of an overall **risk factor** to determine the need for protection. This is arrived at from a series of individual factors which include:

- Number of building occupants and their 'vulnerability' – hospitals and schools would score high, offices would score low
- Building contents – their value/strategic worth
- Type of construction – e.g. reinforced concrete, brick/stone
- Location – close to other buildings or completely isolated
- Country terrain – e.g. high mountainous or flat plain
- Geographical location.

A decision may be made to protect the building, even if the overall risk factor is low, for example where buildings have special inherent risks:

- storage of flammable liquids or explosives
- irreplaceable structure or contents
- essential services are carried out.

Design of the protection system

The design for a protection scheme must be in accordance with *BS6651*. It will be necessary to discuss the proposals with the design team at initial design. The reason is that the system interface with the building must be considered by all parties involved.

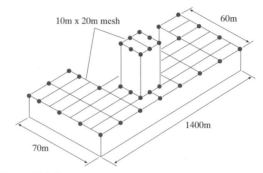

Figure 7.8.1
Air termination for tall conducting structures

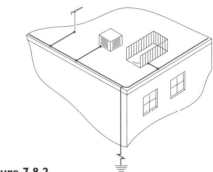

Figure 7.8.2
Bonding to air termination network

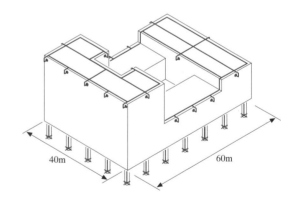

↘ Bonding to reinforced bars   ⊥ Earth electrode pile foundation

Figure 7.8.3
Lightning protection scheme to *BS6651* using reinforced concrete within structure for down conductors

Further reading:
BS6651 Protection of structures against lightning

- Design guidance helps to assess buildings at risk and an approach to protection.
- Depending upon its construction, the structure of a building may be used as the down conductor.

A lightning protection system comprises four main sections:

1 Air termination

For flat roofs, the air termination will consist of horizontal conductors spaced out to form a rectangular grid (Figure 7.8.1): *BS6651* recommends a mesh of 10m × 20m. For **'high-risk'** structures, the mesh should be reduced to 5m × 10m.

2 Earth terminations

Buried earth electrode systems must be provided as close to the structure as possible. The design of the electrode systems will depend on the nature of the site and the **effective resistivity** of the soil.

3 Down conductors

Connections between the air termination network and the earth electrode systems must ensure that lightning discharge currents are conducted safely to earth without any part of the total current being diverted into the building and taking a different path to earth; such diversion of current flow is part of a phenomenon known as **side flashing**.

4 Bonds

All extraneous metalwork in or on the structure with a connection to an earth potential, and not forming part of the lightning protection system, must be bonded to the protection system (Figures 7.8.2-7.8.4).

The detailed systems are comprehensively covered in *BS6651*, together with guidance on the selection of materials.

Use of the structure

In *BS6651*, structures are categorised as **'conducting'** (e.g. steel-framed or reinforced concrete) or **'non-conducting'** (e.g. stone or brick construction).

These are important to the design of the system. For steel-frame and reinforced concrete constructions, the roof (air) termination system can be connected to the structural steelwork at the outer extremities and corners, forming the down conductor system (Figure 7.8.3).

Where the foundations contain sufficient steelwork, *BS6651* allows their use as the earth electrode system.

Detailed design of the roof (air) termination system

Metal-covered roofs

With a metal roof covering, it must be bonded to the (separate) air termination network. Its use as an air termination is not considered in *BS6651*, because the covering may not form continuous current paths to the down

1 Air terminal
2 Down conductor
3 Bond to aerial
4 Bond to vent
5 Bond to reinforcement bars
6 Bond to metal staircase
7 Bond to metal window frame
8 Bond to vent pipe
9 Bond to steel door/frame
10 Test clamp
11 Indicating plate
12 Main earthing terminal of electrical installation
13 Earth termination point

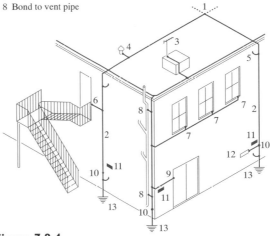

Figure 7.8.4
Bonding to prevent side flashing

conductors and/or the sheet thickness may be insufficient to limit the current density to the required level.

Non-metal roof coverings

The air termination network conductors can be secured to the roof surface by three principal methods:

- The use of purpose-made fixings which space the conductors above the level of the roof. The fixing is secured with adhesive or 'built into' the roof surface.
- The use of purpose-made saddles to locate the conductors closer to the roof but still affording a space between the conductor and the roof surface. The saddle is secured with adhesive or 'built into' the roof surface.
- The use of straps made from a material which is compatible with the roof membrane, the conductors being in direct contact with the roof. The straps are secured to the roof membrane with an adhesive.

All fixing materials must be durable for roof exposure and the fixings must be rigid enough to withstand the mechanical forces associated with lightning current flow, without excessive movement.

The code allows the use of covered conductors for air terminations, but a bare conductor system is preferred. ■

Further reading in the Guide:

7.9   Design for fire safety

- Fire can directly affect building users by heat or smoke. It can also affect the stability of the structure and the safety of adjacent buildings.
- *The Building Regulations* contain requirements for achieving safety in the event of fire.
- The safety requirements are intended for people in and around the building, including in adjacent buildings.

Fire precautions

The Building Regulations make requirements that have to be met in order to provide a level of safety in fire for persons in and around buildings. One way to achieve the standard of safety – particularly where the design is straightforward – is to design to the guidance laid out in the Approved Document B, Fire Safety. Alternative approaches may be suitable when a design is complex. Such approaches include fire safety engineering which considers the circumstances of a particular case where for example, recommendations in the Approved Document cannot be met. The guidance in this Unit is limited to the Approved Document route. The requirements of other authorities should also be considered where relevant, which may include those of the company insuring the building. The Loss Prevention Council publish a *Code of Practice for the construction of buildings*.

The Approved Document addresses several aspects of roof design, some of which are directed at flat roofs and some of which have to be interpreted for them. This Unit addresses only flat roofs and refers the designer to paragraphs and Sections in the Approved Document B. The principles underlying behaviour in a fire are given in **Unit 4.9**.

The guidance (references are to the Approved Document) comprises three main areas; fire resistance; flame spread and fire penetration; other matters.

Fire resistance

The fire resistance of a construction is monitored and recorded in terms of three fundamental parameters:

- Loadbearing capacity – does the system collapse under the test load? (Figure 7.9.1)
- Integrity – do flames, hot or cold gases, penetrate the component to cause damage to adjacent areas? (Figure 7.9.2)
- Insulation – does the component contain the energy of the fire by preventing transfer by conduction? (Figure 7.9.3)

The tests for these parameters are given in *BS476: Parts 21-23: 1987*.

The stability, integrity and insulation of a system can be enhanced using passive fire protection materials. These materials may be subject to reaction to tests such as *BS476: Parts 4, 6 and 7*.

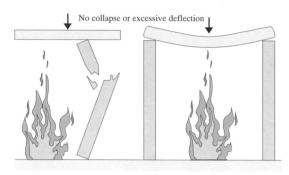

Figure 7.9.1
Fire resistance: loadbearing capacity criterion – no collapse or excessive deflection

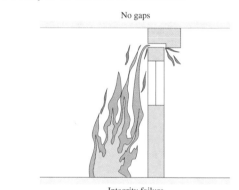

Figure 7.9.2
Fire resistance: integrity criterion – no gaps

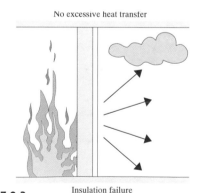

Figure 7.9.3
Fire resistance: insulation criterion – no excessive heat transfer

Further reading:
Approved Documents B, as amended 1992, and K of the Building Regulations • BS476 Fire tests on building materials and structures: Parts 4, 6-7, 21-23

© BFRC / CIRIA: Flat Roofing: Design and Good Practice. 1993

- Fire resistance has three parameters: stability, integrity and insulation.
- Fire hazard must be considered for fires within and outside the building.
- Roofs, as structural elements, are required to provide fire resistance where the roof supports other structures, performs the function of a floor or provides an escape route.

Roofs are elements of structure but are required to provide fire resistance in limited circumstances only.

- Where the roof structure supports elevations to which it is connected, i.e. if the collapse in fire of a roof would then lead to instability of the walls on which it is supported or to which it is connected which themselves need fire resistance, the roof itself is required to provide fire resistance to the same standard as the remainder of the structure. Only the loadbearing capacity would be required for the fire resistance. The standard required is set out in Table 7.9.4 of this Unit, which is based upon Table A2 of the Approved Document.
- Where the roof performs the function of a floor (car park, or terrace for example), fire resistance from below is required for the roof and to the same standard as the remainder of the building; all three aspects of fire resistance would be required (Section 7). The standard required is laid out in Tables A1 (line 4b) and A2 of the Approved Document. The Table A1, in note 3, indicates that a suspended ceiling may contribute to the performance. There are controls on the nature of the ceiling (Table A3) which are of particular importance where surfaces of the ceiling are concerned.
- Where a means of escape route is provided over the roof (paras 2.28 and 5.3), the part of the roof forming the escape route and its supporting structure, together with any opening within 3m of the escape route, should be fire resisting to the 30 minute standard set out in Table A1 of the Approved Document (line 4a). There are additional requirements for the safety of persons using the route over the roof – see Table 7.9.1.

Table 7.9.1
Escape routes over flat roofs
(based on Para 2.28 of Approved Document B)

If more than one escape route is available from a storey, or part of a building, one of those routes may be by way of a flat roof, provided that:

a. The roof is part of the same building from which escape is being made.

b. The route across the roof leads to a storey exit.

c. The part of the roof forming the escape route and its supporting structure, together with any opening within 3m of the escape route, is fire-resisting (see Appendix A, Table A1 of the Approved Document).

d. The route is adequately defined and guarded by walls and/or protective barriers which meet the provisions in Approved Document K, ramps and guards.

Flame spread and fire penetration

This aspect of fire safety recognises hazards from fires within the building and external to it. The three criteria used are:

- External surface flame spread – limitations on roof coverings near a boundary which would not otherwise give adequate protection against fire spread over them (Section 14).
- Fire penetration – choice of materials to resist fire penetration from an adjacent burning building (Section 14).
- Internal flame spread – if appropriate, control with respect to spread on any internal exposed roof surface including rooflights (para 6.8, 14.5-6).

There are limitations on the flame spread and fire penetration characteristics of roof coverings near a boundary which would otherwise not give adequate protection against fire spread over and through them. This aspect does not deal with roof support structure but with build-up finishes which may consist of one or more layers of material. The principle concern is with fire initiated from outside a building.

Overall performance of roofs
The classification of roof coverings is by reference to *BS476: Part 3: 1958* as described in paras A6, 18 and 19 of the Approved Document. The BS test classifies a roof covering in terms of its ability to resist penetration from an external fire and its ability to control flame spread over the surface. The performance is designated in terms of a double letter, e.g. AA, which relates to the dual properties – penetration and flame spread.

Note: The Approved Document points out that this is not the most recent version of the Standard. The 1975 version uses a different notation to describe roof performance. The Approved Document however offers no guidance for comparison between the two versions. This Guide follows the Approved Document in retaining the notation from the 1958 version of the Standard.

continued ▶

Further reading in the Guide:
4.9 Fire behaviour

- The performance of the whole roof construction contributes to its fire safety and must be considered by testing or notional performance.
- Notional performance tables do not cover all roof constructions considered in this Guide.

Table 7.9.2
Limitations on roof coverings

Designation of external covering of roof or part of roof	Minimum distance from any point on relevant boundary			
	Less than 6m	At least 6m	At least 12m	At least 20m
AA, AB, or AC	–	–	–	–
BA, BB, or BC	x	–	–	–
CA, CB, or CC	x	A	B	–
AD, BD, or CD	x	A	B	B
DA, DB, DC, or DD	x	x	x	A
Thatch or wood shingles, if performance under *BS476: Part 3: 1958* cannot be established	x	A	B	A

Notes:

– Acceptable

x Not acceptable

A Not acceptable on any of the following buildings:

  a. Terraces of three or more houses.

  b. Industrial, storage or other non-residential purpose group buildings of any size

  c. Any other buildings with a cubic capacity of more than 1500m³

  And only acceptable on other buildings if the part of the roof is no more than 3m² in area and is at least 1.5m from any similar part, with the roof between the parts covered with a material of limited combustibility.

B Not acceptable on any part of the buildings listed under a, b, or c. above.

  Separation distance considerations do not apply to roofs of a pair of semi-detached houses.

Proximity to boundaries

The proximity of buildings to the boundary bears heavily on the choice of materials and resulting classifications permitted as roof coverings (Table 7.9.2). There is less control over the choice of materials and construction the greater the distance from the boundary, and materials with good flame spread and penetration properties can be used right up to the boundary. There is no control over ratings designated AA, AB or AC – the better ratings. Roofs designated with the lower ratings have severe restrictions, not only on their relationship to a boundary, but also on the type and extent of occupancies for which they may be used.

Notional performance

The notional performance (in terms of the fire test) of certain common roof coverings is given in Table 7.9.5 which addresses flat roof coverings that provide the best performance (AA). It is important to note that the rating is dependent on the support material – since the rating has a penetration aspect to it. Suitable support systems are given in Part (i) of the Table. It can be seen in the table that the notional performance examples are generally for a membrane directly on to a deck. This closely reflects the combination of materials that might be encountered in a cold deck construction.

No examples of notional performance are given for typical warm deck roof construction on high thermal efficiency insulants or for ballasted or inverted warm deck construction. Guidance on the performance of particular combinations not given a notional rating will have to be demonstrated by test. Membrane manufacturers may have appropriate certification of performance.

Internal flame spread – rooflights

Since roof lights form part of the internal lining of a room or circulation space, flame spread over the internal surfaces is also controlled in the same way as internal linings – in addition to controls on the external flame spread.

Plastic rooflights are classified, if possible, according to *BS476: Parts 6 and 7* from which they are designated Class 0-3. Para A19 of the Approved Document explains the manner in which they are classified if the performance under the *BS476* tests is not possible.

The better materials include unwired glass at least 4mm thick, and rigid thermoplastic sheet consisting of polycarbonate or unplasticised PVC which, if they achieve Class 1 spread of flame, may be regarded as having an AA rating. They can therefore be used in any of the circumstances shown for such materials in Table 7.9.3. There are limitations on the use of rooflight material which achieves a Class 3 rating. These are shown in Table 7.9.3. Restrictions include the area of rooflight, the minimum distance between them and the nature of the intervening material.

The external flame spread classification of the rooflight material (under *BS476: Parts 6 and 7* or under the alternative classification para A19) and its location in a building determines its permitted proximity to a boundary – Table 7.9.3.

Further reading:
Approved Document B, as amended 1992, of The Building Regulations • BS476 Fire tests on building materials and structures Parts 3, 6-7, 21-23

Chapter	1	2	3	4	5	6	7	8	9	10	11
Contents	Introduction	History	Regulatory Methods	Principles	Surveys	Constraints & Targets	Design Selection	Calculations	Detail Design Principles	Evaluation of Design	Built-up Roofing
Page	1	19	31	45	83	95	105	165	189	217	221

146

© BFRC / CIRIA: *Flat Roofing: Design and Good Practice. 1993*

- Rooflights require special considerations for both internal and external flame spread.
- Fire spread beneath the roof deck is an important consideration for fire safety which can influence the overall design of the roof.

Table 7.9.3
Plastic rooflights:
limitations on use and boundary distance

Minimum classification on lower surface[A]	Space which rooflight can serve	Minimum distance from any point on relevant boundary to rooflight with an external surface classification[B] of:		
		TP(a)	AD BD CA CB CC CD OR TP(b)	DA DB DC DD
1. TP(a) rigid	any space except a protected stairway	6m[C]	n/a	n/a
2. Class 3 or TP(b)	a. balcony, veranda, carport, covered way, or loading bay, which has at least one longer side wholly or permanently open	n/a	6m	20m
	b. detached swimming pool			
	c. conservatory, garage or outbuilding, with a maximum floor area of 40m			
	d. circulation space[D] (except a protected stairway)	n/a	6m[E]	20m[E]
	e. room[D]			

Notes:

n/a – Not applicable

[A] See also the guidance to B2

[B] The classification of external roof surface is explained in Appendix A.

[C] No limit in the case of any space described in 2a. b. and c

[D] Single skin rooflight only, in the case of non-thermoplastic material

[E] The rooflight should also meet the provisions of Figure 7.9.1.

Polycarbonate and PVC rooflights which achieve a Class 1 rating by test, may be regarded as having an AA designation.

None of the above designations are suitable for protected stairways – see para 6.12.

(B2, Appendix A and para 6.12 refer to the Approved Document.)

Other matters

- Fire-stopping – control of fire spread between compartments where roofs pass over the top of a compartment wall (Section 8).
- Division of concealed spaces – control of fire spread through cavities below flat roofs (para 9.11).
- Use of materials – materials of limited combustibility are required in certain circumstances (Table A7).

Fire-stopping

Fire spread between compartments has to be controlled where roofs pass over the top of a compartment wall (para 8.23-27) and should function for the duration of the required fire resistance of the compartmentation.

The Approved Document describes how the continuity of the junction between wall and roof has to be maintained (para 8.23). Where the roof is not fire resisting, control of fire spread over the compartment wall is achieved by control of flame spread characteristics of the upper surface (para 8.24 of the Approved Document). Under certain circumstances, combustible material is allowed over the wall itself provided it is properly embedded in mortar or other suitable material over the width of the wall (para 8.25 of the Approved Document). Alternatively, the wall may be taken up through the roof for a height of at least 375mm above the top surface of the adjoining roof covering (para 8.27 of the Approved Document).

Concealed spaces

Fire spread through cavities below flat roofs is controlled by the provision of cavity barriers. The number required is such that the maximum dimension in any direction is limited to 20m (Table 14 of the Approved Document). This may, however, conflict with the requirements of ventilation for cold deck roofs. There are no concessions for internal surfaces having superior flame spread characteristics. There is no requirement for cavity barriers in the roof spaces in individual dwellings.

Materials of limited combustibility

In the provision of suitable roof systems, the Approved Document mentions the use of materials of limited combustibility as meeting some of the requirements. Table A7 of the Approved Document outlines the sort of materials that would be suitable; non-combustible materials are included.

continued ▶

Critical factors

- Establish limitations on roof coverings.
- Check whether rooflights are likely to be required.
- Assess for presence of voids which may need control for fire safety.
- Notional fire performance.
- Rooflights.
- Fire spread in cavities.

Further reading in the Guide:
4.9 Fire behaviour

- Minimum periods of fire resistance are provided for different purpose groups and heights of buildings.

Table 7.9.4
Minimum periods of fire resistance

Purpose group of building	Minimum periods (minutes) for elements of structure in a ground or upper storey (basements are not covered in this extract)[H]			
	Height (m) of top floor above ground, in building or separating part of building			
	not more than 5	not more than 20	not more than 30	more than 30
1. Residential (domestic):				
a. flats and maisonettes	30[E]	60[D]	90	120
b. and c. dwelling houses	30[E]	60	not relevant	not relevant
2. Residential:				
a. Institutional[A]	30[E]	60	90	120[B]
b. other residential	30[E]	60	90	120[B]
3. Office:				not permitted
– not sprinklered	30[E]	60	90	
– sprinklered[F]	30[E]	30	60	120[B]
4. Shop and commercial:				not permitted
– not sprinklered	60	60	90	
– sprinklered[F]	30[E]	60	60	120[B]
5. Assembly and recreation:				not permitted
– not sprinklered	60	60	90	
– sprinklered[F]	30[E]	60	60	120[B]
6. Industrial:				not permitted
– not sprinklered	60	90	120	
– sprinklered[F]	30[E]	60	90	120[B]
7. Storage & other non-residential:				
a. any building or part not described elsewhere				not permitted
– not sprinklered	60	90	120	
– sprinklered[F]	30[E]	60	90	120[B]
b. car park for light vehicles:				
i. open-sided park[G]	15[CE]	15[C]	15[C]	60
ii. any other park	30[E]	60	90	120[B]

Notes:

[A] Multi-storey hospitals designed in accordance with the NHS Firecode documents should have a minimum 60 minutes standard.

[B] Reduced to 90 minutes for elements not forming part of the structural frame.

[C] Increased to 30 minutes for elements protecting the means of escape.

[D] Refer to 7.12 of the Approved Document regarding the acceptability of 30 minutes in flat conversions.

[E] Increased to a minimum of 60 minutes for compartment walls separating buildings.

[F] 'Sprinklered' means that the building is fitted throughout with an automatic sprinkler system meeting the relevant recommendations of *BS5306: Part 2*: i.e. the relevant occupancy rating together with the additional requirements for life safety.

[G] The car park should comply with the relevant provisions in the guidance on requirements B3, Section 11 of the Approved Document.

[H] Single storey buildings are subject to the periods under the heading 'not more than 5'. If they have basements the basement storeys are subject to the period appropriate to their depth.

Further reading:
Approved Document B of The Building Regulations • BS476 Fire tests on building materials and structures Parts 21-23 • BS5306 Part 2 Fire extinguishing installations and equipment on premises

- Notional designations of fire performance do not cover all the roof construction combinations considered in this Guide.

Table 7.9.5
Notional designations of roof coverings

Part i: Flat roofs covered with bitumen felt

A flat roof comprising bitumen felt should (irrespective of the felt specification) be deemed to be of designation AA if the felt is laid on a deck constructed of any of these materials:

| Deck of 6mm plywood, 12.5mm wood chipboard, 16mm (finished) T&G or 19mm (finished) plain edged timber boarding | Deck of compressed straw slab | Deck of screeded woolwool slab | Profiled fibre reinforced cement or steel deck (single or double skin) with or without fibre insulating board overlay | Profiled aluminium deck (single or double skin) with or without fibre insulating board overlay | Concrete or clay pot slab (in situ) or precast) |

and has a surface finish of:

a. bitumen-bedded stone chippings covering the whole surface to a depth of at least 12.5mm
b. bitumen-bedded tiles of a non-combustible material
c. sand and cement screed, or
d. macadam

Part ii: Pitched or flat roofs covered with fully supported material

Covering material	Supporting structure	Designation
1. Aluminium sheet 2. Copper sheet 3. Zinc sheet 4. Lead sheet 5. Mastic asphalt 6. Vitreous enamelled steel 7. Lead/tin alloy coated steel sheet 8. Zinc/aluminium alloy coated steel sheet 9. Pre-painted (coil coated) steel sheet including liquid-applied pvc coatings	1. Timber joists and: tongued and grooved boarding, or plain edged boarding	AA*
	2. Steel or timber joists with deck of: woodwool slabs, compressed straw slab, wool chipboard, fibre insulating board, or 9.5mm plywood	AA
	3. Concrete or clay pot slab (in situ or precast) or non-combustible deck of steel, aluminium, or fibre cement (with or without insulation)	AA

Notes:
* Lead sheet supported by timber joists and plain edged boarding may give a BA designation.

Further reading in the Guide:
4.9 Fire behaviour

7.10 Design for wind resistance

- Wind uplift must be considered when selecting roofing components.
- Uplift can be resisted by the dead weight of roof construction above the level where uplift acts.
- Wind uplift pressure at perimeters of a flat roof may be up to twice that in the main area of the roof.

The effects of wind on all parts of a building envelope can be significant, and the design of elements to resist them is a key task. For flat roofs, of particular significance are the wind uplift pressures that can be generated, and how the roof construction responds to these pressures. **Unit 4.10** describes the principles of the interaction of buildings and wind.

Roofs comprise a number of different components or layers, each fixed back to the roof deck or roof structure. The following areas need to be considered:

- Wind uplift for general areas of roof, together with local variations
- Roof edges
- Ballast; to prevent scour or loss from the roof.

To achieve satisfactory design, it is necessary to:

- Determine wind uplift pressure.
- Identify the critical layer where the uplift pressure will act.
- Check whether the critical layer and overlying construction has sufficient dead weight to resist the uplift pressure.
- Provide any further resistance required by means of attachment or additional dead weight.
- If relying on attachment, decide on suitable mechanical fixing or adhesion method(s), taking account of material strengths and other properties.
- If relying on additional weight, check that it will remain in place when subject to traffic and wind action.
- Finally, ensure that all components and edges are detailed to be sealed and/or secured as necessary to prevent local wind damage leading to progressive widespread damage.

Wind uplift pressure

Unit 4.10 described wind effects in general, and highlighted the need to assess wind uplift pressure. Assessment of wind pressures on buildings in the UK is normally based on the recommendations of *BSCP3: Chapter V: Part 2: 1972* and is described in **Unit 8.4**. A basic wind speed in metres/second is determined from a wind speed map (Figure 8.4.1); its magnitude depends on the building's geographical location. The speed is that of a 3-second gust likely to be exceeded on average once in 50 years at 10m above ground in open, level country.

This speed is adjusted to take account of local topography, ground 'roughness' (reflecting the presence or absence of windbreaks), building size, height above ground, and anticipated exposure life.

The resulting design wind speed may be higher or lower than the basic wind speed, with values ranging from around 25m/s for a low-rise building in a Home Counties town to 60 or 70m/s for a tall building in north-west Scotland.

The dynamic wind pressure is determined from the design wind speed and air density. It varies as the square of this speed; for the two examples just given, corresponding dynamic wind pressures are about 0.4 and 2.2–3.0 kN/m^2.

The roof wind uplift pressure for design is this pressure multiplied by the algebraic difference of external and internal pressure coefficients. The external coefficient is a function of building aspect ratio and the pitch of the roof. Where local suctions are high, as at roof edges, the coefficient may be as large as –2.0 (the minus sign indicating suction or uplift). The internal coefficient takes account of the building's 'permeability', reflecting the variation in internal uplift pressure on a roof between a building with no openings (and hence no increase in internal air pressure due to wind) and, say, a shed with a large opening on the windward face, which would experience increased internal air pressure in strong winds, adding to the external air suction on a flat roof.

Typical values of the external and internal pressure coefficients for a building of modest height in relation to width are –0.8 and +0.2 giving a net pressure coefficient of –0.8 – 0.2 = –1.0, so the average wind uplift pressure calculated on the two example building roofs would be 0.4 and 2.2–3.0 kN/m^2 respectively. Local uplift pressures at edges could be about double these average values. **Unit 8.4** gives a calculation method and worked example for wind uplift pressure.

The critical layer

The principle of the critical layer and its significance for flat roofs is introduced in **Unit 4.10**. As guidance in identifying this layer the following examples are given.

Where a solid (and also heavy) concrete deck is used, this will be the critical layer, and (provided the edges of the waterproofing membrane are sealed) such construction will not be vulnerable to wind uplift (Figure 7.10.1).

On the other hand, in the case of a warm roof constructed on a lightweight metal decking, air can pass through the decking joints. If a vapour control layer (VCL) is placed on the decking, then the VCL will be the critical layer; with no VCL the critical layer would be the overlying insulation (if it had a closed cell structure with tight joints), or even the waterproofing membrane itself (if the insulation were of

Further reading:
BSCP3: Chapter V: Part 2: 1972 Wind loads • BRE Digest 295 Stability under wind load of loose laid external roof insulation boards

Chapter	1	2	3	4	5	6	7	8	9	10	11
Contents	Introduction	History	Regulatory Methods	Principles	Surveys	Constraints & Targets	Design Selection	Calculations	Detail Design Principles	Evaluation of Design	Built-up Roofing
Page	1	19	31	45	83	95	105	165	189	217	221

© BFRC / CIRIA: Flat Roofing: Design and Good Practice. 1993

- Stone for ballast must be of sufficient size to be unaffected by wind scour.
- Loose-laid external insulation boarding must also be checked for uplift effects.
- The critical layer is where the net effects of wind uplift forces are greatest.

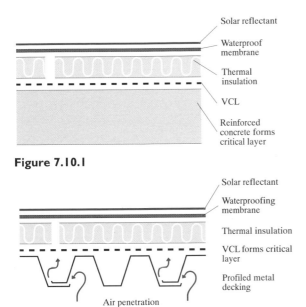

Figure 7.10.1

Figure 7.10.2

Figure 7.10.3

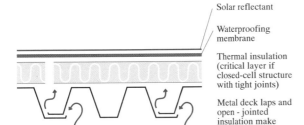

open cell structure and/or laid loose-jointed) (Figures 7.10.2, 7.10.3). Such light construction would need careful checking to safeguard the roof against wind uplift.

A particular exception to the critical layer definition, also to be checked, is the loose-laid external insulation boarding often used to improve the thermal properties of an existing roof without disturbing the waterproofing membrane. Here the wind can get under the boarding and produce uplift, especially when the boarding is not fastened through or bonded to the membrane. In such cases, even though there

may be a 'true' critical layer lower down in the roof construction, the boarding must also be checked (*BRE Digest 295* gives specific guidance on checking).

Resistance to uplift from dead weight

Unit dead weights of the critical layer and permanent overlying layers can be calculated from *BS648*. Table 8.4.6 gives useful supplementary data. The ratio of total unit dead weight to wind uplift pressure can then be calculated as a 'factor of safety' against wind uplift.

There are no standard recommendations for the appropriate factors of safety which should be used. The wind speeds used in calculations are an extreme case of that which is likely to be experienced during the life of the roof, and therefore some inherent margin exists for more frequently experienced conditions. Some judgement by the designers is required to ascertain a reasonable value. The following argument is one way of doing so.

If the factor of safety is greater than, say, 1.4, then the available dead weight is clearly sufficient on its own to resist wind uplift. If it is less than 1.0 then the weight is equally clearly insufficient on its own, so that additional measures (attachment or extra dead weight) will be needed. If the factor of safety lies between 1.0 and 1.4, judgement is needed to decide whether the construction is adequate. If, for example, the critical layer is a VCL that is to be bitumen-bonded to metal decking, then the bonding will probably suffice to give adequate resistance (this may be checked as described below). On a small roof surrounded by properly flashed upstands, there may well be adequate resistance to uplift. On the other hand, a large area of open flat roof with a unit dead weight : wind uplift pressure ratio of 1.05 should certainly be provided with additional resistance, as the margin of safety against local intense gusting is barely adequate.

Waterproof coverings of mastic asphalt are normally laid over an impermeable roof deck, such as concrete, and rely on their self-weight to resist wind uplift forces. However, should asphalt be used over an air permeable deck or in areas of extremely high exposure, they should be assessed in the manner described for adhered membranes.

Other factors than wind uplift, may also have to be considered - for example, scouring. These issues are discussed later in this unit. *continued* ▶

Critical factors

- Calculation of wind uplift.
- The greatest uplift pressures occur at roof edges.
- Each element of the roof must be adequately secured against wind effects.
- Identify critical layer.

- If the available dead weight is insufficient, further resistance may be provided by attaching upper layers physically, using mechanical fixings and/or adhesive bonding, and/or by additional dead weight such as stone ballast or paving slabs.
- Ballast for additional dead weight must be secure in wind forces or there will be a risk of damage to the roof or people and property near the roof.

Additional resistance to uplift

Additional resistance, if needed, can be provided by attaching the roof to the underlying construction – using either **mechanical fixings** or **adhesion** – and/or by **additional dead weight.** Each method is considered below in more detail.

Additional dead weight

The commonest ways of providing additional dead weight on a flat roof are by the use of ballast (gravel or crushed stone) applied overall, or by paving slabs laid locally where wind uplift forces are highest – usually near edges of the roof. Where the roof is to be paved overall, the paving weight may of course be included in the dead weight used in initial checks against uplift. If the roof is to be trafficked, paving slabs are in any event a preferable solution to ballast, which can be displaced in time, or which could damage the insulant in an inverted warm deck roof.

Ballast for roofs laid on an air impermeable structure, such as a concrete slab, will not itself be affected by wind uplift. The ballast used must be of sufficient depth to provide the necessary overall dead weight resistance to uplift: calculation is straightforward once the ballast density has been determined, in addition, the stones must be large enough to withstand being moved or even carried away by the wind. Consequences of wind 'scour' could include loss of restraining dead weight locally, leading to roof uplift; redistribution of ballast loading with consequent damage to roof structure, especially if lightweight; and, in extreme cases, stones being blown off the roof causing damage to property and even injury to people.

BRE Digest 311 offers a method of checking for wind scour, so that an adequate stone size can be specified. If this size is found to be excessive, paving slabs can be substituted where wind pressures are greatest (always at upwind corners), or alternatively a parapet can be introduced (or heightened) to provide local shelter against scour. This last alternative will not always be practical, and will of course have visual implications for the building overall; but, on the other hand, if some form of protective barrier is needed at the roof edge, then a solid parapet would fulfil this role and also reduce or even eliminate the need for extra dead weight.

Adhesive fixing

Adhesion or bonding is an attachment method traditionally used to secure built-up roofing and board insulation with a bituminous compound as the bonding agent, but is also applicable to polymeric single ply membranes. Full or partial bonding may be adopted: in the former, the bonding agent is applied as a continuous overlay, while partial bonding involves patches or strips of bonding agent between which the secured layer has to span, as it does with mechanical fixings, when subject to uplift.

The bonding agent (especially when bitumen-based) can be an effective vapour control layer, and indeed, when full-bonding is specified, care is needed to avoid the inadvertent provision of a VCL that could interfere with the intended performance of the roof. **Units 7.7** and **8.2** give further guidance on assessing VCLs.

Unlike mechanical fixings which can secure a number of layers to the anchoring layer, adhesion can bond only two adjacent layers. It is therefore usually necessary to bond adjacent layers in turn to ensure protection against uplift.

The strength of an adhesive connection between two layers depends on:

- the cleavage strength of the bonding agent itself (see Figure 7.10.4)
- the bond strength to both adjacent layers (see Figure 7.10.5)
- the laminar strength of the adjacent layers, i.e. their resistance to being torn into thinner layers (see Figure 7.10.6).

Mechanical fixings

Mechanical fixings may secure one or more layers of the roof. Because they rely on adequate anchorage over a small embedment area to withstand uplift forces, such fixings are normally secured directly into the roof deck itself rather than to relatively much weaker layers such as the insulation. 'Through' fixings will of course then restrain intermediate layers as well as the secured layer. Separate fixings may have already been used to secure lower levels of roof components.

Fixings for roofing are usually one of four types:

- Hammered, forming their own holes through the secured layer and down into the anchoring layer (usually the deck). Plain nails are suitable for anchorage in timber decks. Hardened nails can be suitable for anchoring into concrete decks. Where suitable, hammered fixings are often the cheapest and quickest solution.

Further reading:
BRE Digest 311: Wind scour of gravel ballast on roofs

Chapter	1	2	3	4	5	6	7	8	9	10	11
Contents	Introduction	History	Regulatory Methods	Principles	Surveys	Constraints & Targets	Design Selection	Calculations	Detail Design Principles	Evaluation of Design	Built-up Roofing
Page	1	19	31	45	83	95	105	165	189	217	221

- In adhesive fixed systems the lamination strength of all the components is important.

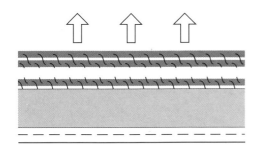

Figure 7.10.4

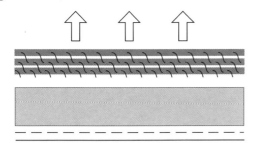

Figure 7.10.5

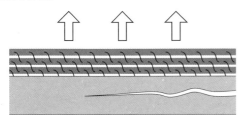

Figure 7.10.6

- The self-drilling, self-tapping, or 'drive' screw with a steep helical thread for aluminium and steel decks. This is a common choice; it develops improved withdrawal resistance by thread bearing, as if it had been secured by a nut.
- Screwed into pre-drilled holes. These are an alternative method of fixing particularly into concrete, with plastic or fibrous plugs in the holes which expand and grip the hole sides when the screws are inserted and tightened.
- Expanded into pre-drilled holes. These are often significantly stronger than screwed fixings, relying on the expansion of metal (or sometimes tough plastic) 'wings' which grip the hole sides as the fixings are tightened.

Care is needed, when installing fixings in substrates of varying strength or geometry, that the fixing is located in the appropriate location with sufficient pull-out resistance; for example in the crowns rather than the valleys of trapezoidal metal deck, or away from the voids in 'hollow pot' concrete decks.

The safe resistance of a fixing is a function of:

- pull-out resistance in the deck or other anchoring layer – influenced by fixing size, shape, embedment length, and 'grip' of the anchoring layer (see Figure 7.10.7)
- 'tear-out' resistance of the anchoring layer – influenced by the layer's splitting strength or resistance to delamination (see Figure 7.10.8)
- 'pull-through' resistance of the upper layers – influenced by their shearing and tensile strength and the size of fixing head (see Figure 7.10.9)
- compressive strength of 'weak' layers, especially the thermal insulation when it is on or near the top layer of the roof build-up (see Figure 7.10.10).

The last two considerations generally lead to the use of large-headed nails, or screws with large diameter washers.

Spacing of fixings must take account of the flexibility and strength of the secured layer(s), which have to span between the fixings when subject to wind uplift. In qualitative terms, weaker and/or thinner materials will need to be secured at close spacings, whereas stronger and/or thicker materials will be secured at wider spacings.

Fixings through the waterproofing membrane must of course be weatherproofed to prevent leakage. This can be achieved by fixing through the first layer of membrane or by detailing an overseal suitable to the membrane material.

Last but not least is the choice of material for fixings. This must be both durable and compatible with other materials; most notably in the latter regard, it is essential that metal fixings used with other metal components are chosen to avoid bimetallic corrosion.

Tables 8.4.3-8.4.6 provide some basic design data for wind uplift resistance for various fixing methods. *continued* ▶

Critical factors

- Compatibility of fixing system and membrane

Further reading in the Guide:

- The mechanical properties of all the roof components are critical to the performance of mechanical fixings.
- The wind forces will vary across the roof and will impinge upon sub-components of the roof such as rooflights.

Testing design proposals

Test facilities are available which can simulate the wind forces likely to act on a roof in service. It is therefore possible to test any proposed form of construction. One such facility is the Building Research Establishment's Real time Wind Uniform Load Follower (BRERWULF).

Other issues

Roofing edges

Special attention is required at roofing edges, verges, overhangs and fascias, for it is at these peripheral locations that local wind pressures are highest and potentially most damaging. Ideally the waterproofing covering must be both fixed down and sealed. Fixing is intended to prevent mechanical damage which, beginning as a small tear or flexing, can eventually cause major problems as the covering is ripped or 'unzipped'. Sealing prevents air getting in below the covering to produce uplift which can debond the covering and/or force it upwards over fixings, again leading to progressive failure.

Fixing of edges of built-up and membrane roofs is often achieved by metal flashings. Asphalt may be secured by keying into rebates. Metal membranes are usually held in place by nails, clips, or lapped rolls. The latter also serve the function of sealing the edge of the covering, which for other materials is achieved by bitumen-bonding or overlapping flashings.

Rooftop buildings

Rooftop buildings or obstructions such as plantrooms or penthouses can create significant local variations in wind speed and therefore wind uplift. The overall design against wind uplift using a more general wind speed should be checked at likely critical areas of the roof.

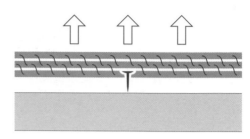

Figure 7.10.7

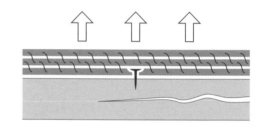

Figure 7.10.8

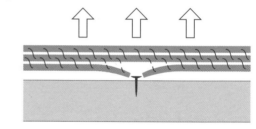

Figure 7.10.9

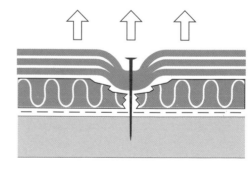

Figure 7.10.10

- The overall performance of the roof may be compromised by local deterioration of the fixing system, by water or repeated mechanical loading.

Unité d'Habitation, Marseilles, France

National Theatre, London, UK

Critical factors

- Wind pressures will be greater at roof edges or other localised areas.
- Rooflights need special consideration.
- Long-term performance.

Rooflights

When rooflights or hatches are incorporated in a flat roof, they will be subject to internal pressure and their means of attachment should be designed accordingly. It is part of the more general need to understand how the performance of each layer or component of a roof system can affect the performance of the whole roof.

Rooflights can also be subject to strong wind forces when opened into the wind. The design of the restraints and supporting structure will need to resist the forces encountered.

Uplift resistance with time

Once the integrity of the fixing system deteriorates, perhaps locally, the whole roof may become more vulnerable to further deterioration. Deterioration will occur if a loose membrane acts as a sail. Or perhaps air infiltration leads to high internal pressures. In the longer term, water ingress or condensation could affect the ability of the roof construction to resist uplift. In extreme cases, deterioration of the roof deck or structure, such as rotting of a timber deck, could reduce its fixing capability. The roof design should therefore be assessed for robustness to deterioration. ■

Heathrow Airport, London, UK

Further reading in the Guide:

7.11 Design for traffic and load spreading

- The source and intensity of local loading must be identified.
- Load intensity on individual roof components is calculated, allowing for load dispersion.
- The components' resistance to local load must be assessed:
  - considering both strength and stiffness
  - to avoid both failure of the component itself and harmful effects on other components receiving support from it.

Estimations of the need for load spreading on flat roofs is needed only where load intensity is high in relation to the strength and stiffness of the roof components. Excessive loading can cause failure of all or part of the roof construction by:

- loading beyond the structural capacity of the roof deck and/or underlying structure, leading to excessive deflection, over-stressing, or even collapse. Avoiding this is the responsibility of the roof structure's designer (see **Unit 4.3**).
- 'punching-through' or puncturing of a roof component (especially the membrane or insulation) leading to water ingress, saturation of underlying components, etc.
- 'squashing' or indentation of a roof component (especially asphalt or insulation) with a consequent risk of local ponding, reduced thermal insulating performance locally, and possible failure by tearing of the membrane and other components.

BS6399: Part 3 gives design imposed loads for two categories of roof: those with no access except for cleaning and repair of the roof; those with access in addition to this. The more general requirements for designing to accommodate traffic on roofs should, however, not be ignored. **Unit 4.11** gives some of the principles which affect the consideration of design for roof traffic.

Approach to design

There is no general or codified approach to the assessment of requirements for load spreading on flat roofs. The approach outlined in this unit is based on the approach in *BS5400: Part 2:* and Department of Transport Departmental Standard *BD21/84*, which are intended to deal with vehicular loads, load dispersion, and assessment of load effects on bridges. In addition, criterion for the resistance of roof membranes and insulation under concentrated loading are not universally agreed. The recommendations in particular manufacturers' literature should be observed (or their technical advice sought when this is unavailable). The guidance below is, however, intended to be generally applicable.

Sources of concentrated loading (see **Unit 4.11**) include:

- Foot traffic
- Vehicles
- Bases or supports to roof-mounted equipment, such as air handling plant
- Roof features such as planter boxes, safety barriers, flagpoles, etc.
- Later additions such as temporary buildings.

It is desirable wherever possible to create a load path to the roof deck/structure, without loading the roof build-up, to support all permanent features directly on the structural deck. This is essential when the features need to be anchored down securely (safety barriers, flagpoles, etc.), but is also preferable for other features such as plinths or planter boxes, etc. This approach ensures that the overlying (and more vulnerable) components, such as the membrane and insulation, are not loaded, and there is therefore no requirement for calculations of local loading effects above the structural deck. It is of course then necessary to consider weathering and thermal insulation at such projections.

Clearly this approach is not applicable for vehicle traffic or (usually) for the addition of features to a roof already built.

Loads through finishes

Where the imposed loads must be transmitted through roof finishes there may opportunities to use load spreading methods which are well established and can hence be termed 'standard solutions'. Many other design solutions require more specific calculation of the likely effects of imposed loads.

'Standard' solutions

Such solutions should be supported by a code of practice or reliable product data (notably an Agrément Certificate), and subject to well-defined loading such as pedestrian access and car traffic. Examples of such solutions are:

- Mastic asphalt subject to foot traffic or used in a roofing car park – provide the appropriate wearing course (based on *BSCP144: Part 4*).
- Built-up bitumen felt subject to continuous foot traffic – provide bitumen macadam, bonded tiles, or a cement screed (based on *BSCP144: Part 3*)

'Calculated' solutions

When 'standard solutions are not appropriate, some calculation or estimation is required of the effects of the imposed loadings on the roof build-up.

The assessments involve three stages:

- Determine loading at point of application on roof.
- Disperse loading through roof to establish loading intensity or critical component(s).
- Determine capacity of roof component(s) and compare with load intensity.

If the component capacity is inadequate, then mitigating measures must be adopted.

Further reading:
BSCP144 Roof coverings Part 3: 1970 Built-up bitumen felt. Part 4: 1970 Mastic asphalt • BS648: 1964 Schedule of weights of building materials • BS5400: Steel, concrete, and composite bridges Part 2: 1978 Specification for loads • BS6399: Loading for buildings Part 1: 1984 Dead and live loads; Part 3: 1988 Imposed roof loads • DTp Departmental Standard BD21/84 The assessment of highway bridges and structures.

Chapter	1	2	3	4	5	6	7	8	9	10	11
Contents	Introduction	History	Regulatory Methods	Principles	Surveys	Constraints & Targets	Design Selection	Calculations	Detail Design Principles	Evaluation of Design	Built-up Roofing
Page	1	19	31	45	83	95	105	165	189	217	221

- If the resistance of a component is inadequate, then other measures will be necessary, such as surface spreaders or delivering loads directly to the structural deck.

- Guidance on loads encountered is available from various sources but not for approaches to assessment.

Load determination

Minimum loads

BS6399: Part 3 recommends as a minimum an allowance for a concentrated load of 1.8kN on roofs where access is provided (other than for maintenance), or 0.9kN minimum where access is for maintenance only. These loads should be considered as acting on a 125mm square patch for checking roof coverings. (If the roof is to have access for specific usage, then the relevant concentrated loads given in *BS6399: Part 1* should be used if higher than those in *BS6399: Part 3*.)

The 'patch' area clearly does not represent a worst case loading intensity such as may arise from the wearing of spiked running shoes, stiletto heels, etc., nor from items with heavily-loaded small bases (e.g. balcony loungers). Such possibilities demand the use of a protective overlay to guard against puncturing or indentation of membrane or insulation: calculations are superfluous, but as an indication it may be noted that contact pressures of 5-10 N/mm^2 are very likely under such footwear–substantially above the capacity of most roofing membranes and insulation materials! Other 'temporary' loads may also be significant–supports of maintenance scaffold for example.

Vehicle loading

Values for vehicle loading may be taken from Department of Transport Departmental Standard *BD21/84*, 'The assessment of highway bridges and structures', as amended 1989. The critical case for roof components will be the single wheel load, which is given in *BD21/84* as in Table 7.11.1.

The single wheel load is taken to be from a tyre inflated at a pressure of 1.1 N/mm^2, and the contact area is taken to be a square or circular patch for calculating local effects. Thus, for a car, the 25kN single wheel load acts on a contact area of 150mm square or 170mm diameter. ('Real' car tyre pressures are of course substantially lower, resulting in reduced load intensity in practice.)

Table 7.11.1
Single wheel loads (based on BD21/84).

Vehicle gross weight (tonnes)	Nominal single Wheel load (kN)
Cars and vans (not exceeding 3)	25
Vehicles generally (3 up to 7.5)	50
Vehicles generally (7.5 up to 40)	100
Fire engines (up to 60kN nominal axle load)	30
Fire engines (up to 120kN axle load)	60

Other concentrated loads

Other loading should be derived from manufacturers' data (for plant and other proprietary items) or by calculation of weight (e.g. for planter boxes). *BS648* gives useful information on component weights. Weight should be divided by contact area to give loading intensity on the roof surface.

Load dispersion

A load applied to the roof surface will be dispersed over a larger area as it spreads down to lower components. *BS5400: Part 2:* gives useful guidance on dispersion, incorporated in the following recommendations:

- Dispersion through asphalt and other non-structural materials (including rigid insulation) can be taken at the rate of 1 unit horizontally in 2 units vertically (i.e. at 26.5° to the vertical).
- Dispersion through structural slabs (including concrete, cement screeds, tiles, and stone paving) can be taken at the rate of 1 in 1, i.e. at 45°.
- No dispersion should be assumed through loose materials (such as stone chippings) or across un-linked joints (e.g. between tiles).

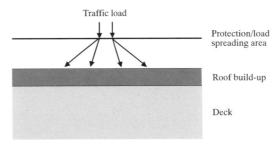

Figure 7.11.1
Load spreading through overlays

Capacity of roof components

Having worked out the load intensity on the top surface of a component, this must now be compared with the component's resistance to puncturing or indentation. This is a property of the particular material, and may also be dependent on the duration of load (many roofing materials will 'creep' under sustained loads). *continued* ▶

Further reading in the Guide:
4.3 Structure and movement • 4.11 Traffic on roofs • 7.4 Design for drainage capacity • 17.2 Insulants: materials

- Some information is available in this Guide for the behaviour of materials under load. Other data should be sought from specific manufacturers.
- The most susceptible of all the layers in the roof build-up will determine the precautions required.

Membranes

- **Paving grade mastic asphalt** (to *BS1446* or *BS1447*) is regarded as capable of supporting a contact pressure of $1.1N/mm^2$, the *BS5400* notional tyre pressure for all road vehicles. However, sustained loading at even low load intensities – and especially in hot weather – will induce 'creep' in the asphalt leading to surface rippling or indentation. Subsequent traffic over such local distortion may, in the long term, lead to failure of the wearing surface. For long-term heavy vehicle parking, an overlay above the asphalt is one way to obviate this problem (see Overlays below).
- **Waterproofing grade mastic asphalt** (to *BS6577* or *BS6925*) can withstand high pressures – when it is fully confined to prevent extrusion. Its capacity when not confined is limited (according to *BS8102*) to $0.65 N/mm^2$. The presence of a finishing coat over the waterproofing asphalt will provide a degree of confinement sufficient to accommodate $1.1N/mm^2$ contact pressure, but this would not be the case if, for example, small tiles were bedded directly onto the waterproofing asphalt: here it is likely that a heavy vehicle would produce a load intensity sufficient to press the tiles into the asphalt. Such a construction build-up is, of course, not recommended.
- **Built-up roofing**, when subject to any loads in excess of normal maintenance traffic, should be protected by an overlay or spreaders. The membrane's resistance to concentrated loading should be established from manufacturer's data but, in the absence of other guidance, the values in *BS8102* can be used. *BS8102* recommends a limit of $0.05N/mm$ for the form of bitumen sheeting as used in damp-proof courses. (Note that this is a very low value compared with the contact pressures quoted above but is also similar in magnitude to the pressure under a human foot – not stiletto heeled.)
- **Metal roof coverings** (lead, copper, etc.) have some resistance to local loading, but unprotected should be limited to maintenance foot traffic. The limiting factor may well be the underlying roof component which – being under a thin flexible metal sheet – is subject to virtually the same load intensity as the metal. Any resulting deformation of the underlay material may distort the metal, leading possibly to accelerated wear and premature failure. Loadings at joints present other difficulties. Particular care is needed that damage to standing seams does not occur.

Other roof coverings should be checked, using strength and creep deformation data provided by the supplier or manufacturer.

Bon Accord, Aberdeen, UK

Insulation

Lightweight board and sheet insulation used in flat roofs has a crushing strength typically in the range $100-700kPa$. This is determined using Test Method No.3 in *BS4370: Part 1*, in which the crushing strength under short-term loading is reported at a strain of 10%, unless crushing has already occurred at a lesser strain. 10% strain means that the sample has compressed by one-tenth of its thickness (e.g. 50mm thick insulation sheet would be only 45mm thick at failure). Such large deformations under local load concentrations might be potentially damaging to coverings in a warm deck roof, but might be acceptable on an inverted roof. Foot traffic for a ballasted roof of this type is likely to produce some local crushing whenever stones are trodden down. Where frequent or heavy traffic is expected, concrete paviours are the preferred finish.

Many insulation manufacturers give recommendations in their literature for limiting pressures on their insulating products. Typically, this might be one-third of the crushing strength for short-term loads and one-fifth for long-term loads; the reduced long-term capacity allows for creep deformation, which is a characteristic of most board insulation products. Thus a board with a crushing strength of $0.3N/mm^2$ at 10% strain may be taken as having a long-term capacity under concentrated loading of $0.06Nmm^2$. The compression under such a load will not in the long term exceed 2%, and in the short term may be very much less. Manufacturers' data on apparent modulus of elasticity for compressive loading is not always available, and in any event is of little relevance since creep effects are so prominent.

For insulating boards on **profiled metal decking**, some manufacturers give recommendations on minimum board thickness related to decking trough width. This is to guard

Further reading:
BS 1446 • BS1447: Specification(s) for mastic asphalt • BS4370: Methods of test for rigid cellular materials • BS5328: Concrete • BS6577: Specification for mastic asphalt for building • BS6677: Clay and calcium silicate pavers for flexible pavements • BS6717 Precast paving blocks • BS6925: Specification for mastic asphalt for building and civil engineering • BS7263: Precast concrete flags, kerbs, channels, edgings and quadrants • BS8102 • BS8204.

- Other factors than direct loading will be important for the roof performance and safety of use. These include:
  - Roof zone depth
  - Drainage
  - Slip resistance
  - Penetration details and guard rails.

---

against 'slumping' of the insulation and membrane into a connected profile reflecting the decking shape, leading possibly to premature failure of the membrane; but this is not a direct consequence of applied loads (see **Unit 17.1**).

Denser insulating materials, such as **'lightweight' cementitious and bituminous screeds**, can have low crushing strengths as compared with concrete. It may therefore be necessary to check these, especially where only a thin membrane is laid over the insulation and load intensities are high. Crushing strengths of 2-5N/mm^2 are typical (refer to manufacturers' data for proprietary screed systems), and long-term load intensity should not exceed about one-third of this crushing strength.

Vapour control layers (VCL)

The VCL (if present) is almost invariably stronger and stiffer than the overlying insulation, and – allowing for load dispersion through the relatively thick insulating material – is unlikely to be the weakest layer in the roof construction.

Structural deck

The structural deck itself (and any non-structural falls) may also need to be checked. Particular attention may be needed for timber-based board and sheet, woodwool, metal decking, and hollow infill blocks used between precast or in situ roof joists or ribs.

Checking roof adequacy

The load intensity on a roof component should be compared with its capacity. This should be done for each of the possibly critical components (typically membrane and insulation).

If the capacity is inadequate, then some form of mitigating measure is necessary.

Mitigating measures

Options include:

- Support loads directly from structural deck, including using raised walkways, with detailing to maintain integrity of weatherproofing and thermal/acoustic insulation.
- Upgrade the roof build-up locally, e.g. by increasing the thickness of an adequately strong component above a weaker one (e.g. board insulation) to disperse the load over a larger area, and hence reduce its intensity on arrival at the top surface of the weaker component. A similar approach on a trafficked roof would increase the thickness of the stronger paving grade asphalt over the weaker waterproofing grade asphalt.
- Provide an overlay.

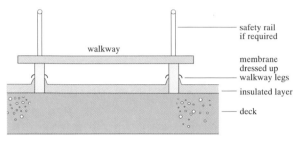

Figure 7.11.2
Traffic walkway to take loads direct to deck

Overlays

Overlays generally comprise a rigid sheet or rigid units such as:

- Thin fibre cement tiles bedded onto the membrane. These are generally only suitable for foot-trafficked areas. Such tiles are vulnerable to impact (such as wheel loads) and have low resistance to heavy point loads.
- Fired-clay or calcium silicate bricks or precast concrete paving blocks designed to function as a flexible or rigid pavement, depending on the underlying roof construction.

Relevant codes of practice for such units and their design are:

- *BS6677* for clay and calcium silicate pavers for flexible pavements.
- *BS6717* for precast concrete paving blocks.
- *BS7263* for precast concrete flags (and often roadway units), of sizes up to 600 by 900mm.

Thickness of these units is typically 50–75mm. Guidance is given in these codes on suitability for use where subject to light and heavy vehicle traffic, to assist choice of thickness related to size and resistance to fracture under wheel loads. A compatible roof construction must be adopted to suit the design assumptions for paving behaviour, i.e. 'flexible' or 'rigid'.

- Natural stone flags laid on a bedding layer or isolated supports. (At present, there is no code of practice: advice on satisfactory performance should be sought from suppliers of the particular stone.)
- In-situ concrete laid in panels, with sealed joints to allow thermal movements. The design of the concrete for durability considerations is covered by *BS5328*. Advice on thickness and bay sizes can be found in *BS8204 Part 2*.

continued ▶

Critical factors

- Compressibility of materials under static or sustained loads.

Further reading in the Guide:
4.3 Structure and movement • 4.11 Traffic on roofs • 7.4 Design for drainage capacity • 17.2 Insulants: materials

Other considerations

Roof zone depth

The combination of roof deck, insulant and membrane will influence the overall requirements for overlays and protection. Roof zone depth requirements may influence the selection of overlays and protection.

Drainage

Local layers of an overlay, such as walkway tiles, may interfere with the preferred drainage arrangement for the roof. Similarly an overall protection layer of, say, a concrete slab may restrict water flow at the membrane level. This may, therefore, require drainage at two levels (see **Unit 7.4**). Where, to improve drainage, paviours are supported on pads or mortar dabs, the local load under the support should be assessed.

Slip resistance

Unit 4.11 described some principles which govern the slip resistance of traffic surfaces. This can be an important safety issue for roofs. Some general conclusions are possible in that smooth, impervious, surfaces are more likely to be slippery, when wet, compared to rough open textured ones. These differences can be seen within materials types, e.g. terrazzo is likely to be more slippery than rougher concrete paviours. The long-term retention of slip resistance is important as this can be reduced by polishing, ice formation, or mould/algae growth.

Penetration details

To provide safe access for pedestrians it is often necessary to provide handrails/guard rails. The location and detailing of such items, because they are likely to penetrate the membrane, needs careful thought.

Approach to a calculation method

Because of the lack of clarity in available guidance, a suggestion is presented here of an approach to calculating the effects of a local load on a typical warm roof, with exposed membrane. The numerical values given are assumed for the convenience of the example. A designer should ensure that the values used for a particular roof are appropriate for the actual materials to be incorporated. As noted earlier in this unit it is preferred to transmit imposed loads directly to the structure beneath without loading the roof build-up. This approach to calculation should only be used where this is not possible.

It is proposed to add a water tank, to be placed on the roof.

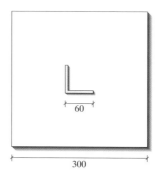

Figure 7.11.3
Steel angle and possible spreader

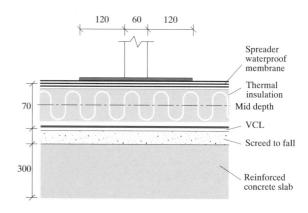

Figure 7.11.4
Section through spreader and roof system

It exerts a load of 2.5 tonnes (including any wind effects), and is supported on four equally-loaded legs, each being a steel angle of section $60 \times 60 \times 6$ mm (see Figure 7.11.3). A structural check shows that the roof structure can support this load; it is necessary to review ways of dealing with the local concentrated load effects on the roof build-up. A warm sandwich roof is assumed to have the following schematic construction (see Figure 7.11.4):

- Three layers of bituminous felt (capacity under compressive load $0.15N/mm^2$); on
- 70mm insulation material (rigid sheet with compressive strength $0.5N/mm^2$ at 10% strain); on

- bituminous felt vapour control layer; on
- lightweight screed laid to falls (compressive strength 2N/mm^2); on
- an in-situ reinforced concrete slab.

Water tank loading may be assumed static, so no dynamic enhancement of loading is necessary. (The equivalent static loads from plant with rotating or other moving components may be twice the plant self-weight or more. Use of anti-vibration mountings or other measures can reduce this magnification factor to perhaps 1.2 times plant self-weight; advice should be sought from a mechanical engineer and/or the plant manufacturer.)

$$2.5 \text{ tonnes} = 2500 \text{ kg},$$
i.e. a weight of $2500 \times 9.81 = 24\,520\text{N}$.
So the force in each leg is $0.25 \times 24\,520 = 6130\text{N}$.

The contact stress under the angle leg (steel area 6.95cm^2) is $6130/695 = 8.8\text{N/mm}^2$. This is greatly above the puncture resistance of bituminous felts (by inspection), and equally will assure failure of the insulation; the legs would slice through the bituminous felt, the insulation, the vapour barrier – and probably the lightweight screed also – before bearing against the concrete slab top surface. Hence measures are needed to spread the loads.

Obvious solutions include:

- Provide upstands in concrete built off the roof slab, and detail the roof construction to ensure weathertightness.
- Provide spreaders under the legs to reduce load intensity on the roofing.

The first option provides a more secure support for the tank, and is normally essential for any item of plant subject to dynamic loads, to prevent it 'wandering' across the roof in use. The second option can be suitable for static items – provided these are stable under wind load, requiring no anchorage to hold them down.

Considering the use of spreaders, it appears that (with a thin felt weatherproofing membrane) the underlying insulation is going to be critical as far as local load intensity is concerned, since there is negligible load dispersion through the felt.

The loading is long-term, so it is appropriate to consider a capacity (for direct load on the top of the insulation) of one-fifth the compressive strength, i.e. in the example used here, $0.2 \times 0.5 = 0.1\text{N/mm}^2$. (Note that this is less than the capacity of the felt membrane, which confirms that the insulation is a more critical component for local loading.) This insulation capacity is associated with a long-term compression strain in the insulation not exceeding 2%. (In reality, load dispersion will reduce load intensity on the underlying insulation material, and hence the compression, as will be shown.) 2% $\times$ 70mm is 1.4mm, which is a surface indentation that is judged unlikely to affect the weather-tightness performance of a three-layer bituminous felt.

Sizing a base spreader to keep the load intensity on its underside at 0.1N/mm^2 under a load of 6130N, the required contact area is not less than $6130/0.1 = 61300$ mm^2, so a square spreader would need a side of at least 247.6 (say 300)mm. The spreader plate thickness would have to give adequate stiffness to spread the load uniformly – for steel, a rule-of-thumb thickness of one-tenth of the clear projection will suffice. The clear projection is one half of the plate length minus the width of the angle support i.e. $(300-60) \times 0.5 = 120\text{mm}$. Therefore the thickness of a square plate would be 120 mm $\div$ 10 = 12mm.

The actual contact pressure under a 300mm square plate would be $6130/(300)^2 = 0.068 \text{ N/mm}^2$ at the top of the insulation; at mid-depth, allowing a 1 in 2 dispersion through the insulation, and neglecting the thickness of the membrane, the loaded area of insulation is $(300 + (2 \times 0.5 \times 35))^2 = 335^2 = 112\,225 \text{ mm}^2$.
So the average compression on the insulation is $6130/112\,225 = 0.055\text{N/mm}^2$ with a corresponding average compression of 2% $\times (0.055/0.1) = 1.09\%$.

On 70mm this represents $1.09 \times 70/100 = 0.76$ mm, which is unlikely to cause distress to the bituminous felt membrane.
The contact pressure at the vapour control layer is here acting over an area of $(300 + (2 \times 0.5 \times 70))^2$ $= 136\,900\text{mm}^2$.

The pressure is therefore $6130/136\,900 = 0.045 \text{ N/mm}^2$ which is acceptable for the most compressible materials, such as a bituminous material with an unconfined bearing capacity of 0.05 N/mm^2 (taken from guidance in *BS8102*) and certainly acceptable for e.g. polythene sheet.
The same contact pressure is acceptable on the lightweight screed under the vapour control layer, for which the safe load intensity is one-third its crushing strength (2N/mm^2), i.e. 0.67 N/mm^2. ■

Critical factors

Further reading in the Guide:

7.12 Design for maintenance

- The design both for new and for replacement roofs and, as far as possible, for the detailing of repairs, should take into consideration the future maintenance and repair of the roof system, and their ease of operation.
- The brief for the building should acknowledge the anticipated life of components. Life-cycle costing should be carried out to assist the design selection process.

Maintenance

Although often not thought of as part of design, consideration of maintenance requirements at the time of initial design is essential. Consideration of maintenance requirements may, however, modify the otherwise preferred design. Flat roof systems and materials will have varying expected lengths of life. It can be expected that the roof finish will require possible replacement and certainly attention during the life of the building.

Where possible, the design should take into consideration what will be required initially to reduce and then to assist (and simplify) the future maintenance and repair of the complete roof installation:

- Good access should be provided to the roof area for personnel, materials and equipment and, at ground level, around the perimeter of the building for placing external scaffolds.
- Removable/replaceable components to allow inspection and repair (e.g. flashings, copings, cappings).
- Details at junctions with adjoining materials that allow the roof to be replaced without wholesale reconstruction of the adjacent building fabric.
- Detailing at pedestals, upstands, balustrades, parapets, penetrations, rooflights, etc., that enable repair and allow for the possible future replacement of the roof system by the application of another system on top.
- Roof-mounted plant, equipment, window cleaning equipment, etc., should be designed with clearance underneath to allow for inspection and repair.
- Roof plan and detailing should be rationalised at:
  - junctions
  - movement joints
  - upstands and skirtings
  - parapets, eaves, verges
  - flank walls, abutments
  - roof heights
  - services penetrations
  - plant and equipment
  - balustrades
  - flashings, drips
  - outlets
  - gutters.

Roof terrace, Arab World Institute, Paris, France

- Adequate distances around and between penetrations, roof-mounted plant or buildings should be provided to give accessibility for repair.
- Protection to the component parts of the roof system from damage by:
  - wind
  - sunlight
  - frost
  - ponding
  - sulphate attack
  - discharge of hot or treated water
  - discharge of chemicals or airborne grease
  - polluted environments
  - physical damage, foot traffic, ladders
  - plant roofs
  - leaves and debris
  - fire or heat
  - contractors' and subcontractors' equipment, whether or not associated with roof construction operations
  - spillages from site operations (e.g. oil).

Particular attention should be given to those areas of membrane that will be inaccessible in the future, for example:
- under hard terraces
- under garden roofs
- under areas hidden by equipment.

Consideration should be given to provision of power supply and water supply at roof level, for future maintenance or repair works. This supply may need special control, to prevent unauthorised use.

Further reading:
BICKERDIKE ALLEN PARTNERS Flat Roof Manual

Chapter	1	2	3	4	5	6	7	8	9	10	11
Contents	Introduction	History	Regulatory Methods	Principles	Surveys	Constraints & Targets	Design Selection	Calculations	Detail Design Principles	Evaluation of Design	Built-up Roofing
Page	*1*	*19*	*31*	*45*	*83*	*95*	*105*	*165*	*189*	*217*	*221*

- Consideration should be given to providing power and water supply supply at roof level for subsequent maintenance.
- Guidance here covers a comprehensive range of advice, from which those responsible may select according to need and terms of appointment.

To anticipate maintenance

The majority of building owners and tenants have been unlikely to consider the roof of their building until a failure occurs. They should be encouraged to institute planned maintenance.

The owner should be well advised during the design process and given comprehensive maintenance documentation following completion. New owners of existing buildings should be encouraged to establish whether such documentation, and associated records, still exist.

In the decision-making process of new building, refurbishment, and even repair, analysis of life-cycle cost should be undertaken (see **Unit 4.15**). The following should be considered:
- anticipated building life or remaining life
- anticipated roof life following installation or repair
- maintenance costs.

These factors cannot be considered in isolation. The occupier of the building must consider their own circumstances:
- are they the owner/occupier?
- are they a tenant?
- who will pay for the work?
- how long has the lease to run?
- does the cost exceed the residual value?
- is the work considered an improvement?

Maintenance implications of roof systems

All systems have their advantages and disadvantages in relation to potential maintenance problems.

Cold deck roof:
- Potentially inadequate support to vapour control layer (VCL).
- Structural deck is at risk of degradation from condensation if VCL penetrated or void ventilation blocked or inadequate.
- Roof finish may be subject to extremes of temperature.
- Roof finish may be subject to physical damage.
- It can be simply inspected, repaired and replaced, (on a like-for-like basis).
- Solar protection can degrade or be disturbed.

Niemeyer House, Rio de Janiero, Brazil

Warm deck roof:
- Roof finish is vulnerable to physical damage, particularly if the underlying insulation is compressible.
- VCL is usually fully supported.
- It can be simply inspected, repaired or replaced, (on a like-for-like basis).
- Roof finish may be subject to extremes of temperature.
- Solar protection can degrade or be disturbed.

Inverted warm deck roof:
- Roof finish is protected from physical damage and solar effects.
- Roof finish is not subject to stresses imposed by movement in insulation.
- Inspection of the roof and minor repairs are complicated by the requirement to lift the ballast layer and any geotextile filter layer. ■

Further reading in the Guide:
4.15 Environmental impact of materials • 20.1 Inspection of the works • 21.1 Planned maintenance • 21.2 Diagnosing defects and remedies

12 Mastic Asphalt	13 Polymeric Single Ply	14 Copper	15 Lead Sheet	16 Other Membranes	17 Thermal Insulants	18 Specification	19 Contracts & Procurement	20 Inspection	21 Maintenance	22 Bibliography	23 Index
263	301	331	353	375	383	393	399	413	429	437	455

Calculations   8

Special Note: *The guidance provided in this Guide assumes that the roof will be exposed to typical UK climatic conditions. Care should be taken for other locations where different conditions may apply.*

- Calculation of roof drainage is essential to ensure removal of rainwater from the roof.
- Inadequate design can lead to water penetration into the building or in extreme cases structural failure of the roof deck.

Calculation of flat roof drainage

The following information is based on the recommendations of *BS6367*.

Whether a roof is to be drained to internal outlets, to chutes and hopper heads, or to eaves gutters, the first stage is to calculate the maximum rate at which water will have to be discharged from that roof. The procedure is as follows:

1 Determine the design rate of rainfall (from meteorological data).
2 Calculate the effective catchment area of the roof.
3 Calculate the rate at which rainwater discharges from the roof (at the design rate of rainfall).

These calculations are carried out assuming that all roof surfaces are impermeable.

Step 1: Determine the design rate of rainfall (I)
The roof drainage system should be able to cope with the design rate of rainfall without overflowing. *BS6367* suggests that a rate of rainfall of 75mm/hour will usually be a satisfactory basis for calculation, although, in some parts of the UK, systems designed for 75mm/hour may surcharge twice a year (Figure 8.1.1). Using a design rate of rainfall of 150mm/hour will reduce the probability of overflow to once every 5 years (Figure 8.1.2). Where outlets are not kept clear the overflow risk will be more frequent.

Drainage systems should be designed so that, should they surcharge, no unacceptable damage will result.

Most flat roofs can accommodate short periods of excess rain provided:

- There is no risk of damage to the structure.
- Outlets are kept clean.
- Waterproof upstands are provided (as recommended in this Unit).
- Consideration is given to discharging overflow through the parapet.

Appendix A of *BS6367* gives further information and recommendations on the selection of an appropriate design rate of rainfall to meet specific levels of risk. The Meteorological Office Advisory Service is able to provide advice on rainfall intensity and storm profiles for a particular area.

Step 2: Calculate the effective catchment area (A_e)
The water to be drained from any flat roof includes that

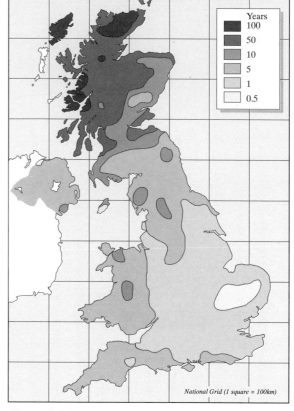

Figure 8.1.1
Period in years between rainfall events of 75mm/hour for 2 minutes

falling directly onto the roof - including the parapets - and that which drains onto it from other roofs and/or adjacent walls.

The effective catchment area is therefore calculated by adding together the various component catchment areas:

- The catchment area of a flat roof is the plan area of the roof including any parapets.
- The catchment area of a sloping roof is equal to the plan area of the roof plus half the maximum area in elevation.
- For a wall the effective catchment area should be taken as half the exposed vertical area of the wall.

Further reading:
BS6367: Drainage of roofs and paved areas

• Calculations use statistical data of likely rainfall and assumptions about water flow characteristics of roofs.

Step 3: Calculate the rate of discharge from the roof (Q)
The rate at which water discharges from the roof at the design rate of rainfall should be calculated using the following formula:

$$Q = \frac{A_e \, I}{3600} \text{ litres/sec.}$$

where: A_e is the effective catchment area (in m²); and

I is the design rate of rainfall (in mm/hour).

Worked example of rainwater runoff

Calculate the rate of run-off Q from the roof shown in Figure 8.1.3.

Step 1: Determine the design rate of rainfall
No serious damage will occur if the drainage system infrequently overflows; a design rate of rainfall of 75mm/hour can therefore be assumed.

Therefore I = 75mm/hour

Step 2: Calculate the effective catchment area (A_e)
Catchment area A_1 = the plan area of the roof

$$A_1 = 24 \times 5.4 = 129.6 \text{ m}^2$$

Catchment area A_2 = the plan area of the roof plus half the maximum area in elevation

$$A_2 = (24 \times 3) + \frac{(24 \times 3.5)}{2} = 114 \text{ m}^2$$

Catchment area A_3 = half the exposed vertical area

$$A_3 = \frac{(5.4 \times 3.5)}{2} + \frac{(3 \times 3.5)}{4} = 12.07 \text{ m}^2$$

The effective catchment area is the sum of the individual catchment areas.

$$A_e = A_1 + A_2 + A_3$$
$$= 129.6 + 114 + 12.07$$
$$= 255.67 \text{ m}^2$$

Step 3: Calculate the rate of discharges from the roof (Q)
The run-off rate Q in litres per second.

$$Q = \frac{I \times A_e}{3600} = \frac{255.67 \times 75}{3600} = 5.33 \text{ litres/sec.}$$

The next stage is to ensure that the drainage system of a given area of roof can cope with the rate of run-off Q. To achieve this select the outlet(s) from tables 8.1.1 – 8.1.6.

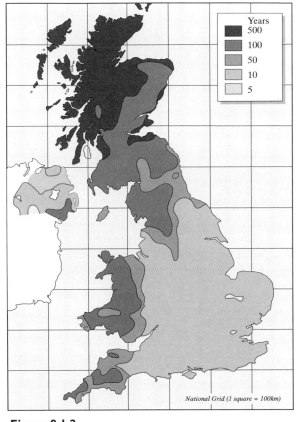

Figure 8.1.2
Period in years between rainfall events of 150mm/hour for 2 minutes

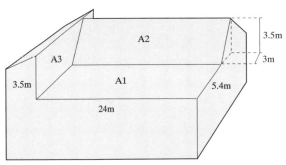

Figure 8.1.3
Calculate the rate of run-off (Q) from the roof shown

continued ▶

Critical factors

• Peak rainfall.
• Frequency of overflow of drainage systems.
• Limitation of drainage by overflows.

Further reading in the Guide:
4.4 Precipitation: rain and snow • 7.4 Design for drainage capacity

- Outlet capacity can be determined from Tables in this Guide, from manufacturers, or British Standards.

Table 8.1.1
Flow capacity (litres/sec.) of outlets, with gravel guard having 75% of circumference open

pipe dia. (mm)	Head of water (mm)													
	5	10	15	20	25	30	35	40	50	60	70	80	90	100
65	0.06	0.21	0.38	0.56	0.79	1.04	1.31	1.60	2.00	2.19	2.35	2.52	2.67	2.81
75	0.08	0.23	0.44	0.67	0.92	1.21	1.52	1.85	2.60	2.90	3.15	3.35	3.56	3.75
100	0.10	0.31	0.56	0.88	1.23	1.60	2.04	2.48	3.48	4.56	5.58	5.96	6.33	6.67
150	0.17	0.46	0.85	1.31	1.83	2.42	3.04	3.73	5.21	6.85	8.63	10.54	12.58	14.73

Height of slots to exceed head of water

pipe diameter

Table 8.1.2
Flow capacity (litres/sec.) of tapered outlets, with gravel guard having 75% of circumference open

pipe dia. (mm)	Head of water (mm)													
	5	10	15	20	25	30	35	40	50	60	70	80	90	100
65	0.10	0.31	0.56	0.85	1.19	1.56	1.98	2.42	3.38	4.46	5.31	5.67	6.0	6.33
75	0.13	0.35	0.65	0.98	1.38	1.81	2.29	2.79	3.90	5.13	6.64	7.90	9.44	11.04
100	0.17	0.46	0.85	1.31	1.83	2.42	3.04	3.73	5.21	6.85	8.63	10.54	12.58	14.73
150	0.25	0.71	1.29	1.98	2.77	3.63	4.58	5.58	7.81	10.27	12.94	15.81	18.85	22.08

Height of slots to exceed head of water

pipe diameter

Gravity drainage

There are three ways the water can be drained from a roof:

- to internal outlets
- through parapet walls via chutes to external hopper heads
- to eaves gutters.

Internal outlets

With this pattern of drainage, the important considerations are:

- the design depth of water (the depth to which water can be allowed to build up on the roof)
- the flow capacity of the outlets
- the dimensions of any gutters or sumps used to obtain the required flow capacity from the outlet.

It is preferable, wherever possible, to design enclosed roofs with more than one outlet. This reduces the risks of damage from an outlet blocking.

Depth of water on roof

BS6367 suggests that, on a roof laid to falls, a water depth of up to 30mm is acceptable if it is confined to relatively small areas around outlets.

Flow capacity of the outlet

Tables 8.1.1-8.1.2 give the flow capacities in litres/second of different sizes of outlets at various of heads of water.

Table 8.1.3
Flow capacity of sumps (litres/sec.)

Total perimeter of sump (mm)	Design depth of water (mm)					
	5	10	15	20	25	30
1200	0.56	1.58	2.90	4.50	6.25	8.22
1600	0.75	2.10	3.60	6.00	8.30	10.90
2000	0.93	2.60	4.85	7.46	10.42	13.70
2400	1.12	3.17	5.80	8.90	12.50	16.44
2800	1.30	3.70	6.78	10.44	14.60	19.20
3200	1.50	4.22	7.75	11.90	16.67	22.00

Table 8.1.4
Flow capacity of chutes (litres/sec.)

Width of chutes (mm)	Design depth of water (mm)					
	5	10	15	20	25	30
300	0.14	0.39	0.73	1.11	1.56	2.01
400	0.18	0.63	0.97	1.50	2.08	3.43
500	0.23	0.66	1.21	1.87	2.60	3.43
600	0.28	0.79	1.45	2.24	3.13	4.11

Outlets draining a roof directly should always be fitted with gravel guards. These flow rates are typical only and reference should be made if possible to manufacturers' information for specific outlets.

Further reading:
BS6367 Drainage of roofs and paved areas

- Flow in gutters is assumed to work under hydraulic gradients, resisted by surface friction.

Table 8.1.5
Flow capacities (litres/sec.) of standard straight drop outlet, without gravel guard

pipe dia. (mm)	Head of water (mm)													
	5	10	15	20	25	30	35	40	50	60	70	80	90	100
65	0.08	0.27	0.50	0.77	1.08	1.42	1.67	1.79	2.00	2.19	2.35	2.52	2.67	2.81
75	0.10	0.31	0.58	0.90	1.25	1.65	2.06	2.38	2.65	2.90	3.15	3.35	3.56	3.75
100	0.15	0.42	0.77	1.20	1.67	2.19	2.77	3.38	4.71	5.17	5.58	5.96	6.33	6.67
150	0.23	0.63	1.17	1.79	2.50	3.29	4.16	5.06	7.06	9.29	11.71	13.42	14.23	15.00

pipe diameter

Table 8.1.6
Flow capacity (litres/sec.) of tapered outlet, without gravel guard

pipe dia. (mm)	Head of water (mm)													
	5	10	15	20	25	30	35	40	50	60	70	80	90	100
65	0.10	0.31	0.56	0.85	1.19	1.56	1.98	2.42	3.38	4.46	5.31	5.67	6.0	6.33
75	0.13	0.35	0.65	0.98	1.38	1.81	2.29	2.79	3.90	5.13	6.64	7.90	9.44	11.04
100	0.17	0.46	0.85	1.31	1.83	2.42	3.04	3.73	5.21	6.85	8.63	10.54	12.58	14.73
150	0.25	0.71	1.29	1.98	2.77	3.63	4.58	5.58	7.81	10.27	12.94	15.81	18.85	22.08

Top diameter not to be less than 1.5 × pipe diameter

Length of taper to equal or exceed top diameter

pipe diameter

Table 8.1.7
Flow capacity of gutters

size of gutter (mm)	Capacity of nominal half-round gutters (litres/sec.)	Capacity of true half-round gutters (litres/sec.)	Minimum outlet diameter (mm)
75			
Outlet at one end	0.27	0.38	50
Outlet at centre	0.54	0.76	50
100			
Outlet at one end	0.55	0.78	65
Outlet at centre	1.10	1.56	65
115			
Outlet at one end	0.78	1.11	65
Outlet at centre	1.56	2.22	75
125			
Outlet at one end	0.96	1.37	75
Outlet at centre	1.92	2.74	90
150			
Outlet at one end	1.52	2.16	90
Outlet at centre	3.04	4.32	100

Having calculated Q for a roof area, it is possible to select the number and diameter of outlets necessary to drain the roof (NB. for enclosed roofs there should always be more than one outlet). If, to accommodate Q, the head of water at the selected outlets has to exceed 30mm, the outlets must be set in a sump or more outlets used.

Dimensions of sumps and gutters
The flow capacities of sumps with different perimeter lengths at various design depths of water are given in Table 8.1.3.

The depth of a sump should be equal to the required head of water (from Tables 8.1.1-8.1.2) plus a safety margin of 25mm.

Flow of water in gutters laid level is assumed in the British Standard to be based on the hydraulic gradient principle, where water will find its own level. It can be noted that the water surface is unlikely to be completely level. At the upstream end of a gutter it is approximately true that the depth will be twice that at the outlet.

The depth of water (see Figure 8.1.4) over the outlet (Y_C) is approximately half the depth of water at the upstream end (Y_U). Freeboard of 2/5 Y_U should be added, to a maximum of 75mm, to establish the gutter depth.

Where the length of gutter from outlet to stop end, or mid-point between outlets, exceeds 50 times Y_U, an additional allowance must be made for frictional resistance.

Outlets in the sole of gutters must be of a diameter 3/4 of the gutter width to be considered a free discharge. Smaller outlets should be placed within a sump in the gutter. *continued* ▶

Town Hall, Seinäjoki, Finland

The width of the sump should be full gutter width and the length 1.5 times the depth of the gutter. Figure 8.1.5 gives capacities of gutters with water depths Y_C, Y_U, and includes an allowance for friction over various lengths (Y_{UF}).

Figure 8.1.5 should be used as follows: Starting at the bottom right-hand side of the chart select a gutter breadth BS(e.g. 200mm), follow vertically up the chart to the flow rate curve (e.g. 3.1 litres/sec.). Read off and note value of Y_U (60mm). Follow horizontally across to the centre axis, noting the depth (Y_C) at the outlet (32mm). Continue to the left, to the curve representing the gutter length (e.g. 10m), and drop vertically into the bottom left-hand section of the value of Y_U (60mm) previously established. Follow right horizontally to the Y_{UF} axis and read off the value (70mm). Add ⅖ freeboard to give a gutter depth (98mm).

Through parapet walls via chutes to external hopper heads

With this pattern of drainage, the important considerations are:

- the design depth of water (the depth to which water can be allowed to build up on the roof)
- the widths of the chutes
- the capacity of the hopper head and outlet in combination.

Design depth of water

BS6367 suggests that, on a roof laid to falls, a water depth of up to 30mm may be acceptable if it is confined to relatively small areas around outlets.

Width of the chute

The flow capacities of different lengths of chute at various design depths of water are given in Table 8.1.4.

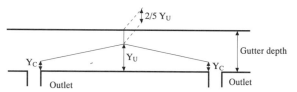

Figure 8.1.4
Establishing the gutter depth

The capacity of the hopper head and outlet in combination:

Tables 8.1.5-8.1.6 give the flow capacities of different diameter outlets at various heads of water. From this, it is possible to select an outlet diameter with a flow capacity to suit the flow of water through the chute.

The dimensions of the hopper head should be such that:

- The length is equivalent to the width of the chute.
- The depth is equal to the required head of water plus a 25mm safety margin.
- The width is sufficient to house the outlet.

Eaves gutters

Table 8.1.7 gives the flow capacities of two common gutter profiles. Manufacturers of eaves gutter systems provide specific data on the flow capacities of their products. These figures can be related to the rate of discharge (Q) from a given roof and an appropriate gutter size and outlet diameter selected.

It is important to remember that the efficiency of all systems will be reduced with time, as they are affected by silt, leaves and other debris. All drainage systems should be designed with a safety factor to take account of this reduction in efficiency. The size of the safety factor is related to the likelihood of debris accumulating in the gutters and the frequency with which they are cleaned.

Other factors which can affect the efficiency of eaves gutter systems are friction loss due to long lengths of gutter and sharp bends (see *BS6367* for further details).

Syphonic drainage

Unit 7.4 commented that manufacturers of syphonic drainage systems provide a design service. The detailed calculation methods for this approach are therefore not given in the Guide. ∎

Further reading:
BS6367 Drainage of roofs and paved areas

Chapter	1	2	3	4	5	6	7	8	9	10	11
Contents	Introduction	History	Regulatory Methods	Principles	Surveys	Constraints & Targets	Design Selection	Calculations	Detail Design Principles	Evaluation of Design	Built-up Roofing
Page	1	19	31	45	83	95	105	165	189	217	221

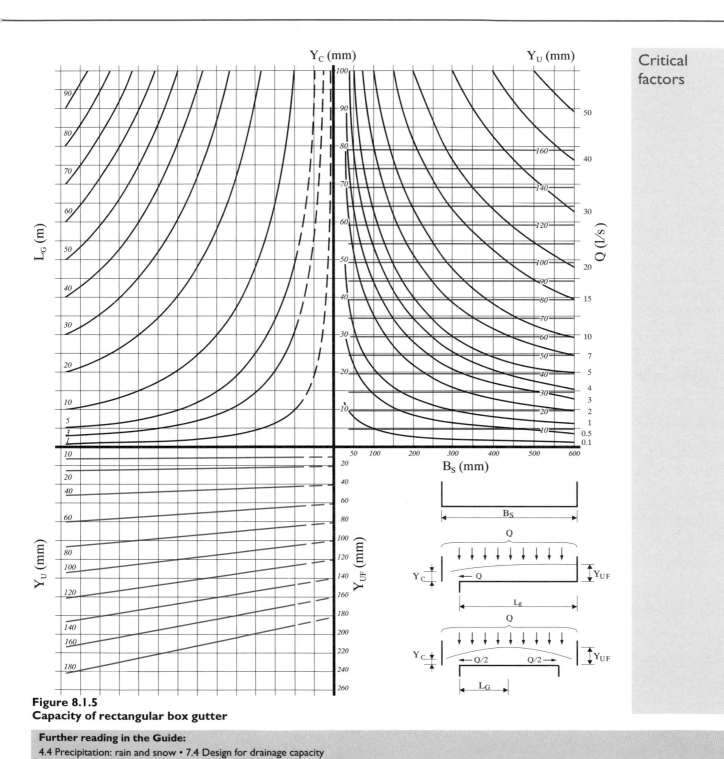

Figure 8.1.5
Capacity of rectangular box gutter

Further reading in the Guide:
4.4 Precipitation: rain and snow • 7.4 Design for drainage capacity

Calculation of thermal performance

- Calculation of the thermal performance is a primary design activity for the whole roof design, as the whole roof construction contributes to thermal performance.
- Minimum statutory requirements are laid down in *The Building Regulations.*
- Thermal performance calculations are also important as part of the prediction/control of condensation.

Building control, or other requirements, will lay down standards of thermal performance of the whole building or components of it. *The Building Regulations* require that 'Reasonable provision shall be made for the conservation of fuel and power in buildings'. The requirement applies to dwellings and other buildings whose floor area exceeds 30m^2.

Guidance on how to comply with the regulation is given in Approved Document L to *The Building Regulations.* Part of this approach is 'to limit the heat loss and where appropriate maximise the heat gains through the fabric of the building'.

The Approved Document considers that, for some buildings with little or no heat usage, insulation will be unnecessary.

Methods of assessment

Approved Document L gives two methods by which the limitation of heat loss can be demonstrated – an **elemental** approach or by **calculation**. The elemental approach is the more straightforward and simple with which to demonstrate compliance. Table 1 of the Approved Document shows the **maximum allowable thermal transmittance** (maximum U value) for the various elements of a construction.

For roofs, the current maximum U values are:

0.25W/m^2 K for dwellings and,
0.45W/m^2 K for other buildings.

Table 2 of the Approved Document also shows the permitted maximum areas of rooflight to be:

15% of the total floor area for dwellings and,
20% of the total roof area for all other buildings.

These assume single glazing. A 'trade off' of either a larger area of glazing, or a higher U value in the general roof, may be gained by using double, triple or emissivity-coated glazing for the rooflights.

The calculation procedure, given as an alternative to the elemental procedure, allows variations in the level of insulation of individual elements and areas of windows and roof lights. This approach requires the designer to show that the heat loss through the envelope of the proposed building is no greater than the rate of heat loss through a notional building – of the same size and shape – designed to comply with the elemental approach.

A further alternative 'calculation approach' is much more sophisticated, but flexible, showing that the **calculated annual energy use** of the proposed building is less than the calculated energy use of a similar notional building designed to comply with the 'elemental approach'. A more detailed discussion of the philosophies embraced in these methods is outside the scope of this Guide.

U value calculation

To calculate a U value is, in effect, to find the inverse of the sum of all the resistances to heat flow for the various component parts of the roof.

The **thermal resistance** (R) for a material is obtained by dividing the thickness (in metres) by its **thermal conductivity** (in W/m K). **Unit 4.5** gives more information on conductivity and briefly describes other forms of heat transfer – convection and radiation. These other mechanisms are not important when calculating the resistance of 'solid' components but need to be considered for air filled cavities and solid/ air interfaces which have a useful resistance to heat transmission.

The **surface resistance** depends on the emissivity of the surface, the direction of heat flow, (in or out of the 'solid' surface), and the degree of exposure of the surface. Thus the weather conditions and the colour of the roof will affect the value of the surface resistance. However, whilst useful to consider in calculations of surface temperatures, these resistances have a relatively small effect on the overall resistance for the roof and standardised values are normally used. In this Guide the values are taken from *CIBSE Guide* and the Approved Document.

In principle the **total resistance** of the roof is expressed as:

$$R_R = R_{INSULATION} + R_{DECK} + R_{MEMBRANES} + R_{CAVITY} + R_{SURFACES} \text{ and any other components}$$

and the U value is simply:

$$U = \frac{1}{R_R}$$

Information on appropriate thermal conductivities is available from manufacturers or from standard guidance documents such as the *CIBSE Guide, Section A3.* As a guide, Table 8.3.2 in **Unit 8.3** gives the typical thermal properties of common roofing materials which can be used in calculations. Designers may however, need to

---

Further reading:
Approved Document L to the Building Regulations • BRE Report 143 Thermal insulation: avoiding risks • CIBSE Guide Volume A section A3 • BS5250 Control of condensation in buildings.

• *The Building Regulations* Approved Document L allows several methods of demonstrating compliance with the regulation. The most widely used is the elemental approach, shown in this Guide.

check specific products' values with manufacturers before finalising designs. Whilst some components may have minimal effect on the overall heat transmission of the roof (e.g. fixings/washers), they can potentially create a local cold bridge which will modify, perhaps locally, the condensation risk calculations (See **Units 7.7** and **8.3**).

Computer programs can be used to carry out thermal performance calculations. Many such programmes are combined with calculation for condensation risk analysis. Designers should ensure that such programs are properly validated to the correct level of reliability.

Specimen calculations

Example 1: This design seeks to meet a required U value of 0.45W/m^2 K. The total thermal resistance required is therefore:

$$\frac{1}{0.45} = 2.22 \text{ m}^2 \text{ K/W}$$

Consider a roof, using the following construction with built-up roofing.

— Membrane
— Insulant
— Vapour control layer
— 60mm (average) sand cement screed
— 150mm dense concrete structural deck

	Resistance (m² K/W)
External surface	0.04
Membrane	0.06
Vapour control layer	0.02
Screed	0.04
Concrete deck	0.12
Internal surface	0.10
Total, excluding insulation	0.38

Therefore the resistance required from the insulant:
= 2.22 −0.38
= 1.84m² K/W

This could be achieved by, say, 41mm of rigid urethane board (design value thermal conductivity = 0.022 W/m K), or 67mm of mineral wool (0.036 W/m K). It would be normal practice to use the next standard, larger, thickness of such a product.

Example 2: Now consider a cold deck roof incorporating a ventilated cavity using the following construction with built-up roofing.

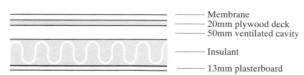

— Membrane
— 20mm plywood deck
— 50mm ventilated cavity
— Insulant
— 13mm plasterboard

	Resistance (m² K/W)
External surface	0.04
Membrane	0.06
Plywood deck	0.14
Ventilated cavity	0.16[a]
Plasterboard	0.08
Internal surface	0.10
Total, excluding insulation	0.58

Therefore the thermal resistance required for the insulant:
= 2.22 - 0.58
= 1.64 m² K/W

This could be achieved using 54mm of mineral wool quilt (0.033 W/m K).

Note: [a]The value for resistance of the cavity is taken, here, as that for an unventilated cavity. The value for a ventilated cavity is complex to calculate and varies across the ventilation path. It is normally considered sufficient to use the value here in calculation of heat loss in relatively simple roofs.

Example 3: If the ventilated roof, shown above, is for a dwelling, the required U value will be 0.25 W/m² K. Thus the total thermal resistance required is 4.00 m² K/W and the insulation would need to provide 4.00 − 0.58 = 3.42 m² K/W. This could be satisfied by 113mm of mineral wool.

Inverted roofs

When calculating the thermal performance of an inverted warm deck roof an allowance must be made for the effects on thermal conductivity, of water and water vapour in and surrounding the insulant. This will generally be achieved by increasing the thickness of the insulant. Some manufacturers recommend an across-the-range increase in insulant thickness of 20%. Other guidance relates the required increase in resistance to the resistance of the construction beneath. For many products, the blanket 20% increase produces a more conservative result and is easier to calculate. ∎

Critical factors

• Building Regulations requirements.
• Several approaches are allowed to meet Building Regulation requirements.
• Validity of data for calculations.

Further reading in the Guide:
4.5 Thermal transmission • 7.6 Design for thermal performance • 7.7 Design for moisture vapour control • 8.3 Calculation of condensation • 17 Thermal insulants

8.3   Calculation of condensation

- Calculation of condensation risk is a primary design activity for the whole roof design.
- Condensation risk calculations are important for the durability of roof constituents, for maintenance of thermal performance, and for the health and safety of occupants.
- *The Building Regulations* include requirements for the control of condensation.

Prediction **by calculation** of moisture vapour conditions within a roof build-up is well established. The factors influencing these predictions and the approaches to condensation control are introduced in **Unit 7.7**. This unit gives the background to the methods of condensation control calculations and shows, by examples, the calculation methods. The control of condensation in cold roofs by ventilation is also described in **Unit 7.7**, where the methods of determination of the required ventilation openings are given.

Calculation of interstitial condensation risk

Principles

The principles of condensation and design approaches to control are discussed in **Units 4.7** and **4.8**. The concepts of **vapour pressure, saturated vapour pressure, relative humidity** and **dewpoint** were introduced in these units. It is an essential scientific phenomenon that differences in composition, concentration or pressure will try to equalise themselves. Two points at differing temperatures will, by energy flow (conduction, convection, radiation), try to bring both to an equilibrium intermediate temperature. The ease with which this is achieved is a function of the initial temperature difference – the driving force – and the ability of the separating medium to allow transfer – the resistance. A calculation method for heat energy transfer is shown in **Unit 8.2**.

The basis for condensation risk assessments is similar: the driving force being the **vapour pressure difference**; and the resistance being the **vapour resistance** of the roof component parts and the whole. The further consideration in condensation is the comparison of the vapour pressure at any point in the construction – as modified by the vapour resistance – and the saturated vapour pressure at that point. From **Unit 4.7**, it will be seen that if the vapour pressure equals the saturated vapour pressure, then moisture must start to condense out.

Approaches to calculations

The relatively simple physics outlined so far becomes more complex in the multi-component construction found in roofs. The processes interact and are to some extent modified by dynamic behaviour. Various calculation methods have been produced over many years as greater understanding has developed. Designers may be familiar with the methods proposed in *BS5250: 1975* and *BS6229: 1982,* or in *CIBSE A10*. Although having some benefit, and utilising essentially similar physical principles, the methods in these documents do not use more recent understanding of the interactions and effects of the assumptions made on the answers generated.

Prediction of condensation by the earlier calculation methods calculated the temperature profiles and hence the saturated vapour pressure and vapour pressure through the structure. Condensation is predicted where the calculated vapour pressure is greater than the saturated vapour pressure. It is, however, not possible for the vapour pressure to exceed the saturated vapour pressure.

The method of calculation described here is based upon that in the later *BS5250* (1989) which is recommended be followed. This is also the method referred to by Approved Document F2.

A fuller comparison of the advantages and disadvantages of the various calculation methods is outside the scope of this Guide and reference should be made to specialist papers (**Chapter 22**). An essential difference with the *BS5250: 1989* method is that whereas earlier methods merely predicted zones of condensation risk, the method now predicts condensation at specific interfaces through the construction, which experiments have shown to be the more likely occurrence.

The risk assessment is a part-calculation/part-graphical method, which is amenable to the use of computer programs. These can be quite simple or heavily developed for complex, interactive calculations. A potential Quality Assurance problem exists in achieving the correct level of validation for such programs – and then maintaining that level during Third Party Certification.

There is considerable benefit in carrying out some calculation by hand (with a calculator) as a better feel for the interactions of components can be achieved in this way. Once established, a computer program can be used to evaluate a larger number of possible options.

Calculation method

A calculation is performed to help assess the risk of condensation. The calculation uses the thermal and vapour resistance characteristics of each element of the construction, and of the whole construction, to model the temperature and vapour pressure distribution. An overall assessment should select external and internal design

---

Further reading:
Approved Document F2 to The Building Regulations • BS5250: Control of condensation in buildings • BS6229: Flat roofs with continuously supported coverings • CIBSE Guide, Volume A, Section A10

- Condensation risk calculations are based upon the evaluation of internal and external environmental conditions and the cumulative vapour resistance of the roof construction.
- The calculations are part calculation, part graphical methods, but rely to some extent on assumptions.

conditions to apply to the calculation method, and also assess whether the amounts of condensate predicted by the calculation are significant.

The process of calculation takes a number of distinct steps which are shown below and then illustrated later in this unit by a worked example:

1 The thermal resistance of each element (resistivity × thickness) is calculated and added to give the overall thermal resistance of the construction.

2 The vapour resistance of each element (resistivity × thickness) is calculated and added to give the overall vapour resistance.

3 The design internal and external temperature and relative humidities (and thus vapour pressures) are selected.

4 The temperatures at each interface within the build-up are calculated from the internal and external temperatures and the individual thermal resistances.

5 The interface saturation vapour pressures are determined by calculation or from a psychrometric chart.

6 The interface saturated vapour pressures are plotted on the vapour pressure/vapour resistance graph. The roof characteristics can be plotted, with cumulative vapour resistance in the direction of flow as the horizontal axis, and vapour pressure as vertical axis (Figure 8.3.3 shows this in a worked example). For an approximate calculation, sufficient at this level of design, it can be assumed that the saturation vapour pressures, between the values calculated, lie on a straight line. (For porous materials, the straight line is accurate between equal saturated vapour pressures of the interfaces, but sags slightly between falling values.)

7 The design internal and external vapour pressures are then added to the graph as a straight line right through the roof build-up.

8 The local vapour pressure cannot in practice be higher than the local saturated vapour pressure determined by the local temperature. Therefore if any of the lines joining the saturated vapour pressures at the interfaces cross the vapour pressure line, interstitial condensation will occur at the first crossover. If the two lines do not cross then condensation will not occur under the conditions assumed.

9 If condensation is predicted by Step 8, the design vapour pressure line plot should be redrawn. The exterior and interior vapour pressures should be joined using lines of minimum length but without crossing the saturation vapour pressure line. Condensation is predicted at each interface where the modified vapour pressure line touches the saturation vapour pressure line.

It is an assumption of this method that condensation will form at an interface (rather than within the components) in the construction. If the plane of condensation is not already at an interface, then adjust its position to the next downstream interface.

10 Calculation of condensation rates can then be carried out either for the general case in Step 8, or most usefully for each of the interfaces highlighted as condensation planes in Step 9. As a first assessment, modifying the assumed design conditions – or perhaps the performance of vapour control layers in Step 8 – may produce sufficient change in the conclusions that no condensation arises (as predicted) (see later for data and assumptions). The condensation rate is calculated by subtracting the mass flow rate of vapour leaving the condensation 'plane' from the mass flow rate entering. This assumes that, during condensation, the vapour pressure corresponding to its temperature and the process of condensation does not significantly raise the temperatures of the plane.

11 Mass flow rates are calculated from a fundamental mass flow equation:

$$G = \frac{\Delta P}{R_v}$$

where G = mass flow rate
ΔP = vapour pressure
R_v = vapour resistance

for each part of the construction between planes where condensation is predicted.

It is usual to calculate condensation build-up over a period of time – e.g. 60 days, 10 days or 1 day. Therefore, this rate must be multiplied up for the total duration. (*BS5250: 1989* has equations which have a figure of 5184 as a multiplier. This is derived from the number of seconds in 60 days.)

Calculation of re-evaporation from a free surface, using the same principles, is possible but should be carried out with caution. Re-evaporation of condensation from porous materials, particularly when actual moisture contents are low, is more complex and therefore more difficult to predict.

continued ▶

Critical factors

- Precision of calculation method.
- Validation of computer programmes for calculations.

Further reading in the Guide:
4.7 Condensation • 4.8 Condensation: pumping • 7.7 Design for moisture vapour control • 8.2 Calculation of thermal performance

- For most calculations of condensation, assumptions will need to be made for internal and external environments, and perhaps for the properties of materials.

  Internal and external environments will change with time and therefore multiple calculations may be required.

Design data and assumptions

The calculations of condensation risk are precise but cannot exactly mimic the real performance of a roof through time, where unpredictable, variable and dynamic environmental conditions will occur internally and externally through the seasons of the year. Calculations are only concerned with diffusion and take no account of air movement through gaps.

Such calculations should therefore be used primarily to give broad consideration to the type of construction and its sensitivity to change in either materials properties or design assumptions. Repeated calculations with modifications to the design parameters allow assessment of the sensitivity to condensation.

The calculation methods, at present, are based on assumptions of steady-state conditions rather than the dynamic flows experienced in practice. However, to carry out the calculations to provide whatever useful predictions are possible, some assumption must be made of internal and external environments. They may be based upon: experience; measurements on other, similar, buildings; reference to standards or guidance documents.

External climate

There is much scope for debate and arguments over the appropriateness of such assumed data. For example, *BS6229* suggested using external winter conditions of −5°C and 90% RH sustained for 60 days. This is an extremely severe condition. It is clear that air temperatures of −5°C will occur during a normal UK winter, but that, on average, temperatures are unlikely to be continually below 0°C for such prolonged periods. It is suggested, in *BS5250: 1989*, that 5°C and 95% RH for a 60-day period be assumed, which is reasonable and should form the basis for the calculation method above, unless more specific climatic data is available. The effects of lower temperatures for shorter periods should not be totally ignored and other calculation checks using, say 0°C and 95% RH for a period of 7 days, and −5°C and 95% RH for ½ or 1 day, may also be appropriate.

Internal climate

Design internal conditions will be affected by the external climatic conditions, the nature of the activities and the extent of comfort control deployed within the building. Specific guidance is therefore more difficult. *BS5250: 1989* suggests two levels: 15°C and 65% RH for dry/moist

Table 8.3.1
Indoor notional psychrometric conditions for flat roof design (from *BS6229*)

Type of building	Temperature	Relative humidity	Vapour pressure
	°C	%	kPa
Houses and flats	20	55	1.285
Offices	20	40	0.935
Schools	20	50	1.169
Factories and heated warehouses	15	35	0.596
Textile factories	20	70	1.636
Swimming pool halls	25	70	2.219

occupancy: 15°C and 95% RH for moist/wet occupancy. (Dry, moist and wet being defined in terms of building use and occupant type – e.g. family with or without young children.) This guidance appears more related to domestic buildings and may be less appropriate for a range of building types.

Control may be achieved for the internal environments of some buildings e.g. air-conditioned office buildings. Other buildings may have relatively consistent internal environments by the nature of the activities therein – e.g. swimming pool halls.

Table 8.3.1 (based on *BS6229*) gives a wider classification of internal environments which are recommended be used in preference to those in *BS5250*. For new buildings more specific information should be available from the building services designers.

For some building services designs, local conditions, close to the roof zone, may be created which modify the general internal environment; e.g. the use of ceiling voids for return air paths in air-conditioned buildings. Such local conditions should be taken into account in the condensation calculations.

Materials data

The calculation method also requires information on the thermal and moisture resistance of the roof components. Generalised data is given by *BS5250* and by the *CIBSE Guide*. Some is represented here (Table 8.3.2). Specific data on the actual grade and type of material to be used should be obtained from manufacturers wherever possible.

Further reading:
Approved Document F2 to The Building Regulations • BS5250: Control of condensation in buildings • BS6229: Flat roofs with continuously supported coverings • CIBSE Guide, Volume A, Section A10

• Where condensation is predicted, an assessment should be made to check whether the predicted levels are acceptable within the specific roof build-up.

Assessment of risk

Where condensation is predicted, some estimation of the consequences of its occurrence will be necessary. Some limited amount of condensation may not be deleterious to the performance of the construction. *The Building Regulations* require prevention of 'excessive condensation'.

Assessment requires the designer to exercise judgement on a number of related issues on the ability of the construction to cater for the predicted condensation. The factors which should be considered are:

1 The condensation rate.

2 The period of time over which condensation is likely to occur.

3 The effects of water accumulation on the materials within the roof construction for example; rotting of wood or other cellulose-based materials or corrosion of fixings.

4 The quantity of water that can be retained before liquid flow occurs.

5 Whether water can be conveniently drained from the construction.

6 Whether condensation will later re-evaporate.

Guidance on allowable levels of condensate is not given in this Guide. Assessments can be made on the basis of previous experience or guidance from component manufacturers. Guidance from such sources, relating to allowable mass of condensate per unit area, requires careful interpretation for effects of material thickness. Allowable condensate values based upon simple classification of physical make-up of roof components (e.g. fibrous/non-fibrous insulation) requires careful consideration of other relevant factors – such as the relative susceptibilities to degradation of wood and mineral fibres. An alternative approach to use, in setting the maximum allowable condensate, is to consider the effect of the moisture on the thermal conductivity of the roof. As the conductivity usually increases with moisture content, condensation may increase the energy losses for the building or could increase the conductivity such that further condensation occurs. *continued* ▶

Table 8.3.2
Thermal and vapour resistivities for roof construction materials[A]

Material	Vapour resistivity (MN.s/g.m)	Thermal resistivity m K/W
Plywood	2000	7
Chipboard	500	7
Dense concrete (2200kg/m³ dry density)	200	0.8
Lightweight concrete (aerated)[B]	50	2.5
Metal deck with unsealed laps	10[C]	-
Vapour control layers	see Table 7.7.2	-
Asphalt	100 000	2
Built-up roofing	10 000	2
Metal sheet membranes (sealed laps)	10 000	-
Polymeric single ply membrane	refer to manufacturer	-
Sand cement screed	200	0.7
Lightweight cement screed	100	1.6
Polyurethane (closed cell)	650	45
Extruded polystyrene	1000	35
Expanded polystyrene	250	30
Cellular glass	10 000	24
Cork board	100	24
Mineral or glass fibre board	5	28

Notes

A Because of the range of materials available within each type and the effects of construction processes, these values can only be taken as notional for calculation purposes. Where necessary, specific values may be able to be determined from manufacturers or independent tests.

B Lightweight concrete, used for structural purposes, made with lightweight aggregate will be influenced by the nature of the aggregates and the mix design. In the absence of specific data from manufacturers, values similar to those of dense concrete of a similar strength may be used.

C Overall vapour resistance of the construction in MN.s/g.

Critical factors

• Validity of assumptions for environmental and materials properties.

• Assessment of acceptability of condensate deposition.

Further reading in the Guide:
4.7 Condensation • 4.8 Condensation: pumping • 7.7 Design for moisture vapour control • 8.2 Calculation of thermal performance

- The calculation methods assess the properties of individual roof components within the overall roof performance.

Worked example

The calculation method described here can be clarified and illustrated by the use of a worked example. The following example uses a combination of elements which might typically be used in flat roof design but should not be taken necessarily as a recommended build-up. The assumed internal and external environmental conditions have been taken as typically average external winter conditions over a 60-day period and, for the internal conditions, to represent a humidity controlled building environment. The vapour pressure for the two conditions are read from a standard psychrometric chart (Figure 8.3.1).

Figure 8.3.1
Psychrometric chart
(The reproduction of the chart here is not sufficiently accurate for calculation. See the Project Notebook.)

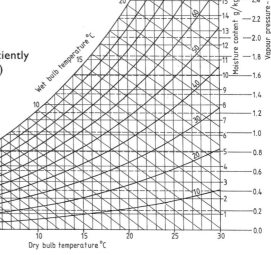

This worked example uses the proforma work sheet to display and record the data as calculated see (Figure 8.3.2). A blank copy of the work sheet is included in the Project Notebook for the use of designers and may be photocopied freely.

The first step in the calculation is to identify the individual layers in the roof build-up and enter them in column A.

In columns B, D, and E the thermal performance is entered from standard data or from manufacturers' information. The thermal performance of the vapour control layer (VCL) is not entered in this case as its contribution to thermal performance is insignificant. It is important to include the VCL in the layer build-up because of its effects on vapour movement.

Having entered the cumulative thermal resistance, the interface temperatures (column F) are calculated using the formula:

$$t_n = t_e + \frac{(t_i - t_e)\,R_{t,n}}{\Sigma R_t}$$

Where t_n = temperature at interface n

t_e = external temperature

t_i = internal temperature

$R_{t,n}$ = cumulative thermal resistance at interface n

ΣR_t = total thermal resistance of roof build-up

Further reading:0
Approved Document F2 to The Building Regulations • BS5250: Control of condensation in buildings • BS6229:00 Flat roofs with continuously supported coverings • CIBSE Guide, Volume A, Section A10

- Variation in physical properties within a single component, e.g. a composite insulation board, may have to be modelled as separate components.

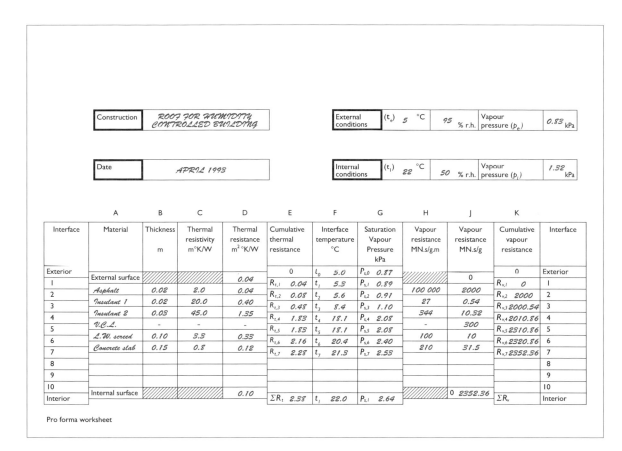

| Construction | ROOF FOR HUMIDITY CONTROLLED BUILDING | | External conditions | (t_e) 5 °C | 95 % r.h. | Vapour pressure (p_e) | 0.83 kPa |

| Date | APRIL 1993 | | Internal conditions | (t_i) 22 °C | 50 % r.h. | Vapour pressure (p_i) | 1.32 kPa |

	A	B	C	D	E	F	G	H	J	K	
Interface	Material	Thickness m	Thermal resistivity m°K/W	Thermal resistance m²°K/W	Cumulative thermal resistance	Interface temperature °C	Saturation Vapour Pressure kPa	Vapour resistance MN.s/g.m	Vapour resistance MN.s/g	Cumulative vapour resistance	Interface
Exterior					0	t_0 5.0	$P_{s,0}$ 0.87		0	0	Exterior
1	External surface			0.04	$R_{t,1}$ 0.04	t_1 5.3	$P_{s,1}$ 0.89		2000	$R_{v,1}$ 0	1
2	Asphalt	0.02	2.0	0.04	$R_{t,2}$ 0.08	t_2 5.6	$P_{s,2}$ 0.91	100 000	0.54	$R_{v,2}$ 2000	2
3	Insulant 1	0.02	20.0	0.40	$R_{t,3}$ 0.48	t_3 8.4	$P_{s,3}$ 1.10	27	10.32	$R_{v,3}$ 2000.54	3
4	Insulant 2	0.03	45.0	1.35	$R_{t,4}$ 1.83	t_4 18.1	$P_{s,4}$ 2.08	344	300	$R_{v,4}$ 2010.86	4
5	V.C.L.	-	-	-	$R_{t,5}$ 1.83	t_5 18.1	$P_{s,5}$ 2.08	-	10	$R_{v,5}$ 2310.86	5
6	L.W. screed	0.10	3.3	0.33	$R_{t,6}$ 2.16	t_6 20.4	$P_{s,6}$ 2.40	100	31.5	$R_{v,6}$ 2320.86	6
7	Concrete slab	0.15	0.8	0.12	$R_{t,7}$ 2.28	t_7 21.3	$P_{s,7}$ 2.53	210		$R_{v,7}$ 2352.36	7
8											8
9											9
10											10
Interior	Internal surface			0.10	ΣR_t 2.38	t_i 22.0	$P_{s,i}$ 2.64		0 2352.36	ΣR_v	Interior

Pro forma worksheet

Figure 8.3.2
Pro forma worksheet

Therefore for interface 2, between the asphalt and the insulant, the temperature t_2

$$= 5 + \frac{(22 - 5)\,0.08}{2.38}$$

$$= 5.6°C$$

The values for saturation vapour pressure (column G) can be calculated from fundamental equations but are more easily taken from standard tables (Table 8.3.3) using temperatures from column F.

Values for vapour resistivity and vapour resistance (columns H, J) are, as for thermal properties, taken from standard data or manufacturers' information. For some materials a notional value is used and here the resistivity value of 100 000 MN.s/g.m for the asphalt layer is such a figure. The cumulative vapour resistance at each interface is then entered in column K. For this example, where a composite insulation board is used, the two components are entered separately as the difference in vapour resistivity between the components could be sufficient to create an interface, even though they are one overall component. *continued* ▶

Further reading in the Guide:
4.7 Condensation • 4.8 Condensation: pumping • 7.7 Design for moisture vapour control • 8.2 Calculation of thermal performance

8.3   Calculation of condensation *continued*

- Calculation of condensation deposition is carried out by comparing the rates of moisture arriving at and leaving interfaces within the roof build-up.
- Re-evaporation calculations are possible but need care to interpret.

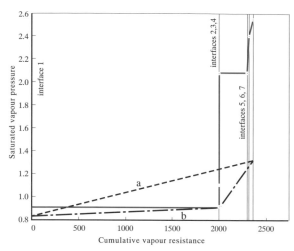

Figure 8.3.3
Graphical representation

At this stage the calculation has produced values for the predicted saturation vapour pressure (column G) and the cumulative vapour resistance (column K) at each of the interfaces in the roof build-up.

A graphical representation of these sets of interface conditions should then be drawn (Figure 8.3.3).

The red line is the plot of the values of saturated vapour pressure against cumulative vapour resistance for the interfaces between layers in the roof build-up. Each interface is indicated with the numbered vertical lines (1 – 7). The external and internal vapour pressures 0.83 and 1.32 KPa are entered on the SVP axis and joined by the dotted black line (a). This line crosses the SVP/vapour resistance plot and condensation is therefore predicted. As described earlier the vapour pressure cannot actually be higher than the saturated vapour pressure so the line is redrawn (b) to stay below the SVP plot. The lines touch only at interface 2 and thus condensation is predicted at the interface between the membrane and the insulant. It is not necessary to redraw the SVP plot to a larger scale in this example as condensation is not predicted at interfaces where the plots are close together.

Calculation of moisture deposition

The graphical prediction method above enables prediction of the occurrence of condensation and at which interface it occurs. It does not predict the amount of moisture which will condense. This is calculated by comparing the rate of moisture arriving at the interface and the rate of moisture escaping from it. In the example above this is the difference between the moisture arriving at and escaping from this underside of the asphalt (interface 2).

Quantity of deposition over 60 days (Q_{60})

$$= \text{time (secs)} \times \left(\frac{Pi - Ps_2}{Rv_{2\text{-}7}} - \frac{Ps_2 - Pe}{Rv_{1\text{-}2}} \right)$$

Pi   = internal vapour pressure
Pe   = external vapour pressure
Ps_2 = saturation vapour pressure at interface 2
$Rv_{2\text{-}7}$ = cumulative vapour resistance between interface 2 and inside the building
$Rv_{1\text{-}2}$ = cumulative vapour pressure between interface 2 and outside the building. In the example

$$Q_{60} = 5184 \left(\left[\frac{1.32 - 0.91}{2352.36 - 2000} \right] - \left[\frac{0.91 - 0.83}{2000} \right] \right)$$

$$= 5184 \quad \left[\frac{0.41}{352.36} - \frac{0.08}{2000} \right]$$

$$= 5184 \, (0.0011235)$$

$$= 5.82 \text{g/m}^2$$

This is a relatively small quantity of condensate which is likely to evaporate in warmer external conditions and increased air movement likely in summer. The lack of deleterious effects on potentially susceptible materials such as organic fibres or ferrous fixings in short-term exposure should, however, be confirmed with manufacturers.   ■

Further reading:
Approved Document F2 to The Building Regulations • BS5250: Control of condensation in buildings • BS6229: Flat roofs with continuously supported coverings • CIBSE Guide, Volume A, Section A10

Table 8.3.3
Saturation vapour pressures for air temperatures 30.9°C to -10°C

Temperature	Saturation vapour pressure kPa									
°C	0.0	0.1	0.2	0.3	0.4	0.5	0.6	0.7	0.8	0.9
30	4.24	4.27	4.29	4.32	4.34	4.37	4.39	4.42	4.44	4.47
29	4.01	4.03	4.05	4.08	4.10	4.12	4.15	4.17	4.19	4.22
28	3.78	3.80	3.82	3.85	3.87	3.89	3.91	3.94	3.96	3.98
27	3.56	3.59	3.61	3.63	3.65	3.67	3.69	3.71	3.74	3.76
26	3.36	3.38	3.40	3.42	3.44	3.46	3.48	3.50	3.52	3.54
25	3.17	3.19	3.21	3.22	3.24	3.26	3.28	3.30	3.32	3.34
24	2.98	3.00	3.02	3.04	3.06	3.07	3.09	3.11	3.13	3.15
23	2.81	2.83	2.84	2.86	2.88	2.89	2.91	2.93	2.95	2.97
22	2.64	2.66	2.68	2.69	2.71	2.72	2.74	2.76	2.77	2.79
21	2.49	2.50	2.52	2.53	2.55	2.56	2.58	2.60	2.61	2.63
20	2.34	2.35	2.37	2.38	2.40	2.41	2.43	2.44	2.46	2.47
19	2.20	2.21	2.22	2.24	2.25	2.27	2.28	2.29	2.31	2.32
18	2.06	2.08	2.09	2.10	2.12	2.13	2.14	2.16	2.17	2.18
17	1.94	1.95	1.96	1.97	1.99	2.00	2.01	2.02	2.04	2.05
16	1.82	1.83	1.84	1.85	1.86	1.88	1.89	1.90	1.91	1.92
15	1.70	1.72	1.73	1.74	1.75	1.76	1.77	1.78	1.79	1.81
14	1.60	1.61	1.62	1.63	1.64	1.65	1.66	1.67	1.68	1.69
13	1.50	1.51	1.52	1.53	1.54	1.55	1.56	1.57	1.58	1.59
12	1.40	1.41	1.42	1.43	1.44	1.45	1.46	1.47	1.48	1.49
11	1.31	1.32	1.33	1.34	1.35	1.36	1.37	1.37	1.38	1.39
10	1.23	1.24	1.24	1.25	1.26	1.27	1.28	1.29	1.29	1.30
9	1.15	1.16	1.16	1.17	1.18	1.19	1.19	1.20	1.21	1.22
8	1.07	1.08	1.09	1.09	1.10	1.11	1.12	1.12	1.13	1.14
7	1.00	1.01	1.02	1.02	1.03	1.04	1.04	1.05	1.06	1.06
6	0.93	0.94	0.95	0.95	0.96	0.97	0.97	0.98	0.99	0.99
5	0.87	0.88	0.88	0.89	0.90	0.90	0.91	0.92	0.92	0.93
4	0.81	0.82	0.82	0.83	0.84	0.84	0.85	0.85	0.86	0.87
3	0.76	0.76	0.77	0.77	0.78	0.78	0.79	0.80	0.80	0.81
2	0.71	0.71	0.72	0.72	0.73	0.73	0.74	0.74	0.75	0.75
1	0.66	0.66	0.67	0.67	0.68	0.68	0.69	0.69	0.70	0.70
0	0.61	0.62	0.62	0.62	0.63	0.63	0.64	0.64	0.65	0.65
-0	0.61	0.61	0.60	0.60	0.59	0.59	0.58	0.58	0.57	0.57
-1	0.56	0.56	0.55	0.55	0.54	0.54	0.53	0.53	0.53	0.52
-2	0.52	0.51	0.51	0.50	0.50	0.50	0.49	0.49	0.48	0.48
-3	0.48	0.47	0.47	0.46	0.46	0.46	0.45	0.45	0.44	0.44
-4	0.44	0.43	0.43	0.43	0.42	0.42	0.42	0.41	0.41	0.40
-5	0.40	0.40	0.39	0.39	0.39	0.38	0.38	0.38	0.37	0.37
-6	0.37	0.37	0.36	0.36	0.36	0.35	0.35	0.35	0.34	0.34
-7	0.34	0.34	0.33	0.33	0.33	0.32	0.32	0.32	0.32	0.31
-8	0.31	0.31	0.30	0.30	0.30	0.30	0.29	0.29	0.29	0.29
-9	0.28	0.28	0.28	0.28	0.27	0.27	0.27	0.27	0.26	0.26
-10	0.26	0.26	0.26	0.25	0.25	0.25	0.25	0.24	0.24	0.24

Critical factors

• Assessment of acceptability of condensate deposition.

Further reading in the Guide:
4.7 Condensation • 4.8 Condensation: pumping • 7.7 Design for moisture vapour control • 8.2 Calculation of thermal performance

12 Mastic Asphalt	13 Polymeric Single Ply	14 Copper	15 Lead Sheet	16 Other Membranes	17 Thermal Insulants	18 Specification	19 Contracts & Procurement	20 Inspection	21 Maintenance	22 Bibliography	23 Index
263	301	331	353	375	383	393	399	413	429	437	455

- Calculation can be used to assess wind uplift pressures, based on standard meteorological data.
- Wind speeds vary across the UK.
- Building location, size and local topography modify the basic wind speed to give a design wind speed.

The calculation method described below is based upon *BSCP3:Chapter V: Part 2: 1972*. A revised British Standard is in preparation; it will take account of information presently contained in *BRE Digest 346*.

Determination of wind uplift pressures must be carried out in the following stages:

- Calculate the design wind speed.
- Calculate the dynamic pressure of the wind above atmospheric pressure.
- Calculate the wind uplift pressure on each part of the roof, taking account of areas with high local uplift such as at roof edges or at changes of level.
- The roof components must resist these wind uplift pressures – with an appropriate margin of safety – by dead weight, by mechanical attachment, by adhesion or by a combination of those means.

The design wind speed

The first step is to determine the basic wind speed in metres per second (m/s), denoted by the letter V. This is read from the wind speed map shown in Figure 8.4.1. Note that wind speeds are not constant over the whole of the UK: in general they increase in severity from the south-east to the north-west.

The basic wind speed V, must be modified to find the design wind speed V_s, by taking into account local factors such as:

- topography;
- ground roughness;
- building size;
- height above ground;
- statistical probabilities related to period of exposure to wind.

V_s is calculated as:

$$V_s = V \times S_1 \times S_2 \times S_3$$

where

S_1 is the topography factor.

The basic wind speed does not take into account topographic features such as hills, valleys, cliffs, escarpments or ridges by which the wind may be accelerated – near the summit – or decelerated – near the foot. The value of S_1 is normally taken as 1.0 provided

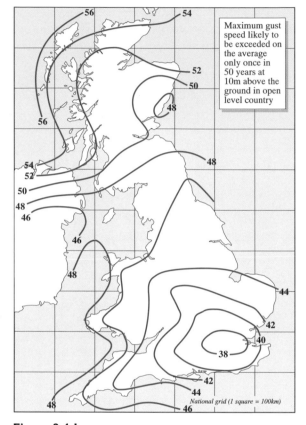

Figure 8.4.1
UK wind speeds
(based upon data from *BSCP3 Chapter V*)

average ground slope within 1 km of the site does not exceed 0.05: a higher value (up to 1.36) must be used if the upward slope is greater (see Appendix D of *CP3: Chapter V: Part 2*).

Factor S_2 takes account of the combined effects of ground roughness, building size and the variation of wind speed with height above ground.

Four categories of ground roughness are identified:

1 Long fetches of open level or nearly level country with no shelter. (Examples are flat coastal fringes, fens, airfields and grassland, moorland or farmland without hedges or walls around the fields)

Further reading:
BSCP3: Chapter V: Part 2 Wind loads • BRE Digest 311 Wind scour of gravel ballast on roofs • BRE Digest 346 The assessment of wind loads

Table 8.4.1
Factor S₂ for ground roughness and building height, for roofing and wind uplift calculations

Building height, H (m)	Ground roughness category			
	1. Open country with no obstructions	2. Open country with scattered windbreaks	3. Country with many windbreaks; small towns; outskirts of large cities	4. Surface with large and frequent obstructions e.g. city centres
3 or less	0.83	0.72	0.64	0.56
5	0.88	0.79	0.70	0.60
10	1.00	0.93	0.78	0.67
15	1.03	1.00	0.88	0.74
20	1.06	1.03	0.95	0.79
30	1.09	1.07	1.01	0.90
40	1.12	1.10	1.05	0.97
50	1.14	1.12	1.08	1.02
60	1.15	1.14	1.10	1.05
80	1.18	1.17	1.13	1.10
100	1.20	1.19	1.16	1.13
120	1.22	1.21	1.18	1.15
140	1.24	1.22	1.20	1.17
160	1.25	1.24	1.21	1.19
180	1.26	1.25	1.23	1.20
200	1.27	1.26	1.24	1.22

2 Flat or undulating country with obstructions such as hedges or walls around fields, scattered wind breaks of trees and occasional buildings. (Examples are most farmland and country estates with the exception of those parts that are well wooded.)

3 Surfaces covered by numerous large obstructions (Examples are well wooded parkland and forest areas, towns and their suburbs and the outskirts of large cities. The general level of roof tops and obstructions is assumed at about 10m, but the category will include built-up areas generally apart from those that qualify for category 4.)

4 Surfaces covered by numerous large obstructions with a general roof height of 25m or more. (The category covers only the centres of large towns and cities where the buildings are not only high, but are also not too widely spaced.).

(Further explanation of ground roughness factors can be found in Appendix A of *CP3: Chapter V: Part 2.*)

S₂ varies depending on building size and the application of the wind loading – whether it is for structural design or cladding design. In this case it is cladding and fixings – Class A in the Code.

Wind speed increases with building height, and S₂ should be adjusted to take account of this.

Having determined the ground roughness factor and the height of the building it is possible to read an appropriate value for S₂ from Table 8.4.1.

S₃ is a statistical factor.
It is almost certain that the design wind speed will be experienced during the life of a permanent building. The longer the building stands the higher this probability becomes. Temporary structures have a lesser chance of being exposed to such a wind speed. In the majority of circumstances S₃ is given a value of 1.0, but a higher value may be adopted if greater security is required. This value corresponds to a wind that will statistically occur on average once in 50 years. (See also Appendix C of *CP3: Chapter V: Part 2.*) continued ▶

Critical factors

• Basic wind speed for location.
• Nature of building geometry.
• Local topography.
• Wind uplift pressure counteracted by roof system.

Further reading in the Guide:
4.10 Wind • 7.10 Design for wind resistance

- The roof design should ensure that the roof system has sufficient capacity to resist the calculated uplift pressures using dead weight, applied loadings, adhesion, or mechanical fixings.
- Calculation of wind uplift pressure should take account of locally more extreme cases such as building perimeters or rooftop constructions.

Dynamic pressure of the wind

The dynamic pressure of the wind above atmospheric pressure (denoted as q) is calculated as:

$$q = 0.613V_s^2 \text{ N/m}^2$$

where V_s is the design wind speed in metres per second calculated above.

Wind uplift pressure

The pressure acting upwards (denoted as F) is calculated as:

$$F = (C_{pe} - C_{pi})q \text{ N/m}^2$$

where:

C_{pe} is the external pressure coefficient.

(C_{pe} is dependent on the shape of the roof and the dimensions of the building. Values for C_{pe} are given in Table 8.4.2.)

C_{pi} is the internal pressure coefficient.

C_{pi} is taken as +0.2 if a dominant opening (such as open loading bay doors in the side of the building) will not be present during a storm. If there is a likelihood of a dominant opening being present or occurring through building failure, C_{pi} is taken as +0.6. (For further information refer to Appendix E of *CP3: Chapter V: Part 2*.)

A negative value of F indicates wind uplift, while a positive value indicates a downward pressure.

q is the dynamic pressure of the wind.

The roof construction must be able to resist this uplift by a suitable margin. **Unit 7.10** discussed an approach to this. Some data on the resistance available for bituminous membranes is shown in Tables 8.4.3 and 8.4.4, and for insulation materials in Table 8.4.5. Table 8.4.6 gives some typical values for the dead weight of roofing materials which can be used in the assessment of adequacy of self dead weight of the roof to resist uplift forces. All of this data should be checked against the actual materials proposed for the roof when these are known.

Worked example

This determines the wind uplift on the roof of the building shown in Figure 8.4.2. The building occupies a city centre site, which from Figure 8.4.1 is known to have a basic wind speed of 42m/s.

Table 8.4.2
External pressure coefficients for overall duopitch roof surface

Building height/ width ratio (h/w)	Roof slope (degrees)	Cpe (negative value indicates uplift)
h/w ≤ 0.5	0	-0.8
	5	-0.9
	10	-1.2
0.5 < h/w ≤ 1.5	0	-1.0
	5	-0.9
	10	-1.1
1.5 < h/w ≤ 6	0	-0.9
	5	-0.8
	10	-0.8

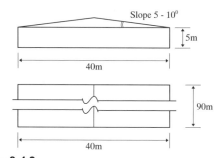

Figure 8.4.2
The building covered by this worked example

Step 1. Calculate design wind speed, V_s.

$$V_s = V \times S_1 \times S_2 \times S_3$$

There are no steep slopes within a 1 km radius.

S_1 (the topography factor) = 1.0

The building is on a city centre site with a height to eaves of 5m above ground level.

S_2 (ground roughness and height above ground factor taken from Table 8.4.1) = 0.60

Assume normal life of building (say 50/60 years).

S_3 (the statistical factor) = 1.0

$$\begin{aligned} V_s &= V \times S_1 \times S_2 \times S_3 \\ &= 42 \times 1 \times 0.60 \times 1 \\ &= 25.2 \text{ m/s} \end{aligned}$$

Further reading:
BSCP3: Chapter V: Part 2 Wind loads • BRE Digest 311 Wind scour of gravel ballast on roofs • BRE Digest 346 The assessment of wind loads

Step 2. Determine the dynamic pressure, q.

$$q = 0.613V_s^2$$
$$= 0.613 \times 25.2^2$$
$$= 389.3 \text{ N/m}^2 \ (= 0.39 \text{ kN/m}^2)$$

Step 3. Calculate the wind uplift pressure, F.

$$F = (C_{pe} - C_{pi})q$$

The external pressure coeficient C_{pe} is greater for the perimeter of the roof than for the general area. Therefore the value of wind pressure, F must be calculated separately for both areas.

The general area

The building height ratio h/w = 5/40 = 0.13, i.e. <0.5. Therefore the value of the external pressure coefficient, C_{pe}, from Table 8.4.2 is –1.2.

For this example, we will assume that the building has no large openings. So C_{pi} is +0.2. Therefore:

$$F = (C_{pe} - C_{pi})q$$
$$= (-1.2 - +0.2) \times 389.3$$
$$= -545\text{N/m}^2$$

The negative value of F signifies an uplift pressure in the general area which the attachment of each layer of the roof must withstand if damage due to wind action is to be avoided in the 'once in 50 years' wind.

Uplift may be wholly or partly resisted by the permanent dead-weight of ballast, finishes, and other construction above the critical layer. In the case of a light membrane, it is conservative to ignore dead-weight and provide uplift resistance either by adhesion or fixings.

To calculate the number of fixings required to resist this wind uplift, simply divide the uplift pressure on a square metre by the safety working resistance of the fixings. If the design pullout strength of a fixing (for the deck and insulation being specified) were to be – say – 0.3kN, then the number of fixings required per square metre in the general roof area would be:

$$\text{fixing per m}^2 = \frac{\text{wind uplift pressure}}{\text{pullout strength of fixings}}$$
$$= \frac{545}{300}$$
$$= 1.8 \text{ or, more practically, 2}$$

Alternatively, if the waterproof covering were to be ballasted with a 50mm depth of 20–40mm gravel ballast, the resistance provided by the ballast can be calculated.

Dead-weight of ballast per m^2
$$= \text{density (kg/m}^3) \times \text{thickness (m)} \times 9.8$$
(the g factor for mass to weight)

The density of 20–40mm gravel is 1600kg/m³

Dead-weight of 50mm gravel ballast per m^2
$$= 1600 \times 0.05 \times 9.8$$
$$= 784\text{N/ m}^2$$

The factor of safety against uplift is therefore
$$\frac{784}{545} = 1.44$$

which is acceptable (subject to the designer's judgement).

The perimeter areas

The maximum local C_{pe} for the perimeter, taken from *BSCP3: Chapter V: Part 2*, is – 2.0. The maximum local C_{pe} effect zone (y) is determined from y = h or 0.15w whichever is the lesser, where h is the building height and w the lesser plan dimension.

The zone y acts around the perimeter for a mono-pitch. For other roof plans, and pitches, guidance on the effect zone should be taken from the Code of Practice.

C_{pi} and q are the same as for the general area so the wind pressure in the perimeter areas is

$$F = (C_{pe} - C_{pi})q$$
$$= (-2.0 - +0.2) \times 389.3$$
$$= -856.5\text{N/m}^2$$

From above, 50mm of gravel ballast provides 784N/m² of uplift by its self-weight. This would not be suficient to restrain the waterproof covering at the perimeter, so more gravel or a more dense ballast must be used. An alternative solution is to provide concrete paving slabs.

The density of paving slabs is typically 2300kg/m³.

Dead weight of 50mm paving slabs per m^2
$$= 2300 \times 0.05 \times 9.8$$
$$= 1128\text{N/ m}^2$$

The factor of safety against uplift is therefore
$$\frac{1128}{856.5} = 1.32$$

which is barely adequate, but can be enhanced above 1.4 by adding the weight of a screed.

Worked examples for uplift of loose-laid insulation boards and for wind scour of gravel ballast are given in *BRE Digests 346* and *311*.

continued ▶

Critical factors

- General uplift pressure.
- Locally more severe uplift.

- Tables of standardised data are available to assess capacity to resist uplift pressures.
- Other specific data will be available from system and materials suppliers.

Table 8.4.3
Safe working resistance of typical polyester based bituminous membranes nailed to timber decking

Fixing	Safe working resistance to wind uplift (kN/m²)	
	Nails at 150mm centres (45 per m²)	Nails at 100mm centres (100 per m²)
Large-headed galvanised clout nails nailed through membrane into minimum 19mm timber boarding	2.0 - 2.7	4.5 - 6.0

Table 8.4.4
Typical bond strength of bitumen bonding to various substrates

Substrate method	Bonding resistance of bond (kN/m²)	Safe working
Dense concrete and cement/sand screed	Partial bond type 3G (to *BS747*) underlayer	4.0
Lightweight concrete or screed and woodwool (pre-felted or pre-screeded)	Partial bond type 3G (to *BS747*) underlayer	3.0
Rigid urethane foams	Partial bond Type 3G (to *BS747*) underlayer	2.0–3.5
Cork	Fully bonded	3.5
Wood fibre	Fully bonded	3.5
Cellular glass	Fully bonded	3.5
Fibre	Fully bonded	3.0[A]
Perlite	Fully bonded	2.5[A]
Polystyrene beadboard overlaid with wood fibre	Fully bonded	3.5

Note:
[A] Tests and practical experience with these boards have shown that the bond to them can be variable. Unless evidence is available to the contrary, mechanically fix through the first layer of roofing. These boards should not be used in exposed locations or without a heavy surfacing of stone chippings or tiles, unless satisfactory evidence of performance is available.

Table 8.4.5
Safe working resistance of common insulation boards fixed to a minimum of 0.7mm thick galvanised steel decking

Insulation board	Method of attachment	Number of fixings[A] per m² for safe resistance to wind uplift							
		Wind uplift pressure (kN/m²)							
		1.0	1.5	2.0	2.5	3.0	3.5	4.0	4.5
Cork, wood fibre, cellular glass, polystyrene beadboard, rigid urethene foam	Bitumen adhesive	0	0	0	0	3	3	4	5
Mineral fibre, perlite[B]	Bitumen adhesive	0	0	3	4	5	6	8	9
Any	Mechanical fixing only	6	6	6	6	7	9	10	11

Notes:
[A] 11 gauge screws with 70mm washers are minimum size to be used. Where mechanical fixings are necessary to supplement or replace a bitumen bond at least four fixings should be used for each board.

[B] Because of the unreliable bond of bituminous roofing to mineral fibre and perlite, fixings must be made through the first layer, which should be a high performance membrane.

Further reading:
BSCP3: Chapter V: Part 2 Wind loads • BRE Digest 311 Wind scour of gravel ballast on roofs • BRE Digest 346 The assessment of wind loads

• Specific checks are needed to confirm the applicability of standardised information.

Table 8.4.6
Dead weights of common flat roofing components

Component	Material	Dead weight (kN/m²)
Surface finishes	Mineral chippings (12-15mm layer)	0.15 - 0.18
	50mm layer, 20 - 40mm stones (1600kg/m³)	0.78
	GRC tiles (18mm)	0.22
	Concrete tiles (25mm)	0.57
	Concrete paving slabs (50mm)	1.13
Membranes and sheeting (*including bonding bitumen)	Two layers felt*	0.07
	Three layers felt*	0.10
	Mineral surfaced layer, extra	0.01
	Bonding bitumen, one layer	0.015
	Bituminous VCL, one layer	0.03
	Polymeric single ply	0.01 - 0.03
	Asphalt (10mm)	0.21
	Asphalt (20mm)	0.42
	Lead+	0.4 - 0.5
	Copper+	0.05 - 0.1
	Zinc+	0.04 - 0.08
Insulation boards (25mm thickness)	Cork	0.03
	Wood fibre - plain	0.06
	Wood fibre - bitumen impregnated	0.07
	Cellular glass	0.035
	Glass fibre	0.045
	Mineral fibre	0.05
	Perlite	0.05
	Polystyrene beadboard, pre-felted	0.02
	Rigid urethane foam	0.01
Screeds	Dense cement - sand (100mm)	2.0
	Lightweight cement - sand (100mm)	1.2 - 1.8
	Aerated concrete (100mm)	0.54
	Vermiculite (100mm)	1.1
Structural decking (+weight dependent on material thickness and profile - see manufacturer's literature; typical values given)	Steel decking+	0.07 - 0.16
	Aluminium decking+	0.03 - 0.06
	Pre-felted reinforced woodwool (50mm)	0.3
	Pre-screeded reinforced woodwool (50mm)	0.3
	Timber (20mm, softwood)	0.1
	Dense reinforced concrete (100mm)	2.4
	Lightweight reinforced concrete (density 1900kg/m³ and 100mm thick)	1.9

Critical factors

• Tables of standard data can provide useful information but should be assessed against the actual materials.

Further reading in the Guide:
4.10 Wind • 7.10 Design for wind resistance

188

Detail design principles 9

9.1 Key diagram

- Wherever there is a change or discontinuity in material or in the roof geometry careful consideration of the associated detail must be given.

- Such details are often 3-dimensional in character and the difficulties to be solved may not be apparent solely from isolated simple sections.

- This schematic key diagram is shown to locate details for a variety of roof designs and conditions. The drawing itself must not be considered appropriate for any particular roof type.

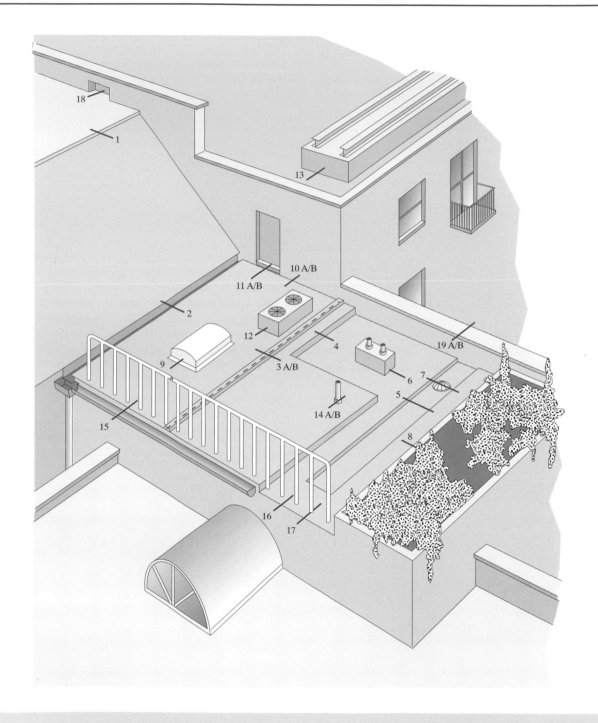

- The roof system is subject to dynamic loads from gravity, wind, temperature changes, humidity changes, air pressure changes.
- The details must allow for suitable construction tolerances and movement.
- The purpose of the schematic diagrams is to identify those aspects that must be considered when approaching the design of specific details.

Key

1	Flat roof to pitched roof
2	Pitched roof to flat roof with gutter
3A	Movement joint - upstand
3B	Movement joint - flush
4	Step
5	Internal gutter
6	Boxed-in pipes or extract
7	Outlet
8	Planted roof
9	Rooflight
10A	Abutment - integral deck
10B	Abutment - accommodating movement
11A	Opening - integral deck
11B	Opening - accommodating movement
12	Plant plinth above waterproofing layer
13	Plinth
14A	Service penetration - cold
14B	Service penetration - hot
15	Eaves with gutter
16	Verge
17	Balustrade fixing
18	Chute
19A	Parapet - integral deck
19B	Parapet - accommodating movement

General

Those areas that must be addressed in the design development fall into risk categories:

A Stability and integrity.
B Discontinuity of material, substrate. or roof geometry and differential movement.
C Water path.
D Convection path.
E Conduction path with risk of cold bridging.
F Fire.
G Condensation.
H Ventilation requirement.

Other considerations must be borne in mind:

- Ease of construction.
- Ease of access for inspection.
- Ease of repair and replacement.
- Method of attachment.
- Material compatibility.

Membranes must not be carried across building movement joints or other structural discontinuities capable of independent movement. Proper movement joints must be provided at such critical points.

Penetrations through roof openings should be minimised. They should be grouped through specially designed and waterproofed service boxes which allow for hot and cold services and their future replacement.

Penetrations or upstands should be located such that sufficient space is allowed between them and other obstructions so the detai can be properly formed.

Membrane laps and upstand heights must be maintained at all details.

Cold bridges through the insulated layer should be avoided. Continuity for insulation around the perimeter details, roof services and penetrations is important. Integrity of the vapour control layer at all points is vital.

Direct excessive imposed loading of the roof finish, particularly point loads, must be prevented. Loads should be evenly distributed.

Internal gutters should be avoided if possible. If necessary, they must be wide enough to be formed properly and to allow for maintenance. ■

Critical factors

- Integrity.
- Provision for movement.
- Material compatibility.
- Provision for discharge of water.
- Consistency between different detail drawings and with the specification.

12 Mastic Asphalt	13 Polymeric Single Ply	14 Copper	15 Lead Sheet	16 Other Membranes	17 Thermal Insulants	18 Specification	19 Contracts & Procurement	20 Inspection	21 Maintenance	22 Bibliography	23 Index
263	301	331	353	375	383	393	399	413	429	437	455

Schematic diagrams

- Deciding upon the type of flat roof construction may be influenced by the range of design solutions to the pitched roof element. They should be considered together.
- The interface between the flat and pitched areas should be detailed to allow the maintenance, repair or replacement of one with the minimum disturbance of the other.

Detail 1
Flat roof to pitched roof

Every effort should be made ensure the insulation is continuous to avoid cold bridges.

Inverted roofs are generally not recommended where abutting a pitched roof, particularly where thermal discontinuity cannot be eliminated. They can be accommodated if the discharge of the roof takes place in a direction away from the pitched roof below.

In situations of high risk the VCL layer should be continuous between roofs. ■

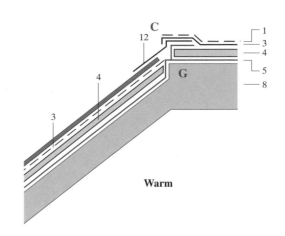

Warm

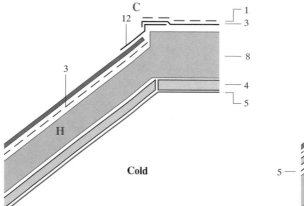

Cold

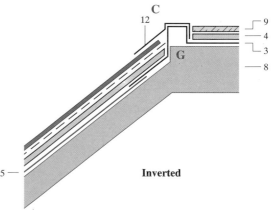

Inverted

Key												
	1	Surface protection	5	Vapour control layer	9	Paving	A	Stability and integrity	D	Convection path	H	Ventilation
	2	Protection layer	6	Filter layer	10	Earth	B	Differential	E	Conduction path		requirement
	3	Water barrier	7	Isolating layer	11	Timber		movement	F	Fire risk		
	4	Insulation	8	Structure	12	Flashing	C	Water path	G	Condensation risk		

Chapter	1	2	3	4	5	6	7	8	9	10	11
Contents	Introduction	History	Regulatory Methods	Principles	Surveys	Constraints & Targets	Design Selection	Calculations	Detail Design Principles	Evaluation of Design	Built-up Roofing
Page	1	19	31	45	83	95	105	165	189	217	221

Detail 2
Pitched roof to flat roof with gutter

When considering cold roof construction, provision must be made for ventilation of the void between insulation and roof finish.

It may be possible to ventilate all sections of the roof in one continuous air flow parallel to the fall line.

The provision of ventilation slots or ventilating components in the pitched roof may be necessary.

Gutter waterproof layers must be taken up sufficiently on the inclined slope under tiles and isolating layers to avoid problems should gutters become blocked or in snow conditions. It is usual practice to require an effective vertical protection of 150mm. ∎

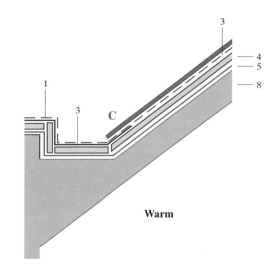

Warm

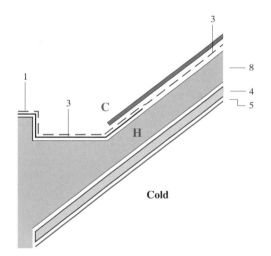

Cold

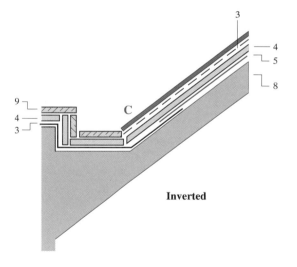

Inverted

Critical factors

- Compatibility of pitched and flat roof design.
- Continuity of insulation.
- Adequate upstands in gutters.
- Ease of maintenance

- Design measures must be taken to mitigate the consequences of differential movement between system components.
  - Use dimensionally stable substrate materials.
  - Isolate the membrane from the substrate by loose laying partial bonding or the incorporation of separating layers.

Detail 3A
Movement joint - upstand

Provision must be made in the detailing of the roof finish to accommodate any movement in the structure or the underlying deck.

Particular problems occur where movement joints in the structure meet abutments or make changes in direction.

Movement joints must be assessed for:

- passage of water
- passage of fire
- passage of heat
- passage of sound
- interruption of drainage
- continuity of vapour control layer
- appearance.

Copings over double upstand kerbs must themselves incorporate allowance for movement. Joints in manufactured copings must incorporate sealed or drained straps.

On very low U-value roof designs, cappings over movement joints may also require insulating. ■

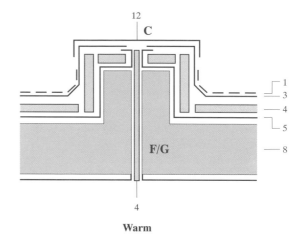

Warm

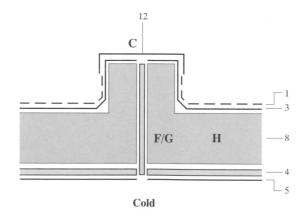

Cold

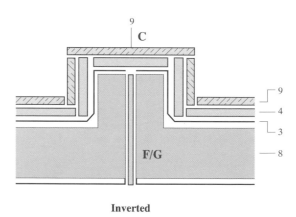

Inverted

Key												
	1	Surface protection	5	Vapour control layer	9	Paving	A	Stability and integrity	D	Convection path	H	Ventilation requirement
	2	Protection layer	6	Filter layer	10	Earth	B	Differential movement	E	Conduction path		
	3	Water barrier	7	Isolating layer	11	Timber	C	Water path	F	Fire risk		
	4	Insulation	8	Structure	12	Flashing			G	Condensation risk		

Chapter	1	2	3	4	5	6	7	8	9	10	11
Contents	Introduction	History	Regulatory Methods	Principles	Surveys	Constraints & Targets	Design Selection	Calculations	Detail Design Principles	Evaluation of Design	Built-up Roofing
Page	1	19	31	45	83	95	105	165	189	217	221

Detail 3B
Movement joint - flush

The preferred way to deal with substantial anticipated movement is to construct upstand kerbs in order to lift the vulnerable joint above the general waterproofing level.

In some instances such as refurbishment, or where drainage across a movement joint may be unavoidable, waterproofing at the general level will be required. This joint must be watertight and remain so over the anticipated life while accommodating the movement expected. ■

Critical factors

• Provision for movement.

• Avoiding stress in the membrane material.

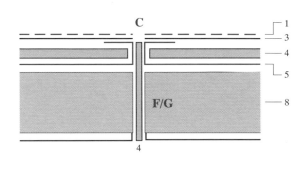

Warm

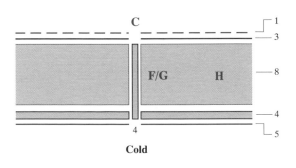

Cold

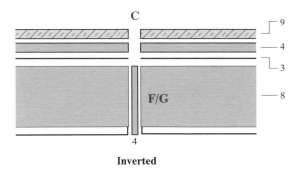

Inverted

- Considerations must be given to the following
  - Differential movement at junctions
  - Continuity of insulation and vapour control layers
  - Protection of vulnerable edges.

Detail 4
Step

Physical protection will be required to insulation at steps to prevent crushing/damage. Where continuity of the insulation is critical the insulating layer must not be interrupted in order to provide this protection.

With flexible deck design additional support may be necessary at the base of the upstand to prevent differential movement transmitting stress to the roof finish. ■

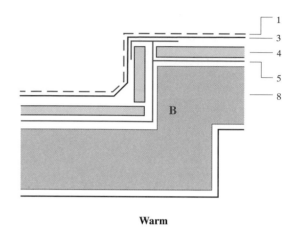

Warm

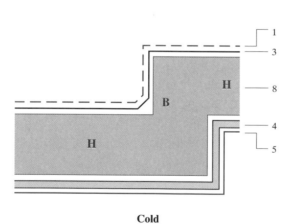

Cold

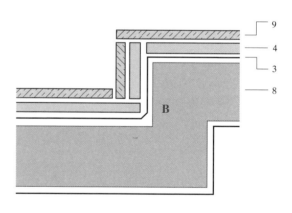

Inverted

Key	1	Surface protection	5	Vapour control layer	9	Paving	A	Stability and integrity	D	Convection path	H	Ventilation
	2	Protection layer	6	Filter layer	10	Earth	B	Differential	E	Conduction path		requirement
	3	Water barrier	7	Isolating layer	11	Timber		movement	F	Fire risk		
	4	Insulation	8	Structure	12	Flashing	C	Water path	G	Condensation risk		

Detail 5
Internal gutter

Where the roof design can arrange for falls to outlet positions the use of box gutters is best avoided.

Internal box gutters should only be used where the roof cannot be designed to fall directly to outlets or external gutters.

The arris of a gutter edge is a potentially vulnerable point. Additional protection or chamfering may be necessary.

Box gutters must be of adequate width to:

- facilitate construction
- enable outlets to perform to design capacity
- accommodate the overall gulley outlet
- allow for maintenance and inspection. ■

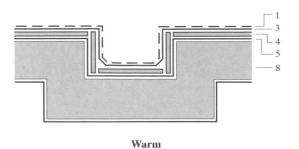

Warm

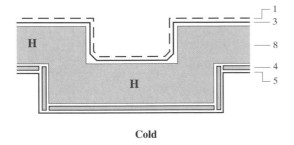

Cold

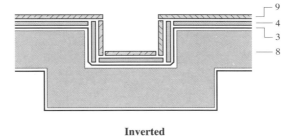

Inverted

- Generally where major service elements pass through the roof the detailing of the waterproofing is most satisfactorily resolved by forming upstand kerbs and providing a purpose made capping.
- Very small penetrations of bituminous membranes may be accommodated by hot pour sealing techniques but the consequences of loss of performance, in relation to the space beneath should be assessed for each case.

Detail 6
Boxed-in pipes or extract

Penetrations through the roof waterproofing system by service pipes, flues, extracts etc should be kept to a minimum and where at all possible grouped together. Areas of penetrations should be kept away from other roof details parapets, abutments outlets, balustrades, etc.

Consideration must be given to:

- differential movement of services and structure
- maintaining the integrity and performance of the total roof insulation
- acoustic performance
- heat transmission from flues to the surrounding membranes and other roof components.

Purpose-made cappings to falls are recommended; they may require insulation. ∎

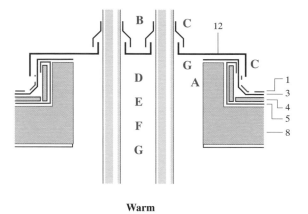

Warm

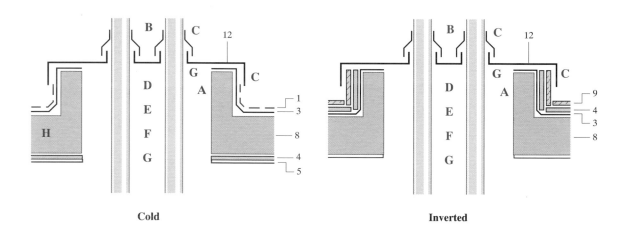

Cold

Inverted

Key	1	Surface protection	5	Vapour control layer	9	Paving	A	Stability and integrity	D	Convection path	H	Ventilation
	2	Protection layer	6	Filter layer	10	Earth	B	Differential	E	Conduction path		requirement
	3	Water barrier	7	Isolating layer	11	Timber		movement	F	Fire risk		
	4	Insulation	8	Structure	12	Flashing	C	Water path	G	Condensation risk		

Chapter	1	2	3	4	5	6	7	8	9	10	11
			Regulatory			Constraints &	Design		Detail Design	Evaluation of	Built-up
Contents	Introduction	History	Methods	Principles	Surveys	Targets	Selection	Calculations	Principles	Design	Roofing
Page	1	19	31	45	83	95	105	165	189	217	221

Detail 7
Outlet

Both box gutters and rainwater outlets must be installed at the correct height in relation to the surrounding waterproofing. Care must be taken to ensure there is no build up of material dressed into the gutter or outlet. This can create local ponding and inhibit water flow. Dishing prior to the outlet or gutter can overcome some of these problems.

Insulation of rainwater pipes and collars may be required to prevent condensation on the pipe surface but this may create the necessity for trace heating.

Downpipe connections should be designed to accommodate vertical movement on responsive structures.

If the outlet flange is set at the insulation top level, local compression of the insulation should be avoided by the use of collars at fixing points or incompressible blocks between them. ■

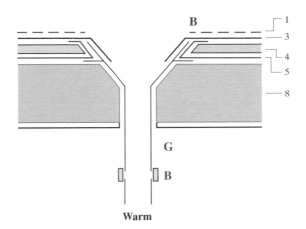

Warm

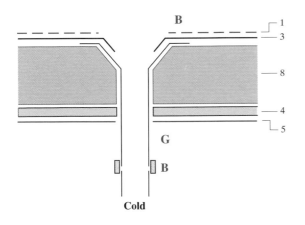

Cold

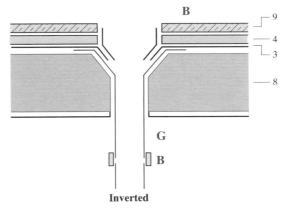

Inverted

Critical factors

- Group services.
- Insulated capping may be necessary
- Provision of adequate falls.
- Avoid material build-up which might interfere with water flow.
- Allow for maintenance of services

12 Mastic Asphalt	13 Polymeric Single Ply	14 Copper	15 Lead Sheet	16 Other Membranes	17 Thermal Insulants	18 Specification	19 Contracts & Procurement	20 Inspection	21 Maintenance	22 Bibliography	23 Index
263	301	331	353	375	383	393	399	413	429	437	455

- Roof gardens should be designed and executed to give trouble-free performance for the life of the building. Repairs and replacement may be prohibitively expensive.
- The designer will need to consider:
  - the additional total and local loading
  - correct falls to ensure drainage
  - water retention for planting
  - roof damage and gardening activity protection
  - measures to secure trees against wind uplift
  - irrigation.

Detail 8
Planted roof

Waterproofing to roof gardens will generally be of the inverted roof design although a warm roof is also feasible. In this latter case insulation of high compressive strength will be required and the membrane must be more fully protected to prevent subsequent physical damage.

Although the detail indicated for the cold roof is feasible it will not perform hygrothermally as a cold roof.

Independent drainage of planters will be required in order to prevent excessive water build up. Drainage layers must be incorporated in the build up with filter layers to prevent the leaching of soil into the drainage layer.

Care over choice of plant species must be made in order to avoid root damage.

Incorporation of movement joints under roof gardens should be avoided wherever possible but if not, require very particular attention.

Upstand heights above soil level must be maintained at a minimum of 150mm or the waterproofing layer continuous over the upstand. Upstands must be protected. ■

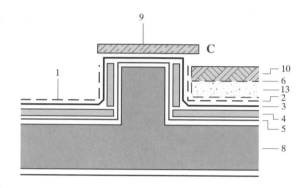

Warm

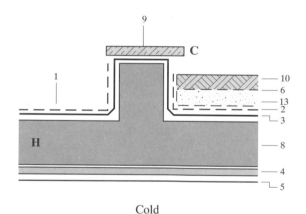

Cold

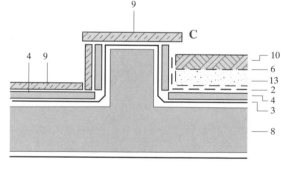

Inverted

Key	1	Surface protection	5	Vapour control layer	9	Paving	A	Stability and integrity	D	Convection path	H	Ventilation
	2	Protection layer	6	Filter layer	10	Earth	B	Differential	E	Conduction path		requirement
	3	Water barrier	7	Isolating layer	11	Timber		movement	F	Fire risk		
	4	Insulation	8	Structure	13	Drainage layer	C	Water path	G	Condensation risk		

Detail 9
Rooflight

Rooflight upstands should be treated as upstands elsewhere in respect of minimum height etc.

Particular care must be given to the detailing of lightweight upstands or proprietary rooflights on responsive decks. Reinforcement of the upstand junction may be necessary. ■

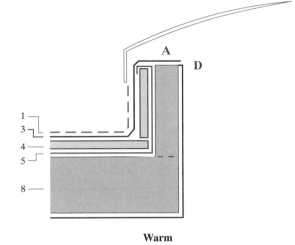

Warm

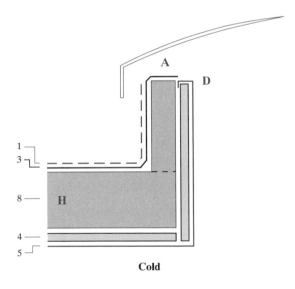

Cold

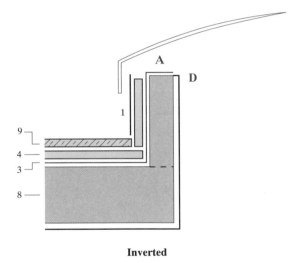

Inverted

12	13	14	15	16	17	18	19	20	21	22	23
Mastic Asphalt	Polymeric Single Ply	Copper	Lead Sheet	Other Membranes	Thermal Insulants	Specification	Contracts & Procurement	Inspection	Maintenance	Bibliography	Index
263	301	331	353	375	383	393	399	413	429	437	455

- Full width cavity trays must be provided through walls to prevent the bypass of water. Laps in these trays must be sealed and weep holes provided.

- Lead flashings should not exceed 1.5m in length.

- If thermal upgrading of the roof is likely during the building life it is recommended that cavity trays should terminate 75mm above the upstands for waterproofing.

- Cavity trays and flashings are separate components.

Detail 10A
Abutment - integral deck

Minimum height for skirtings is 150mm.

Skirtings generally must be protected against degradation by solar radiation. Some membranes may also require physical protection.

Cavity trays should be taken through the full thickness of the wall to discharge over the flashing.

Flashings must be housed well into the wall. The purpose of the flashing is to protect the head of the waterproofing upstand and to deflect water from above, including that from the cavity tray. Flashings should cap upstands by a minimum of 75mm. ■

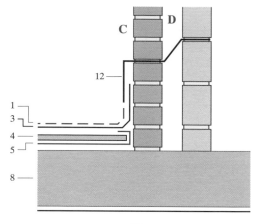

Warm

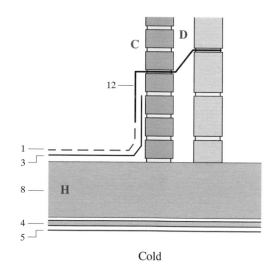

Cold

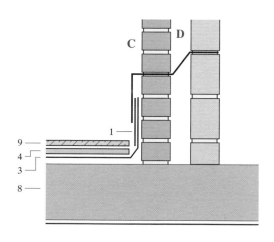

Inverted

Key													
	1	Surface protection	5	Vapour control layer	9	Paving	A	Stability and integrity	D	Convection path	H	Ventilation
	2	Protection layer	6	Filter layer	10	Earth	B	Differential	E	Conduction path		requirement
	3	Water barrier	7	Isolating layer	11	Timber		movement	F	Fire risk		
	4	Insulation	8	Structure	12	Flashing	C	Water path	G	Condensation risk		

Detail 10B
Abutment - accommodating movement

Where provision for movement is incorporated flashings must be fully supported.

Ideally, flashings should be dressed over fillets to ensure water does not pond on the flat sections and drain internally through the laps.

Upstands must act monolithically with the deck. ■

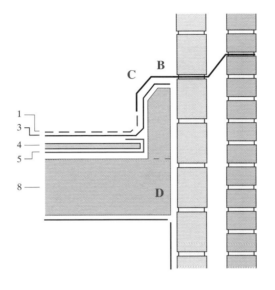

Warm

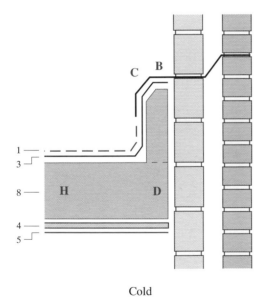

Cold

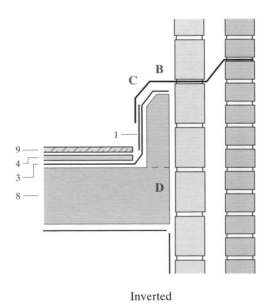

Inverted

- Openings on to the roof will require the formations of upstands. These upstands may need to accommodate movement.
- Consideration should be given to the extent and nature of traffic which may access the roof and what protection to the roof is appropriate.

Detail 11A
Opening - integral deck

A minimum height of 150mm should be maintained at upstands. Ideally this upstand height should be continued at the same level on either side of door openings, ensuring consistency of detailing.

Falls should be designed such that water drains away from any opening.

Consideration must be given to the protection of exposed membranes on upstands.

Cill trays and water bars should be provided to prevent water ingress under the threshold. ■

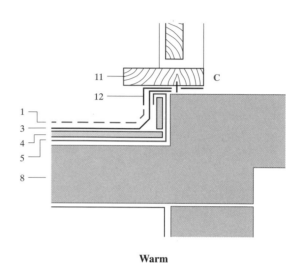

Warm

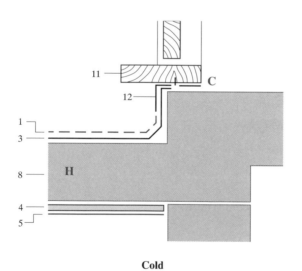

Cold

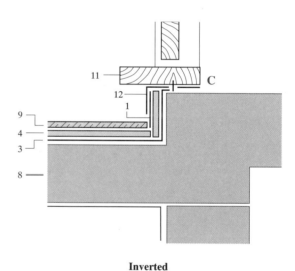

Inverted

Key											
	1	Surface protection	5	Vapour control layer	9	Paving	A	Stability and integrity	D	Convection path	H	Ventilation requirement
	2	Protection layer	6	Filter layer	10	Earth	B	Differential movement	E	Conduction path		
	3	Water barrier	7	Isolating layer	11	Timber	C	Water path	F	Fire risk		
	4	Insulation	8	Structure	12	Flashing			G	Condensation risk		

Chapter	1	2	3	4	5	6	7	8	9	10	11
Contents	Introduction	History	Regulatory Methods	Principles	Surveys	Constraints & Targets	Design Selection	Calculations	Detail Design Principles	Evaluation of Design	Built-up Roofing
Page	1	19	31	45	83	95	105	165	189	217	221

Detail 11B
Opening - accommodating movement

Where provision for movement is allowed for, flashing must be adequately supported with bridging pieces.

In all cases of openings adequate hardstanding should be provided to protect the roof and where appropriate these should be connected to walkways.

Where possible construct upstands integrally with the deck. ■

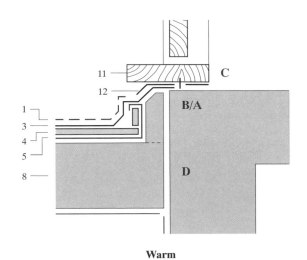

Warm

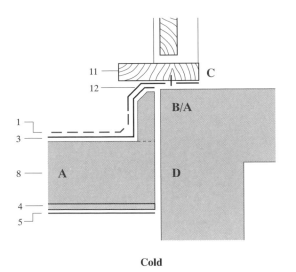

Cold

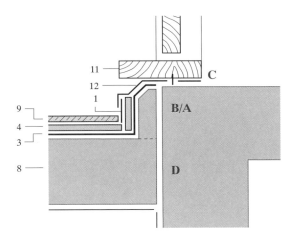

Inverted

Critical factors

• Incorporate water bars to avoid bypassing of the waterproofing.

• Maintain constant upstand heights.

- Local loadings must be assessed particularly on lightweight decks.

- Where possible roof mounted items should be raised to give access to roof finishes.

- Assessment of the effect upon the roof drainage must be given at an early stage in the design process.

- Particular care must be given to the detailing of lightweight upstands or proprietary roof lights on responsive decks. Reinforcement of the upstand junction may be necessary.

Detail 12
Plant plinth above
waterproofing layer

Where possible, placing of plant or equipment directly onto waterproofing should be avoided as it introduces possible long-term maintenance problems.

In any event this application would only be suitable for static loads stable under wind loading and requiring no fixings to hold them down.

Calculations must be carried out to assess the imposed loadings and the capacity of the structure and insulation to cater for these loadings.

Protection and load spreading layers must be incorporated over waterproof membranes.

Consideration should be given to a special provision for plant located in corral with their own drainage and waterproofing system kept separate from the main roof. ■

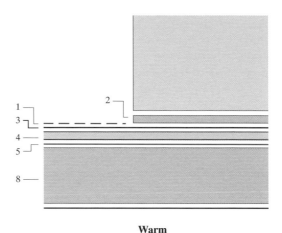

Warm

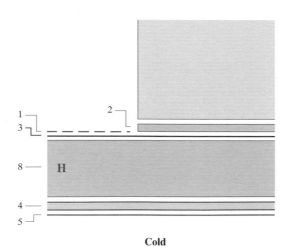

Cold

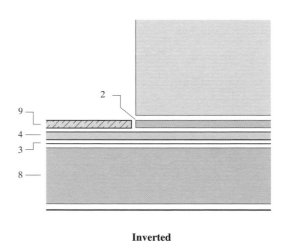

Inverted

Key													
	1	Surface protection	5	Vapour control layer	9	Paving	A	Stability and integrity	D	Convection path	H	Ventilation
	2	Protection layer	6	Filter layer	10	Earth	B	Differential	E	Conduction path		requirement
	3	Water barrier	7	Isolating layer	11	Timber		movement	F	Fire risk		
	4	Insulation	8	Structure	12	Flashing	C	Water path	G	Condensation risk		

Detail 13
Plinth

The most satisfactory way of detailing support elements for major components is to form raised plinths that avoid penetrating the waterproof layer.

This type of solution raises the vulnerable details above the general level of the roof surface.

The waterproofing of the plinth will depend primarily on the size and nature of the element to be secured. Generally the plinth top surface will be dressed in Code 5 lead.

If a significant number of fixing/penetrations of the waterproofing layer are necessary consideration should be given to a secondary base placed over the waterproofing layer.

Drainage on top of the plinth and between rails must be considered and adequate falls provided. ■

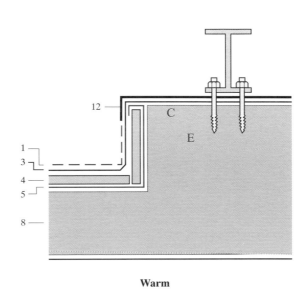

Warm

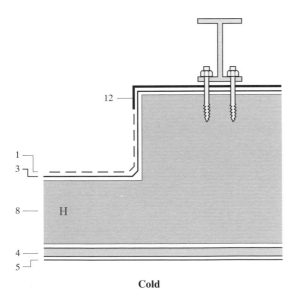

Cold

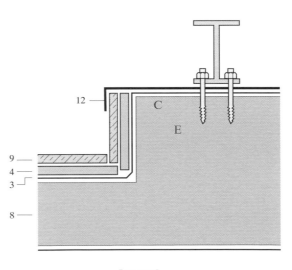

Inverted

Critical factors

- Long-term maintenance and demounting of equipment so as not to disturb waterproofing.

- Assess compression resistance of insulation.

12	13	14	15	16	17	18	19	20	21	22	23
Mastic Asphalt	Polymeric Single Ply	Copper	Lead Sheet	Other Membranes	Thermal Insulants	Specification	Contracts & Procurement	Inspection	Maintenance	Bibliography	Index
263	301	331	353	375	383	393	399	413	429	437	455

- Pipes and services passing through the roof finish must be sleeved and weathered. This should be insulated to prevent condensation forming on their surface.
- Where pipes are grouped together they must be spaced so that each pipe can be adequately weathered.

Detail 14A
Service penetrations - cold

The following aspects need to be considered when detailing pipes passing through the waterproofing layer:

- group together where possible in a box
- locate away from other roof features
- weathering of services
- insulate services and sleeves to avoid cold bridging and the risk of condensation
- provide adequate support and protection to the membrane
- design should minimise heat loss by convection. ■

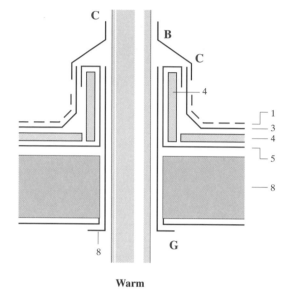

Warm

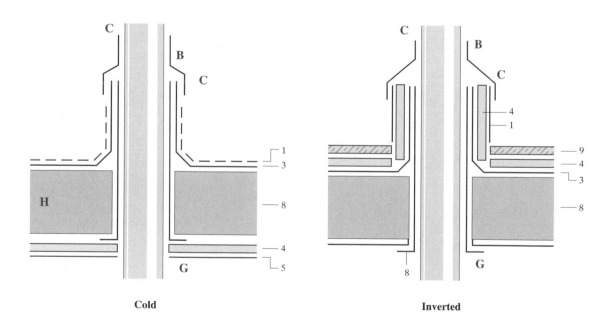

Cold   **Inverted**

Key												
	1	Surface protection	5	Vapour control layer	9	Paving	A	Stability and integrity	D	Convection path	H	Ventilation
	2	Protection layer	6	Filter layer	10	Earth	B	Differential	E	Conduction path		requirement
	3	Water barrier	7	Isolating layer	11	Timber		movement	F	Fire risk		
	4	Insulation	8	Structure	12	Flashing	C	Water path	G	Condensation risk		

Detail 14B
Service penetrations - hot

Additional when considering the penetration for hot services the following points need to be borne in mind:

- Sleeving of services to allow for movement on hot services and to provide a support for the roof finishes
- Fireproofing of very hot services such as flues to ensure heat is not transmitted in any manner to the roof finish.

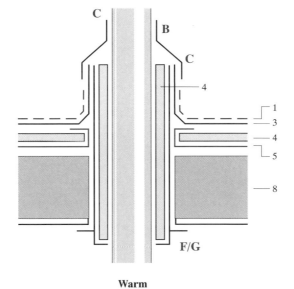

Warm

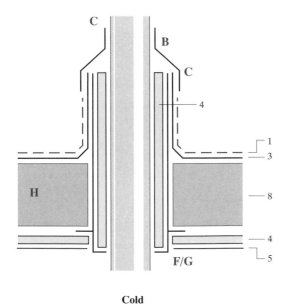

Cold

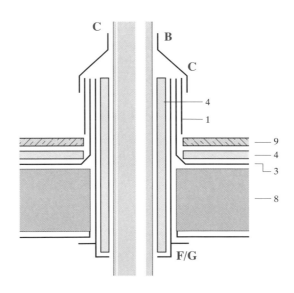

Inverted

Critical factors

- Provision for movement.
- Insulation.
- Support to membrane.

12	13	14	15	16	17	18	19	20	21	22	23
Mastic Asphalt	Polymeric Single Ply	Copper	Lead Sheet	Other Membranes	Thermal Insulants	Specification	Contracts & Procurement	Inspection	Maintenance	Bibliography	Index
263	301	331	353	375	383	393	399	413	429	437	455

• Water must be allowed to flow easily off roofs at those points intended. It may be advisable to reduce insulation thickness at eaves edges to allow for build-up on the waterproof membrane and ensure that the water flow is not impeded.

Detail 15
Eaves with gutter

Overhanging eaves should be used when at all possible where rainwater discharges into gutters. The drip must project into the gutter and stand clear of the fascia.

Drips should be a minimum of 75mm.

Consideration must be given to preventing cold bridging at eaves. This may require insulation of soffit and fascias. ■

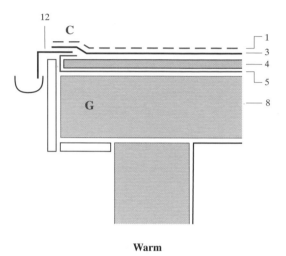

Warm

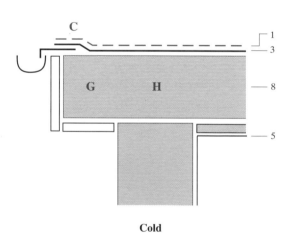

Cold

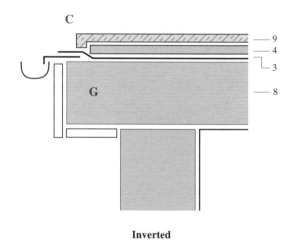

Inverted

Key											
1	Surface protection	5	Vapour control layer	9	Paving	A	Stability and integrity	D	Convection path	H	Ventilation requirement
2	Protection layer	6	Filter layer	10	Earth	B	Differential movement	E	Conduction path		
3	Water barrier	7	Isolating layer	11	Timber			F	Fire risk		
4	Insulation	8	Structure	12	Flashing	C	Water path	G	Condensation risk		

Chapter	1	2	3	4	5	6	7	8	9	10	11
Contents	Introduction	History	Regulatory Methods	Principles	Surveys	Constraints & Targets	Design Selection	Calculations	Detail Design Principles	Evaluation of Design	Built-up Roofing
Page	1	19	31	45	83	95	105	165	189	217	221

Detail 16
Verge

Where inverted roofs are proposed, special attention will be required to prevent wind uplift, or dislodging of perimeter insulation and ballasting.

Where upstands are provided they must be of adequate height to ensure that water is not discharged over the edge. For waterproof membranes this is typically 75mm. For metals where bay disciplines reduce total water flow to verges this may be reduced. ■

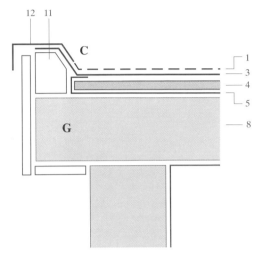

Warm

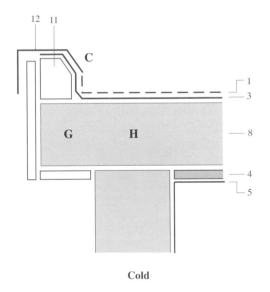

Cold

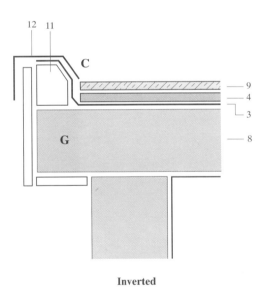

Inverted

| 12 | 13 | 14 | 15 | 16 | 17 | 18 | 19 | 20 | 21 | 22 | 23 |
Mastic Asphalt	Polymeric Single Ply	Copper	Lead Sheet	Other Membranes	Thermal Insulants	Specification	Contracts & Procurement	Inspection	Maintenance	Bibliography	Index
263	301	331	353	375	383	393	399	413	429	437	455

- Any penetration of the waterproof layer must be sufficiently robust to avoid flexing and stressing of the membrane.

Detail 17
Balustrade fixing

Where possible, penetration of the waterproofing layer by balustrades should be avoided. Movement and the difficulty of satisfactorily forming the membrane around the posts make these details particularly vulnerable.

Supports for railings should be on raised kerbs or plinths integral with the deck, this will allow satisfactory weatherproofing independent of the railing or barrier (see **Detail 19**). Where this is not possible such as on lightweight decks considerations should be given to separate bases placed above the waterproofing layer.

Where safety barriers are being considered they must be designed to withstand the loadings required by Approved Document K of the *Building Regulations*. ∎

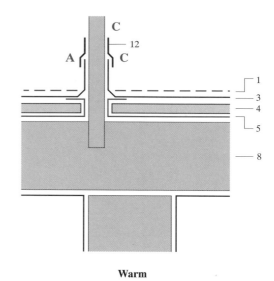

Warm

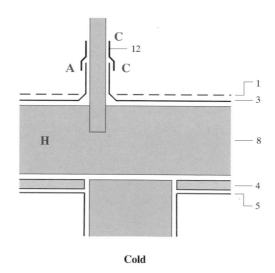

Cold

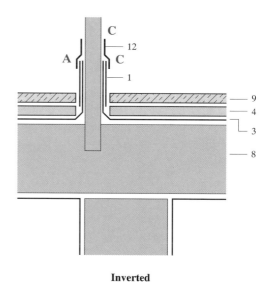

Inverted

Key											
	1	Surface protection	5	Vapour control layer	9	Paving	A	Stability and integrity	D	Convection path	H	Ventilation requirement
	2	Protection layer	6	Filter layer	10	Earth	B	Differential movement	E	Conduction path		
	3	Water barrier	7	Isolating layer	11	Timber			F	Fire risk		
	4	Insulation	8	Structure	12	Flashing	C	Water path	G	Condensation risk		

Chapter	1	2	3	4	5	6	7	8	9	10	11
Contents	Introduction	History	Regulatory Methods	Principles	Surveys	Constraints & Targets	Design Selection	Calculations	Detail Design Principles	Evaluation of Design	Built-up Roofing
Page	1	19	31	45	83	95	105	165	189	217	221

Detail 18
Chute

Chutes present a unique set of detailing problems. They should be avoided if at all possible.

To facilitate laying and dressing of membranes, chute openings should be formed at least 300mm in size, both horizontally and vertically.

The chute height must be co-ordinated with skirting heights generally so that flashing and cavity tray details can be continuous in one plane.

Typically, whatever membrane is used, the external chute arrangement and flashing will be formed in Code 5 lead.

Consideration may be given to the use of pre-formed chute components. ■

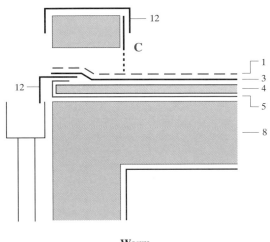

Warm

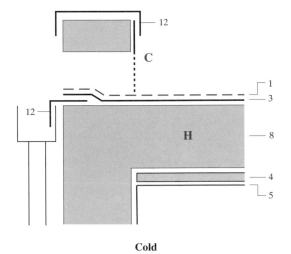

Cold

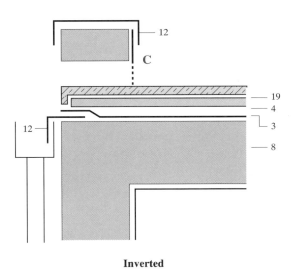

Inverted

Critical factors

- Avoid penetrations if possible.
- Check loadings of safety barriers.

• Where parapets also form safety barriers the waterproofing should be treated as for an abutment and should include for cavity trays and flashing as there are likely to be exposed sections of the wall above membrane level.

Detail 19A
Parapet - integral deck

Parapet detailing must address the following aspects:

• guarding/safety performance of parapet
• longitudinal movement of wall and coping
• under copings, dpcs/cavity trays
• adequate laps in flashings and physical restraint
• termination of insulation
• restraint of upstand waterproofing
• allowance for movement in discontinuous deck and wall
• protection of membrane
• adequate overhang of copings and provision of falls on copings. ■

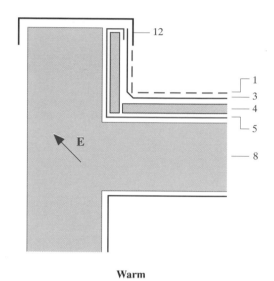

Warm

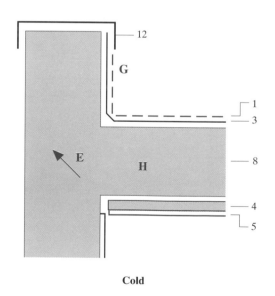

Cold

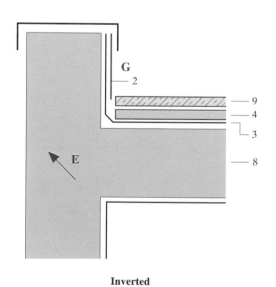

Inverted

Key	1	Surface protection	5	Vapour control layer	9	Paving	A	Stability and integrity	D	Convection path	H	Ventilation
	2	Protection layer	6	Filter layer	10	Earth	B	Differential	E	Conduction path		requirement
	3	Water barrier	7	Isolating layer	11	Timber		movement	F	Fire risk		
	4	Insulation	8	Structure	12	Flashing	C	Water path	G	Condensation risk		

Detail 19B
Parapet - accommodating movement

Where parapet junctions have to accommodate movement an upstand will be necessary. This upstand should act monolithically with the deck, and the waterproof membrane isolated from the upstand wall.

Protection of the junction will be undertaken by copings or flashings depending upon the height of the parapet. ■

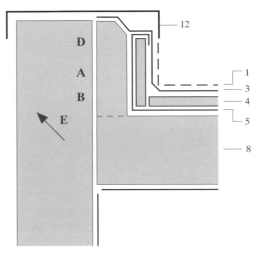

Warm

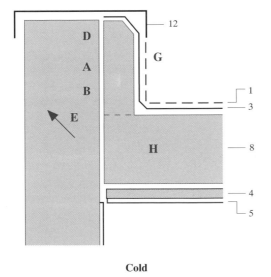

Cold

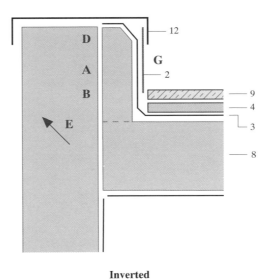

Inverted

12	13	14	15	16	17	18	19	20	21	22	23
Mastic Asphalt	Polymeric Single Ply	Copper	Lead Sheet	Other Membranes	Thermal Insulants	Specification	Contracts & Procurement	Inspection	Maintenance	Bibliography	Index
263	301	331	353	375	383	393	399	413	429	437	455

Evaluation of design 10

10.1 Evaluation checklist

- At any stage of the design process an evaluation of the roof design may be needed.
- Evaluation should be carried out against the requirements (constraints and targets) established by the designer at that stage and in terms of the suggested specification headings.
- Evaluation of designs can be made in a variety of ways against different criteria, for example life cycle costs, environmental considerations or risk of premature failure.

It is important for the success of a building or building element that some review or evaluation of the proposed design takes place before construction. A flat roof is no exception to this. An evaluation will, in essence, compare the proposed design against the **constraints** and **targets** of the project. In this Guide the concept and detail explanation of the kinds of requirements that might have to be satisfied are given in **Unit 6.1**. These form the basis of a checklist, which is used in **Unit 7.1** to sequence the design selection process. As the **design selection** procedures in the various units of **Chapter 7** are followed, a number of prompts are given for staged review or evaluation of the decisions reached at that time. There is also the suggestion to record the decision made, where appropriate, on a design checklist. In this way the evolution of the design can be noted. Once the individual decisions are made and reviewed it is useful to assess the whole package of decisions against the **constraints** and **targets**.

There are many possible ways of evaluating a design for a flat roof: on the basis of lowest initial cost, some form of lowest acceptable risk of failure, a whole life-cycle cost (see **Unit 4.14**), or an environmental assessment such as that under the BREEAM system. All of these have useful facets and drawbacks. The balance of these different approaches will vary with designer and client attitudes.

This Guide does not try to develop any of these approaches specifically but provides the framework in which information and decisions can be recorded. A suggested roof evaluation checklist has been devised using the headings discussed in **Unit 6.1**.

Designers may find this approach helpful, so the checklist is therefore included in loose leaf form in the Project Notebook. This checklist does not incorporate a 'scoring' system for the various aspects although designers may wish to create one for themselves. To illustrate how such a framework might be used, an example of the evaluation checklist, completed, for an imaginary roof design, is shown in Figure 10.1.1.

Project: *Meadow cottage*		Type of work: *New build*	
Evaluate design proposals against summary requirements	Design headings from Unit 7.1	Dimensions/ geometry	Structural deck and falls (Units 7.1 & 7.5)
Headings described in Unit 6.1 — Summary design requirements / Roof design proposal		*Roof zone 500. 2 areas of 6m x 12m*	*250 RC on frame*
Client programme/ budget	*Occupy June '93 Roof £10,000*		
Form/function	*Roof terrace possibility*	*OK for space*	*OK for loads*
Context	*Height restriction 4.5m*		*OK*
Structural	*High winds probable. Basic wind speed 48m/s*		*OK*
Climate control	*Severe rainfall, cold winters*		*OK*
Internal environment control	*Building Regulations $U = 0.25 \ W/m^2 K$*		*Use insulation to create falls?*
Durability/ working life	*Minimum maintenance 25 years life*		
Health & safety	*No fumes from site work*		*OK*
Environmental impact	*Desirable: Low energy materials*		*Possible problem*
Security	*No unauthorised access to roof*		*OK*
Construction method	*Fast track*		
Design process	*Fast track. design must finish week 3*		
Site processes	*Difficult access in lane*		*On site mixer*
Contract administration			
Notes		*OK*	*OK*

Chapter	1	2	3	4	5	6	7	8	9	10	11
Contents	Introduction	History	Regulatory Methods	Principles	Surveys	Constraints & Targets	Design Selection	Calculations	Detail Design Principles	Evaluation of Design	Built-up Roofing
Page	1	19	31	45	83	95	105	165	189	217	221

Further reading:

218

© BFRC / CIRIA: Flat Roofing: Design and Good Practice. 1993

- A proforma is provided to assist evaluation and to record design decisions. It also acts as a prompt to the designer—as many boxes as possible should be evaluated.
- A proforma may be helpful in a quality management system.

Evaluation by: BC **Date of evaluation:** 17.6.92 **BFRC/CIRIA: Flat Roofing Design and Good Practice**

Roof configur-ation (Unit 7.2)	Membrane (Unit 7.3)	Drainage system (Unit 7.4)	Thermal insulation (Unit 7.5)	Vapour control (Unit 7.7)	Finishes (Units 7.10 & 7.11)	Health & safety (Unit 3.4)	Details	Cost	Time	Notes
Warm	Mastic asphalt on sheathing felt	Perimeter outlets 6 per area @75ø	50mm board. Overall roof U value 0.52	Metal foil/bitumen felt below insulant	Solar reflective paint on MA	Perimeter lightning protection fixings	Complex movement joint at junction of areas	£13.000	10 weeks	
Slow to get watertight	Slow?	OK	OK	OK	OK			Too high		Rethink Budget?
OK	OK	OK	OK	OK	Special surface?					Consider terrace in detail
	OK	Sewer connection?	OK	OK	OK					
	OK	Watch outlet positions	OK	OK	OK					
OK	OK	OK	OK	OK	OK					
OK	OK	Cold bridges	PROBLEM	Joint sealing	OK					Reconsider design for U value requirements
OK	Watch surfaces	Regular maintenance	OK	OK	Regular maintenance required					Discuss maintenance with client
OK	Possible problem with access	OK	OK	OK	OK	Fire OK, lightning OK				
OK	Probably OK	OK	Possible problem	Probably OK	OK					Clarify client preferences
OK	OK	OK	OK	OK	OK					
Slow to complete waterproofing							Complex			
OK – lots of standard details	OK	Probably OK	OK but site cutting	Sealing joints?	OK	Slow?	Slow at critical stage			Check critical path
Complex sequences	Slows applications	OK	OK	OK	OK					
Probably OK if schedule controlled	Just OK	OK	Redesign, but in principal OK	Problem with inspections	Solar paint and terrace conflict	OK	Have to accept complications	Redesign?		Decision: Review design before construction can start

Critical factors

- Evaluation against constraints and targets
- Validity of assessment method and criteria
- Based on UK climate conditions

Further reading in the Guide:
4.14 Life-cycle costing • 6.1 Design requirements: Constraints and targets • 7.1 Design selection: general approach

12 Mastic Asphalt	13 Polymeric Single Ply	14 Copper	15 Lead Sheet	16 Other Membranes	17 Thermal Insulants	18 Specification	19 Contracts & Procurement	20 Inspection	21 Maintenance	22 Bibliography	23 Index
263	301	331	353	375	383	393	399	413	429	437	455

Built-up roofing 11

11.1 General description

- Built-up roofing consists of two or more layers of a bitumen sheet, bonded with hot bitumen.
- The bitumen sheet consists of a reinforcing base impregnated and coated with bitumen or modified bitumen.
- Several different reinforcing bases are used, with polyester bases now being the general purpose, quality material.

Basis of technology

Nature of materials

The built-up membrane has been a standard type of continuous waterproofing system for industrial flat roofs throughout the world for the best part of a century. It now finds application in all types of flat roofs.

A bitumen roofing 'felt' is essentially a preformed layer of reinforced bitumen. The term 'felt' is not generally used in this Guide, as it no longer aptly describes the composition of the modern high performance bitumen roofings in common use, the prime components of which are the bitumen and the base, which fulfils the dual roles of carrier at the manufacturing stage and reinforcement for the permanent roofing membrane.

A built-up roofing membrane consists of two or more superimposed layers of a bitumen roofing sheet, bedded and bonded with hot applied bitumen, or fused together by the torch application method, to form a continuous impermeable composite membrane. Cold applied bitumen adhesives are sometimes used in place of hot bitumen to bond roof membranes on small roofs or for minor repairs.

Special high performance bitumen sheets may be used for single layer systems. This is more common where a single layer of roofing is applied to an aged but otherwise sound built-up system as part of a refurbishment programme.

General considerations

From an engineering point of view, the built-up membrane may be viewed as a slab of bitumen, reinforced at various depths by the bases embedded in each of the preformed layers of which the built-up membrane is composed, along with the bonding layers that hold them together.

A particular advantage of the built-up system is that it affords the roofing designer the opportunity to choose from a range of mutually compatible materials and so to combine separate product features into a single composite membrane to meet the requirements of a particular roof construction.

Multiple layering reduces the reliance for success on achieving faultless workmanship in each layer. A fault in one layer will usually be covered by a subsequent one. However, this does not mean that any lower levels of skill in its applicators are acceptable than for other membranes; nor that supervision can be less; nor that a flood test, if appropriate, need not be carried out to prove the system installed.

The technology therefore involves the adaptation of factory-made sheets to create waterproof three dimensional roof forms by multilayering, cutting and forming on site. It continues to be skill-based with relatively few pre-formed components.

Constituent materials

The reinforcing base

The base plays an important role in the performance and durability of the built-up membrane. It gives to the roofing product and finished membrane:

- Dimensional stability
- Puncture resistance
- Crack-bridging capability and fatigue endurance
- Nail-holding strength and tear resistance
- Practical handling and forming characteristics.

The compositions, including weights and dimensions, of the common types of bitumen roofing are given in *BS747 Specification for Roofing Felts*. The different classes are designated by a type number which relates to the nature of the base, see Table 11.1.1.

Table 11.1.1
BS747 Types of reinforcing base

Type 1	Fibre felt (coded white - to be withdrawn)
Type 3	Glass fibre tissue (coded red)
Type 4A(i)	Black sheathing felt (for use with mastic asphalt)
Type 5	Non-woven polyester (coded blue) $125g/m^2$ and $350g/m^2$

Note:
The colour coding is along one edge to aid visual identification.

The stiffness of the base in traction (i.e. the force required per unit extension) determines how well it will be able to perform, when movement occurs in the substrate below, thus inducing a strain into the membrane. For instance, this movement could be a crack occurring in a screed used to form falls, or in the butt joint between timber boards used for the deck. The movement that occurs may be a permanent opening, or it may vary, depending on temperature and moisture conditions.

Further reading:
BS 747: Specification for roofing felts • BS 3690: Part 1 Bitumens for building and civil engineering. Specification for bitumens for roads and other paved areas • BS3690: Part 2 Bitumens for building and civil engineering. Specification for bitumens for industrial applications.

- The 'ideal' membrane combines a base of high stiffness in tension, with a low stiffness matrix, to provide the best combination of characteristics to resist movement and maintain waterproofing integrity.
- Multiple layering offers advantages in achieving optimum membrane characteristics.
- The two main grades of bitumen for roofing are known as 'penetration' grade (for base impregnation and polymer blending) and 'oxidised' (for normal coatings and site bonding).

A bitumen sheet for built-up roofing should, ideally, combine a high stiffness base (such as polyester) and a lower modulus matrix to allow strain to be dissipated (and also to allow flexibility for ease of application). As the waterproofing integrity of a bituminous membrane critically depends on preserving the physical continuity of the bitumen, the moduli of the bases are matters of technical importance.

In addition to its advantages in coping with movement in the deck below the membrane, the polyester base confers two other benefits. The first is a general improvement in mechanical toughness and general puncture resistance. No flat roof membrane should be without at least one layer of polyester, and certainly not where there is access to the roof. The second is the tear resistance, which makes the polyester reinforced first layer suitable in cases where the membrane is to be nailed or mechanically fixed to the deck. The fibres of the base should arrest the development of any tear, although stiffness of the base should anyway prevent the strains in the membrane which would cause tearing.

The bitumen coating
The different types of bitumen and modified bitumen coatings used on the reinforcing base to form the roofing product may be summarised as follows:

- 'penetration' grade – for the impregnation of bases and for blending with polymers
- 'oxidised' grade – for standard bitumen coatings and for bonding on site
- 'modified' grades – for proprietary coatings with varying bitumen matrix properties.

BS747 only covers bitumen sheets with 'oxidised' bitumen coatings. For 'modified' products reference should be made to Agrément Certificates.

There are two main types of proprietary coating modification, both of which can be processed on roofing product manufacturing machines. The first is the modification by means of an addition of compatible thermoplastic rubber, such as styrene butadiene styrene (SBS). The second is the modification by means of atactic polypropylene (APP) with or without complementary additives (see below).

Bonding bitumen
The traditional bonding adhesive for use with bituminous roofings is hot applied oxidised bitumen. Bitumen is favoured because:

- it offers good bedding properties and evens out minor surface irregularities
- it adds to the impermeability and movement capability of the system
- it provides almost instant adhesion
- it is exceptionally durable if protected from direct exposure to solar radiation
- it is a relatively innocuous substance.

The amount of bitumen per bonding layer varies between 1.5 and 1.8kg/m^2, and corresponds to a layer mean thickness of between 1.5mm and 1.8mm.

Cold-applied bitumen based adhesives are available for roofing work, more particularly for DIY applications. The setting time for such adhesives will depend on outdoor temperature and on the nature of the solvent used. It may take several days for the full strength of the adhesive to be developed.

Proprietary rubber-modified bitumen bonding compounds are also available for special situations requiring the greatest degree of flexibility in the membrane, although the normal oxidised compound is suitable for the great majority of applications. Not all thermo-plastic rubbers are equally resistant to prolonged heating and storage at high temperature. Care is need in their use.

Bitumen primer
Bitumen primer is used to seal porous substrates such as concrete, cementitious screed or brickwork. It may also be used to form a suitable key for subsequent bitumen bonding to the crowns of profiled metal deck. Most primers consist of penetration grade bitumen with a viscosity modifier such as white spirit to accelerate drying.

Generic types
Bitumen products
Bitumen is produced by the fractional distillation of crude oil. The grades and principal characteristics are described in *BS3690*.
continued ▶

Critical factors

- Choose the appropriate combination of components to give a final membrane with optimum properties.
- Built-up roofing systems should now incorporate at least one layer of polyester base material, preferably in the top layer.

Further reading in the Guide:
11.2 Built-up roofing: Performance in use • 11.4 Built-up roofing: Additional information

- The two main polymer modifiers to bitumen for coatings in roofing products are a thermoplastic rubber and a form of polypropylene.
- These two forms of polymer modification confer very different characteristics on the resulting products.
- Bitumen or pitch extended polymer sheets form a class of materials between conventional built-up systems and the wholly polymer types.

As stated above the two main grades of bitumen roofing products are the 'penetration' grade and the 'oxidised' grades. An oxidised bitumen is a penetration grade whose rheological properties have been substantially changed by reaction with air ('blown') at elevated temperature. The purpose is to reduce the temperature susceptibility of the bitumen and thus to make it more suitable for the intended use. More detail is given in **Unit 11.4**.

Modification with thermo-plastic elastomers (SBS)

The purpose of modification with rubber is to change the inherent rheological properties of bitumen from predominantly visco-elastic to elastic. The proportion of thermoplastic rubber employed depends mainly upon the balance of end properties required. There is no unique recipe.

Experience shows that sheets with SBS-modified coatings are compatible with traditional bitumen-based sheets and with conventional bonding bitumens. Consequently, mixed systems are technically possible. It is particularly cost effective for the top layer of a built-up system to be composed of an SBS-modified sheeting.

Products for application by torching can be formulated with SBS-modified or unmodified oxidised bitumen coatings. Although these do not have the same high temperature and slump resistances as the APP materials (see below), they can nonetheless be torch applied successfully, and the rubber-modified variants require less heat than the other types.

A roofing product variant employing this general type of rubber modification consists of a heavily modified bitumen sheeting made without an embedded reinforcement, or with no more than a lightweight glass tissue applied to the bottom face of the sheeting. The special feature of such sheetings is their highly extensible properties, which makes them convenient for stretching over awkward roofing details. They are best used for general work areas in combination with polyester reinforced underlayers.

The general technical features offered by rubber modified bitumen coatings are:

- Improvement in low temperature flexibility and pliability, which is particularly important for unrolling thick products, (say more then 3mm thick) at low temperature, or when forming roof details with thick materials in the cold season.

- Improvement in the adhesion between the coating and its mineral granule or other factory applied finish.
- A substantial increase in the fatigue endurance of the bitumen coating. This is brought about by the greatly improved resilience of the rubber-modified bitumen which permits a fast and near complete recovery following a period of induced strain.

Modification with APP

The purpose of modification with APP is to produce a heavy coating of high melting point bitumen particularly suited to the torch welding method of bonding. This is primarily an application convenience, for use in situations where hot bitumen or cold adhesives are not appropriate, but where the use of a naked flame is permitted and safe. Unlike the SBS modification, APP does not alter the rheological nature of the bitumen. APP-modified roofings are generally not suitable, nor intended for, application by the traditional 'pour and roll' method using hot bitumen.

In general, APP-modified coatings offer a high degree of slump resistance at elevated temperature, usually up to 140°C. They can also be flexible at low temperature if formulated accordingly. Softening points are raised from about 110°C for oxidised and rubber-modified bitumens to about 145°C, or more for those modified with APP.

The APP-modification of the bitumen is especially advantageous for torch applied roofings because it confers to the coating a well-defined and pronounced melting point. This feature contrasts with that for oxidised and rubber-modified coating types. The well-defined melting point enables the coating surface to melt rapidly on reaching its softening point, and to form a free-flowing molten layer of bitumen on the heated side, which then serves as the adhesive and bedding layer for the roofing as it is unrolled onto the substrate.

APP-modification does not confer elastic properties on the bitumen at service temperatures on a roof. The rheology of such blends is more like that of high softening point oxidised bitumens, the principal difference being in the domain of temperature susceptibility and the high resistance to creep at normal service temperatures.

The limitations are that torch-applied roofings are restricted to substrates which are not likely to be damaged by temporary exposure to a naked flames, and the risk of fire needs to be addressed and safety precautions taken accordingly.

Further reading:

Chapter	1	2	3	4	5	6	7	8	9	10	11
Contents	Introduction	History	Regulatory Methods	Principles	Surveys	Constraints & Targets	Design Selection	Calculations	Detail Design Principles	Evaluation of Design	Built-up Roofing
Page	1	19	31	45	83	95	105	165	189	217	221

- Bitumen roofing sheets covered by *BS747* are designated with different code letters to identify different surface finishes and intended uses.

The features and principal benefits conferred by APP-modification of the bitumen are:

- high slump/creep resistance
- suitability for torch applied sheetings
- greater resistance to blistering pressures generated in wet and porous substrates
- generally harder and less prone to foot marking under service temperature conditions
- advantageous for repair and maintenance.

Bitumen/Pitch extended sheets
In addition to the materials described above, there are others which are derived from bitumen or pitch extended polymers.

The bitumen or pitch extended polymer roofings belong to a class which sits between the wholly polymer or elastomeric sheets, on the one hand, and the reinforced bitumen based sheets on the other. They are proprietary products covered by Agrément Certificates and always require to be used in accordance with the manufacturers' instructions. This class of sheet material is formed from a homogeneous blend of polymers extended with bitumen or with pitch. The sheeting contains no separate reinforcing base, but may incorporate a uniform dispersion of short natural or synthetic fibres within the polymer blend.

These are not strictly improved traditional bitumen roofings, but rather flexible polymer-dominant sheets compatible with bitumen-based sheets and suitable for incorporation into built-up systems. They also differ, in that plastics or rubber sheet forming machinery is used in the manufacture of such products, unlike the modified bitumens roofings which are made on bitumen roofing machines.

Such types of sheeting, more particularly the pitch extended variants, offer particular technical features such as resistance to spillages of petroleum solvents or other chemicals which otherwise attack bitumen.

Form / surface finishes

Bitumen roofing products are designated with different code letters to identify different surface finishes and intended uses, as defined in *BS747*, see Table 11.1.2.

Some general characteristics may be summarised as follows:

- Rolls of bitumen sheet are generally 1m wide. To provide some consistency in handling, rolls of thick intermediate or top layers are shorter (typically 8 to 16m), whilst those of lighter weight are 16 to 20m in length.
- bitumen sheets are not supplied by weight. Roll weights stated on wrappers are intended to aid identification and site handling. Typical roll weights are in the range 25 to 40kg.
- Bonding bitumen is generally supplied in paper-wrapped kegs, sold by nominal weight, typically 45kg.
- Fine aggregate surfaced cap sheets are available in white, grey, green and brown, and in aluminium flakes. Metal-faced cap sheets include copper, aluminium and stainless steel.

Table 11.1.2
BS747 **Finish/function code letters**

Code	Type	Use
B	fine granule	suitable for lower layers under protection
E	mineral granule	for top layers with a decorative/protective finish in a choice of colours
G	perforated	venting base layer in glass fibre felt for partial bonding
U	underlayer	polyester first layer/nailing felt

Note:
Metal foil faced products are also available but they are not classified in the BS.

Workability

High performance built-up roofing is suitable for covering flat, pitched or vertical surfaces. Its moderate stiffness modulus (see **Unit 11.2**) allows it to be formed over large radius curved surfaces and hyperbolic roof forms. However, it cannot be formed into small three dimensional shapes and details without cutting and folding. ∎

Critical factors

- Many of the newer products are not covered by the British Standard. Some of these are covered by Agrément Certificates.

Further reading in the Guide:
11.4 Built-up roofing: additional information

11.2   Performance in use

- Built-up membranes using modern materials are expected to have a useful life in excess of 25 years.
- Bitumen sheets are durable over this length of time, although some stiffening will occur.
- Consideration should be given to the durability of the materials and the performance of the system as a whole.

Movement characteristics

Material behaviour

The different types of roofing sheet have different self-movement characteristics. For example:

- Glass tissue bases confer a dimensional stability which makes them suitable for torch-on applications.
- Glass/polyester composite bases combine the benefits of dimensional stability with high tear resistance and tensile strength.
- Lightweight polyester based membranes may exhibit unevenness due to expansion of the base under hot-lay conditions, but this is not deleterious to performance.

The main benefits and limitations of these bases are summarised in Table 11.2.1.

Accommodation of movement

The ability of the membrane to accommodate cyclic building movements, will depend upon the choice and number of layers used to form the membrane, and on the type of attachment to the substrate through which the effect of movements are communicated to the membrane. The durability of bituminous membrane systems is in practice largely governed by mechanical considerations, in particular those related to fatigue endurance.

In general, endurance of a membrane will be increased by:

- increasing the thickness/number of layers in the built-up system
- locating the high performance polymer modified sheet(s) uppermost
- partial attachment to substrate, subject to meeting the wind loading or slope requirements

The effect of replacing a fully bonded first layer (e.g. *BS747* Type 3B) by a partially bonded layer (*BS747* Type 3G) is to raise the tolerable amplitude of substrate movement by about 30%, when used beneath high performance membranes, and by about 90% when used beneath two layers of *BS747* Type 3B glass-based materials, all for a given number of cycles.

A property often referred to in roofing terminology is the 'stiffness' modulus of the base. The greater the stiffness modulus of the base, the harder it is to stretch the finished roofing sheet. As the two sides of any crack in the substrate move apart, the membrane by itself will not restrain them, no matter how stiff it is. However, a stiff base in the membrane prevents large strains from

Table 11.2.1
Benefits and limitations of different bases

Product	Benefits	Limitations
Glass tissue/woven glass	• high modulus (300-1000N/mm) • high dimensional stability • rot proof • cosmetic durability	• low elongation (=2-3%) • fragile • low tear resistance • water can wick along strand
Glass/polyester (mixed non-woven fibres)	• high modulus (=400N/mm) • high dimensional stability • rot proof • cosmetic durability • improved resistance to crack propagation • moderate nail holding strength	• low elongation
Polyester	• modulus (100 to 350 N/mm) • high elongation (over 20%) • rot proof • general toughness • nailable • high puncture resistance • high tear resistance	• moderate dimensional stability • less flexible • heavier weights

developing at any point in the bituminous matrix. The strains are limited by being spread over a greater area by plastic or elastic deformation in shear of the bonding medium and/or the matrix. This will occur until, ultimately, the capacity of a component material in the system to accept plastic deformation is reached, and failure of that weakest part in tension will occur, resulting in partial delamination. However, this would only occur at extreme strain, which should be prevented by good design in the first instance

The 'low strain stiffness modulus' of the base is defined as the modulus for strains up to about 2% elongation, and is regarded as the stiffness value of practical importance for built-up roofing systems.

Further reading:
BS747 Specification for roofing felts

© BFRC / CIRIA: Flat Roofing: Design and Good Practice. 1993

- 'High performance' materials must now be used to achieve the best results in terms of resistance to movement, particularly cyclic movements which induce fatigue into the membrane.
- Good fire ratings can be obtained with the use of finishing layers such as stone chippings.
- Whilst SBS modified materials have the best low temperature flexibility, APP modified materials show the best creep resistance at high ambient temperatures.

Table 11.2.2
Indicative ranking of selected specification options

Bond	Specification	RJMC[D]
Full	3B+3B+3B	1.0
Full	3B+5U+3B	1.2
Partial[C]	3G+3B+3B	1.9
Partial[C]	3G+5B+3B	2.0
Full	3B+5B	2.8
Full	P180+P180[A]	3.7
Full	5U+5B	4.0
Full	3B+5U+5B	5.4
Full	3B+P250E[B]	5.7
Partial[C]	3G+P180+P180[A]	6.6
Partial[C]	3G+5U+5B	7.0

Notes:
[A] Typical proprietary polyester roofing: 180g/m² base.
[B] Typical proprietary polyester roofing: 250g/m² base: elastomeric coating.
[C] Partial attachment by nailing or use of venting base sheet Type 3G.
[D] RJMC = relative joint movement capability

Fatigue endurance
If a crack that is bridged is 'live' – that is, moving – then fatigue may become an issue for the membrane. The modern polyester bases have conferred an important technical benefit in respect of the fatigue endurance of the membrane system. The benefit comes from the substantially greater order of ultimate elongation than their predecessor base materials. This is usually 20% as a minimum, as compared with the few percent elongations obtained with the traditional Classes 1 and 3 roofing felts.

It is not that the greater elongation potential of the polyester base can be fully utilised with impunity, but that the sheets' capacity to endure repeated strains of the order likely to be experienced in a roof system (less than 1%) is substantially increased. This represents a smaller proportion of the ultimate elongation of polyester than of other base materials. This under utilisation of mechanical properties corresponds to an increase in the fatigue endurance of the base and therefore of the membrane under normal service conditions.

For the purposes of general comparison, the performance potential of a membrane may be gauged by the relative amplitude of substrate joint movement to cause fatigue failure in a given number of cycles. Table 11.2.2, which is indicative only, ranks selected specification options of one company's products in ascending order of relative joint movement capability. However, in selecting any particular system, the overall performance must be considered. Partial bonding, which can assist fatigue resistance, may not be suitable in areas of significant wind uplift.

Key properties

Thermal performance
Built-up roofing membranes do not contribute significantly to the thermal resistance of the system (**see Units 4.5 and 7.6**).

SBS-modified bitumen-coated materials have greater low temperature flexibility than oxidised and APP-modified coatings.

At high ambient temperatures both oxidised and SBS-modified bitumen coatings exhibit similar softening characteristics, but in both cases the propensity for slipping is dependent on the grade of bonding bitumen. By contrast, since APP-modified materials are applied by torching, the coating bitumen also forms the bonding agent, with the result that very high creep resistance is obtained at maximum ambient temperatures.

Fire Resistance
An AA fire rating will be obtained with any built-up roofing specification, surfaced with a 12.5mm layer of chippings or cementitious tiles or concrete slabs on a suitable substrate (see **Unit 7.9**).

Ratings for proprietary membranes will be given in the relevant Agrément Certificates or in the independent fire rating certificates available from the manufacturers.

Wind resistance
Due to the manufacturing process, the bond strength of the bitumen coating with the reinforcing base exceeds that of the membrane and its adhesive under normal design conditions. Delamination of individual high performance layers is thus extremely unlikely.

Traffic resistance
Protection is required where the membrane will be exposed to anything other than light maintenance traffic.

Acoustic performance
Built-up roofing makes no significant contribution to the acoustic performance of a roof (**see Unit 4.12**).

continued ▶

Critical factors

Resistance to damage from movements will be enhanced by:

- increased overall thickness
- high strength/ stiffness material at the top
- polymer modified sheetings in the top layer
- partial attachment to the substrate.

Check that the surface finish chosen is suitable for the fire rating required.

Accommodation of movement.

Protection from ultra-violet radiation.

Further reading in the Guide:
4.5 Thermal performance • 4.12 Acoustic performance • 7.6 Design for thermal performance • 7.9 Design for fire safety • 11.1 Built-up roofing: general description

Lloyds, Bristol

Durability

Expected life
Built-up membranes designed in accordance with the recommendations given in this Guide, and subject to normal timely maintenance, are expected to give a useful service life in excess of 25 years, depending upon the build-up of components.

Natural ageing
When reviewing the performance of built-up roofing systems, a distinction needs to be made between the durability of the materials and that of the system.

Oxidised (blown) bitumen is known to be very durable if protected from direct exposure to solar radiation and mechanical attrition. It will harden through absorption of oxygen and loss of volatiles, and will become stiffer, but it will not lose its adhesive nor its waterproofing characteristics. However, the risk of mechanical rupture, if stressed, increases as the bitumen hardens and becomes less compliant. It is for this important reason that proper consideration must always be given to the properties of reinforcement in the roofing materials, and to design measures which mitigate membrane stresses generated by building movements and induced loadings.

In addition to embrittlement, surface crazing may develop. In the long term, the upper coating may become porous, but the built-up membrane will continue to perform satisfactorily, provided a highly inert base such as glass and/or polyester is used. The lower levels of coating will remain completely waterproof.

If surface crazing is observed the membrane may only require additional solar protection to considerably extend

Further reading:

its life. Breakdown of the total membrane is more likely to be due to extremes of substrate movement which are greater than can be accommodated and which is manifest in splits and cracks through all layers.

Experience with APP-modified bitumens (**see Unit 11.1**) goes back nearly 30 years, and that with SBS-modified bitumens some 25 years. The evidence of durability is generally satisfactory for properly formulated and installed products.

The glass and polyester base materials will not, in themselves, perish and are therefore long-lasting.

Freemans distribution centre, Peterborough, UK

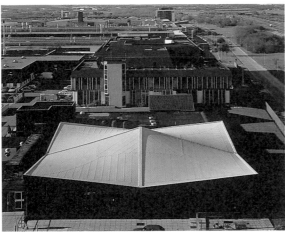

Signet House, Basildon, UK

Water and biological effects

A built-up membrane roof should always be designed and constructed with adequate falls provided. The ponding of clean rainwater will not harm glass or polyester based materials. However, such regular ponding may cause the unwanted and possibly harmful deposits of general detritus, powders, decaying organic matter and local concentrations of corrosive substances from roof vents. The wetting and drying of muddy deposits can tend to damage and cause some crazing in the bitumen coating on the top layer.

An advantage of the built-up membrane is that it can accommodate temporary flooding of the roof where the deck is designed to support the load associated with such conditions.

Built-up roofing is not generally affected by insects. Fungi, moss, lichens and moulds may form on the surface of the membrane, but are not generally detrimental to the membrane. They should be removed by the application of suitable fungicides during maintenance inspections.

Chemical and heat effects

Bitumen does not react chemically with the common materials used in building. However, solvent-based adhesives may affect certain materials. Hydrocarbon solvents and chlorinated hydrocarbon solvents derived from crude oil, more especially those with a low volatility, will tend to soften bitumen, if present in sufficient quantity for prolonged periods.

In the event of serious damage to the roof covering by chemicals, it will normally be necessary to replace the affected areas.

Some food and industrial processes give rise to potentially harmful powder or liquid discharges, as may vents above industrial or commercial kitchens. Specialist advice should be sought in case of doubt.

Solar radiation and high temperatures can lead to loss of volatiles from the materials and to surface oxidation.

Environmental impact
see **Unit 4.15**. ■

Further reading in the Guide:
4.15 Environmental impact of materials

11.3 Selection, design and application

- In making the detailed selection of the components of a built-up roofing membrane, the lowest layer is chosen first, followed by the top layer/finishes and finally any intermediate layers.
- The first layer may be fixed to the substrate by full bonding or by various forms of partial attachment. Loose laying (ballasted) is another option.

Supermarket, New Malden, UK

Selection

Layers in build-up

Once the concept of a built-up membrane has been selected, a number of decisions must still be made on the roof configuration and the membrane's detailed build-up.

The membrane generally comprises

- a first layer to ensure the appropriate connection to the substrate
- a top layer which provides or receives the desired finish
- optional intermediate layers to build up the performance capability of the system beyond that provided by the other layers alone.

Table 11.3.1
Dimensional co-ordination

	Minimum sizes (mm)		
	head lap	side lap	offset
Vapour control -			
Single layer	100	50	-
Double layer	100	50	1/2 roll
BS 747 Type 3G venting	100	50	-
Underlayer or base	75	50	1/3 roll[A]
top layer or cap sheet	75	50[B]	1/3 roll[A]

Notes:
[A] 1/2 roll if venting layer omitted
[B] 75mm often used: check with manufacturers

Intermediate layers augment the overall strength and thickness of the composite membrane to such a level as may be judged necessary with respect to:

- puncture resistance and general membrane toughness.
- movement capability/fatigue endurance of the membrane.

An intermediate layer will generally be required where the first layer is nailed or mechanically fixed to the deck, or where the first layer is a partially bonded, perforated roofing felt.

Dimensional coordination

In setting out bitumen sheets, either as a vapour control layer or waterproof membrane, the dimensional discipline set out in Table 11.3.1 applies.

BS747 Type 3G is loose laid in the roof field but details must be fully bonded.

A bituminous vapour control layer should extend beyond the insulation to allow a minimum 75mm lap to the waterproofing

Successive layers of waterproofing are generally laid in the direction of the fall.

Further reading:
BS747: Specification for roofing felts

- The choice of finish to the top layer will depend on fire rating, appearance, the access needs and special maintenance requirements.
- Intermediate layers are used to build up the overall strength and toughness of the system.

Table 11.3.2
Substrates and methods of attachment

Roofs up to and including 10° slope	
Substrate	Method of attachment of first layer of waterproofing
Plywood, woodwool, concrete, screeds, chipboard, rigid polyurethane or polyisocyanurate	Partial bond
Cork, cellular glass, wood fibreboard	Full bond
Mineral fibre	Full bond
	Full bond and mechanically fix through first layer of high performance material
Perlite	Full bond
	Full bond and mechanically fix through first layer of high performance material
Timber boarding	1st layer Type 5U nailed at 200mm centres

Priming metal deck prior to bonding vapour control layer

Critical factors

Selection of the first layer and its attachment in relation to all the factors involved, including:

- wind loads
- the nature of the substrate
- the strength of the substrate
- movement considerations.

Substructures

The first layer will be selected principally according to the substrate to which it is applied. The aim is to achieve the correct method of attachment to minimise risks of blistering and wind damage, and to limit the possible membrane stresses induced by differential movement between the substrate and roof covering (see Table 11.3.2).

Partial attachment of the membrane gives a reduced risk of membrane blistering due to trapped moisture, and a significant increase in movement capability of membrane. The disadvantages are an increased vulnerability to wind because of the reduced contact area between membrane and substrate, and a risk of lateral spread of water beneath the membrane in the event of leakage.

While the method of attachment depends primarily on the nature of the substrate, there may be instances where it will be dictated by wind loads or by roof slope considerations. In these circumstances, where a substrate is of a type normally requiring a partial bond, the first

layer of *BS747* Type 3G felt should be omitted and an insulating board, such as cork or bitumen impregnated fibre board, interposed which will provide both a surface suitable for full bonding and a degree of venting below the membrane.

Application

The complete range of attachment options comprises:

- Fully bonding with hot bitumen or cold roofing adhesive.
- Partial bonding by means of a perforated roofing (*BS747* Type 3G) in combination with hot applied bitumen, or by frame bonding using an unperforated first layer with either hot bitumen or cold adhesive. (The use of the *BS747* Type 3G perforated roofing gives a bonded area of about 20% to the substrate beneath.)
- Partial attachment by nailing or screws and washers through a suitable first layer, offering the requisite resistance to tearing at nail or fixing heads. (The recommended roofing felt for this purpose is the polyester reinforced roofing to *BS747* Type 5U or better.)
- Partial attachment by torch application of proprietary materials which allow partial bonding whilst sometimes also forming the first waterproofing layer as well.
- No attachment (loose laying), subject to ballasting or other loading to counter wind uplift. *continued* ▶

Further reading in the Guide:
11.1 Built-up roofing: general description

Where the substrate is judged to give an insufficient margin of laminar strength in respect of wind uplift, even when a fully bonded method of attachment is employed, the laminar strength of the system may be increased by using supplementary mechanical fixings driven into the deck through a high tear strength roofing as first layer. Polyester reinforced sheets are particularly suitable for extreme wind loading cases. A finish of stone aggregate in chipping compound will increase the resistance to wind uplift.

Where the wind loads exceed 3.6kN/m² specialist advice should be sought. The need for supplementary fixings may influence the choice of decking material which has to be able to receive and hold such fixings under the design loadings.

Protection

The relevant factors in selecting the finish are:

- fire designation (*BS476*: Part 3)
- aesthetic and/or solar reflectivity considerations
- roof access and roof traffic demands
- special technical or maintenance needs, such as finishes resistant to chemical contaminations or harmful deposits in powder form, etc.

The normal permanent finishes are:

- The decorative/protective mineral surfacing, 'E' class to *BS747* (see **Unit 11.1**), or its proprietary equivalents.
- Metal faced membrane (aluminium, copper, stainless steel)
- Minimum 10mm layer of stone aggregate in bitumen or gritting compound.
- Proprietary walkway tiles set in a bitumen bonding compound.
- Precast concrete paving slabs.
- Stone ballasting as required for inverted roofing systems.

Loose-laid 3G felt

Applying and spreading hot bitumen. Partial bonding is obtained through the holes in the 3G felt.

Further reading:

Chapter	1	2	3	4	5	6	7	8	9	10	11
Contents	Introduction	History	Regulatory Methods	Principles	Surveys	Constraints & Targets	Design Selection	Calculations	Detail Design Principles	Evaluation of Design	Built-up Roofing
Page	1	19	31	45	83	95	105	165	189	217	221

Cutting flashing for soil vent pipe

Fitting flashing

Torch welding flashing to main roofing sheet

Flexible walkway tiles

Roof paints can give a measure of protection to the built-up membrane, while the coating remains in good condition, but this is unlikely to exceed a few years. Furthermore, the reflective properties of the treatment may be affected by local environmental conditions and will lose the reflective properties if covered by surface deposits of dust and grime. Designers should be sure that the building owner clearly understands the need to clean and re-coat the surface every few years or as soon as bare patches appear. The designer should also ensure that the coating does not reduce the intended fire rating of the roof covering, and should seek advice from the manufacturer.

The separately applied finishes will generally be used on a top layer of bitumen sheet with a sanded finish. Thick roofing products, in excess of about 3mm thick, should not be used as the top layer beneath walkway tiles. The height of steps at laps, if excessive, would make the proper even bedding of the tiles difficult to achieve.

Steps at laps can be avoided by using a thinner, lightweight sheet for the top layer, in addition to the normal specification. Excessive quantities of bonding bitumens should not be used for levelling up. ∎

Critical factors

Roof paints should only be used as a surface finish in special circumstances.

Further reading in the Guide:

12 Mastic Asphalt	13 Polymeric Single Ply	14 Copper	15 Lead Sheet	16 Other Membranes	17 Thermal Insulants	18 Specification	19 Contracts & Procurement	20 Inspection	21 Maintenance	22 Bibliography	23 Index
263	301	331	353	375	383	393	399	413	429	437	455

11.4　Additional information

- The manufacture of bitumen roofing products involves:
  - impregnation of a base carrier with bitumen or modified bitumen
  - coating to seal and waterproof the sheet
  - application of surface finishes

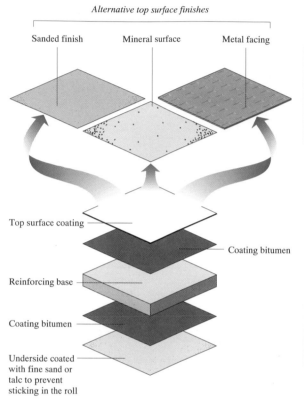

Figure 11.4.1
Composition of typical bitumen sheet

Table 11.4.1
Grades of bitumen used in built-up roofing

Nominal grade	Softening point °C: ring and ball	Penetration dmm at 25°C	P.I.
85/25	80 - 90	20 - 30	3.3
95/25	90 - 100	20 - 30	4.5
105/35	100 - 110	30 - 40	6.2
115/15	110 - 120	10 - 20	5.3

Table 11.4.2
Roof pitch and grades of bitumen

Pitch	Grade	Supplementary mechanical fixings
up to 1:14 (4°)	95/25 or 105/35	-
1:11 (5°)[1]	95/25 or 105/35	-
1:5.5 (10°)	115/15 only	50mm centres along head of roll[2]
above 20°	115/15 only	consult supplier

Notes
1　Use 115/15 if very exposed to sunlight or on highly insulated warm deck.
2　Except for APP-modified material.

Manufacture

BS747 gives an outline of the typical manufacturing process. An exploded 'anatomical view' of a typical bitumen sheet is shown in Figure 11.4.1.

The manufacture of a bitumen roofing on a conventional roofing machine requires the use of a base or carrier, whose composition and mass per unit area depends on the type of product being made. The base may require pre-impregnation with a soft bitumen to expel moisture and air from its interstices, more especially if the base is close-textured, dense and of appreciable thickness.

The base is then coated with bitumen containing filler to a thickness appropriate to its function and method of application.

The amount of filler does not to exceed 40% by mass of the filled coating. The modern proprietary roofings generally use a coating modified with a compatible polymer system to enhance the characteristics of coating in one or more respects. However, care is required to ensure compatibility of the coating with the material used to saturate the base, if delamination risks are to be avoided.

Finally, the bitumen-coated base is surfaced with fine sand or other suitable material to prevent sticking in the roll and to provide the appropriate surface finishes required on the top and bottom faces (according to intended use).

Further reading:
BS747 Specification for roofing felts • BS3690: Part 2 Bitumens for building and civil engineering. Specification for bitumen for industrial applications

• Some test methods for bitumen roofing products are included in British Standards, others are given in UEATc's M.O.A.Ts; drafts exist for a number of European standards.

Grades of bitumen

The grades and principal characteristics of bitumens are set out in *BS3690*. As described in **Unit 11.1**, the two main grades of bitumen for *BS747* roofing products are the 'penetration' grade and the 'oxidised' grades.

Oxidised bitumens are characterised by two numbers, (e.g. 95/25). The first of these is the temperature in degrees Celsius of the ring and ball softening point as measured by a standard petroleum industry test. The second is a measure of softness at a standard temperature, usually 25°C, as determined by the penetration in hundredths of a centimetre of a standard loaded needle in 5 seconds. For most bitumens there is a linear relationship between the temperature and the corresponding logarithm of penetration.

The characteristics of the grades of bitumen used in flat roofing are summarised in Table 11.4.1.

Table 11.4.2 shows the grades used for bonding on different roof pitches.

Bitumen primers

A suitable primer should have the following characteristics when tested in accordance with *BS2000: Part 72*:

• minimum volatile solvent content 40% by mass
• maximum viscosity (STV at 25°C, 4mm orifice) 10s.

Test methods

The test methods for bitumen products are summarised in Table 11.4.3. ■

Table 11.4.3
Test methods for built-up roofing materials

(i) British Standards (BSI)

Tensile strength	BS 2576 / BS 747
Elongation to break	BS 2576 / BS 747
Burst strength	BS 3137
Tear strength	BS 747
Low temperature flexibility	BS 747
Bitumen content	BS 5284
Mass of base	BS 5284
Mineral or surfacing material	BS 5284

(ii) European Union of Agrément Technical Committee (UEAtc)

M.O.A.T 27: 1983	General directives for the assessment of roof waterproofing systems.
M.O.A.T 30: 1984	Special directives for the assessment of reinforced waterproof coverings in atactic polypropylene (APP) polymer bitumen.
M.O.A.T 31: 1984	Special directives for the assessment of reinforced waterproof coverings of styrene-butadiene-styrene (SBS) elastomer bitumen.

(iii) Draft European Standards

A number of standards are in the course of preparation. Current drafts may be subject to change before final publication. They cover the determination of:

• length, width, straightness and flatness
• visible defects
• thickness and mass per unit area
• watertightness
• joint strength (shear and peel)
• water vapour transmission properties
• tensile properties
• impact resistance
• resistance to static perforation
• tear resistance
• relevant properties for wind uplift resistance
• chemical resistance
• effects of water
• dimensional stability at elevated temperatures
• resistance to heat ageing
• resistance to artificial weathering
• form stability under changing temperature
• flexibility at low temperature
• flow properties at elevated temperature
• granule adhesion

Critical factors

Further reading in the Guide:

11.5   Design details

- Wherever there is a change or discontinuity in material or in the roof geometry careful consideration of the associated detail must be given.

- Such details are often 3-dimensional in character and the difficulties to be solved may not be apparent solely from isolated simple sections.

- This schematic key diagram is shown to locate details for a variety of roof designs and conditions. The drawing itself must not be considered appropriate for any particular roof type.

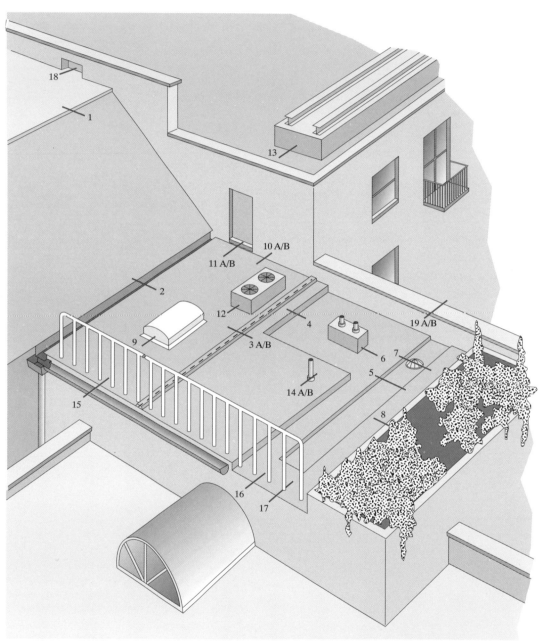

Key

1	Flat roof to pitched roof
2	Pitched roof to flat roof with gutter
3A	Movement joint - upstand
3B	Movement joint - flush
4	Step
5	Internal gutter
6	Boxed-in pipes or extract
7	Outlet
8	Planted roof
9	Roof light
10A	Abutment - integral deck
10B	Abutment - accommodating movement
11A	Opening - integral deck
11B	Opening - accommodating movement
12	Plant plinth above waterproof layer
13	Plinth
14A	Service penetration - cold
14B	Service penetration - hot
15	Eaves with gutter
16	Verge
17	Balustrade fixing
18	Chute
19A	Parapet - integral deck
19B	Parapet - accommodating movement

- The roof system is subject to dynamic loads from gravity, wind, temperature changes, humidity changes, air pressure changes.
- The details must allow for suitable construction tolerances and movement.

Notes

General

Those areas that must be addressed in the design development fall into risk categories:

A   Stability and integrity
B   Discontinuity of material, substrate. or roof geometry and differential movement
C   Water path
D   Convection path
E   Conduction path with risk of cold bridging
F   Fire
G   Condensation
H   Ventilation requirement.

Other considerations must be borne in mind:

- Ease of construction
- Ease of access for inspection.
- Ease of repair and replacement.
- Method of attachment.
- Material compatibility.

Membranes must not be carried across building movement joints or other structural discontinuities capable of independent movement. Proper movement joints must be provided at such critical points.

Penetrations through roof openings should be minimised.They should be grouped through specially designed and waterproofed service boxes which allow for hot and cold services and their future replacement.

Penetrations or upstands should be located such that sufficient space is allowed between them and other obstructions so proper forming of the detail is feasible.

Membrane laps and upstand heights must be maintained at all details.

Cold bridges through the insulated layer should be avoided. Continuity for insulation around the perimeter details, roof services and penetrations is important. Integrity of the vapour control layer at all points is vital.

Direct excessive imposed loading of the roof finish, particularly point loads, must be prevented. Loads should be evenly distributed.

Internal gutters should be avoided if possible. If necessary, they must be wide enough to be formed properly and to allow for maintenance.

The details illustrate the deck in generic form. The thickness of kerbs will depend upon the the material used and will affect the actual detailing of components for particular situations.

Built-up roofing

1. The following details illustrate the 'side of roll' condition in which separate pieces of sheet are used for upstands.

2. An angle fillet of 50mm × 50mm is included in all upstand/kerb details excluding pipe penetrations but larger or shallower angle fillets can also be used.

3. If chippings are to be used for solar protection, consideration should be given to appropriate protection of upstands, for example by using separate pieces of mineral surfaced sheet.

4. The details show a fully bonded, 2-layer waterproofing system.

5. In warm deck roofs it is general good practice to lap and bond the vapour control layer to the waterproofing at perimeters and all details.

6. Metal cover flashings should provide a minimum 75mm cover to upstands.

Special note

For each of the generic conditions shown in this Unit, there are various good practice solutions. Some good practice solutions involve particular components, materials and/or methods developed by individual suppliers or manufacturers, and benefit from their experience. Some solutions may also have to be modified according to the particular circumstances of the individual contract.

The detailed solutions shown in this Unit therefore represent only a selection of possible routes to good practice in design and installation. They indicate appropriate general methods for this particular membrane material, to show how the principles for different roof configurations (set out in Unit 9.1) may be translated into practical building. An understanding of these methods and principles will help the designer to assess not only the problems, but also the likely range of alternative possible solutions. *continued* ▶

continued ▶

Critical factors

- Integrity.
- Provision for movement.
- Material compatibility.
- Provision for discharge of water.
- Check for consistency between different detail drawings and with the specification.

Further reading in the Guide:
9 Detail design principles

12 Mastic Asphalt	13 Polymeric Single Ply	14 Copper	15 Lead Sheet	16 Other Membranes	17 Thermal Insulants	18 Specification	19 Contracts & Procurement	20 Inspection	21 Maintenance	22 Bibliography	23 Index
263	301	331	353	375	383	393	399	413	429	437	455

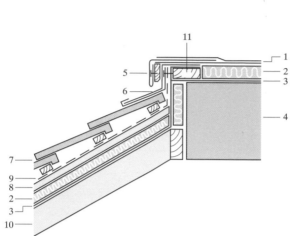

Warm deck roof.

1. Built up roofing
2. Insulation
3. Vapour Control Layer
4. Deck
5. Mineral faced elastomeric layer with welted drip
6. Minimum code 4 lead flashing with copper clips at 500mm centres
7. Roof tiling
8. Counter battens
9. Under tiling membrane (vapour permeable)
10. Timber rafters
11. Pre-treated timber bearer

Inverted warm deck roof.

1. Stainless steel restraint strapping
2. Concrete paving slabs on pads
3. Filter layer
4. Insulation
5. Built up roofing
6. Screed to falls
7. Deck
8. Mineral faced elastomeric layer with welted drip.
9. Minimum code 4 lead flashing with copper clips at 500mm centres
10. Roof tiling
11. Under tiling membrane (vapour permeable)
12. Counter battens
13. Timber rafters
14. Pre-treated timber bearer
15. Vapour control layer

Fig 11.5.1 (1) Flat roof junction with pitched roof

Welted drips are formed on timber battens to throw the water clear of the upstand. The downturn should be a minimum of 50mm. Timber edge battens should be of sufficient size to give adequate bearing on to the deck.

Should the pitched roof be of cold deck roof design the ventilation of this roof must be independent of the flat roof element if thermal integrity is to be maintained.

In situations of high condensation risk the vapour control layer should be continuous between roofs. Support must be provided for the vapour control layer.

Reduce water step at edge of flat roof by reduced timber thickness or stepped insulation.

Note that vapour-permeable membranes for underslating have different support requirements.

Fig 11.5.1 (2) Flat roof junction with pitched roof

It is generally inadvisable to form eaves details with inverted roofing. In the event of such details being unavoidable the following factors must be considered:

1 Effective restraint to paving to stop movement due to wind or thermal expansion of insulation.

2 Effective protection of the insulation from sunlight.

3 Avoidance of cold bridging.

4 Solar protection to built-up roofing where it is exposed.

Lightweight composite inverted roof insulation with cementitious overlay may require greater restraint.

The exact detailing of 9 will be dependant upon exposure. Flashings may be secured by clips of lead, copper or stainless steel: they may be fixed through tiles in severely exposed situations.

Proprietary edge trim could be used in lieu of a welted drip provided it allows discharge of rainwater away from vertical face of flashing.

Chapter	1	2	3	4	5	6	7	8	9	10	11
Contents	Introduction	History	Regulatory Methods	Principles	Surveys	Constraints & Targets	Design Selection	Calculations	Detail Design Principles	Evaluation of Design	Built-up Roofing
Page	1	19	31	45	83	95	105	165	189	217	221

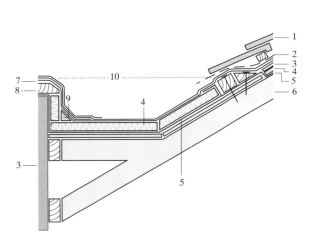

Warm deck roof.

1. Roof tiling
2. Under tiling membrane (vapour permeable)
3. Counter batten
4. Insulation
5. Vapour control layer
6. Rafters
7. Built up roofing
8. Pre-treated timber bearer
9. Angle fillet minimum 50mm x 50mm
10. Warm deck construction maintained up slope to height of upstand

Warm deck roof.

1. Pre-formed coping with butt straps
2. Weather sealed fixing to one side only
3. Pre-treated timber spacers
4. Fire stop (if required)
5. Non combustible insulation (compressible)
6. Minimum code 4 lead flashing
7. Mineral surfaced elastomeric layer
8. Built up roofing
9. Insulation
10. Vapour control layer
11. Deck
12. Insulating blocks
13. Angle fillet 50mm x 50mm

Fig 11.5.2 Pitched roof junction to flat roof with gutter

The membrane must be taken up the inclined pitch higher than the level of the adjoining flat roof. This ensures that if the gutter is blocked for some reason water will not pass into the building but on to the lower roof.

The lower tiling battens should be fixed through strips of membrane laid over the under-tiling membrane.

Care should be taken to avoid a backfall below the bottom course of tiling.

Fig 11.5.3A (1) Upstand movement joint

Insulating blocks avoid the need to insulate the upstands, but are not practical for high upstands. In very low U-value designs both upstands and capping may require insulation. Copings are secured on one side only allowing independent movement of upstands

If upstands are of excessive height mechanical restraint of the membrane will be necessary. *continued* ▶

12 Mastic Asphalt	13 Polymeric Single Ply	14 Copper	15 Lead Sheet	16 Other Membranes	17 Thermal Insulants	18 Specification	19 Contracts & Procurement	20 Inspection	21 Maintenance	22 Bibliography	23 Index
263	301	331	353	375	383	393	399	413	429	437	455

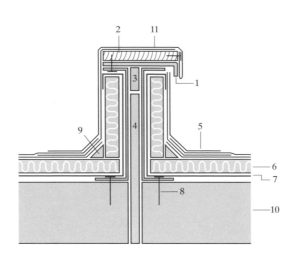

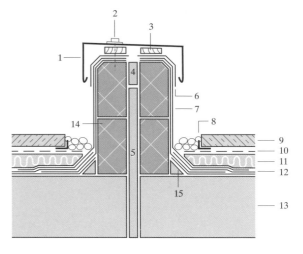

Warm deck roof.
1. Pre-formed metal capping fixed one side only
2. Pre-treated plywood or timber capping
3. Fire stop (if required)
4. Non-combustible (if required) insulation - compressible.
5. Built-up roofing
6. Insulation
7. Vapour control layer
8. Pre-formed metal or other kerbs fixed to deck
9. Insulation angle fillets 50mm x 50mm
10. Deck
11. Mineral surfaced elastomeric layer

Fig 11.5.3A (2) Upstand movement joint
This detail illustrates upstands which are insulated separately during the roofing works.

Inverted warm deck roof.
1. Pre-formed coping with butt straps
2. Weather sealed fixing to one side only
3. Pre-treated timber spacers
4. Fire stop
5. Non combustible insulation
6. Minimum code 4 lead flashing
7. Mineral surfaced elastomeric layer
8. Pebbles 20mm - 40mm
9. Concrete paving slabs on pads
10. Filter layer
11. Insulation
12. Built up roofing
13. Deck
14. Insulating blocks
15. Angle fillet 50mm x 50mm

Fig 11.5.3A(3) Upstand movement joint
Minimum upstand height of 150mm above finished roof level must be maintained.

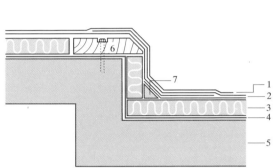

Warm deck roof.

1. Mineral surfaced elastomeric layer
2. Built up roofing
3. Insulation
4. Vapour control layer
5. Deck
6. Timber batten bolted to deck
7. Insulation fillet 50mm x 50mm

Inverted warm deck roof.

1. Stainless steel restraint strap
2. Stainless steel insulation retaining clip
3. Concrete paving slabs on pads
4. Filter layer
5. Insulation
6. Built up roofing
7. Deck
8. Insulation with cementitious topping
9. Pebbles 20mm - 40mm
10. Insulation fillet 50mm x 50mm

Fig 11.5.4 (1) Step

The insulation requires physical protection at the arris. It may be necessary to consider alternative details in areas of high condensation risk.

In these cases the insulation and vapour control layer would be continuous from horizontal to vertical planes.

With flexible deck design additional support may be necessary at the base of the upstand to prevent differential movement transmitting stress to the waterproofing.

Where the upstand is high, mechanical restraint of the membrane may be required.

Fig 11.5.4 (2) Step

Physical restraint of the upstand insulation is provided by clips from the paving surface. Overhang of the paving must be kept to a minimum to prevent tipping. Surface restraint strapping aids prevention of slabs being dislodged.

If the roof field insulation is laid first, upstand insulation should be restrained by pebbles at the perimeter.

continued ▶

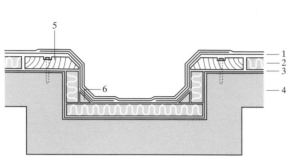

Warm deck roof.

1. Built up roofing
2. Insulation
3. Vapour control layer
4. Deck
5. Timber batten bolted to deck
6. Insulation fillet 50mm x 50mm

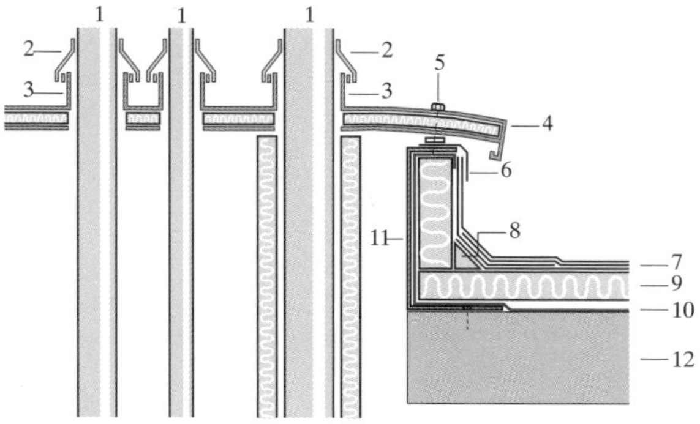

Warm deck roof.

1. Service penetrations
2. Weathering collars secured to services
3. Upstands on penetration capping
4. Purpose-made coated steel or stainless steel capping insulated as necessary
5. Weather-sealed bolt & strip fixing
6. Minimum code 4 lead flashing or pre-formed rigid metal flashing
7. Built-up roofing
8. Insulation fillet 50mm x 50mm
9. Insulation
10. Vapour control layer
11. Pre-formed metal or timber kerb fixed to deck
12. Deck

Fig 11.5.5 (1) Internal gutter.

Where possible internal box gutters are best avoided, the roof falls being configured to directly discharge into roof outlets or external gutters. Upstands should be detailed as shown previously.

Insulation must be protected and support provided on the arris. In situations of risk of cold bridging it may be necessary to ensure the insulation is continuous and provide support by the use of a metal angle.

Box gutters on inverted roofs should be avoided wherever possible as water flow may reduce insulation efficiency. Adequate support must be provided to the edge paving slabs in order to prevent tipping.

Fig 11.5.6 (1) Boxed-in pipes or services

Where possible service penetrations should be grouped together to minimise the number of weatherproofing details required. Cappings to these penetrations should be insulated.

Cold services should be insulated to prevent condensation forming where they pass from inside to outside.

Flues must be insulated to prevent heat being transmitted to the roof finish either by convection or by conduction through the penetration capping.

Services must be provided with weathered aprons.

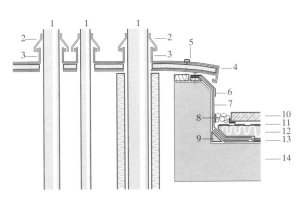

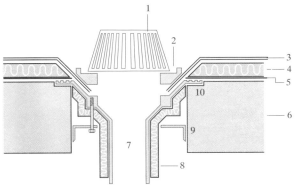

Inverted warm deck roof.

1. Service penetrations
2. Weathering collars secured to services
3. Upstand on penetration capping
4. Purpose made insulated (if necessary) capping with membrane coated steel or stainless steel facing
5. Weather sealed bolt
6. Minimum code 4 lead flashing or preformed rigid metal flashing

7. Mineral surfaced elastomeric layer
8. Pebbles 20mm-40mm
9. Insulation fillet 50mm x 50mm
10. Concrete paving on pads
11. Filter layer
12. Insulation
13. Built up roofing
14. Deck

Warm deck roof.

1. Removable grating
2. Clamping ring
3. Built up roofing
4. Insulation
5. Vapour control layer

6. Deck
7. Down pipe
8. Insulation collar
9. Fixing Bracket
10. Outlet flange

Fig 11.5.6 (2) Boxed-in pipes or services

If insulated kerbs are required see Figure 11.5.9(2)

Fig 11.5.7 (1) Outlet

The insulation thickness is reduced around the outlet position to facilitate water flow and prevent ponding.

Insulation in the form of a factory applied collar may be required to the outlet, but consideration should be given to the risk of ice forming inside the outlet as a result.

The vapour control layer may be dressed into the outlet clamp but only if this does not effect the waterproof seal.

It is not possible to turn back the vapour control layer over the insulation.

The outlet should be secured to the deck and on responsive decks the down pipe connection must be designed to accommodate vertical movement.

continued ▶

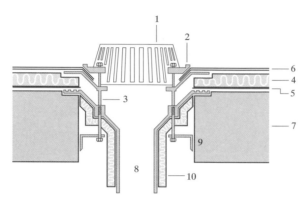

Warm deck roof.

1. Removable grating
2. Clamping ring
3. Extension flange (see notes)
4. Insulation
5. Vapour control layer
6. Built up roofing

7. Deck
8. Downpipe
9. Fixing bracket
10. Insulation collar

Inverted warm deck roof.

1. Removable grating
2. Adjustable seating
3. Pebbles 20mm-40mm
4. Concrete paving slabs on pads
5. Filter membrane
6. Insulation

7. Built up roofing
8. Deck
9. Down pipe
10. Insulation collar
11. Fixing bracket
12. Clamping ring

Fig 11.5.7 (2) Outlet

This alternative arrangement avoids compression of the insulation around the outlet by use of an outlet with an extension flange. There are other ways of achieving this.

Fig 11.5.7(3) Outlet

Two-level outlets should be specified with inverted roofs as they maximise drainage above the filter membrane/ insulation and hence insulation efficiency.

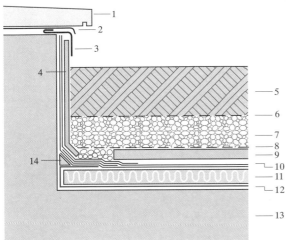

Warm deck roof.
1. Precast concrete coping fixed to upstand
2. dpc
3. Code 4 lead flashing
4. Protection board
5. Top soil
6. Filter layer
7. Drainage layer
8. Filter layer
9. Protection layer
10. Built up roofing
11. Insulation
12. Vapour control layer
13. Deck
14. Insulation fillet 50mm x 50mm

Inverted warm deck roof.
1. Precast concrete coping fixed to upstand
2. dpc
3. Code 4 lead flashing
4. Protection board
5. Top soil
6. Filter layer
7. Drainage layer
8. Filter layer
9. Protection layer
10. Insulation
11. Built up roofing
12. Deck
13. Insulation fillet 50mm x 50mm

Fig 11.5.8 (1) Roof planter

Finished top soil levels must be maintained at a minimum of 150mm below adjacent capping levels.

Built up roofing in both horizontal and vertical planes must be protected from physical damage by gardening operations and plant roots.

A drainage layer is provided to prevent waterlogging of the planting medium. The filter layer prevents leaching of the soil into the drainage layer.

Fig 11.5.8(2) Roof planter

continued ▶

12 Mastic Asphalt	13 Polymeric Single Ply	14 Copper	15 Lead Sheet	16 Other Membranes	17 Thermal Insulants	18 Specification	19 Contracts & Procurement	20 Inspection	21 Maintenance	22 Bibliography	23 Index
263	301	331	353	375	383	393	399	413	429	437	455

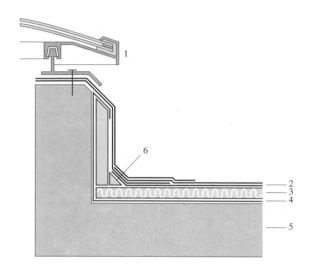

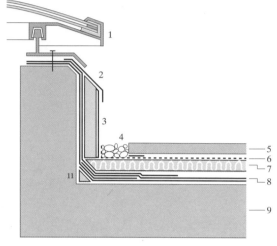

Warm deck roof.

1. Proprietary rooflight
2. Built up roofing
3. Insulation

4. Vapour control layer
5. Deck
6. Fillet 50mm x 50mm

Inverted warm deck roof.

1. Proprietary roof light
2. Preformed rigid metal flashing
3. Insulation board with cementitious topping
4. Pebbles 20mm-40mm

5. Concrete paving on pads
6. Filter layer
7. Insulation
8. Built up roofing
9. Deck

Fig 11.5.9(1) Rooflight upstand

The same principles apply at roof light opening as with door openings and perimeter abutments. A minimum upstand height of 150mm must be provided. If proprietary rooflights (including upstands) are used careful consideration must be given to:

1 Their fixings in order to prevent flexing being transmitted to the membrane.

2 Maintenance of minimum upstand height.

3 Satisfactory key to the rooflight kerb.

4 Chemical and heat compatibility with the waterproofing application.

Fig 11.5.9(2) Rooflight upstand

Kerbs should be insulated continuously with the deck insulation, in low U-value designs.

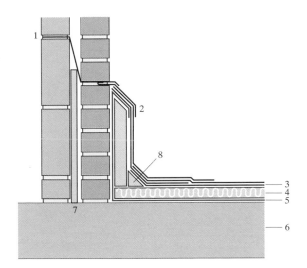

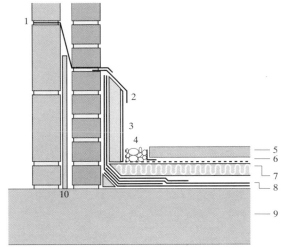

Warm deck roof.

1. Cavity tray
2. Minimum code 4 lead flashing
3. Built up roofing
4. Insulation
5. Vapour control layer
6. Deck
7. Cavity wall insulation
8. Insulation fillet 50mm x 50mm

Inverted warm deck roof.

1. Cavity tray
2. Rigid preformed metal flashing
3. Insulation board with cementitious topping
4. Pebbles 20mm-40mm
5. Concrete paving on pads
6. Filter layer
7. Insulation
8. Built up roofing
9. Deck
10. Cavity wall insulation

Fig 11.5.10A(1) Abutment integral deck

In cases of junctions between abutting walls and decks where no relative movement is possible the roof covering may be dressed up and bonded to the wall for a distance of not less than 150mm above the finished roof level. It is not normally recommended that upstands are taken more than 300mm up the face of the wall. If weather proofing protection is required above this level some form of wall cladding should be considered. If the felt has to be taken up higher then consideration should be given to a mechanical fixing at the top.

The upper edge of the vertical leg of the covering should be protected by a separate lead cover flashing set into the wall and dressed down over the covering.

Fig 11.5.10A(2) Abutment integral deck

Vertical insulation may be secured against the upstand in abutment situations.

Necessity for a fixing can be avoided if a rigid metal flashing is used, for example structural aluminium or stainless steel, and if restraint at its lower edge is provided by adjacent insulation or pebbles. Alternatively, suitable adhesives are available. *continued* ▶

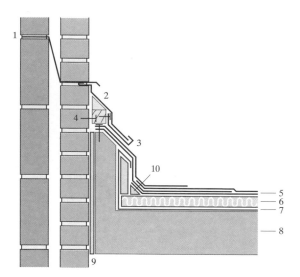

Warm deck roof.

1. Cavity tray
2. Minimum code 4 lead flashing
3. Copper clips at 500mm centres
4. Pre-treated timber support batten
5. Built up roofing
6. Insulation
7. Vapour control layer
8. Deck
9. Provision for movement
10. Angle fillet 50mm x 50mm

Inverted warm deck roof.

1. Cavity tray
2. Minimum code 4 lead flashing or rigid preformed metal flashing
3. Clips at 500mm centres
4. Pre-treated timber support batten
5. Insulation board with cementitious topping
6. Pebbles 20mm-40mm
7. Concrete paving on pads
8. Filter layer
9. Insulation
10. Built up roofing
11. Deck
12. Provision for movement

Fig 11.5.10B(1) Abutment accommodating movement

Where provision for vertical or horizontal movement has to be accommodated in instances where a flexible deck abuts a rigid element a detail must be developed to prevent flexing of the membrane.

Where the gap to be bridged is significant rigid support to the lead flashing must be provided. The support should be weathered to prevent ponding and possible ingress of water through laps in the lead. Laps in lead should be a minimum of 100mm.

In low U-value designs it may be necessary to insulate the upstand.

Consideration should be given to convection heat losses between the roof and the wall. Because of the anticipated movement and self-supporting requirements, a preformed metal flashing may be advised. However, fixing, movement and joint waterproofing should be considered.

Fig 11.5.10B(2) Abutment accommodating movement

Direct mechanical fixing of upstand insulation may be necessary or by the use of rigid flashing.

Consideration should be given to convection heat losses between the roof and the wall. Because of the anticipated movement and self-supporting requirements, a preformed metal flashing may be advised. However, fixing, movement and joint waterproofing should be considered.

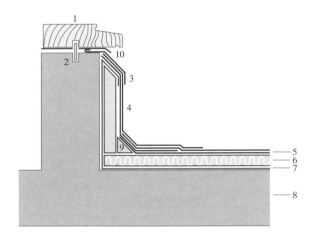

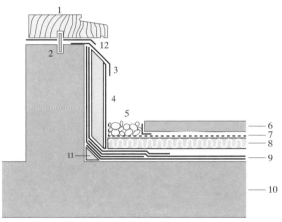

Warm deck roof.

1. Cill
2. Water bar
3. Minimum code 4 lead flashing
4. Mineral surfaced elastomeric layer
5. Built up roofing
6. Insulation
7. Vapour control layer
8. Deck
9. Insulation fillet 50mm x 50mm
10. Dpc

Inverted warm deck roof.

1. Cill
2. Water bar
3. Preformed rigid metal flashing
4. Insulation board with cementitious topping
5. Pebbles 20-40mm
6. Concrete paving slab on pads
7. Filter layer
8. Insulation
9. Built up roofing
10. Deck
11. Insulation fillet 50mm x 50mm
12. Dpc

Fig 11.5.11A(1) Opening on to roof integral deck

Thresholds should have a minimum height of 150mm above the finished roof level, with the roof ideally formed to provide falls away from the opening. This detail is appropriate for all conditions where differential movement between deck and wall is not expected.

Water bars should be provided to prevent water being blown in under the cill. Cill trays may also be necessary.

The use of rigid metal flashing allows easier square cutting to the top of the insulation upstand in this and other insulation abutment situations (10A and B, 19A and B,13).

Fig 11.5.11A(2) Opening on to roof integral deck

If provided, vertical insulation should be secured against the upstand in all abutment situations.

Necessity for fixing the insulation can be avoided if a rigid metal flashing is used (3), for example structural aluminium or stainless steel, and if restraint at its lower edge is provided by adjacent insulation or pebbles. Alternatively, a suitable adhesives are available.

continued ▶

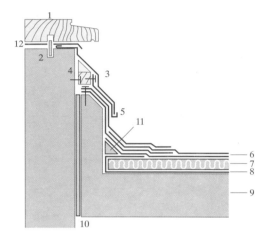

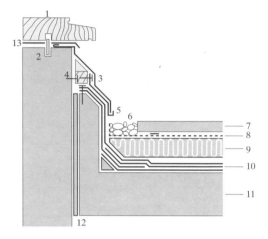

Warm deck roof.

1. Cill
2. Water bar
3. Minimum code 4 lead flashing or rigid preformed metal
4. Pre-treated timber support batten
5. Clips at 500mm centres

6. Built up roofing
7. Insulation
8. Vapour control layer
9. Deck
10. Provision for movement
11. Angle fillet 50mm x 50mm
12. Dpc

Inverted warm deck roof.

1. Cill
2. Water bar
3. Minimum code 4 lead flashing or rigid preformed metal
4. Pre-treated timber support batten
5. Clips at 500mm centres
6. Pebbles (20-40mm)

7. Concrete paving on pads
8. Filter layer
9. Insulation
10. Built up roofing
11. Deck
12. Provision for movement
13. Dpc

Fig 11.5.11B(1) Opening on to roof accommodating movement

Where provision for vertical or horizontal movement has to be accommodated and in instances where a flexible deck abuts a rigid element a detail must be developed to prevent flexing of the membrane.

Where the gap to be bridged is significant rigid support to the lead flashing must be provided. The support should be weathered to prevent ponding and possible ingress of water through laps in the lead. Laps in lead should be a minimum of 100mm.

In low U-value designs it may be necessary to insulate the upstand as per 11.5.10A and 11.5.10B.

Consideration should be given to convection heat losses between the roof and the wall. Because of the anticipated movement and self-supporting requirements, a preformed metal flashing may be advised. However, fixing, movement and joint waterproofing should be considered.

Fig 11.5.11B(2) Opening on to roof accommodating movement

Consideration should be given to convection heat losses between the roof and the wall. Because of the anticipated movement and self-supporting requirements, a preformed metal flashing may be advised. However, fixing, movement and joint waterproofing should be considered.

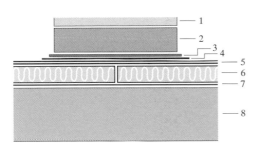

Warm deck roof.

1. Equipment	5. Built up roofing
2. Plinth	6. Insulation
3. Bitumenised protection board	7. Vapour control layer
4. Mineral surfaced elastomeric layer	8. Deck

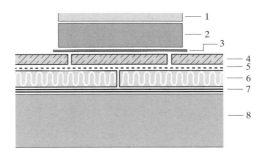

Inverted warm deck roof.

1. Equipment	5. Filter layer
2. Plinth	6. Insulation
3. Bitumenised protection board	7. Built up roofing
4. Concrete paving	8. Deck

Fig 11.5.12(1) Plinth above waterproofing layer

This detail is suitable for static loads stable under wind load, requiring no fixings to hold them down. The base is provided to spread the load to ensure that the felt is not damaged by compression of the insulation.

Wherever possible static loads should be supported on plinths or piers constructed off the structural deck. Where this is not feasible,

1 The details should include a suitable load-spreading board appropriate to the load and the compression resistance of the insulation.
2 The membrane supplier should be consulted to determine acceptable loadings and compatibility with the load-spreading board.
3 The additional bitumen sheeting and protection board layer provides protection against damage during construction.

Fig 11.5.12(2) Plinth above waterproofing

Additional load spreading is provided in the case of inverted roofs by the concrete paving slabs. See other notes under 11.5.12(1). *continued* ▶

12 Mastic Asphalt	13 Polymeric Single Ply	14 Copper	15 Lead Sheet	16 Other Membranes	17 Thermal Insulants	18 Specification	19 Contracts & Procurement	20 Inspection	21 Maintenance	22 Bibliography	23 Index
263	301	331	353	375	383	393	399	413	429	437	455

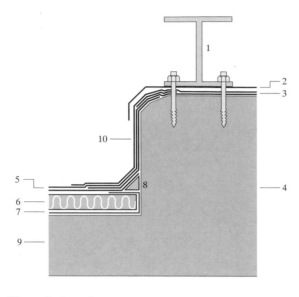

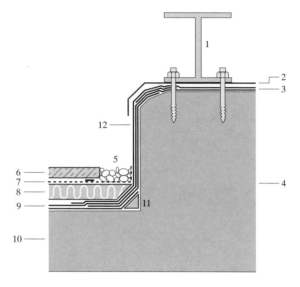

Warm deck roof.

1. Cradle track
2. Code 5 lead flashing
3. Built up roofing
4. Plinth
5. Built up roofing
6. Insulation
7. Vapour control layer
8. Angle fillet 50mm x 50mm
9. Deck
10. Mineral surfaced elastomeric layer

Fig 11.5.13(1) Plinth

Bolt holes may require sealing individually or by use of a bedded sealing plate.

Designs should allow for fittings to be demountable without affecting the waterproofing.

Inverted warm deck roof.

1. Cradle track
2. Code 5 lead flashing
3. Built up roofing
4. Plinth
5. Pebbles 20mm - 40mm
6. Concrete paving on pads
7. Filter layer
8. Insulation
9. Built up roofing
10. Deck
11. Angle fillet 50mm x 50mm
12. Mineral surfaced elastomeric layer

Fig 11.5.13(2) Plinth

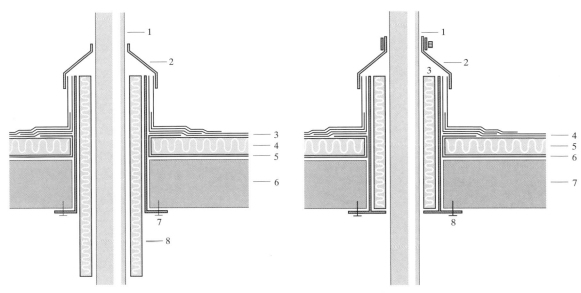

Warm deck roof.
1. Service penetration (cold)
2. Weather collar secured to pipe
3. Built up roofing
4. Insulation
5. Vapour control layer
6. Deck
7. Metal sleeve secured to deck
8. Insulation

Warm deck roof.
1. Service penetration (hot)
2. Weather collar secured to pipe
3. Non-combustible insulation
4. Built up roofing
5. Insulation
6. Vapour control layer
7. Deck
8. Metal sleeve secured to deck

Fig 11.5.14A(1) Service penetration (cold)

Penetration of pipes through the roof should be kept to the minimum. The use of proprietary moulded collars avoids the need for complex star cutting and forming of water proofing layers around the penetration. Circular fillets are desirable for site formed collars but are required to be purpose made for the penetration size and are rarely used.

Generally it is advisable to sleeve all pipes to ensure that flexing of the deck or the services does not transmit movement to the roof finish.

Cold pipes may require insulation to prevent condensation forming on their surface this should be continued into the area below the roof deck.

Pipes should have weather collars positioned a minimum height to allow a 150mm upstand in the roof finish.

Fig 11.5.14A(2) Service penetration (hot)

Particular care must be taken with timber decks to ensure sufficient separation is maintained. *continued* ▶

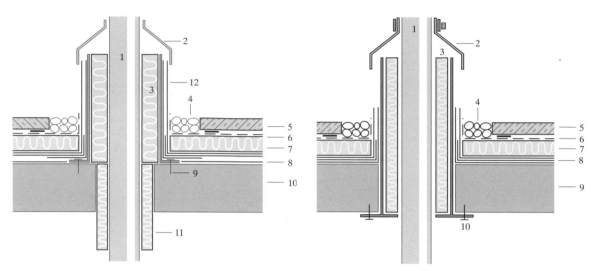

Inverted warm deck roof.

1. Service penetration (cold)
2. Weather collar secured to pipe
3. Insulation
4. Pebbles 20mm-40mm
5. Concrete paving on pads
6. Filter layer
7, Insulation
8. Built up roofing
9. Metal sleeve secured to deck
10.Deck
11.Pipe insulation
12.Mineral surfaced elastomeric layer

Inverted warm deck roof.

1. Service penetration (hot)
2. Weather collar secured to pipe
3. Non-combustible insulation
4. Pebbles 20mm-40mm
5. Concrete paving on pads
6. Filter layer
7. Insulation
8. Built up roofing
9. Deck
10.Metal sleeve secured to deck

Fig 11.5.14B(1) Service penetration (cold)

The same thickness of insulation around the pipe may not be necessary above and below the deck.

Fig 11.5.14B(2) Service penetration (hot)

Hot pipes such as flues must be sleeved and insulated with non-combustible insulation to prevent heat being transferred to the roof finish.

Metal hoods can also transmit heat to the waterproofing layer and adequate ventilation gaps between hood and finish must be kept.

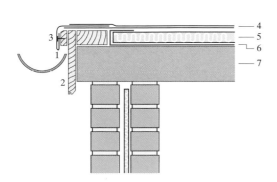

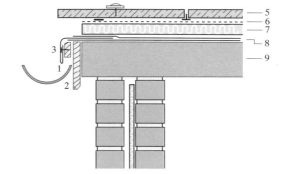

Warm deck roof.

1. Mineral faced elastomeric layer with welted drip
2. Fascia
3. Pre-treated timber batten (minimum 25mm thick x 50mm high) secured to deck or fascia as appropriate.

4. Built up roofing
5. Insulation
6. Vapour control layer
7. Deck

Inverted warm deck roof.

1. Mineral faced elastomeric layer with welted drip.
2. Timber fascia
3. Pre-treated timber batten (minimum 25mm thick x 50mm high) secured to deck or fascia as appropriate
4. Stainless steel restraint strapping

5. Concrete paving on pads
6. Filter layer
7. Insulation
8. Built up roofing
9. Deck

Fig 11.5.15(1) Eaves with gutter

Eaves should be formed to ensure that water is discharged into the gutter via an adequate welted drip. The welted drip should not be less than 50mm providing minimum 25mm projection beyond the fascia.

The fascia board should also be provided with a drip and stand clear of the face of the wall. The precise detailing and fixing of the fascia should be appropriate to its expected durability. For example a softwood fascia may require replacement and will require re-decoration before the membrane is replaced. It should be detailed to allow such works without disturbing the membrane.

The vapour control layer can be either turned back minimum 75mm over the insulation or taken over the fascia/batten.

Insulation should be protected at the edge by an upstand fascia or a timber bearer.

Consideration must be given to cold bridging at eaves, and insulation under the facia and soffit boards may be required.

Fig 11.5.15(2) Eaves with gutter

On eaves to inverted roofs insulation and protection requires physical restraint to prevent movement due to wind uplift and thermal expansion.

The precise detailing and fixing of the fascia should be appropriate to its expected durability. For example a softwood fascia may require replacement and will require re-decoration before the membrane is replaced. It should be detailed to allow such works without disturbing the membrane.

The vapour control layer can be either turned back a minimum 75mm over the insulation or taken over the fascia/batten.

Solar protection should be provided to the built-up roofing where it is exposed.

continued ▶

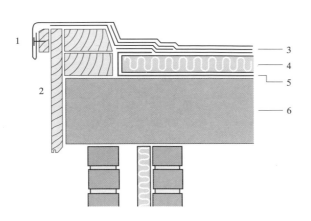

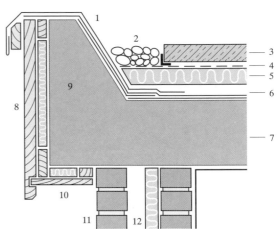

Warm deck roof.

1. Mineral elastomeric layer with welted drips
2. Timber fascia
3. Built up roofing
4. Insulation
5. Vapour control layer
6. Deck

Inverted warm deck roof.

1. Mineral faced elastomeric layer
2. Pebbles 20mm-40mm
3. Concrete paving on pads
4. Filter membrane
5. Insulation
6. Built up roofing
7. Deck
8. Timber fascia
9. Concrete upstand
10. Timber soffit
11. Brickwork
12. Insulation

Fig 11.5.16(1) Verge

Verges must provide and adequate check to prevent the discharge of water over the roof side. A minimum of 75mm upstand is recommended.

The precise detailing and fixing of the fascia should be appropriate to its expected durability. For example a softwood fascia may require replacement and will require re-decoration before the membrane is replaced. It should be detailed to allow such works without disturbing the membrane.

The vapour control layer can be either turned back minimum 75mm over the insulation or taken over the fascia/batten.

Fig 11.5.16(2) Verge

The precise detailing and fixing of the fascia should be appropriate to its expected durability. For example a softwood fascia may require replacement and will require re-decoration before the membrane is replaced. It should be detailed to allow such works without disturbing the membrane.

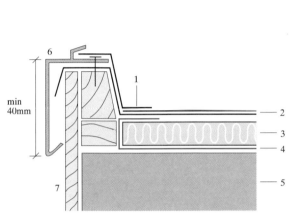

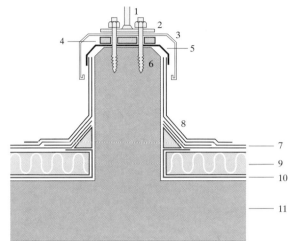

Inverted warm deck roof.
1. Mineral faced elastomeric layer
2. Built up roofing
3. Insulation
4. Vapour control layer
5. Deck
6. Aluminum or grp edge trim
7. Fascia

Warm deck roof.
1. Balustrade
2. Baseplate
3. Metal coping
4. Stainless steel spacer
5. Code 5 lead flashing
6. Holding down bolts
7. Built-up roofing
8. Angle fillet 50mm x 50mm
9. Insulation
10. Vapour control layer
11. Deck

Fig 11.5.16(3) Verge trim termination – alternative

Manufacturers advice should be followed regarding provision for thermal movement of metal edge trims.

Fig 11.5.17(1) Balustrade fixing

Bolt fixing holes must be sealed by compressing a non-setting mastic under the base plate.

Minimum heights of upstands should be 150mm above the finished roof level.

On plinths of excessive height mechanical restraint of the upstand membrane may be required.

Flashings should provide a minimum of 75mm cover to the top of felt upstands. *continued* ▶

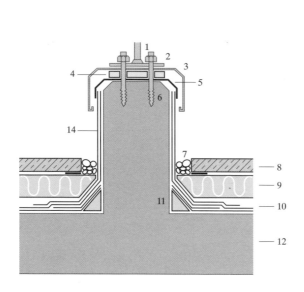

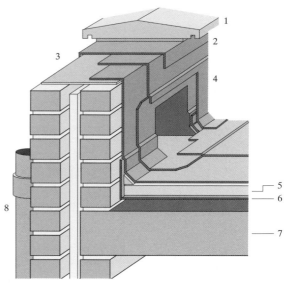

Inverted warm deck roof.

1. Balustrade
2. Baseplate
3. Metal coping
4. Stainless steel spacer
5. Code 5 lead flashing
6. Holding down bolts
7. Pebbles (20-40mm)
8. Paving on pads
9. Insulation
10. Built-up roofing
11. Angle fillet 50mm x 50mm
12. Deck
13. Plinth
14. Mineral surfaced elastomeric layer

Warm deck roof.

1. Coping
2. Dpc
3. Slate closer
4. Built up roofing
5. Insulation
6. Vapour control layer
7. Deck
8. Down pipe

Fig 11.5.17(2) Balustrade fixing

Designs incorporating independent bases must take into account *BS6399: Part 1 (1984)* and *The Building Regulations*, the effect of local loadings on the roof structure and the compressive strength of the insulation.

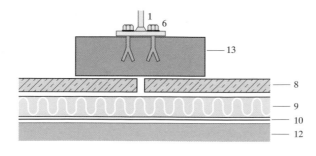

Fig 11.5.18 Chute

This detail is shown as an end of roll condition where generally details have been shown as edge of roll.

Where possible the use of chutes should be avoided. If they are to be used then they should be of sufficient size such that they can be adequately formed in the first instance and cleaned and maintained subsequently. A minimum of 300mm horizontally and vertically is recommended. If not turned back over the insulation the vapour control layer should lap the upstand underlayer by a minimum of 75mm.

The height of adjacent flashings should be consistent with the chute size.

Proprietary parapet outlets are available which have leaf guards and spigots suited to standard rainwater goods.

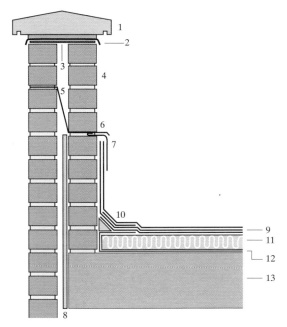

Warm deck roof.

1. Coping
2. Dpc
3. Slate Closer
4. Brickwork
5. Cavity tray
6. Weep holes
7. Minimum code 4 lead flashing

8. Cavity insulation
9. Built-up roofing
10. Angle fillet 50mm x 50mm
11. Insulation
12. Vapour control layer
13. Deck

Inverted warm deck roof.

1. Coping
2. Dpc
3. Slate closer
4. Brickwork
5. Cavity tray
6. Weep holes
7. Preformed rigid metal flashing
8. Insulation board with cementitious topping

9. Pebbles 20mm-40mm
10. Concrete paving on pads
11. Filter layer
12. Insulation
13. Built up roofing
14. Deck
15. Cavity wall insulation

Fig 11.5.19A(1) Parapet abutment

Dpc under copings must be supported by slate or some other form of cavity closer.

Cavity trays must protrude over flashings and be sealed at laps which should be a minimum of 100mm. Weep holes should be provided at 900mm centres.

Copings should be weathered and provided with adequate overhangs and drips. Mechanical fixing of the copings may be necessary.

Under no circumstances should a lead cavity tray be used unless provision for movement is made.

Fig 11.5.19A(2) Parapet abutment

Insulation to the upstand membrane is strongly recommended as it reduces heat ageing of the membrane, protects the membrane from damage and eliminates the risk of cold bridging of the wall/ceiling abutment.

continued ▶

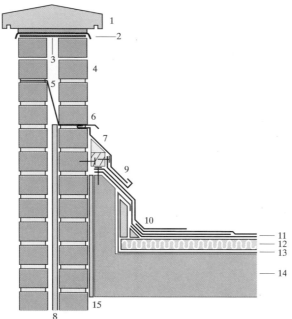

Warm deck roof.

1. Coping
2. Dpc
3. Slate closer
4. Brickwork
5. Cavity tray
6. Weep holes
7. Code 4 lead flashing
8. Cavity insulation
9. Copper clips at 500mm centres
10. Angle fillet 50mm x 50mm
11. Built up roofing
12. Insulation
13. Vapour control layer
14. Deck
15. Provision for movement

Inverted warm deck roof.

1. Coping
2. Dpc
3. Slate Closer
4. Brickwork
5. Cavity tray
6. Weep holes
7. Code 4 lead flashing
8. Cavity insulation
9. Copper clips at 500mm centres
10. Insulation board with cementitious topping
11. Pre-treated timber support batten
12. Pebbles 20mm-40mm
13. Concrete paving on pads
14. Filter layer
15. Insulation
16. Built up roofing
17. Deck
18. Provision for Movement

Fig 11.5.19B(1) Parapet abutment accommodating movement

Where upstands are formed to accommodate movement between deck and parapet they should be a minimum of 150mm high and the cover flashing depth a minimum of 75mm.

Consideration should be given to convection heat losses between the roof and the wall. Because of the anticipated movement and self-supporting requirements, a preformed metal flashing may be advised. However, fixing, movement and joint waterproofing should be considered.

Fig 11.5.19B(2) Parapet abutment accommodating movement

Consideration should be given to convection heat losses between the roof and the wall. Because of the anticipated movement and self-supporting requirements, a preformed metal flashing may be advised. However, fixing, movement and joint waterproofing should be considered. ■

Mastic asphalt 12

12.1 General description

- Mastic asphalt comprises asphaltic cement and graded aggregates.
- It has the characteristic of being solid or semi-solid at normal temperatures, but workable for spreading by trowel at elevated temperature.
- The workability of asphalt means that complex details can be formed, in an essentially seamless waterproofing membrane.

Pearl Assurance Headquarters, Peterborough. Water garden over car park

Basis of technology

Mastic asphalt has a long history of use for roofing in buildings. It ranks as one of the 'traditional' roofing systems, with a well-developed vocabulary of detailing and application methods.

As a molten material mastic asphalt is extremely versatile and workable. The mastic asphalt craftsman can apply the material to various complex details and configurations, including membrane penetrations, whilst still producing a continuous seamless waterproofing layer.

The essential ingredients of mastic asphalt are asphaltic cement, and suitably graded fine and coarse aggregates. Together they form a cohesive, voidless, impermeable mass, which is solid or semi-solid under normal temperature conditions, but sufficiently fluid when brought to a suitable temperature, to be spread by means of a hand float without compaction.

Mastic asphalt may be modified by inclusion of polymers. They have the beneficial effect of improving flexibility at lower temperatures. Polymer modified mastic asphalts are not yet covered by British Standards. Individual products may carry Agrément Certificates.

General considerations

Mastic asphalt is a suitable roofing option for a wide variety of situations, including roof gardens and trafficked areas, such as car park roofs and decks, where its ability to combine a directly trafficable surface with waterproofing is advantageous.

Asphalt performs best when used on a stable, low movement deck such as in-situ reinforced concrete. When laid on softer, more compressible insulating materials, mastic asphalt's resistance to mechanical damage is reduced. Increased thermal movements when laid above the insulation can give rise to failure from restrained thermal fatigue.

Asphalt is intrinsically heavier than most other membrane systems, although this may be offset in certain comparisons for specific applications by not requiring a separate ballasting system against wind uplift.

Asphalt is relatively inflexible at normal exposed temperatures in the UK and is therefore less tolerant of movement than some comparable systems. Attention to detailing is essential to ensure that this vulnerability does not lead to premature diminution of performance.

The material can have advantages in refurbishment works, which can be undertaken using mastic asphalt on a 'strip and re-cover' procedure, thus avoiding the necessity for temporary roof coverings.

Constituent materials

Asphaltic cement

Asphaltic cement is defined in *BS6925: 1988* as 'bitumen or a mixture of refined lake asphalt with bitumen and/or asphaltite having adhesive qualities suitable for the manufacture of mastic asphalt'.

Bitumen is normally a viscous liquid (sometimes solid), consisting essentially of hydrocarbons and their derivatives. It is substantially non-volatile, and softens (thus becoming more workable) when heated. It is found naturally in rock and lake asphalt, and is also manufactured by distillation of petroleum.

Lake asphalt, is found in surface deposits and comprises bitumen and finely-divided mineral matter. After treatment to remove unwanted components such as water and organic matter, it is known as refined lake asphalt.

A further naturally-occurring material often used in mastic asphalt is asphaltite. This is a substance allied to bitumen but with a higher softening point and greater stability and strength. It is used in flooring grades only.

Asphaltic cement thus consists of bitumen, refined lake asphalt, asphaltite or blends of these with one another.

Further reading:
BS6925 Specification for mastic asphalt for building and civil engineering (limestone aggregate) • MACEF Paving Handbook • MACEF Roofing Handbook.

- Mastic asphalt is suitable not only for normal roofing, but also for areas subject to traffic, such as car park roofs/decks.

- Asphalt performs best on stable, low movement decks.

Table 12.1.1
Methods of surface protection for mastic asphalt

Type of surface	Surface protection
Sloping or vertical upstands and kerbs	Reflective paint or mineral/aluminium faced aluminium faced roofing felt
Flat roof	Stone chippings laid loose or in bonding compound
	Ballast laid loose
	Proprietary paving tiles
	Pre-cast concrete paving slabs laid over external board insulation
Access roof or walkway (where exposed) or terrace deck	Proprietary paving tiles
Gutters	Usually reflective paint but wider gutters may have bonded stone chippings or proprietary paving tiles – laid over external board insulation.

Aggregates

The natural occurrence of mineral matter with bitumen in rock and lake asphalts was found to produce a more stable waterproofing material than bitumen alone. Subsequently, aggregates were incorporated in the production process for mastic asphalt, the grading and proportions of fine and coarse aggregate influencing the performance of the finished product. As a result, there is now a variety of mastic asphalts with different performance characteristics.

The fine aggregate used is naturally-occurring limestone rock crushed and suitably graded.

Coarse aggregate is clean igneous or calcareous rock or siliceous material obtained from natural deposits either directly or by screening, crushing or other mechanical process, and again suitably graded.

Form / surface finishes

Mastic asphalt is a formless material and the technique of laying it in a molten state results in a seamless membrane. It is typically black or dark grey, unless coloured by pigment. Ageing produces a lighter grey colour.

Mastic asphalt is a strong durable material. However, consideration should be given to the provision of protection against damage that can be caused by misuse, in particular that resulting from impact damage. Mastic asphalt should be protected against point loadings which can cause indentation and damage to insulation installed below the mastic asphalt.

For warm deck or cold deck roof specifications the surface finish may be mineral aggregate chippings consisting of limestone, granite, gravel, calcined flint, calcite, feldspar, etc. They may be bonded or loose laid with chippings of 20mm or more, on roofs not exposed to wind scour, with adhesion achieved around outlets and perimeters using a bitumen dressing compound.

Where chippings cannot be used for aesthetic or weight restriction reasons, a suitable white reflective paint may be used. However, this offers minimal protection on insulated horizontal areas and regular repainting is essential (see also **Unit 11.3**). Paint coatings are the normal protection to skirtings and vertical work. They should be applied as soon as practicable after laying the mastic asphalt. Proprietary products are available designed specifically for use with mastic asphalt. All paints must in themselves be capable of withstanding thermal cycling, without imposing undue stress on the mastic asphalt.

A high standard of protection is essential where the mastic asphalt is laid directly over an insulant. In such cases the asphalt is exposed most significantly to solar heat gain and loss (mainly through radiation) and will thus be subject to significant thermal movements or, if restrained, to thermal stresses.

The methods of surface protection most commonly used are summarised in Table 12.1.1.

For heavy duty applications such as roofing car parks and service decks, the MACEF *Paving Handbook* provides advice on surface treatment and protection.

Workability

Because the whole waterproofing sheet is formed insitu, there is more reliance on the operatives' skill to control the process completely. Well-trained and experienced operatives can achieve this consistently, and this emphasises the need to employ suitable specialist firms. ∎

Critical factors

- A layer of chippings is a more effective solar protection on an asphalt surface than reflective paints, although these are important on upstands and other details,

- A high standard of solar protection is required when it is used directly over insulation, to limit the extent of the differential temperature induced movements that may occur.

- Mastic asphalt roofs should be protected from mechanical damage and impact risks.

Further reading in the Guide:
12.3 Mastic asphalt: selection, design and application

12 Mastic Asphalt	13 Polymeric Single Ply	14 Copper	15 Lead Sheet	16 Other Membranes	17 Thermal Insulants	18 Specification	19 Contracts & Procurement	20 Inspection	21 Maintenance	22 Bibliography	23 Index
263	301	331	353	375	383	393	399	413	429	437	455

12.2 Performance in use

- A well designed mastic asphalt roof is expected to have a useful life in excess of 25 years.
- The natural 'age hardening' of mastic asphalt is a slow process which takes place over many years.
- The inverted warm deck roof specification is particularly suited to mastic asphalt, as it protects the membrane from both thermal stressing and mechanical damage.

Movement characteristics

At normal exposure temperatures mastic asphalt is relatively inflexible. At higher temperatures it can accommodate imposed movements by plastic deformation. It can also accommodate 'slow' imposed movements by plastic deformation, but is prone to fracture if subject to shock or impact loading. The use of an isolating layer on horizontal surfaces is an important contribution to good performance, as it separates the mastic asphalt from much movement of the roofing below. However, care may be needed to minimise local restraints to movement.

The inverted warm deck roof specification is particularly suitable for mastic asphalt roof coverings, because of the protection provided to the principal waterproofing membrane and the consequent reduction in thermal movements and physical damage. This may be expected to improve the service life, in comparison with other arrangements of the roofing elements.

Although warm deck roof specifications (i.e. insulation immediately beneath the mastic asphalt) can perform satisfactorily, an effective solar reflective treatment is essential. However, the life expectancy of such a construction will be less than with a roof design in which the membrane is fully protected.

Key properties

Thermal performance
Mastic asphalt has a relatively high thermal conductivity (see **Unit 12.4**) and so does not contribute significantly to the overall thermal resistance of a roof (see **Units 4.5** and **7.6**).

Fire resistance
Mastic asphalt is one of the materials listed with designation AA in *The Building Regulations*. Asphalt, therefore, fulfils these requirements with regard to fire resistance for use on any class of building, without restriction.

Asphalt fulfils all the requirements for a roof covering, as given in *BS5588: Part 1* section 1.1 and achieves the highest rating (P60) under the test requirements of *BS476: Part 3: 1975*. The P60 rating relates to external fire exposure roof tests carried out as described under Clause 6.2 and 6.3 confirming that fire penetration did not occur in less than one hour.

The Armada Centre, Plymouth, UK

Guidance on the comparison between this rating and the AA rating in the Approved Document to *The Building Regulations* is not available (see **Unit 7.9**).

Wind resistance
Mastic asphalt is applied over a loose-laid sheathing felt, needing no form of attachment to the deck. The self-weight of asphalt waterproofing is typically about $0.5kN/m^2$ and, over an impermeable deck, this is sufficient to resist wind uplift. However, should the deck be air permeable, or the exposure conditions be severe, an assessment should be made as described in **Units 4.10 7.10** and **8.4**).

Providing edge details are properly formed and designed to reduce the free entry of air beneath the membrane, the presence of insulation beneath the mastic asphalt should not affect the wind resistance capabilities of a mastic asphalt roof covering when installed over a concrete roof deck. For applications over flexible roof decks, consideration may have to be given to the mechanical fixing of some insulants.

Further reading:
BRE Digest 144 Asphalt and built-up felt roofings: durability • BS5588: Fire precautions in design, construction and use of buildings • BS476: Part 3 Fire tests on building materials and structures. External fire exposure roof test • BS5284: Methods. Sampling and testing of mastic asphalt and pitchmastic used in building • MACEF Paving Handbook.

- Asphalt roofs have proved to be resistant to wind uplift, even though they are laid unbonded to the deck, given care at perimeter details.
- Asphalt is very resistant to water and biological agencies; however, it is affected by solvents.

However, to avoid possible wind uplift problems at perimeters, care should be taken to ensure the correct fixing of metal flashings, which may form part of the weatherproof roof design. This issue does not arise if the mastic asphalt is finished forming a skirting or upstand.

Traffic resistance
Asphalt can be designed to provide surfaces with a high degree of resistance to traffic. Reference should be made to the *MACEF Paving Handbook*.

Asphalt, like most non-metallic waterproof membranes, has a low compressive strength when unconfined. It is vulnerable, in particular, to concentrated loads such as occur under the legs of plant and machinery. These can cause indentation or, at worst, puncturing of the asphalt.

Consequently, plant, machinery, pipework etc should be supported on plinths or bases constructed from the roof slab. These bases should incorporate a chase or rebate allowing the formation of a standard mastic asphalt skirting.

Acoustic performance
The mass of asphalt, usually associated with a heavy stiff supporting deck, will contribute to acoustic insulation. Its consistency contributes to reducing transmission of structure-borne impact sound.

Durability

Expected life
BRE Digest 144 indicates that a properly designed and laid mastic asphalt roof can prove capable of 50-60 years service. Numerous examples exist of satisfactory performance in excess of this period, but the normal target for roofing grade is to seek a life in excess of 25 years.

Natural ageing
It is well documented that bituminous materials undergo a natural 'age setting' process during service. There is supporting evidence for this with samples taken from roofs where the mastic asphalt is in excess of 40 years of age and is still performing satisfactorily. The 'age hardening' of mastic asphalt is the slow process of stabilisation of the bitumen binder after melting and cooling.

Surface oxidation of mastic asphalt takes place, but no significant overall change occurs. No detrimental effect on the material's waterproofing properties is likely from this.

As with all materials, the life expectancy of a mastic asphalt roof covering will depend upon various factors, notably correct detailing, specification, installation, and maintenance. However, the general principle of protecting the mastic asphalt from the effects of solar heat gain must be considered the most important factor.

Water and biological effects
Mastic asphalt is impervious to water and snow, and will not be adversely affected by them, providing the roof construction is designed to accommodate imposed loadings.

No significant biological change occurs with age. Mastic asphalt is non-toxic, vermin-proof and rot-proof. It provides no support for organic growth.

Chemical and heat effects
Whilst mastic asphalt is a durable material, contamination with oil, fuel and most organic solvents must be avoided. Spillages from vehicles may cause localised softening. Thus, the internal levels of multi-storey car parks will, for example, require periodical hosing to remove oil or fuel deposits. However roof top car parks are usually washed sufficiently by normal rainfall. Proprietary coatings are available offering a degree of protection to mastic asphalt.

In situations where mastic asphalt may come into contact with industrial liquors, acids, effluents etc. specialist advice may be sought from the Mastic Asphalt Technical Advisory Centre (MATAC).

Bitumen is soluble in many organic solvents, notably dichloromethane (which are used in testing mastic asphalt, as outlined in *BS5284*).

As with other bitumen-based and similar membranes, asphalt should be isolated and insulated from heat sources such as flames.

Environmental impact

See **Unit 4.15**　　■

Critical factors

- Mastic asphalt should be separated from movements in the supporting deck by an isolating layer.
- Effective protection from temperature rise from solar gain.

Further reading in the Guide:
4.5 Thermal performance • 4.10 Wind • 4.15 Environmental impact of materials • 7.6 Design for thermal performance • 7.10 Design for wind resistance • 8.4 Calculation of wind uplift • 12.4 Mastic asphalt: additional information

12.3 Selection, design and application

- There is a well established vocabulary of detailing roofs in mastic asphalt.
- Asphalt is normally laid on a separating membrane.
- Asphalt can be bonded to suitably primed brick and concrete upstand details.

Selection

General

For general roof work, mastic asphalt is normally applied in two coats, each of nominal 10mm thickness. Being a hand laid material, all finished thicknesses are nominal and subject to tolerances in practice. As a guide, a thickness tolerance of ± 10% may be considered acceptable.

Roof gardens

Three-coat mastic asphalt is a suitable specification for waterproofing to roof gardens and terracing or other buried applications.

The asphalt should be applied in full before the construction of the gardens or terraces. Before it is covered, the asphalt should be inspected carefully for visible faults. A full water test should normally be carried out on the membrane, although effective electronic methods are becoming available. A typical test may last approximately 48 hours and include water spray on surfaces which are to be covered but which cannot be included in the static water test.

When designing roof gardens the following principles should be given special attention:

- The asphalt should be protected by external grade board insulant or similar means from subsequent digging operations. An alternative is loose laid gravel laid on a glass fibre filter, to prevent blockage of the outlets.
- All drainage should be provided at the mastic asphalt waterproofing layer.
- All pedestrian areas should have adequate falls.
- Where horizontal areas of mastic asphalt are to be left uncovered, they should be insulated in accordance with the remainder of the roof, and be covered with surface protection appropriate to their function.

Substructures

Mastic asphalt roofing should be applied to structures with characteristics conforming with those described in *BS6229: 1982.*

Where insulation is to be used below mastic asphalt, it is important to choose a material which is not damaged or distorted when the hot asphalt is applied. *CP144: Part 4* limits the choice to lightweight concrete (lightweight aggregate with cement, or aerated concrete), granulated cork slabs, or fibre insulation board (now rarely used). However, other materials have been introduced successfully since this code was published in 1970. Those adopted for warm roof construction include polyisocyanurate foams, cellular glass, perlite, and expanded polystyrene (with wood fibreboard or cork overlaying the polystyrene to act as a heat protection layer).

In general, movement joints are only required where designed and incorporated into the building structure. A twin kerb with a metal capping is the preferred type of detail. Expansion joints are not required solely for the mastic asphalt covering.

Application

General techniques

The speed of mastic asphalt application is controlled by the continuous availability of molten material. The rate of application can therefore be increased dramatically by the use of 'hot charge' material supply. This involves the delivery to site of molten material in mechanically-agitated thermostatically-controlled mixers, capable of carrying up to 16 tonnes of material (the equivalent of approximately $320m^2$ of two-coat 20mm covering). Critical factors include:

- access to point of laying
- distance to transporter
- method of transfer
- height of building
- the number of asphalters on site.

The rate of production will depend not only on the accessibility factors, but also on the amount of the labour-intensive items, such as skirtings and collars. These are more time-consuming than clear horizontal areas.

The formation of bay joints in all asphalting is critical. The bay joints between coats are staggered so that the first coat of asphalt acts as a 'strapping' for the second. Junctions between contiguous bays should not be less than 150mm from the corresponding junction in the preceding coat. The edge of a previously laid bay is warmed and cleaned by the application of hot mastic asphalt, which is then removed before the joint with the new material is made.

Further reading:
BS 6229 Code of practice for flat roofs with continuously supported coverings • CP 144: Part 4 Roof coverings: Mastic asphalt • BS 747: Specification for roofing felts • BS1369: Part 1 Specification for expanded metal and ribbed lathing.

- Expanded metal lathing is used to support asphalt on details, such as upstands, where the background material cannot support it directly.
- With careful planning, backed-up by hot charge supply, the application rate of mastic asphalt can be considerably faster than traditionally achieved.

Delivering and spreading mastic asphalt

Pour butting up to a bay joint - second layer

Old covering partly stripped. New work close butted obviating the need for a temporary roof

Contact with moisture may produce 'blowing' within the mastic asphalt, which should be pierced and made good whilst the mastic asphalt is still warm. During periods of rain the 'blowing' will tend to be extensive and the repairing or puncturing of these blows during the laying operation then becomes very difficult.

The protection of mastic asphalt during installation is vital, in particular prior to cooling.

After the application of the final coat of asphalt, sand is scattered over the surface and rubbed in with a wooden float to break up the bitumen-rich layer which will have come to the surface.

All repair work to a mastic asphalt surface should be performed by a specialist mastic asphalt contractor. If it is necessary to remove an area of mastic asphalt, the lines of the cuts should be covered with molten mastic asphalt until the underlying material has softened. Blisters or cracks should be repaired (on the same principle) in accordance with *CP144: Part 4*. In no circumstances should a hammer and chisel be used to cut cold mastic asphalt (see **Unit 20.6**).

Underlays

For limited access roofs, horizontal mastic asphalt is normally laid on a separating membrane of black sheathing felt complying with *BS747* Type 4A(i), which is laid loose with lap joints of 50mm. This isolates the mastic asphalt from minor substructure movement, eliminates the risk of 'blowing' by allowing   *continued* ▶

Further reading in the Guide:

the lateral escape of trapped air and moisture, and acts as a long term vapour pressure relief layer. For substrates containing bitumen, non-bituminised building paper may be required between the felt and the substrate to prevent adhesion.

In specifications incorporating mastic asphalt roofing for vehicle traffic, the black sheathing felt membrane is replaced by a glass fibre tissue separating layer which is less compressible than sheathing felt. This is again laid loose, with laps of 50mm.

Attachment to upstands
Black sheathing felt is also used as the separating membrane behind expanded metal lathing where this is used to provide a key to vertical surfaces. *CP144: Part 4* recommends the use of bitumen coated or galvanised expanded metal lathing complying with *BS1369*. (The mesh can be used on normal weight concrete and other surfaces but is not normally necessary.)

Concrete surfaces in general, vertical or sloping (over 10°), will normally be treated with a proprietary bitumen/rubber emulsion primer before application of the mastic asphalt. Chemical damage to the mastic asphalt and reduced bond to the concrete can be caused by excessive use of mould oil on formwork.

For keying mastic asphalt to brickwork, particularly old brickwork, a light application of a suitable proprietary bitumen/rubber emulsion primer is recommended. Blistering or loss of bond may be experienced if mastic asphalt is applied direct to sand-lime bricks or to brickwork bedded in unduly hygroscopic mortars.

Bitumen-coated expanded metal lathing and sheathing felt can be used on most vertical surfaces which will not successfully accept a direct mastic asphalt application. Secure fixings throughout are essential.

Detailing the attachment of asphalt at insulated upstands requires great care. Mastic asphalt cannot be applied vertically direct to an insulant, due to the insulant's inability to provide a secure fixing for expanded metal lathing and to the heat retention effects during application and in service. One solution is to add a timber or plywood facing to the vertical insulation, so that the normal key of sheathing felt and expanded metal lathing can be formed. Efficient solar protection is required for such upstands.

Perimeter upstand tucked into chase with corner fillet.

Working asphalt around a roof penetration.

Bay joints laid with fall to outlet.

Further reading:

Chapter	1	2	3	4	5	6	7	8	9	10	11
Contents	Introduction	History	Regulatory Methods	Principles	Surveys	Constraints & Targets	Design Selection	Calculations	Detail Design Principles	Evaluation of Design	Built-up Roofing
Page	*1*	*19*	*31*	*45*	*83*	*95*	*105*	*165*	*189*	*217*	*221*

Protection

Temporary protection

It is essential that mastic asphalt roofing is fully protected from:

- mechanical and impact damage, including damage from contractors' plant, equipment and materials
- trafficking by following trades
- contamination by spillage of solvents, diesel fuel and paints.

Protection to the mastic asphalt can be provided by covering with plywood sheeting and, if oil or fuel spillage is a consideration, by the inclusion of layers of polythene sheet.

As an alternative, a single sacrificial layer of mastic asphalt may be applied early in the contract to provide temporary waterproofing. The main mastic asphalt roof covering may then follow at a later date when construction trafficking has ceased.

Permanent protective finishes

Permanent protective finishes should be specified, appropriate to the eventual function. With each system, and particularly with solar reflective paints, the maintenance requirements imposed by the finish should be carefully considered.

The choices for vertical surfaces and skirtings are:

- compatible solar reflective paint
- mineral surfaced polyester-based bitumen sheeting
- protection boards (roof gardens only)
- lightweight faced insulation (inverted roofs only).

For horizontal surfaces:

Maintenance access only -
- bonded 12mm limestone chippings
- compatible solar reflective paint
Access roofs -
- proprietary promenade tiles bedded on compatible bitumen or other adhesive
- additional coat of paving grade mastic asphalt
For inverted warm deck roofs -
- 50mm concrete paving slabs on paving supports on filter membrane on extruded polystyrene insulation.

Safety issues

During manufacture and installation mastic asphalt gives off bitumen fumes.

These fumes can contain polycyclic aromatic compounds, but these are of high molecular weight and boiling point and are more complex ring systems than those considered to be a potential carcinogenic hazard. Recent reports have concluded from the available information, knowledge and experience that:

- Bitumens are of a low order of acute toxicity.
- The amount of bitumen in mastic asphalt is relatively small (approximately 15%) when compared with oxidised bitumen materials used in built-up roofing.
- There is no evidence that bitumens are associated with long-term effects resulting from normal use over extended periods.

The Health and Safety Commission has not established an approved Occupational Exposure Standard for bitumen fume. However, the American Conference of Government Industrial Hygienists has adopted a threshold limit value of bitumen fumes for an 8-hour Time Weighted Average of $5mg/m^3$ and it is recommended that exposures are controlled below this figure. A survey of studies has concluded that inhalation exposures of polycyclic aromatic compounds during handling and use of bitumens will be extremely low if total fume exposures are kept below $5mg/m^3$. ■

Critical factors

- Protection provided to avoid damage during construction.

Further reading in the Guide:
20.6 Site processes: remedial works and testing

12.4 Additional information

- Mastic asphalt is manufactured in batches by blending the asphaltic cement and the graded aggregates, and supplied to site in blocks for remelting.
- Mastic asphalt exhibits flow characteristics within the normal range of ambient temperatures and this is reflected in some of its other physical properties and detailing disciplines.

Symphony Hall, Birmingham, UK

Manufacture

The manufacture of mastic asphalt is a batch production process. The raw materials are fine and coarse aggregates and asphaltic cement. These materials are pre-heated and fed in controlled amounts into a heated mixer capable of processing up to 10 tonnes of material. The mixture is continually agitated at a controlled temperature for 3-4 hours and following satisfactory laboratory testing of samples is discharged into steel moulds to form convenient sized blocks for transport and re-melting on site.

Blocks typically weigh approximately 25kg. They are transported on pallets for unloading by forklift truck or loose loaded on to a 'tipper' lorry for discharge where adequate storage space exists.

Further reading:
CP 144: Part 4 Roof coverings: Mastic asphalt • BS 6229: Code of practice for flat roofs with continuously supported coverings • BS5284: Methods, sampling and testing mastic asphalt and pitchmastic for use in building.

- The additional weight of mastic asphalt compared to other roof waterproofing materials is both an advantage and a disadvantage. Appropriate selection and design will maximise the former and minimise the latter.

Dorchester Hotel, London

Mastic asphalt can also be delivered to the site as a 'hot charge'. The molten material is delivered in thermostatically controlled, agitated mixers.

The mastic asphalt industry in the UK produces approximately 250 000 tonnes of material per year, half of which is roofing grade material. (The remaining tonnage covers paving, flooring and tanking production.)

Whether the material is transported to the site in a molten condition, or remelted on site, the total duration of heating and the type of plant used should be such that the properties of the mastic asphalt will not be impaired. (See *CP144: Part 4*).

Properties of mastic asphalt

Weight
The mass of mastic asphalt varies due to a number of factors, principally the differing proportions of constituents utilised in its manufacture.

In general mastic asphalt roofing is applied in two or three coats. Table 12.4.1 gives superficial mass and weight for a single coat of 10mm thickness and the commonest horizontal total thicknesses recommended in *CP 144: Part 4*. The density of asphalt is taken as 2400 kg/m³, i.e. 2.4 kg/m² per millimetre of thickness.

Table 12.4.1
Thickness and weight of mastic asphalt

Asphalt thickness (mm)	Mass (kg/m²)	Weight kN/m²
10	24	0.24
13	31	0.31
20	48	0.47
25	60	0.59

Thermal conductivity
Mastic asphalt has a thermal conductivity (k value) of between 0.43 and 1.15 W/m K. It does not therefore contribute significantly to the overall thermal insulation of a roof structure. A k value of 0.50 W/m K may be assumed for design purposes.

Thermal expansion
The coefficient of cubic expansion may be taken as 15×10^{-5} per °C.

Vapour resistivity
The vapour resistivity of asphalt can be assumed to be not less than 100 000MN.s/g.m

Tensile and flexural strength
Mastic asphalt has low tensile and flexural strengths, and consequently must be continuously supported on horizontal and inclined surfaces. It is unable to span or project horizontally without a high risk of fracture, and requires continuous lateral support on vertical and near-vertical surfaces.

Test methods
Test methods for mastic asphalt are given in *BS5284*. ■

Critical factors

- Mastic asphalt can accommodate slow applications of loads, by plastic deformation, but sudden loads are more likely to lead to fracture.

12.5 Design details

- Wherever there is a change or discontinuity in material or in the roof geometry careful consideration of the associated detail must be given.

- Such details are often 3-dimensional in character and the difficulties to be solved may not be apparent solely from isolated simple sections.

- This schematic key diagram is shown to locate details for a variety of roof designs and conditions. The drawing itself must not be considered appropriate for any particular roof type.

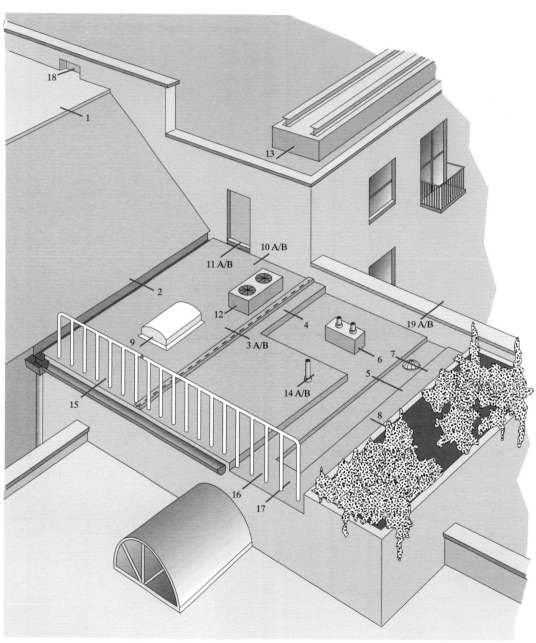

Key

1	Flat roof to pitched roof	8	Planted roof	14B	Service penetration - hot
2	Pitched roof to flat roof with gutter	9	Roof light	15	Eaves with gutter
3A	Movement joint - upstand	10A	Abutment - integral deck	16	Verge
3B	Movement joint - flush	10B	Abutment - accommodating movement	17	Balustrade fixing
4	Step	11A	Opening - integral deck	18	Chute
5	Internal gutter	11B	Opening - accommodating movement	19A	Parapet - integral deck
6	Boxed-in pipes or extract	12	Plant plinth above waterproof layer	19B	Parapet - accommodating movement
7	Outlet	13	Plinth		
		14A	Service penetration - cold		

- The roof system is subject to dynamic loads from gravity, wind, temperature changes, humidity changes, air pressure changes.
- The details must allow for suitable construction tolerances and movement.

Notes

General

Those areas that must be addressed in the design development fall into risk categories:

A   Stability and integrity
B   Discontinuity of material, substrate. or roof geometry and differential movement
C   Water path
D   Convection path
E   Conduction path with risk of cold bridging
F   Fire
G   Condensation
H   Ventilation requirement.

Other considerations must be borne in mind:

- Ease of construction
- Ease of access for inspection.
- Ease of repair and replacement.
- Method of attachment.
- Material compatibility.

Membranes must not be carried across building movement joints or other structural discontinuities capable of independent movement. Proper movement joints must be provided at such critical points.

Penetrations through roof openings should be minimised.They should be grouped through specially designed and waterproofed service boxes which allow for hot and cold services and their future replacement.

Penetrations or upstands should be located such that sufficient space is allowed between them and other obstructions so proper forming of the detail is feasible.

Membrane laps and upstand heights must be maintained at all details.

Cold bridges through the insulated layer should be avoided. Continuity for insulation around the perimeter details, roof services and penetrations is important. Integrity of the vapour control layer at all points is vital.

Direct excessive imposed loading of the roof finish, particularly point loads, must be prevented. Loads should be evenly distributed.

Internal gutters should be avoided if possible. If necessary, they must be wide enough to be formed properly and to allow for maintenance.

The details illustrate the deck in generic form. The thickness of kerbs will depend upon the the material used and will affect the actual detailing of components for particular situations.

Mastic asphalt

1. The following details include examples of different types of upstand substrate to mastic asphalt. Where not stated otherwise, two-coat vertical work to 13mm thickness on a primed substrate is assumed. Substrates of timber, lightweight concrete and metal require three-coat work to 20mm thickness on expanded metal lathe secured over the separating membrane.

2. All timber bearers and battens should be pre-treated, offsite, preferably with water-borne preservatives and should be dry when fixed.

3. Asphalt kerbs applied to brickwork and concrete should be turned into a minimum 25mm × 25mm chase, preferably with the lower edge chamfered.

4. Where mastic asphalt is dressed over lead flashings, the minimum thickness of asphalt must be maintained.

5. Mastic asphalt to insulated upstands requires effective solar reflective treatment. Mineral or metal surfaced high-performance bitumen sheet is recommended.

Special note

For each of the generic conditions shown in this Unit, there are various good practice solutions. Some good practice solutions involve particular components, materials and/or methods developed by individual suppliers or manufacturers, and benefit from their experience. Some solutions may also have to be modified according to the particular circumstances of the individual contract.

The detailed solutions shown in this Unit therefore represent only a selection of possible routes to good practice in design and installation. They indicate appropriate general methods for this particular membrane material, to show how the principles for different roof configurations (set out in Unit 9.1) may be translated into practical building. An understanding of these methods and principles will help the designer to assess not only the problems, but also the likely range of alternative possible solutions.   *continued* ▶

continued ▶

Critical factors

- Integrity.
- Provision for movement.
- Material compatibility.
- Provision for discharge of water.
- Check for consistency between different detail drawings and with the specification.

Further reading in the Guide:
9 Detail design principles

12 Mastic Asphalt	13 Polymeric Single Ply	14 Copper	15 Lead Sheet	16 Other Membranes	17 Thermal Insulants	18 Specification	19 Contracts & Procurement	20 Inspection	21 Maintenance	22 Bibliography	23 Index
263	301	331	353	375	383	393	399	413	429	437	455

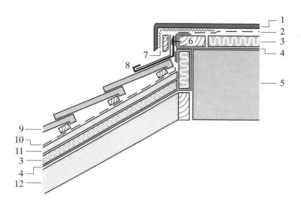

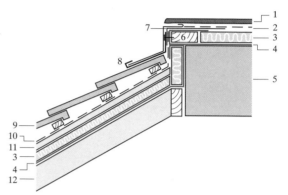

Warm deck roof.

1. 20mm two coat mastic asphalt
2. Separating layer
3. Insulation
4. Vapour control layer
5. Deck
6. Pre-treated timber bearer
7. Expanded metal lathing secured to bearer
8. Minimum code 4 lead flashing with copper clips at 500mm centres
9. Roof tiling
10. Under tiling membrane (Vapour permeable)
11. Counter battens
12. Rafters

Warm deck roof.

1. 20mm two coat mastic asphalt
2. Separating layer
3. Insulation
4. Vapour control layer
5. Deck
6. Pre-treated timber bearer
7. Polyester-based bitumen sheeting
8. Minimum code 4 lead flashing with copper clips at 500mm centres
9. Roof tiling
10. Under tiling membrane (vapour permeable)
11. Counter battens
12. Rafters

Fig 12.5.1 (1) Flat roof junction with pitched roof

Expanded metal lath should be taken over the junction of differing substrates.

The use of lead clips their spacing and method of fixing will depend on the location, orientation and exposure of the building.

In situations of high condensation risk the vapour control layer should be continuous between roofs support must be provided for the vapour control layer.

The timber edge batten should be of sufficient size to give adequate bearing on the deck.

Fig 12.5.1(2) Flat roof junction with pitched roof

The use of lead drips is not now generally recommended due to the thermal movement and low bond strength between the two materials.

Asphalt thickness should be maintained over the lead flashing. This can be achieved with the perimeter timber bearer rebated to allow for the thickness of lead.

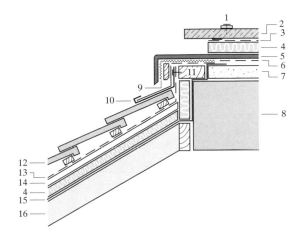

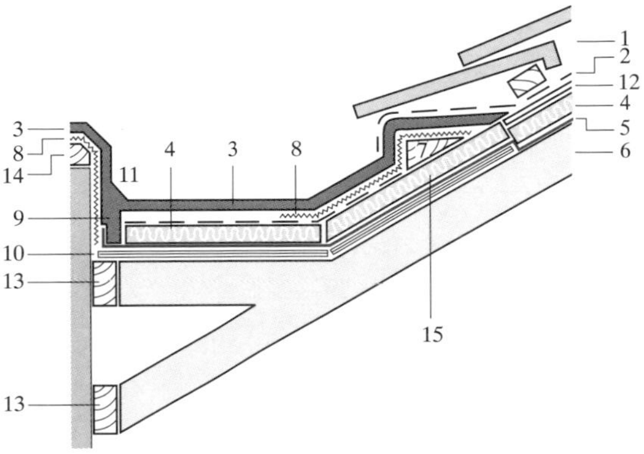

Inverted warm deck roof.
1. Stainless steel restraint strapping
2. Concrete paving slabs on pads
3. Filter layer
4. Insulation
5. 20mm two coat mastic asphalt
6. Separating layer
7. Screed to falls
8. Deck
9. Expanded metal lathing secured to bearer
10. Minimum code 4 lead flashing with copper and drip batten clips at 500mm centres
11. Pre-treated timber bearer
12. Roof tiling
13. Under tiling membrane (vapour permeable)
14. Counter batten
15. Vapour control layer
16. Rafters

Warm deck roof.
1. Roof tiling
2. Under tiling membrane
3. 20mm two coat mastic asphalt three coat to upstands
4. Insulation
5. Vapour control layer
6. Rafters
7. Tilting fillet
8. Expanded metal lath on separating membrane
9. Mastic asphalt downstand
10. Plywood layer secured to rafters
11. 50mm angle fillet
12. Counter battens
13. Wall plate
14. Timber plate
15. Insulation with plywood facing

Fig 12.5.1 (3) Flat roof junction with pitched roof

It it generally inadvisable to form eaves details with inverted roofing. In the event of such details being unavoidable the following factors must be considered:

1 Effective restraint to paving to stop movement due to wind or thermal expansion of insulation.
2 Effective protection of insulation from sunlight.
3 Avoidance of cold bridging lightweight composite inverted roof insulation with cementitious overlay may require greater restraint.
4 Effective solar protection to exposed mastic asphalt.

Fig 12.5.2 Pitched roof junction to flat roof with gutter

Expanded metal lath should be used to provide a good key on the inclined and vertical elements and over changes in the substrate material.

The membrane must be taken up the inclined pitch higher than the level of the adjoining flat roof. This ensures that if the gutter is blocked for some reason water will not pass into the building but on to the lower roof.

Support under the upstand is important. If any differential movement is expected here a free standing kerb may be required.

The mastic asphalt leg or downstand is appropriate for insulation that is not softened by direct contact during installation. For polystyrene insulant, an 'earth dry' sand/cement infill should be used.

12 Mastic Asphalt	13 Polymeric Single Ply	14 Copper	15 Lead Sheet	16 Other Membranes	17 Thermal Insulants	18 Specification	19 Contracts & Procurement	20 Inspection	21 Maintenance	22 Bibliography	23 Index
263	301	331	353	375	383	393	399	413	429	437	455

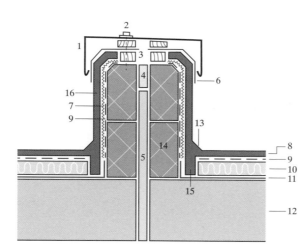

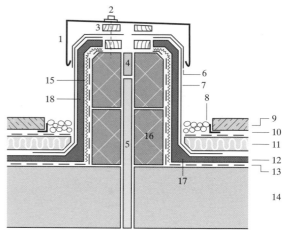

Warm deck roof.

1. Preformed coping with butt straps
2. Weather sealed fixing to one side only
3. Pre-treated timber spacers
4. Fire stop
5. Non-combustible insulation
6. Minimum code 4 lead flashing
7. Expanded metal lath secured to blocks at 100mm centres
8. 20mm 2-coat mastic asphalt
9. Separating layer
10. Insulation
11. Vapour control layer
12. Deck
13. 50mm fillet
14. Insulation blocks (lightweight)
15. Mastic asphalt downstand
16. 20mm 3-coat mastic asphalt

Inverted warm deck roof.

1. Pre-formed coping with butt straps
2. Weather sealed fixing to one side only
3. Pre-treated timber spacer
4. Fire stop (if required)
5. Non combustible insulation (if required)
6. Minimum code 4 lead flashing
7. Mineral coated elastomeric protection layer
8. Pebbles 20mm-40mm
9. Concrete paving on pads
10. Filter layer
11. Insulation
12. 20mm 2-coats mastic asphalt
13. Separating layer
14. Deck
15. Expanded metal lath secured to blocks
16. Insulating blocks (lightweight)
17. 50mm fillet
18. 20mm 3-coat mastic asphalt

Fig 12.5.3A (1) Upstand movement joint

Expanded metal lath is required if blocks are of lightweight concrete. The EML must be securely fixed to the blockwork over the separating membrane.

Insulating blocks avoid the need to insulate the upstand. In very low U-value designs both upstands and cappings require insulation.

Cappings are secured on one side only allowing independent movement of upstands.

The mastic asphalt leg or downstand is appropriate for insulation that is not softened by direct contact during installation. For plastic foam insulants an 'earth dry' sand/cement infill should be used.

Fig 12.5.3A (2) Upstand movement joint

Minimum upstand heights must be maintained.

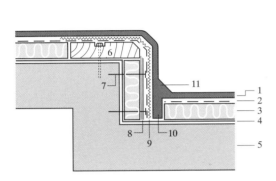

Warm deck roof.

1. 20mm two coat mastic asphalt 3-coat to upstand and solar reflective treatment
2. Separating layer
3. Insulation
4. Vapour control layer
5. Deck
6. Timber batten bolted to deck
7. Mechanical fixing
8. Plywood layer
9. Expanded metal lath
10. Mastic asphalt downstand
11. 50mm fillet

Inverted warm deck roof.

1. Stainless steel restraint strap
2. Stainless steel insulation retaining strap
3. Insulation with cementitious topping
4. Pebbles 20m - 40mm
5. Concrete paving on pads
6. Filter layer
7. Insulation
8. 20mm two coat mastic asphalt 3-coat to upstand
9. Separating layer
10. Deck
11. Expanded metal lath or primer as required
12. 50mm fillet

Fig 12.5.4 (1) Step

Upstand insulation is covered in a plywood layer which both secures the insulation and provides a suitable substrate for securing the expanded metal lath and mastic asphalt finish. The thickness of the mastic asphalt should be consistent across the detail.

The mastic asphalt leg or downstand is appropriate for insulation that is not softened by direct contact during installation. For polystyrene insulants, an 'earth dry' sand/cement infill should be used.

For uninsulated upstands, expanded metal lath would not be required (see general notes). The timber batten provides support at the arris.

Fig 12.5.4 (2) Step

Physical restraint of the upstand insulation is provided by clips from the paving surface. Overhang of the paving must be kept to a minimum to prevent tipping. Surface restraint strapping aides prevention of slabs being dislodged. Clearance between upstand insulation and paving is essential to stop paving load being transferred to the mastic asphalt at the base of the upstand.

If the roof field insulation is laid first, restraint to the lower edge of the upstand insulation should be provided by the pebbles.

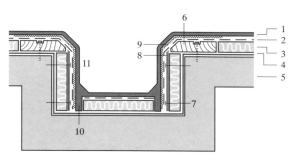

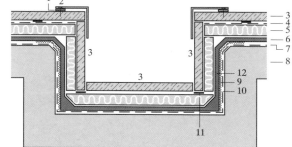

Warm deck roof.
1. 20mm two coat mastic asphalt
2. Separating layer
3. Insulation
4. Vapour control layer
5. Deck
6. Timber batten bolted to deck
7. Mechanical fixing
8. Plywood layer
9. Expanded metal lath, or primer as required
10. Mastic asphalt downstand
11. 20mm 3-coat mastic asphalt and solar reflective treatment

Inverted warm deck roof.
1. Stainless steel restraint strap
2. Stainless steel paving restraint clip
3. Concrete paving slabs on pads
4. Filter layer
5. Insulation
6. 20mm 2-coat mastic asphalt
7. Separating layer
8. Deck
9. Expanded metal lath secured to deck, or primer, as required
10. 50mm fillet
11. Polyester-based bitumen cap sheet strip
12. 20mm 3-coat mastic asphalt

Fig 12.5.5 (1) Internal gutter

Where possible internal box gutters are best avoided, the roof falls being configured to directly discharge into roof outlets or external gutters.

Expanded metal lath is continued over changes in the substrate material in order to prevent cracking. Plywood is provided on the upstands to protect and secure the insulation and provide a solid fixing for the expanded metal lath.

For uninsulated upstands, expanded metal lath would not be required (see general notes). The timber batten provides support at the arris.

Fig 12.5.5 (2) Internal gutter

Where possible, box gutters should be avoided for inverted roofs, as effective U-values may be reduced by water flow under the insulation.

Adequate support must be provided to the edge paving slabs in order to prevent tipping.

The paving slabs are oversailed in order to provide protection to continuous insulation.

The vertical paving slabs are retained in position by clips fixed to the horizontal paving restraint strip.

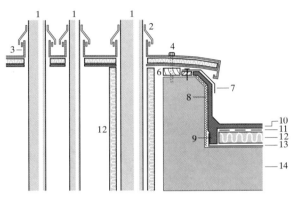

Warm deck roof.

1. Service penetration
2. Apron flashing secured to service
3. Upstand on penetration capping
4. Weather seal bolt fixings
5. Purpose made insulated capping with membrane coated metal facing
6. Pre-treated timber spacers
7. Minimum code 4 lead flashing
8. Expanded metal lath secured to upstand, or primer, as required
9. Mastic asphalt downstand
10. 20mm two coat mastic asphalt and solar reflective treatment
11. Separating layer
12. Insulation
13. Vapour control layer
14. Deck

Warm deck roof.

1. Service penetration
2. Apron finishing secured to service
3. Upstand on penetration capping
4. Weather seal bolt fixings
5. Purposed made insulated capping with membrane coated metal facing
6. Pre-treated timber spacers
7. Code 4 lead flashing
8. Expanded metal lath secured to upstand
9. Mastic asphalt downstand
10. 20mm two coat mastic asphalt 3-coat to upstand and solar reflective treatment
11. Separating layer
12. Insulation
13. Vapour control layer
14. Deck
15. Plywood facing

Fig 12.5.6 (1) Boxed-in pipes or services

Mastic asphalt should be provided with a downstand at upstands and expanded metal lath is required as a key to lightweight concrete timber or metal securely fixed to the structure at 100mm centres.

Where possible service penetrations should be grouped together to minimise the number of weather proofing details required. Cappings to these penetration should be insulated.

Cold services should be insulated to prevent condensation forming where they pass from inside to outside.

Flues must be insulated to prevent heat being transmitted to the roof finish either by convection or by conductor through the penetration capping.

Services must be provided with weathered aprons.

The mastic asphalt leg or downstand is appropriate for insulation that is not softened by direct contact during installation. For polystyrene insulants, an 'earth dry' sand/cement infill should be used.

Fig 12.5.6(2) Boxed-in pipes or services

In this alternative, the upstand kerbs are insulated, requiring a plywood facing and expanded metal lath as a key to the mastic asphalt.

In all such insulated upstand situations, effective solar reflective treatment can be provided by a mineral-surfaced high-performance bitumen sheet flashing.

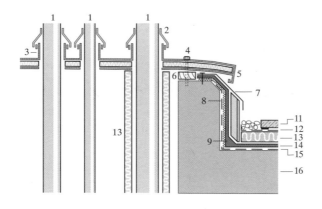

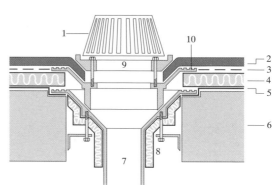

Inverted warm deck roof.

1. Service penetration
2. Apron flashing secured to service
3. Upstand on penetration capping
4. Weather seal bolt fixing
5. Purpose made insulated capping with membrane coated metal facing
6. Pre-treated timber spacers
7. Pre-formed rigid metal flashing
8. Expanded metal lath or primer as required
9. Mastic asphalt fillet 50mm
10. Pebbles 20-40mm
11. Concrete paving slabs on pads
12. Filter layer
13. Insulation
14. 20mm 2-coat mastic asphalt 3-coat to upstand
15. Separating layer
16. Deck

Fig 12.5.6 (3) Boxed-in pipes or services

Warm deck roof.

1. Removable grating/guard
2. 20mm 2-coat mastic asphalt
3. Separating layer
4. Insulation
5. Vapour control layer
6. Deck
7. Downpipe connection
8. Insulation collar
9. Clamp ring
10. Extension flange

Fig 12.5.7 (1) Outlet

The flanges of outlets must be primed with bitumen primer. For single flange outlets, the insulation thickness should be reduced around the outlet position to form a sump. This facilitates water flow and prevents ponding.

Insulation in the form of a factory applied collar may be required to the outlet.

Double flange outlets are also available to suit various thicknesses of insulation. These enable mastic asphalt to be dressed directly into the clamp ring and avoid local depression of the insulation.

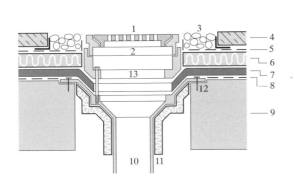

Inverted warm deck roof.

1. Removable grating	8. Separating layer
2. Adjustable seating	9. Deck
3. Pebbles 20mm-40mm	10. Downpipe
4. Concrete paving slabs on pads	11. Insulation collar
5. Filter layer	12. Outlet flange
6. Insulation	13. Clamped ring
7. 20mm two coat mastic asphalt	

Inverted warm deck roof.

1. Precast concrete coping fixed to upstand	8. Filter layer
2. Dpc	9. Concrete paving slabs on pads
3. Minimum code 4 lead flashing	10. Insulation
4. Protection board	11. 30mm 3-coat mastic asphalt
5. Top soil	12. Separating layer
6. Filter layer	13. Deck
7. Drainage layer	14. 20mm 2-coat mastic asphalt

Fig 12.5.7(2) Outlet

Two-level outlets should be specified with inverted roofs, as they maximise drainage above the filter layer and hence insulation efficiency.

Fig 12.5.8 Roof planter

Finished top soil levels must be maintained at a minimum of 150mm below adjacent capping levels.

Mastic asphalt in both horizontal and vertical planes must be protected from physical damage by gardening operations and plant roots.

A drainage layer is provided to prevent waterlogging of the planting medium. The filter layer prevents leaching of the soil into the drainage layer.

Roof gardens with mastic asphalt are generally of the inverted roof thermal design. Should warm roof design be considered insulation with high compressive strength should be specified.

12 Mastic Asphalt	13 Polymeric Single Ply	14 Copper	15 Lead Sheet	16 Other Membranes	17 Thermal Insulants	18 Specification	19 Contracts & Procurement	20 Inspection	21 Maintenance	22 Bibliography	23 Index
263	301	331	353	375	383	393	399	413	429	437	455

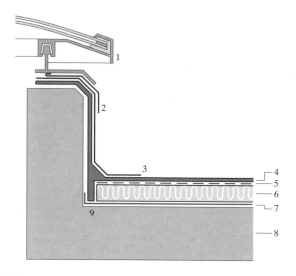

Warm deck roof.
1. Proprietary rooflight
2. Code 4 lead flashing
3. Mineral surface elastomeric layer
4. 20mm mastic asphalt 3-coat on upstand
5. Separating layer
6. Insulation
7. Vapour control layer
8. Deck
9. Mastic asphalt downstand

Inverted warm deck roof.
1. Proprietary rooflight
2. Rigid metal restraint flashing
3. Insulation board with cementitious topping mechanically fixed
4. Pebbles 20mm-40mm
5. Concrete paving on pads
6. Filter layer
7. Insulation
8. 20mm 2-coat mastic asphalt 3-coat on upstand
9. Separating layer
10. Deck

Fig 12.5.9(1) Rooflight upstand
The same principles apply at roof light openings as with door openings and perimeter abutments. A minimum upstand height of 150mm must be provided. If proprietary roof lights including upstands are used careful consideration must be given to their fixings in order prevent flexing being transmitted to the membrane.

With lightweight concrete, timber or metal upstands a key must be provided by the use of expanded metal lath secured to the upstand over a separating layer.

The mastic asphalt leg or downstand is appropriate for insulation that is not softened by direct contact during installation. For polystyrene insulants, an 'earth dry' sand/cement infill should be used.

Fig 12.5.9(2) Rooflight upstand
Kerbs should be insulated continuously with the deck insulation.

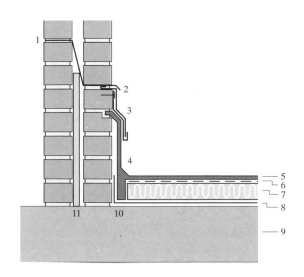

Warm deck roof.
1. Cavity tray
2. Minimum code 4 lead flashing
3. 25 × 25mm chase to key mastic asphalt
4. 13mm 2-coat mastic asphalt and solar reflective treatment
5. 20mm 2-coat mastic asphalt
6. Separating layer
7. Insulation
8. Vapour control layer
9. Deck
10. Mastic asphalt downstand
11. Cavity wall insulation

Warm deck roof.
1. Cavity tray
2. Minimum code 4 lead flashing
3. Insulation board with plywood, mechanically fixed, faced with expanded metal lath
4. 20mm 3 coat mastic asphalt and solar reflective treatment
5. 2 coat 20mm mastic asphalt
6. Separating layer
7. Insulation
8. Vapour control layer
9. Deck
10. Mastic asphalt downstand
11. Cavity wall insulation

Fig 12.5.10A(1) Abutment-integral deck

In cases of junctions between abutting walls and decks where no relative movement is possible the roof covering may be dressed up the wall directly. With new brickwork the mastic asphalt will be on average 13mm thick laid in two coats and keyed into 25mm × 25mm chase in the brickwork at the top and pointed in sand and cement mortar on completion. On metal, timber or lightweight concrete the fixing of expanded metal lath as a key is advised. Highly porous brickwork or concrete will require priming before mastic asphalt is applied.

The upper edge of the vertical key of the covering should be protected by a separate lead counter flashing set into the wall and dressed down over the covering. Mastic asphalt downstands should be provided at the abutment.

Cross refer to Figure 12.5.11A(1) where insulation is required.

Fig 12.5.10A(2) Abutment -integral deck: additional insulation

A preformed rigid metal flashing can be used in place of (2). If so care must be taken to ensure adequate attachment to brickwork to resist thermal and wind induced movement.

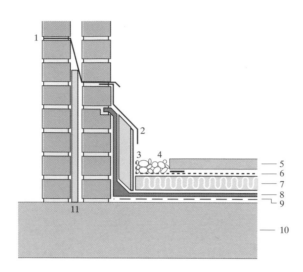

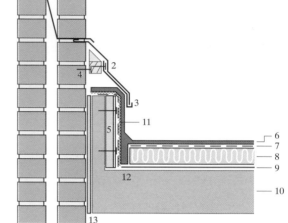

Inverted warm deck roof.

1. Cavity tray
2. Rigid metal flashing
3. Insulation board with cementitious topping
4. Pebbles 20mm-40mm
5. Concrete paving on pads
6. Filter layer
7. Insulation
8. 20mm 2-coat mastic asphalt 13mm 2-coat upstand
9. Separating layer
10. Deck
11. Cavity wall insulation

Warm deck roof.

1. Cavity tray
2. Minimum code 4 lead flashing or rigid pre-formed
3. Copper clips at 500mm centres
4. Pre-treated timber support batten fixed to brickwork
5. Insulation board with plywood mechanically fixed
6. 20mm mastic asphalt (3 coat on upstand) and solar reflective treatment
7. Separating layer
8. Insulation
9. Vapour control layer
10. Deck
11. Expanded metal lath
12. Mastic asphalt downstand
13. Provision for movement

Fig 12.5.10A(3) Abutment-integral deck

Skirtings must be protected from solar degradation.

Fig 12.5.10B(1) Abutment – accommodating movement

Junctions between abutting walls and decks are particularly vulnerable to relative movement.

In cases where relative movement is possible, an independent skirting or kerb is to be constructed along the edge of the deck that makes contact with the wall.

The roof covering is dressed over the kerb without contact with the wall. A separate counter flashing is set into the wall and dressed over the weatherproofed kerb. The kerb is required to be a minimum of 150mm above finished roof level.

Consideration should be given to convection heat losses between the roof and the wall.

Because of the anticipated movement and self-supporting requirements, a preformed metal flashing may be advised. However, fixing, movement and joint waterproofing should be considered.

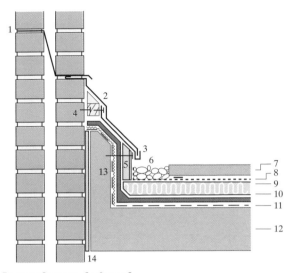

Inverted warm deck roof.
1. Cavity tray
2. Minimum code 4 lead flashing or rigid pre-formed metal flashing
3. Clips at 500mm centres
4. Pre-treated support batten
5. Insulation board with cementitious topping
6. Pebbles 20mm-40mm
7. Concrete paving on pads
8. Filter layer
9. Insulation
10. 20mm mastic asphalt (3 coat on upstand)
11. Separating layer
12. Deck
13. Expanded metal lath secured to upstand, or primer, as required
14. Provision for movement

Warm deck roof.
1. Cill
2. Water bar
3. Minimum code 4 flashing
4. Insulation board with plywood face
5. 20mm two coat mastic asphalt (3 coat to upstand) and solar reflective treatment
6. Separating layer
7. Insulation
8. Vapour control layer
9. Deck
10. Mechanical fixing
11. Expanded metal lath secured to plywood

Fig 12.5.10B(2) Abutment – accommodating movement

Consideration should be given to convection heat losses between the roof and the wall. Because of the anticipated movement and self-supporting requirements, a preformed metal flashing may be advised. However, fixing, movement and joint waterproofing should be considered.

Fig 12.5.11A(1) Opening onto roof – integral deck

Thresholds should have a minimum height of 150mm above finished roof level, with the roof ideally formed to provide falls away from the opening. This detail is appropriate for all conditions where differential movement between deck and wall is not expected.

Waterbars should be provided to prevent water being blown in under the cill, together with a cill tray as appropriate.

Vertical insulation will be required to be mechanically fixed to the upstand.

The upstand should be protected with a layer of mineral surfaced polyester based bitumen capsheet in situations where abrasion is likely. Surface protection of proprietary walkway tiles is also recommended for any regular access ways.

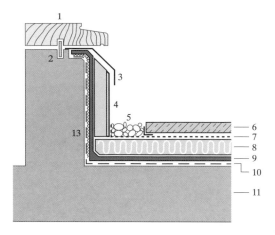

Inverted warm deck roof.

1. Cill
2. Water bar
3. Rigid pre-formed metal flashing
4. Insulation board with metal flashing cementitious topping
5. Pebbles 20mm-40mm
6. Concrete paving on pads
7. Filter layer
8. Insulation
9. 20mm 2-coat mastic asphalt (3-coat to upstand) and solar reflective treatment
10. Separating layer
11. Deck
13. Expanded metal lath secured to upstand, or primer, as required

Fig 12.5.11A(2) Opening on to roof – integral deck

Vertical insulation if required should be restrained by (upper) rigid metal flashing and by (lower) sole insulation or pebbles. If this is not practical, it may be bonded to the upstand with compatible adhesive.

Warm deck roof.

1. Cill
2. Water bar
3. Minimum code 4 lead flashing or rigid pre-formed metal flashing
4. Pre-treated timber support batten
5. Clips at 500mm centres
6. Expanded metal lath secured to upstand, or primer, as required
7. 20mm 2-coat mastic asphalt, (3-coat to upstand) and solar reflective treatment
8. Separating layer
9. Insulation
10. Vapour control layer
11. Deck
12. Provision for movement

Fig 12.5.11B(1) Opening onto roof – accommodating movement

Where provision for vertical or horizontal movement has to be accommodated and in instances where a flexible deck abuts a rigid element a detail must be developed to prevent flexing of the membrane.

Where the gap to be bridged is significant rigid support to the lead flashing must be provided. The support should be weathered to prevent ponding and possible ingress of water through laps in the lead. Laps in the lead should be minimum of 100mm. Rigid metal flashings are recommended where regular foot traffic or mechanical abrasion is expected.

Consideration should be given to convection heat losses between the roof and the wall.

Because of the anticipated movement and self-supporting requirements, a preformed metal flashing may be advised. However, fixing, movement and joint waterproofing should be considered.

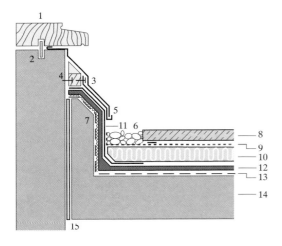

Inverted warm deck roof.

1. Cill
2. Water bar
3. Code 4 lead flashing
4. Pre-treated timber support batten
5. Clips at 50mm centres
6. Pebbles 20mm-40mm
7. Expanded metal lath
8. Concrete paving on pads
9. Filter layer
10. Insulation
11. Mineral surfaced elastomeric layer
12. 20mm 2-coat mastic asphalt, (3-coat to upstand)
13. Separating layer
14. Deck
15. Provision for movement

Inverted warm deck roof.

1. Equipment
2. Plinth
3. Bitumenised protection board
4. Concrete paving on pads
5. Filter layer
6. Insulation
7. 20mm mastic asphalt
8. Separating membrane
9. Deck

Fig 12.5.11B(2) Opening onto roof - accommodating movement

Consideration should be given to convection heat losses between the roof and the wall.

Because of the anticipated movement and self-supporting requirements, a preformed metal flashing may be advised. However, fixing, movement and joint waterproofing should be considered.

Fig 12.5.12 Plinth above waterproofing layer

Load spreading is provided in the case of inverted roofs by the concrete paving slabs. To avoid heavier loads being transfered through paving supports, fibre cement surfaced lightweight insulation could be used, but the compressive strength of the insulation should be assessed in all situations.

© BFRC / CIRIA: Flat Roofing: Design and Good Practice. 1993

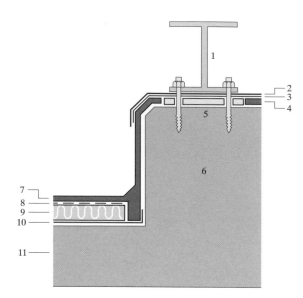

Warm deck roof.

1. Cradle track
2. Code 5 lead flashing
3. Elastomeric felt layer
4. 20mm 2-coat mastic asphalt
5. Stainless steel spacer
6. Plinth

7. 20mm 2-coat mastic asphalt, 3-coat on upstand and solar reflective treatment
8. Separating layer
9. Insulation
10. Vapour control layer
11. Deck

Inverted warm deck roof.

1. Cradle track
2. Code 5 lead flashing
3. Mineral surfaced elastomeric felt layer
4. 20mm 2-coat mastic asphalt
5. Stainless steel spacer
6. Plinth
7. Pebbles 20mm-40mm

8. Concrete paving slabs on pads
9. Filter layer
10. Insulation
11. 20mm 2-coat mastic asphalt
12. Separating layer
13. Deck

Fig 12.5.13(1) Plinth.

Bolt holes may require sealing individually or by use of a bedded sealing plate.

A stainless steel spacer plate is used to prevent any transmission of load into the asphalt.

Fig 12.5.13(2) Plinth

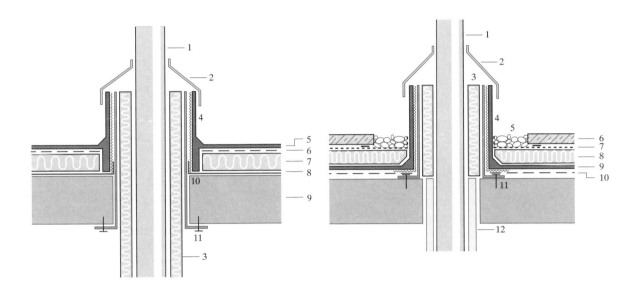

Warm deck roof.
1. Service penetration (cold)
2. Weather collar secured to pipe
3. Insulation
4. 20m 3-coat mastic asphalt upstand on expanded metal lath with solar reflective paint finish
5. 20mm 2-coat mastic asphalt
6. Separating layer
7. Insulation
8. Vapour control layer
9. Deck
10. Mastic asphalt downstand
11. Metal sleeve secured to deck

Inverted warm deck roof.
1. Service penetration (cold)
2. Weather collar secured to pipe
3. Insulation
4. 20mm 3-coat mastic asphalt upstand on expanded metal lath with solar reflective paint finish
5. Pebbles (20-40mm)
6. Concrete paving on pads
7. Filter layer
8. Insulation
9. 20mm 2-coat mastic asphalt
10. Separating layer
11. Metal sleeve secured to deck
12. Pipe insulation

Fig 12.5.14A(1) Service penetration (cold)

Penetration of pipes through the roof should be kept to the minimum.

Generally it is advisable to sleeve all pipes to ensure that flexing of the deck or service does not transmit movement to the roof finish.

Cold pipes may require insulation to prevent condensation forming on their surface this should be continued into the area below the roof deck.

Pipes should have weather collars positioned a minimum height to allow 150mm upstand in the roof finish.

Sleeves will require to have a key formed in expanded metal lath.

The mastic asphalt leg or downstand is appropriate for insulation that is not softened by direct contact during installation. For polystyrene insulants an 'earth dry' sand/cement infill should be used.

Fig 12.5.14A(2) Service penetration (cold)

The same insulation thickness around the pipe may not be necessary above and below the deck.

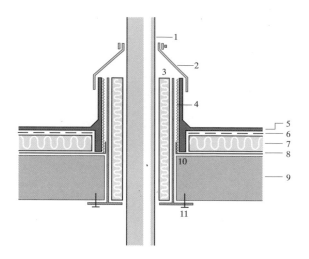

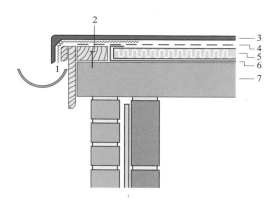

Warm deck roof.

1. Service penetration (hot)
2. Weather collar secured to pipe
3. Non-combustible insulation
4. 20mm 3-coat mastic asphalt upstand on expanded metal lath with solar reflective finish
5. 20mm mastic asphalt
6. Separating layer
7. Insulation
8. Vapour control layer
9. Deck
10. Mastic asphalt downstand
11. Metal sleeve secured to deck

Warm deck roof.

1. Expanded metal lath
2. Pre-treated timber bearer
3. 20mm mastic asphalt
4. Separating layer
5. Insulation
6. Vapour control layer
7. Deck

Fig 12.5.14B Service penetration (hot)

Hot pipes such as flues must be sleeved and insulated with non combustible insulation to prevent heat being transferred to the roof finish.

Particular care must be taken with timber decks to ensure sufficient separation is maintained.

Metal hoods can also transmit heat to the waterproofing layer and adequate ventilation gaps between hood and finish must be kept.

Fig 12.5.15(1) Eaves with gutter

Eaves should be formed to ensure that water is discharged into the gutter via an adequate drip. The drip, if it is formed in mastic asphalt, will require to have a key of expanded metal lath. The use of lead drips is not now generally recommended due to the differential thermal movement and low bond strength between the two materials.

The fascia board should also be provided with a drip and stand clear of the face of the wall.

Insulation should be protected at the edge by an upstand fascia and timber bearer.

Consideration must be given to cold bridging at eaves, and insulation under the fascia and soffit boards may be required. Consider also the detailing and durability of the fascia board so that maintenance and replacement will not disturb the mastic asphalt.

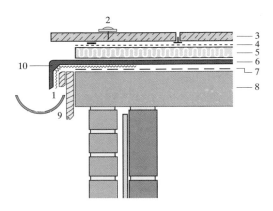

Inverted warm deck roof.

1. Expanded metal lath
2. Stainless steel restraint strapping
3. Concrete paving on pads
4. Filter layer
5. Insulation
6. 20mm 2-coat mastic asphalt
7. Separating layer
8. Deck
9. Timber fascia
10. Solar reflective finish

Warm deck roof.

1. 13mm 2-coat mastic asphalt with solar reflective paint finish
2. 13mm 2-coat mastic asphalt with solar reflective paint finish
3. 20mm 2-coat mastic asphalt
4. Separating layer
5. Insulation
6. Vapour control layer
7. Deck
8. Mastic asphalt drip edge or proprietary trim
9. Expanded metal lath

Fig 12.5.15(2) Eaves with gutter

Eaves drainage of inverted roofs should be avoided whenever possible, as effective U-values may be reduced by water flow below the insulation and restraint to paving may be difficult to achieve.

On eaves to inverted roofs the insulation and protection requires physical restraint to prevent wind uplift and being dislodged.

Effective solar reflective finish must be provided to exposed mastic asphalt.

Fig 12.5.16(1) Eaves

Insulation of verges in both warm and inverted thermal designs may be necessary where the thermal conductivity of the deck and U-value of the system combine to give a risk of cold bridging. Verges must provide an adequate check to prevent the discharge of water over the roof side a minimum of 75mm upstand is recommended.

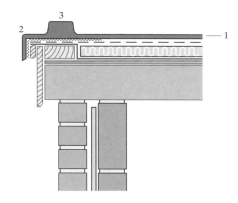

Warm deck roof.
1. 20mm two coat mastic asphalt
2. 20mm three coat mastic asphalt

3. Expanded metal lath
4. Mastic asphalt drip edge

Fig 12.5.16(2) Eaves

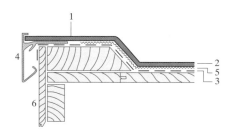

Warm deck roof.
1. 20mm two coat mastic asphalt
2. 20mm three coat mastic asphalt

3. Optional solid asphalt water check

Fig 12.5.16(3) Eaves

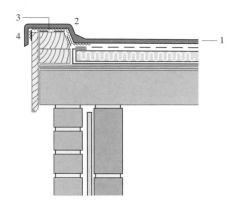

Inverted warm deck roof.
1. Mineral surfaced elastomeric layer
2. Pebbles 20mm - 40mm
3. Concrete paving on pads
4. Filter layer
5. Insulation

6. 20mm 2 coat mastic asphalt
7. Separating layer
8. Deck
9. Timber fascia
10. Concrete upstand

Fig 12.5.16(4) Eaves

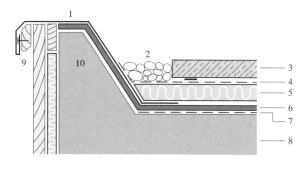

Cold deck roof.
1. Solar reflective paint to water check
2. 20mm two coat mastic asphalt
3. Separating layer

4. Proprietary trim fixed with corrosion resistant screws at 300mm centres joint lapped and sleeved to manufacturers recommendations.
5. Expanded metal lath
6. Fascia board

Fig 12.5.16(5) Eaves

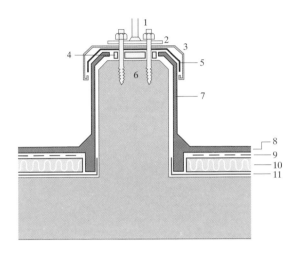

Warm deck roof.

1. Balustrade
2. Base plate
3. Metal coping
4. Stainless steel spacer
5. Code 5 lead flashing
6. Holding down bolts
7. 13mm 2-coat mastic asphalt

8. 20mm 2-coat mastic asphalt
9. Separating layer
10. Insulation
11. Vapour control layer
12. Mastic asphalt downstand
13. Deck

Inverted warm deck roof.

1. Balustrade
2. Base plate
3. Metal coping
4. Stainless steel spacer
5. Code 5 lead flashing
6. Holding down bolts
7. 13mm 2-coat mastic asphalt
8. Mineral surface elastomeric layer

9. Pebbles (20-40mm)
10. Concrete paving on pads
11. Filter layer
12. Insulation
13. 20mm 2-coat mastic asphalt
14. Separating layer
15. Deck
16. Base

Fig 12.5.17(1) Balustrade fixing

Bolt fixing holes must be sealed by compressing a non-setting mastic under the base plate.

Minimum heights of upstands should be 150mm above the finished roof level.

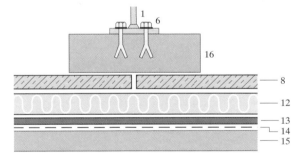

Fig 12.5.17(2) Balustrade fixing

Designs incorporating independent bases must take into account *BS6399*: Part 1 (1984) and *The Building Regulations*, the effect of local loadings on the roof structure and the compressive strength of the insulation.

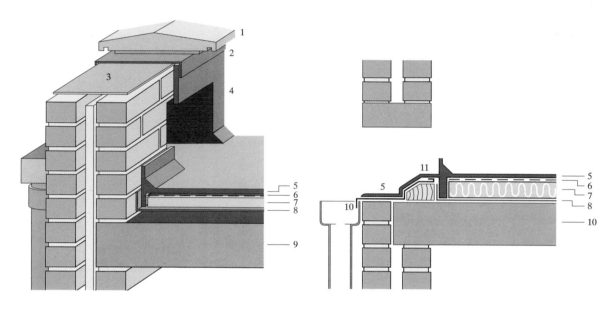

Warm deck roof.
1. Coping
2. Dpc
3. Slate closer
4. 13mm mastic asphalt skirting
5. 20mm 2-coat mastic asphalt
6. Separating layer
7. Insulation
8. Vapour control layer
9. Deck

Warm deck roof.
5. 20mm 2-coat mastic asphalt
6. Separating layer
7 Insulation
8. Vapour control layer
9. Deck
10. Code 5 lead tray
11. Timber batten secured to deck

Fig 12.5.18(1) Chute

Where possible use of chutes should be avoided. If they are to be used then they should be of sufficient size such that they can be adequately formed in the first instance and cleaned and maintained subsequently. A minimum of 300mm horizontally and vertically is recommended.

Given its seamless nature mastic asphalt can be readily dressed into openings.

The height of adjacent flashings should be consistent with the chute size.

Fig 12.5.18(2) Chute

Alternative proprietary chute outlets are available complete with gratings.

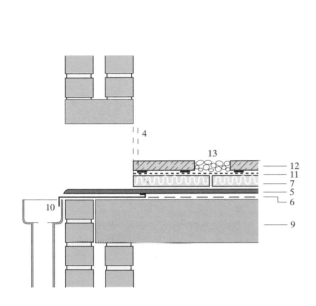

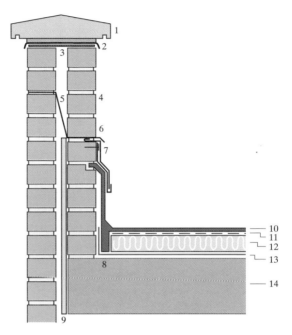

Inverted warm deck roof.

1. Coping
2. Dpc
3. Slate closer
4. 13mm mastic asphalt skirting
5. 20mm 2-coat mastic asphalt
6. Separating layer
7. Insulation
8. Vapour control layer

9. Deck
10. Code 5 lead tray
11. Filter layer
12. 50mm concrete paving on spacers, across chute opening only
13. 20-40mm pebbles

**Fig 12.5.18(3) Chute section
to illustrate mastic asphalt termination**

Warm deck roof.

1. Coping
2. Dpc
3. Slate closer
4. Brickwork
5. Cavity tray
6. Weep holes
7. Code 4 lead flashing restrained by copper clips

8. Mastic asphalt downstand
9. Cavity wall insulation
10. 20mm mastic asphalt
11. Separating layer
12. Insulation
13. Vapour control layer
14. Deck

Fig 12.19A(1) Parapet abutment

Dpc under copings must be supported by slate or some other form of cavity closer.

Cavity trays must protrude over flashings and be sealed at laps which should be a minimum of 100mm. Weep holes should be provided at 900mm centres.

Copings should be weathered and provided with adequate overhangs and drips. Mechanical fixing of the copings may be necessary.

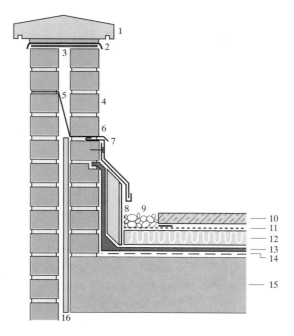

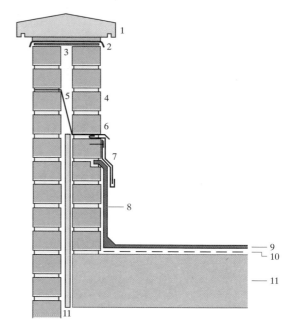

Inverted warm deck roof.

1. Coping
2. Dpc
3. Slate closer
4. Brickwork
5. Cavity tray
6. Weep holes
7. Code 4 lead flashing
8. Insulation board with cementitious topping
9. Pebbles (20-40mm)
10. Paving slabs on pads
11. Filter layer
12. Insulation
13. 20mm mastic asphalt
14. Separating layer
15. Deck
16. Cavity wall insulation

Cold deck roof.

1. Coping
2. Dpc
3. Slate closer
4. Brickwork
5. Cavity tray
6. Weep holes
7. Code 4 lead flashing restrained by copper clips
8. 13mm 2-coat mastic asphalt skirting
9. 20mm 2-coat mastic asphalt
10. Separating layer
11. Deck

Fig 12.5.19A(2) Parapet abutment

Insulation of the upstand membrane is strongly recommended as it reduces heat ageing of the membrane, protects the membrane from damage and eliminates the risk of cold bridging of the wall/ceiling abutment.

Fig 12.5.19A(3) Parapet abutment

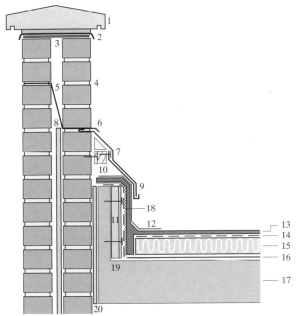

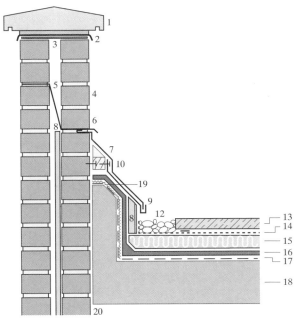

Warm deck roof.

1. Coping
2. Dpc
3. Slate closer
4. Brickwork
5. Cavity tray
6. Weep holes
7. Code 4 lead flashing
8. Insulation
9. Copper clips at 500mm centres
10. Pre-treated timber support batten
11. Insulation board with cementitious topping
12. Mineral surfaced elastomeric layer
13. 20mm mastic asphalt
14. Separating layer
15. Insulation
16. Vapour control layer
17. Deck
18. Expanded metal lath
19. Mastic asphalt downstand
20. Provision for movement

Inverted warm deck roof.

1. Coping
2. Dpc
3. Slate closer
4. Brickwork
5. Cavity tray
6. Weep holes
7. Code 4 lead flashing
8. Insulation
9. Copper clips at 500mm centres
10. Pre-treated support batten
11. Insulation board with cementitious topping
12. Pebbles (20-40mm)
13. Concrete paving on pads
14. Filter layer
15. Insulation
16. 20mm mastic asphalt
17. Separating layer
18. Deck
19. Expanded metal lath
20. Provision for movement

Fig 12.5.19B(1) Parapet abutment-accommodating movement

Where upstands are formed to accommodate movement between deck and parapet they should be a minimum of 150mm high and the cover flashing depth a minimum of 75mm.

Consideration should be given to convection heat losses between the roof and the wall.

Because of the anticipated movement and self-supporting requirements, a preformed metal flashing may be advised. However, fixing, movement and joint waterproofing should be considered.

Fig 12.5.19B(2) Parapet abutment-accommodating movement

Consideration should be given to convection heat losses between the roof and the wall. Because of the anticipated movement and self-supporting requirements, a preformed metal flashing may be advised. However, fixing, movement and joint waterproofing should be considered.

Polymeric single-ply 13

13.1 General description

- A wide range of polymeric materials fall within the scope of this section. Their characteristics and range of properties make classification difficult.
- Some distinctive characteristics exist between thermoplastic materials and elastomeric types, but the materials all tend to be offered for use in similar contexts.

Basis of technology

Nature of materials

Polymeric single-ply roofing materials are manufactured from high molecular weight synthetic polymers, with or without a fabric carrier (base). They are suitably compounded with other additives and then formed into a sheet by calendering, extrusion or spreading techniques. The process used for making polymeric sheeting reflects the nature of the polymer and the final properties required.

The choice of polymers is wide and the spectrum of properties exhibited makes description and classification difficult. In describing polymeric single-ply roofing, emphasis tends to be placed on the nature of polymers and the underlying range of common and distinctive properties.

In Europe, where approximately one-sixth of flat roofs are now being waterproofed by polymers, and with many bitumen manufacturers modifying their products with polymers, or marketing polymeric sheeting independently, the division between the industries is becoming less distinct.

This Guide cannot provide definitive information for the selection of a specific polymeric roofing product, but aims to provide a background against which specifiers may judge manufacturers' proposals for specific projects.

Table 13.1.1 provides a broad classification for polymeric waterproofing materials, based on the more general polymers and blends.

Properties, even with the same class of polymer, can vary widely and it is normal for manufacturers to include plasticisers or oils, filler and pigments, as well as trace additives, to improve flexibility, flame resistance, UV and bacteriological resistance and to allow cross-linking.

Table 13.1.1
Polymers: general classification

	Hot melt	Thermoplastic	Elastomeric	Thermoset
Effect of increase in temperature	Fluidity, no strength	Softening, reduced strength	No change, slight loss	No change, marginal loss
% Cross-linking	–	–	5	>10
Examples:	Bitumen Polymer, Polymer Modified[A]	EVA, VET PVC, CPE CSM[B]	IIR, EPDM CR, PIB	Epoxy, PU Polyester

Notes:
[A] some elastomeric properties
[B] some plastic properties

General considerations

Single-ply membranes are generally light in weight. Their flexibility renders them particularly suitable for lightweight constructions which tend to flex in response to dynamic loads. They are most likely to be successful on large, simply shaped areas, with few penetrations and little traffic or access. Complexities of roof junctions or penetrations result in difficult details, as with other sheet waterproofing materials, but these can be designed and installed satisfactorily, using existing techniques.

In the refurbishment of existing roofs, single-ply membranes can, in many cases, be laid directly over the old without the need for stripping up. However, the need for separation/protection layers between the new and old waterproofing should be checked.

These materials offer a smooth surface, which facilitates inspection and integrity testing. Repairs are quickly and easily carried out with a piece of membrane and simple heat or solvent-welding hand tools.

- Single-ply membranes are normally formulated to be inherently flexible.
- Single-ply membranes are normally used without surface coatings or chipping finishes. In this condition, the identification of areas of damage is easier and repairs can be readily executed.

Elephant and Castle, London, UK

Constituent materials

The precise chemical composition is not relevant here. The general classification given is only a guide. Mixtures of polymers are becoming increasingly common and the significance attributable to a polymer name, in terms of implying a specific range of properties, is limited.

A general description of the principal materials can be given as follows:.

- PVC: Polyvinylchloride, made flexible by the addition of plasticisers (stabilisers and pigments are added for resistance to UV light).
- CPE: Chlorinated polyethylene, with enhanced flexibility by a chlorination process.
- CSM: Chlorosulphonated polyethylene, with enhanced flexibility by a chlorosulphonation process. (On external exposure its properties are further modified giving a greater measure of toughness and elasticity).
- VET: Polyvinylchloride, made flexible by blending with ethylene vinyl acetate (EVA). (The EVA component is a resin modifier which acts as a stable plasticiser for the PVC).
- PIB: Polyisobutylene is naturally flexible.
- IIR: Polyisobutylene/isoprene, a butyl rubber, is naturally flexible. It often has ethylene propylene diene monomer (EPDM) added to increase its resistance to 'ozone cracking' when under strain.
- EPDM: Ethylene propylene diene monomer is naturally flexible.

Form/surface finishes

Single-ply membranes are most commonly supplied in thicknesses between 1.0mm and 4.0mm. There is an increasing tendency to use the thicker membranes.Single-ply membranes do not normally require any surface coatings or chippings. They are available in many colours, including white and black, mostly of neutral tone as, due to a build-up of dust and other matter on flat roofs, dark coloured materials can appear lighter and light coloured materials darker. The texture can be glossy, matt or pattern embossed. Some are embossed with the product name, which is useful for future recognition.

Although they are not normally affected by occasional light foot traffic, protective walkways should be provided where regular traffic is expected (i.e. maintenance of HVAC plant etc.) These walkways can be made of proprietary non-slip membranes, rubber or concrete tiles.

Workability

Single-ply roofing membranes can offer an economic solution for all types of building, but especially for those where the speed of installation is an important element. The installation does not require the use of heavy plant or naked flames, although some small specialist equipment, such as hot air welders, may be required. Significant reductions can be achieved in terms of installation time, compared to other types of system.

It is, however, important to ensure that the membrane is installed by competent, trained operatives in order that a watertight roof is achieved at the first attempt. As a result, the supply of materials is normally restricted only to those roofing contractors who are licensed or authorised by the manufacturer/supplier concerned.

■

Critical factors

- Although materials are often referred to by their main polymer constituent, there can be as great a variation in properties within a group as between groups of products.
- There are no British Standards for these materials. Agrément Certificates provide a source of detailed information to help evaluate the suitability of a particular product.

Further reading in the Guide:
4.13 Durability of materials

13.2 Performance in use

- The expected life of single-ply roofing systems is normally stated to be in excess of 25 years.
- Polymers are degraded by heat and by ultra-violet light and polymer systems are formulated to reduce the effects of these influences.

Movement characteristics

Installed as part of a mechanically fastened, fully adhered or loose laid ballasted system, the membranes are capable of withstanding normal substrate movements without failure. In many cases, the membrane can even be carried straight over structural expansion joints, provided that the movement is only in one plane. However, specialist advice should be sought on this.

When the waterproofing membrane is held in position by the strength of an adhesive, a correct balance of the cohesive and adhesive strength is needed to facilitate the membrane bridging substrate gaps without losing adhesion. The technique of over-taping such gaps is used in order to reduce the localised extension of the membrane. Homogeneous polymeric membranes have the extensibility, and some carrier based materials have the strength, to accommodate localised stretching over gaps. Use of the UEAtc cyclic test procedure has shown that polymer roofing can endure many cycles, without failure, even after heat ageing and when tested at low temperatures.

Under ballasted and mechanically-fixed conditions, the membrane rides over gaps without developing stresses. Possible problem areas relate to membrane penetration by the ballast, which can also shift over time under wind action.

Mechanical attachment significantly isolates the waterproofing membrane from the building movement, but introduces a new set of strains and stresses at the point of fixing, resulting from the wind forces. Extensive wind testing indicates that polymeric membranes, with and without fabric carriers, can resist these cyclic strains, although the mechanism is different. For these applications, the nature of the polymeric membrane and any carrier, together with the fixing distance and geometry are critical. If these are not resolved, these cyclic strains can cause irreversible extension of the membrane, which is generally referred to as 'permanent set'.

The tension induced into the membrane by normal relaxation shrinkage, is another form of movement which must be accommodated by the polymer sheets. It is exacerbated at low temperatures.

Key properties

Thermal performance
Polymeric single-ply membranes do not contribute significantly to the thermal resistance of the roof system (see **Units 4.6** and **7.6**).

Fire resistance
Single-ply materials in the finished roof form are normally self-extinguishing and, depending upon the roof construction as a whole, will achieve an AA or AB rating when tested according to *BS476: Part 3*. The individual manufacturer should be consulted when specific performance is required (see **Unit 7.9**).

Wind resistance
By their nature, polymeric single-ply, membranes do not contribute to wind resistance, which must be provided by mechanical fixings, adhesives or ballasting.

Traffic resistance
In common with all other roof waterproofing materials, polymeric membranes can suffer mechanical damage if abused. Their comparative thinness makes them more vulnerable in this respect.

Acoustic performance
Polymeric single-ply materials make no significant contribution to the acoustic performance of a roof (see **Unit 4.12**).

Durability

Expected life
Most single-ply membranes have a life expectancy of at least 25 years.

Natural ageing
Ultra-violet radiation in time degrades virtually all polymeric materials (see Unit 4.13). Single-ply membranes therefore incorporate stabilisers, fillers and pigments to enhance their resistance. Heat will accelerate the degradation processes and surface temperatures in the UK can be as high as 80°C plus for dark colours, or 50°C for white, solar reflective membranes. Low surface temperatures may reach -20°C.

Single-ply membranes are formulated to resist oxidation, although most polymers will harden slightly, due to cross-linking processes.

Further reading:

- As with other systems, polymeric single-ply roofs are designed to minimise the effects of deck movements on the membrane.
- Tests have shown that these materials have a high fatigue resistance under cyclic movements.
- Many polymeric roofing materials can be recycled for the production of new sheeting.

Whilst the physical properties of the cross-linked polymers will not change significantly due to fluctuations in temperature, the flexibility and softness of the thermoplastic polymers will vary with the temperature.

In the long term, the combination of heat and UV light will result in degradation of the polymer system. It is within the scope of the individual manufacturer to formulate the product to reduce significantly the effects of heat and light such that the anticipated life of the product exceeds the design requirements.

Some components in the roof build up may not be compatible. PVC, and some other membrane materials, for example, should be separated from bitumen surfaces with a barrier layer to avoid plasticiser migration and reduction in material properties. Compatibility with all components needs to be carefully checked with the relevant suppliers.

Water and biological effects

All the polymeric membranes will resist the passage of water through them and are therefore suitable for exposure to rain and snow. Ponding water will not cause these materials to rot. Some polymeric membranes are susceptible to water wicking into the carrier. In such cases, sealing of cut edges forms part of the recommended system.

The polymers used in waterproofing are resistant, to a wide range of chemicals, and generally unaffected by bacteria. Some polymers, which contain plasticisers, oils and water-absorbing residues, are more susceptible to biological attack than others, which contain certain chemical groupings or cross-linking additives. Manufacturers select their ingredients to minimise adverse effects. Protracted conditions of heat and humidity which encourage such bacterial attack or surface growth seldom arise in roofing systems.

The inverted roofing systems, in which the waterproofing membrane is placed under the ballasted insulation, reduces the overall membrane exposure, but is more demanding of the membrane's chemical and biological resistance, since water can be trapped at the membrane surface. Some products contain biocides to control this process.

Chemical and heat effects

Where specific chemicals, singly or in combination, are likely to come into contact with roof membranes advice from membrane manufacturers and other authoritative sources should be sought.

Single-ply membranes are unlikely to be affected chemically by solid discharges. If any unusual material (e.g. flour, powdered milk, starch, chocolate, etc.) is likely to be discharged onto the roof the supplier should be consulted about its effect.

Liquid discharges of a cold, aqueous nature are unlikely to affect single-ply membranes, which are resistant to most acids and alkalis. Liquid discharges from copper or ferrous metals may cause staining of light coloured materials.

Hot discharges, such as overflows from boilers, may have an effect on thermoplastic materials and, if these are expected to be of long duration or frequent, protection should be provided. The discharge of liquid organic materials such as vegetable oil, mineral oil or diesel will harm many of the materials. Exhausts from engines, extraction ducts from chemical plant, etc. likely to contain these materials should be directed away from the roof.

Organic solvents, such as petrol or white spirit, can cause swelling, softening and degradation of a polymeric membrane, although small amounts may evaporate without causing damage. The exact effects depend upon the membrane, the concentration of the liquid and the time and conditions of contact.

Environmental impact

See **Unit 4.13** ■

Critical factors

- The effects of chemicals on the materials should be carefully checked, where the membrane may be affected.
- Solvents can cause significant damage and degradation to polymer systems.

Further reading in the Guide:
4.13 Durability of materials • 4.12 Acoustic behaviour • 4.5 Thermal transmission • 7.6 Design for thermal performance • 7.9 Design for fire safety

13.3   Selection, design and application

- Single-ply membranes are either:
  - loose-laid with mechanical attachment to the deck
  - loose-laid and ballasted
  - fully or partially bonded to the deck or insulation
- Seams between sheets are formed by heat or solvent welding or by the use of adhesives.

Selection

The different types of polymeric single-ply membrane and their general characteristics have been described in other sections (see **Units 13.1 and 13.4**). The choice of one material rather than another will be the result of an evaluation of a variety of different factors, which have been described at various points in this Guide. As the different materials all do the primary task of providing a watertight roof, it is the more subtle differences which may govern the final choice.

Substructures

Substrates for polymeric single-ply membranes should give a sound base for the material and good support for the lap sealing operation.

In some cases there will be a need for a protection or separation layer between the waterproofing membrane and the underlying surface. This can be to protect it either from a rough and/or abrasive surfaces or from chemical incompatibility. Protective layers will be required between the membrane and surfaces of bitumen, asphalt and unsuitable plastic foam insulations. The requirement for separation varies according to the specific polymer type. Protective and separation layers typically consist of polyester fleece or glass fibre tissue.

There are many varieties of insulation materials available, many of which can be used with single-ply systems. The insulation must provide continuous smooth support for the membrane, be compatible with the other roof components, have sufficient compressive and laminar strength and provide the required degree of fire resistance. Some insulations are not compatible if they are in direct contact with some membranes.

For insulants of low compressive strength, fixings with a secondary wide thread just below the head of the screw are normally specified to stop the washer being depressed.

The inherent flexibility of single-ply membranes and their specialised methods of attachment, cope with the normal thermal movement experienced on flat roofs and therefore no further provisions for movement are required in the membrane. However, where considerable movement is expected (i.e. connections to existing buildings, etc.), expansion or movement joints should be provided. Various options exist, for example the conventional double kerb detail, and the system suppliers will advise on appropriate methods.

Hot air welding by hand

Solvent welding

Laying the membrane

References to other documents:
SINGLE PLY ROOfiNG ASSOCIATION (SPRA) Guide on Design Criteria for Single Ply Roofing Membranes

- Coated metal components are used to assist in the forming of upstands and other details.
- Single-ply membranes are also available preformed into large sheets tailored to a particular roof geometry.

Machine welding at a seam

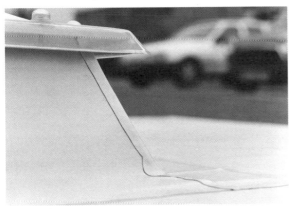
Upstand corner trim

Fixing the insulation boards

Application

General techniques

Single-ply membranes can be easily formed to follow the contours of the substrate and are readily trimmed and fitted to shape. They can be satisfactorily installed without the need for naked flames or hot bituminous compositions, using heat or solvent-welding or by adhesive seaming techniques. Which method is used depends on the type of single-ply roofing membrane employed. Joints in thermoplastic membranes are heat or solvent-welded, whilst elastomeric membranes use special adhesives.

Substrates should be dry, particularly for adhesive fixing. Manufacturers and contractors supply guidance on the precise requirements with respect to their systems.

The membrane may also be obtained in pre-welded blanket form for installation in one piece. However, care is required to deal with the difficulty of handling such a blanket up to roof level, avoiding excessive localised loads on the roof deck, and with the need for accuracy in tailoring the sheet off site.

Single membrane roofs are often used for their speed of installation. Poor sequencing of operations, particularly with fast programmes can result in delays to the roofing operation, with resulting pressures to complete areas before they are ready – this may result in the correct procedures for laying and testing being overlooked.

With the exception of CSM, thermoplastic polymeric membranes retain their welding characteristics indefinitely, facilitating repair and allowing the membrane to be cut for new structures to be built into the roof deck and then welded to restore the waterproofing integrity. CSM materials require surface preparation and special adhesives to achieve a sound repair. Similarly, mechanical damage resulting in penetration of the membrane may quickly and easily be repaired by welding a patch over the damaged area.

continued ▶

Critical factors

- The needs for separation layers between the deck/insulation and the membrane should be carefully considered.
- Check the compatibility of insulation material with the particular membrane material.
- Solvent welds are very dependant on weather conditions.

Further reading in the Guide:
20.5 Site processes: general

Attachment

There are three methods of securing single-ply membrane roofs:

- Loose-laid membranes, mechanically secured either with metal bars screwed to the decking or with screw fastenings through large washers at joints, and often at intermediate locations. In both cases, fixings are also required around the roof perimeter and at penetrations. It is essential that the disposition and types of fixings are based on calculation, against anticipated wind uplift.
- Membranes laid loose below insulation and ballasted with either paving or aggregate have the advantage of protection from traffic damage and from UV light exposure. The amount of ballast must be sufficient to resist calculated wind uplift. The operations of insulant and ballast laying have attendant risks of accidental damage to the membrane.
- Adhered systems, fully or partially-bonded to the insulating layer or the decking, demand material compatibility and secure fastening of the insulation to resist wind uplift. Adhesive and laminar strengths need to be considered. Priming may be necessary on some surfaces.

Executing details

The formability of the membrane materials, coupled with the recommended jointing techniques allows all features to be effectively detailed. However, seam jointing and detail forming both require skill and knowledge of the membrane characteristics.

Details can be executed by cutting, forming and welding the membrane insitu, or by the provision of proprietary preformed membrane shapes or by the use of coated metal sections.

Coated metal components usually consist of galvanised steel to which the polymeric material has been factory bonded. These metal sheets are supplied preformed and may be cut to the required dimensions on site. The galvanising can be expected to protect the cut edges of the metal. However, details are usually designed so that the edges of the metal are not exposed to actual running water. Properly installed, these metal sections can be expected to last as long as the membrane.

During the life of most roofs some modifications take place, for example installing new pipe penetrations, which require waterproofing. When using single-ply materials, the same care and skill is needed as for new roofs. Correct identification of the existing material is important.

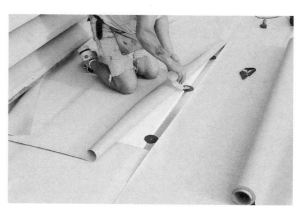

Mechanical fasteners

Adequate provision of information in maintenance manuals will be of great benefit. In some cases, the provision of spare rolls of roofing material at the time of the original work may be an appropriate measure.

Protection

Only in special cases are protective layers required between membranes and ballast and between membranes and insulation in the case of the inverted roof. Additionally, in the case of inverted roofs, there is sometimes a requirement for a filter layer between the insulation and the ballast.

Safety issues

Solvents

Solvents and solvent-based adhesives are invariably highly flammable and must be stored and used in flame and spark proof conditions. All sources of ignition should be eliminated and 'No Smoking' precautions strictly observed. Welding equipment, gas burners, pilot lights, non-flameproofed electrical equipment, including electric motors, heaters and switches, all represent potential sources of ignition and must be made safe. Plant and equipment should be connected to a common earth to prevent static discharge.

Solvent based adhesives and welding solutions should be stored in accordance with the *Highly Flammable Liquids and Liquid Petroleum Gas Regulations 1972* in a secure, well ventilated, flameproof store under lock and key and protected from the weather.

Further reading:
Highly flammable liquids and liquid petroleum gas regulations 1972 • HEALTH & SAFETY EXECUTIVE Control of substances hazardous to health regulations

Cutting flashing for service penetration

Fitting flashing

Hot air welding flashing to roof

The *Control of Substances Hazardous to Health Regulations* (1988) (COSHH) lists chemicals and classifies them according to the degree of hazard. The solvents used for single ply installation are listed and the allowable solvent vapour levels are quoted as Occupational Exposure Limits as 8hr (long-term) and 10 minutes (short-term) Time Weighted Averages.

The well ventilated environment on a roof will normally ensure that the limits are not exceeded, but appropriate checks should be carried out. In the case of use in a confined area or very close work, the operative should wear the appropriate face mask.

Hot-air welding
Burns from skin contact with the hot metal of welding tools are the major hazard and due precautions should be taken to prevent direct skin contact. Single-ply membranes are self-extinguishing and will not ignite and burn in the normal course of installation. Over-application of hot air during welding will result in scorching and carbonisation of the membrane, but ignition will not occur.

Hot air welding equipment is generally electrically powered requiring heavy duty supply cables, subject to standard safety provisions. ■

Critical factors

Further reading in the Guide:

13.4   Additional information

- Polymers are complex chemicals, whose properties are influenced by many characteristics, including the nature and structure of the molecular chains.

- The main methods used to form polymeric roofing sheets are calendering, spreading and extrusion. Elastomeric products are vulcanised.

Nature of materials

Long-chain polymers exist in nature, in materials such as wool, cotton, leather and natural rubber. Natural rubber can be cross-linked to enhance its elastomeric properties, a process traditionally referred to as 'vulcanisation' which is also used for synthetic rubbers. A general classification of polymers was given in Table 13.1.1 (**see Unit 13.1**). An explanation of polymer structure and its effects on the properties and behaviour of the materials is beyond the scope of this Guide. Some general points may, however, be made.

The chemical nature of the components of a polymer, the length, twisting and entanglement of the molecular chains, and the nature and frequency of the cross-links between them, will alter the material's response to a stress and, hence, the mechanical properties. This will determine whether it is 'resistant' or 'compliant' and whether its elasticity allows recovery or not. It will also affect the temperature sensitivity and influence whether the material will flow freely on a hot day, or soften only under a hot air gun, or not flow at all.

The flow properties have a practical application significance in the ability to make hot melt or hot air welded joints, thus converting narrow sheeting into a continuous waterproof covering. True elastomers cannot be hot welded and different adhesive and chemical bonding systems are used, some requiring the application of heat and pressure.

Different types of material

With polymeric materials, there can be no simple property categorisation. Many anomalies exist. Plastics such as PVC and CPE have recovery properties. PIB, which has rubbery properties, is in fact a thermoplastic. Polyurethane can be thermoplastic, elastomeric or thermoset. These features can be further distorted by the fact that polymers are generally compounded with plasticisers and fillers, designed to modify the balance of properties for the application.

The following gives a guide to the jointing characteristics of the materials described in **Unit 13.1**:

Can be heat or solvent-welded:
- PVC – Polyvinylchloride.
- CPE – Chlorinated polyethylene.
- CSM – Chlorosulphonated polyethylene (when new, but the subsequent reactivity means that modified techniques may be required for any jointing carried out

after exposure).
- VET – Vinyl ethylene terpolymer.
- PIB – Polyisobutylene.

Requires solvent-based adhesives:
- IIR – Butyl rubber.
- EPDM – Ethylene propylene diene monomer (using a special adhesive tape, welding can be achieved).

Carriers, normally either a woven polyester or a non-woven glassfibre, are sometimes employed at the centre of the sheet thickness. This alters the properties of the sheet by comparison with homogeneous products. Carriers are sometimes used as a backing which can facilitate the bonding process or provide a separation layer.

In laminate construction, the surface layer differs from an underlayer. Clearly, added strength and UV protection can be provided in the outer layer, while adhesive properties are given by the underlayer.

Manufacture

The manufacturing process used for polymeric sheeting reflects the nature of the polymer and the final properties required. For calendering and extrusion, the materials are blended and then formed into a plastic dough, using a combination of heat and pressure. Some polymeric materials require very little compounding and can be formed by calendering or extrusion into the final product. However, the more rubbery polymers require heavier duty mixing equipment to disperse the added ingredients, which may amount to 70% – 80% of the final composition. The sheeting formed by 'calendering' or 'extrusion' has to be carefully cooled to avoid locking in stresses and produce a stable sheet.

PVC single-ply materials can be made by calendering and by a 'spreading' process. In this, the polymer and other additives are dispersed in the plasticiser to produce a liquid material known as a 'plastisol'. This plastisol is coated onto a release substrate by spreading and then subjected to a heating process which causes the PVC to absorb the plasticiser, forming a solid but flexible sheet upon cooling. During this spreading process, it is possible to encapsulate glass or polyester reinforcement with the PVC layer.

With some polymers (e.g. butyl rubber and EPDM), a vulcanisation step is required to convert the softer unvulcanised sheet into the elastomeric product supplied

Further reading:

Chapter	1	2	3	4	5	6	7	8	9	10	11
Contents	Introduction	History	Regulatory Methods	Principles	Surveys	Constraints & Targets	Design Selection	Calculations	Detail Design Principles	Evaluation of Design	Built-up Roofing
Page	1	19	31	45	83	95	105	165	189	217	221

© BFRC / CIRIA: Flat Roofing: Design and Good Practice. 1993

- Laminate construction of a sheet enables different properties to be given to the upper and lower surfaces.
- The tensile strength, elongation and the tear strength are influenced by the presence of a fabric carrier in the sheet construction.

Table 13.4.1
Test methods for polymeric single-ply roofing materials

(i) British Standards (BSI)

It is current practice to use certain British Standard test methods in the assessment of polymeric single ply materials though the composition of the materials themselves is not covered by British Standards.

Tensile strength	BS2782 (1976) Method 320A-320F BS903 (1989) Part A2 (Vulcanised and Thermoplastic rubbers)
Elongation to break	BS2782 (1978) Method 320A-320F BS3424 (1982) Part 4 Method 6
Tear strength	BS2782 (1976) Method 308A BS3424 (1982) Part 5 Method 7B
Water vapour resistance/ Water vapour permeability	BS3177 (1959)

(ii) European Union of Agrément Technical Committee (UEATc)

The M.O.A.T. directives are each a programme of various tests in the assessment of products for which an Agrément Certificate is being sought.

M.O.A.T 27: 1983	General directives for the assessment of roof waterproofing systems.
M.O.A.T 29: 1984	Directives for the assessment of Roofing Systems using pvc sheets without reinforcement, loose laid under heavy protection and not compatible with bitumen.
M.O.A.T 46: 1988	Special directives for the Assessment of Roof Waterproofing Systems with non-reinforced Vulcanised EPDM.
M.O.A.T. 1991 (un-numbered):	Supplementary guide for the assessment of mechanically fastened roof waterproofing.

for roofing. This can be achieved by subjecting the sheeting to heat and, in most cases – to pressure, in either a continuous or batch vulcanising process. The latter system involves interlayering the unvulcanised calendered sheet with a fabric and winding on a roll which is placed in a steam heated pan for a considerable time, dependent on the temperature and pressure. On removal, the separating fabric is stripped out.

The traditional method of forming large sheets off-site involves a separate factory process, in which the vulcanised sheeting is unrolled and overlapped with sheeting already in position. A special tape is inserted between the overlap and a portable press then moves in stages along the overlap joint to make a vulcanised seal.

A newer method, now well established, is to joint the length of sheeting together almost as it emerges from the calender. The material is in the unvulcanised stage and the two sheets can fuse together under heat and pressure. The joint formed in this way is virtually imperceptible.

Properties

The characteristics of polymeric single-ply roofing materials of the same generic type may vary from one manufacturer to another. The test methods used and the tests carried out to establish the mechanical characteristics of the product are likely to depend on the country of origin of the product.

Tensile strength

The tensile strength of a material that has a fabric core, tends to reflect the strength of the core material and, in turn, the deformation and ultimate failure of the membrane under strain. Tensile strength is an important property in relation to the membrane's ability to resist wind uplift and other imposed stresses although the fixing density is more significant. Values range between $7kN/mm^2$ and $20kN/mm^2$.

The elongation behaviour of a material with an integral carrier may be influenced by the carrier material, with reduced elongation and increased tensile strength. Elongation ranges from around 20% for materials with polyester fabric carriers to around 300% for homogeneous materials; glass fibre carriers fall between the two.

Tear strength

Test methods for tear strength have suffered from poor reproducibility and the exact relevance of the criteria is not established. Most methods introduce a cut of some description into the material and then measure the force required to propagate this cut.

A high tear strength will be of benefit when fastening by mechanical fasteners which puncture the membrane, and also in resisting mechanical damage due to traffic.

Test methods

The test methods for polymeric single-ply materials are summarised in Table 13.4.1.

European standards are being developed to cover a similar range of characteristics to those for built-up roofing (see Table 11.4.3). ∎

Critical factors

- In the absence of British or CEN standards, take care when comparing the quoted properties of different products; results obtained in tests will vary with the test method used.

Further reading in the Guide:

12 Mastic Asphalt	13 Polymeric Single Ply	14 Copper	15 Lead Sheet	16 Other Membranes	17 Thermal Insulants	18 Specification	19 Contracts & Procurement	20 Inspection	21 Maintenance	22 Bibliography	23 Index
263	301	331	353	375	383	393	399	413	429	437	455

13.5 Design details

- Wherever there is a change or discontinuity in material or in the roof geometry careful consideration of the associated detail must be given.

- Such details are often 3-dimensional in character and the difficulties to be solved may not be apparent solely from isolated simple sections.

- This schematic key diagram is shown to locate details for a variety of roof designs and conditions. The drawing itself must not be considered appropriate for any particular roof type.

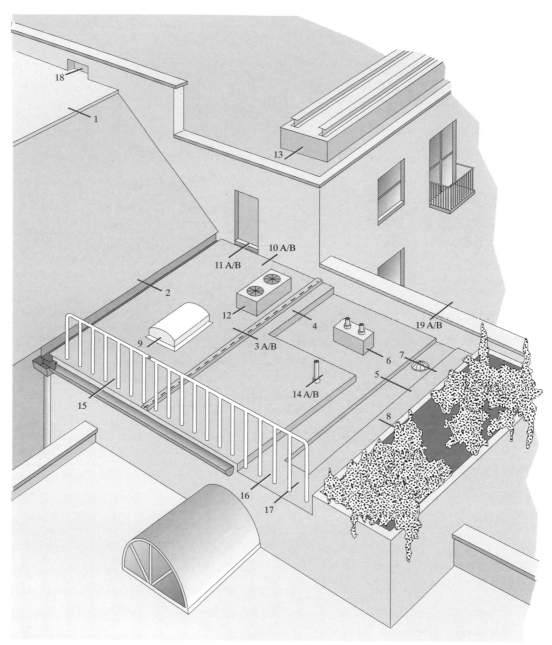

Key

1	Flat roof to pitched roof	8	Planted roof	14B	Service penetration - hot
2	Pitched roof to flat roof with gutter	9	Roof light	15	Eaves with gutter
3A	Movement joint - upstand	10A	Abutment - integral deck	16	Verge
3B	Movement joint - flush	10B	Abutment - accommodating movement	17	Balustrade fixing
4	Step	11A	Opening - integral deck	18	Chute
5	Internal gutter	11B	Opening - accommodating movement	19A	Parapet - integral deck
6	Boxed-in pipes or extract	12	Plant plinth above waterproof layer	19B	Parapet - accommodating movement
7	Outlet	13	Plinth		
		14A	Service penetration - cold		

- The roof system is subject to dynamic loads from gravity, wind, temperature changes, humidity changes, air pressure changes.
- The details must allow for suitable construction tolerances and movement.

Notes

General

Those areas that must be addressed in the design development fall into risk categories:

A   Stability and integrity
B   Discontinuity of material, substrate. or roof geometry and differential movement
C   Water path
D   Convection path
E   Conduction path with risk of cold bridging
F   Fire
G   Condensation
H   Ventilation requirement.

Other considerations must be borne in mind:

- Ease of construction
- Ease of access for inspection.
- Ease of repair and replacement.
- Method of attachment.
- Material compatibility.

Membranes must not be carried across building movement joints or other structural discontinuities capable of independent movement. Proper movement joints must be provided at such critical points.

Penetrations through roof openings should be minimised.They should be grouped through specially designed and waterproofed service boxes which allow for hot and cold services and their future replacement.

Penetrations or upstands should be located such that sufficient space is allowed between them and other obstructions so proper forming of the detail is feasible.

Membrane laps and upstand heights must be maintained at all details.

Cold bridges through the insulated layer should be avoided. Continuity for insulation around the perimeter details, roof services and penetrations is important. Integrity of the vapour control layer at all points is vital.

Direct excessive imposed loading of the roof finish, particularly point loads, must be prevented. Loads should be evenly distributed.

Internal gutters should be avoided if possible. If necessary, they must be wide enough to be formed properly and to allow for maintenance.

The details illustrate the deck in generic form. The thickness of kerbs will depend upon the the material used and will affect the actual detailing of components for particular situations.

Polymeric single-ply

1.The following details illustrate examples of different generic types of polymer in different attachment modes. Since such detailing is proprietary it must not be assumed that it will be suitable for all products within a generic type. Their purpose is to illustrate how principles of detailing are applied in different situations.

2. Welding by hot air and solvent will vary with proprietary system.

Special note

For each of the generic conditions shown in this Unit, there are various good practice solutions. Some good practice solutions involve particular components, materials and/or methods developed by individual suppliers or manufacturers, and benefit from their experience. Some solutions may also have to be modified according to the particular circumstances of the individual contract.

The detailed solutions shown in this Unit therefore represent only a selection of possible routes to good practice in design and installation. They indicate appropriate general methods for this particular membrane material, to show how the principles for different roof configurations (set out in Unit 9.1) may be translated into practical building. An understanding of these methods and principles will help the designer to assess not only the problems, but also the likely range of alternative possible solutions. *continued* ▶

Critical factors

- Integrity.
- Provision for movement.
- Material compatibility.
- Provision for discharge of water.
- Check for consistency between different detail drawings and with the specification.

Further reading in the Guide:
9 Detail design principles

12 Mastic Asphalt	13 Polymeric Single Ply	14 Copper	15 Lead Sheet	16 Other Membranes	17 Thermal Insulants	18 Specification	19 Contracts & Procurement	20 Inspection	21 Maintenance	22 Bibliography	23 Index
263	301	331	353	375	383	393	399	413	429	437	455

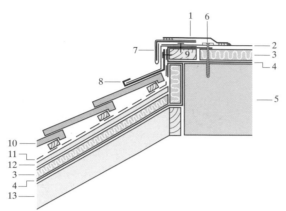

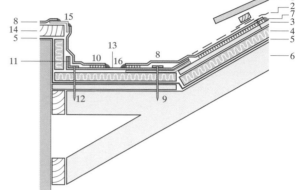

Warm deck roof.
- **PVC**
- **Mechanically fixed**

1. Welded membrane cover strip
2. Membrane
3. Insulation
4. Vapour control layer
5. Deck
6. Mechanically fixed metal bar
7. Membrane coated metal profile clipped to galvanised steel angle secured to bearer

8. Minimum code 4 lead flashing with copper clips a 500mm centres
9. Pre-treated timber bearer
10. Roof tiling
11. Under tiling membrane (vapour permeable)
12. Counter battens
13. Rafters

Warm deck roof.
- **PVC**
- **Mechanically fixed**

1. Roof tiling
2. Under tiling membrane
3. Ply layer
4. Insulation
5. Vapour control layer
6. Rafters
7. Mechanical fastener, securing membrane to ply deck sealed with mastic
8. Membrane cover strip heat-welded (minimum 38mm)

9. Metal support, mechanically fixed
10. Membrane heat-welded
11. Metal angle
12. Mechanical fastener
13. Single-ply membrane
14. Pre-treated timber bearer
15. Membrane-coated metal plate
16. Lap sealant

Fig 13.5.1 Flat roof junction with pitched roof

It is usual practice to provide supplementary mechanical fixing at details irrespective of the method of attachment. This may be for the avoidance of sheer slippage or to restrain the membrane during construction.

Junctions between the membrane coated metal profiles must be adequately detailed and sealed to prevent water penetration. These details must allow for thermal movement as necessary.

In flexible deck situations additional support at the junction of horizontal and pitched elements will be required to reduce differential movement.

The critical component is the PVC-coated profile which:

- restrains the exposed edge of the membrane
- forms a drip detail
- provides a weldable top surface compatible with the membrane.

The detail allows repair/alteration to pitched or flat sections without disturbing the other.

Fig 13.5.2 Pitched roof junction to flat roof with gutter

Expansion gaps must be provided between metal angles and straps.

The membrane must be taken up the inclined pitch higher than the level of the adjoining flat roof. This ensures that if the gutter is blocked for some reason water will not pass into the building but onto the lower roof.

It is usual practice to include a membrane coated metal plate across the junction between the roof planes.

In situations of high condensation risk the vapour control layer should be continuous between roofs. Support must be provided for the vapour control layer.

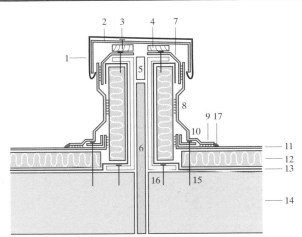

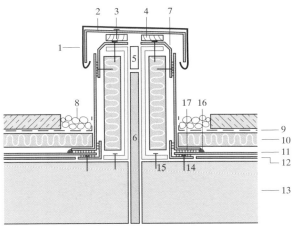

Warm deck roof.
- PVC
- **Mechanically fixed**

1. Pre-formed membrane-coated metal coping with butt straps
2. Fixing strap
3. Strap fixing
4. Pre-treated timber spacers
5. Fire stop
6. Non-combustible insulation
7. Membrane-coated metal angle
8. Membrane solvent or heat-welded to angle and adhered to insulation
9. Membrane-to-membrane weld
10. Membrane-coated metal angle
11. Single-ply membrane
12. Insulation
13. Vapour control layer
14. Deck
15. Mechanical fastener
16. Pre-formed metal kerbs
17. Lap sealant

Fig 13.5.3A (1) Upstand movement joint
Junctions between the membrane coated metal profiles must be adequately detailed and sealed to prevent water penetration. These details must allow for thermal movement as necessary.

Some membranes may require additional metal plates fixed to upstands to provide a surface for adhesion.

Required distances for solvent and heat welding vary with membrane type and manufacturers detail.

Cappings are secured on one side only allowing independent movement of upstands.

If insulating blocks are used in place of the insulated upstand, consideration must be given to the long term security of the bedding joints.

It may be necessary to include a cover strip on the soffit of the expansion gap to restrain the compressible insulation.

Inverted warm deck roof.
- CPE
- **Mechanically fixed**

1. Pre-formed coping with butt straps
2. Fixing strap
3. Strap fixing
4. Pre-treated timber spacers
5. Fire stop
6. Non-combustible insulation
7. Membrane solvent or heat-welded to membrane-coated metal angle
8. Pebble ballast (20--40mm)
9. Filter layer
10. Insulation
11. Single-ply membrane
12. Fleece protection layer
13. Deck
14. Membrane-coated angle
15. Pre-formed metal kerbs
16. Lap sealant
17. Membrane-to-membrane weld

Fig 13.5.3A (2) Upstand movement joint
If insulated upstands are necessary consideration should be given to the means of vapour control.

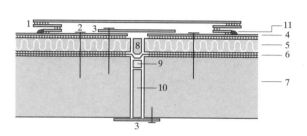

Warm deck roof.
- **PVC**
- **Fully adhered**

1. Bellows formed from heat-welded membrane
2. Mechanical fixing
3. Membrane-coated metal plate, fixed one side only
4. Membrane adhered to insulation
5. Insulation

6. Vapour control layer adhered to deck with dip at point of movement joint.
7. Deck
8. Compressible filler
9. Fire stop
10. Non-combustible insulation
11. Lap sealant

Warm deck roof.
- **EPDM**
- **Fully adhered**

1. Fleece-backed membrane strip, adhesive-welded to main membrane
2. 40mm diameter foam polyethylene tube
3. Fleece-backed membrane fully adhered
4. Kerb formed from insulation bonded to main insulation
5. Insulation

6. Fleece-backed membrane strip bonded to vapour control layer with dip at point of movement joint
7. Vapour control layer bonded to deck
8. Deck
9. Fire stop
10. Non-combustible insulation
11. Membrane-coated metal plate, fixed one side only.

Fig 13.5.3B (1) Movement joint (flush)

Flush joints should only be considered where:

- it is not possible to construct upstand kerbs
- only minor movement is anticipated
- foot traffic is for inspection only.

The metal plate is provided to cover the joint and provide support to the bellows membrane.

The compressible filler should be compatible with the insulation.

The maximum joint amplitude will vary with the type of membrane. A bellows detail is appropriate for relatively large amplitude movement with reinforced membranes.

The vapour control layer is dipped at the joint position to accommodate movement.

Fig 13.5.3B (3) Movement joint (flush)

Movement is accommodated by the formation of a roll in the membrane material.

The vapour control layer integrity is maintained by the introduction of a secondary membrane layer bonded to the vapour control layer on both sides of the joint.

In conditions of high condensation risk consideration should be given to a continuity of thermal transmittance across the joint.

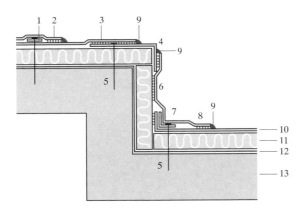

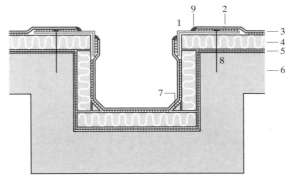

Warm deck roof.
- **PVC**
- **Mechanically fixed**

1. Mechanical bar fixing
2. Membrane heat-welded
3. Membrane solvent or heat-welded
4. Membrane-coated metal angle
5. Mechanical fastener
6. Membrane adhered

7. Membrane-coated metal angle
8. Membrane heat-welded
9. Lap sealant
10. Membrane
11. Insulation
12. Vapour control layer
13. Deck

Warm deck roof.
- **VET**
- **Fully adhered**

1. Membrane-coated metal angle
2. Membrane heat-welded to angle
3. Membrane adhered to insulation
4. Insulation adhered to vapour control layer
5. Vapour control layer adhered to deck

6. Deck
7. Insulation fillet
8. Mechanical fastener
9. Lap seal

Fig 13.5.4 Step

Expansion gaps between sections of material profile are usually covered by a standard butt strap.

Additional restraint to upstand insulation may be required using mechanical fixings.

Some polymeric single-ply products do not require full adhesion to upstand insulation.

With flexible deck design, additional support may be necessary at the base of the upstand to prevent differential movement transmitting stress to the roof finish.

Fig 13.5.5 Internal gutter

Where possible internal box gutters are best avoided, the roof falls being configured to directly discharge into roof outlets or external gutters.

The insulation fillet also ensures consistent bonding across the 90° angle and assists water flow in the gutter. Fillets are not generally required in mechanically fixed systems or new constructions.

A timber block could have been provided at the external angle, the metal profile omitted and the membrane run continuously; however, this form would provide reduced resistance to impact or abrasion at the arris.

VET is bitumen-compatible. Therefore all adhesion excluding that to the metal angle could be by bitumen bonding.

In responsive decks, support must be provided at the external angle.

© BFRC / CIRIA: Flat Roofing: Design and Good Practice. 1993

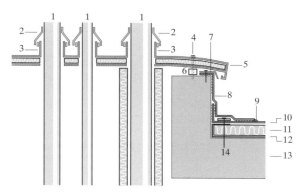

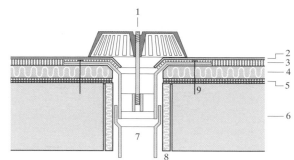

Warm deck roof.
- **EPDM**
- **Mechanically fixed**

1. Service penetration
2. Apron flashing required to service
3. Upstand on penetration capping
4. Weather seal bolt fixing
5. Purpose-made insulated capping with membrane-coated metal facing
6. Spacers

7. Membrane-coated metal capping secured to upstand.
8. Membrane fully adhered
9. Lap sealant
10. Membrane
11. Insulation
12. Vapour control layer
13. Deck
14. Metal bar mechanically fixed

Warm deck roof.
- **PVC**
- **Fully adhered**

1. Removable grating/guard
2. Membrane
3. Adhesion layer
4. Insulation bonded to VCL
5. Vapour control layer bonded to deck

6. Deck
7. Down pipe
8. Insulation collar
9. Mechanical fastener

Fig 13.5.6 Boxed-in pipes or services

Mechanical fixings should be provided close to the upstand. They should be located to isolate the upstand membrane from wind induced tension in the roof field membrane.

Elastomeric membranes are generally sealed at laps which should be fully adhered and be a minimum of 75mm.

Where possible, service penetrations should be grouped together to minimise the number of weather proofing details required. Cappings to these penetrations should be insulated.

For thermo-plastic membranes, membrane-coated metal trim may be fixed to the top of the upstand with the membrane solvent/heat welded to it. Fillets have been shown as they may be existing in a refurbishment situation where VET has been selected for bitumen compatibility.

Fig 13.5.7 Outlet

The detail in a mechanically fixed system is similar with a mechanical fixing and membrane overlap being provided at the outlet position. Solvent welding on the detail is then omitted.

Where membrane coated accessories are available then current practice is to site the outlet flange at the membrane level. If the outlet is of the cast, clamp ring type or there is a risk of local compression of the insulation then fixing on support stools or extension flange products are recommended.

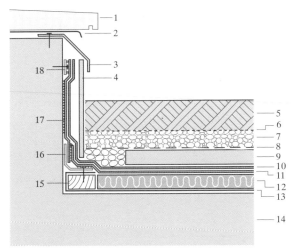

Warm deck roof.
* **PVC**
* **Mechanically fixed**

1. Pre-cast concrete coping fixed to upstand
2. Dpc
3. Rigid metal or lead flashing
4. Protection board
5. Top soil
6. Filter layer
7. Drainage layer
8. Filter layer
9. Protection layer
10. Polyester fleece layer
11. Membrane
12. Insulation
13. Vapour control layer
14. Deck
15. Pre-treated timber battens
16. Membrane-coated metal angle
17. Membrane-adhered to upstand
18. Membrane-coated metal strip

Warm deck roof.
* **PVC**
* **Mechanically fixed**

1. Proprietary rooflight with kerbs
2. Membrane adhered to upstand
3. Membrane-coated metal angle fixed to deck
4. Membrane heat-welded
5. Membrane
6. Insulation
7. Vapour control layer
8. Rooflight fixing
9. Deck
10. Lap sealant

Fig 13.5.8 Roof planter

Finished top soil levels must be maintained at a minimum of 150mm below adjacent coping levels.

Single-ply membranes in both horizontal and vertical planes must be protected from physical damage by gardening operations and plant roots.

A drainage layer is provided to prevent water-logging of the planting medium. The filter layer prevents leaching of the soil into the drainage layer.

Intermediate adhesion of the upstand membrane at (17) may not be required for some membranes.

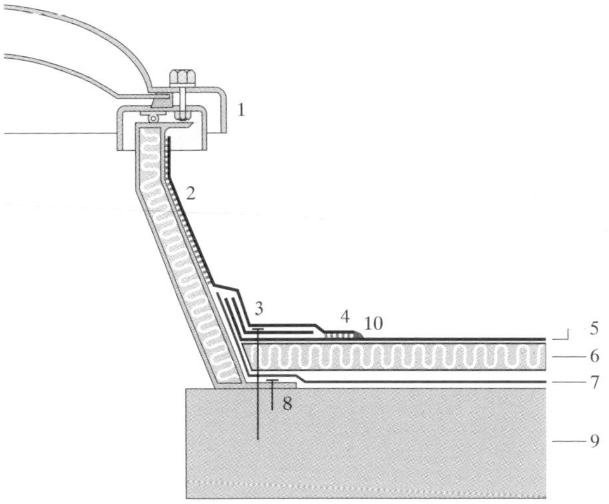

Fig 13.5.9 Rooflight upstand

Insulation in this detail is provided within the body of the roof light and the smooth outer surface of the roof light provides a good finish to adhere the upstand membrane. The rooflight supplier should be consulted to ensure compatibility in this respect.

The horizontal membrane is turned up the rooflight upstand and secured by purpose made angles.

Some membrane suppliers details include restraint near the rooflight kerb by a bar or by a series of individual fasteners. In such cases the angled metal section is omitted and the vapour control layer is dressed under the membrane at the fastener. Rooflight fixings and membrane fasteners indicated in the drawing are linearly separated.

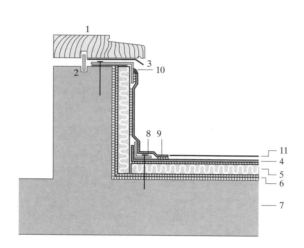

Warm deck roof.
- **PVC**
- **Fully adhered**

1. Cill
2. Water bar
3. Code 4 lead flashing
4. PVC membrane solvent-welded to insulation
5. Insulation bonded to VCL
6. Vapour control layer bonded to deck

7. Deck
8. Membrane-coated metal angle
9. Membrane welded
10. Lap seal
11. Protection layer

Warm deck roof.
- **PIB**
- **Ballasted**

1. Cavity tray
2. Code 4 lead flashing
3. Profiled metal flashing clipped to wall plate
4. Fleece-backed membrane adhered to upstand
5. Pebbles (20-40mm)

6. Fleeced-backed membrane
7. Insulation
8. Vapour control layer
9. Deck
10. Cavity wall insulation

Fig 13.5.9A Opening onto roof-integral deck

Thresholds should have a minimum height of 150mm above finished roof level, with the roof ideally formed to provide falls away from the opening.

This detail is appropriate for all conditions where differential movement between deck and wall is not expected.

Water bars should be provided to prevent water being blown in under the cill.

Fig 13.5.10A Abutment-integral deck

The upstand membrane is adhered to a previously coated brickwork upstand ensuring total bonding. Additional mechanical support is provided by the profiled metal flashing wall plate. In some systems if the skirting is quite high it is hung loose being only bonded at intervals.

Profiled metal flashing (3) could be formed in lead and should set into the joint as (2). This would result in a simpler mechanical restraint at the head of the upstand.

Chapter	1	2	3	4	5	6	7	8	9	10	11
Contents	Introduction	History	Regulatory Methods	Principles	Surveys	Constraints & Targets	Design Selection	Calculations	Detail Design Principles	Evaluation of Design	Built-up Roofing
Page	1	19	31	45	83	95	105	165	189	217	221

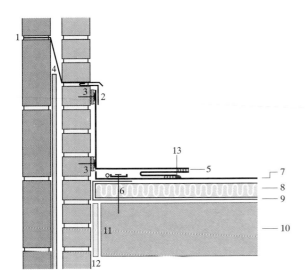

Warm deck roof.
- **PVC**
- **Mechanically fixed**

1. Cavity tray
2. Minimum code 4 lead flashing
3. Membrane-coated metal strip
4. Cavity insulation
5. Membrane welded to form bellows
6. Perimeter mechanical fixing with PVC cord
7. Membrane
8. Insulation
9. Vapour control layer sealed to upstand
10. Deck
11. Compressible filer
12. Provision for movement
13. Lap sealant

Fig 13.5.10B (1) Abutment-accommodating movement

Junctions between abutting walls and decks are particularly vulnerable to relative movement unless structurally connected in a positive way. Single-ply membranes can be configured either by pre-forming or forming on site into details that will accommodate the movement.

It may be necessary to provide compressible insulation at the junction between the deck and elevation to control convection losses.

A bellows arrangement permits large amplitude movement but this should be consistent with the movement capability of flashings and compressible insulation.

Adhesion may be required for certain thermoplastic membranes.

Warm deck roof.
- **EPDM**
- **Mechanically fixed**

1. Cavity tray
2. Minimum code 4 lead flashing
3. Membrane adhered to upstand
4. Lap sealant
5. Unvulcanised EPDM flashing and lap splice centred over fastener
6. Metal bar fastener
7. Polyethylene roll
8. Movement joint filler
9. Membrane
10. Insulation
11. Vapour control layer
12. Deck
13. Provision for movement

Fig 13.5.10B(2) Abutment-accommodating movement

12 Mastic Asphalt	13 Polymeric Single Ply	14 Copper	15 Lead Sheet	16 Other Membranes	17 Thermal Insulants	18 Specification	19 Contracts & Procurement	20 Inspection	21 Maintenance	22 Bibliography	23 Index
263	301	331	353	375	383	393	399	413	429	437	455

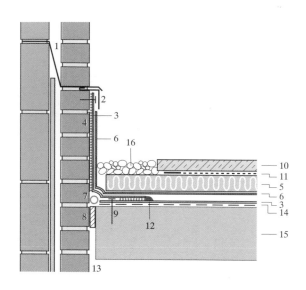

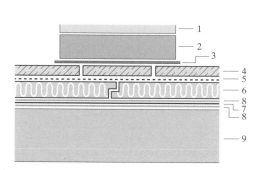

Inverted warm deck roof.
- **PVC**
- **Mechanically fixed**

1. Cavity tray
2. Metal cover flashing
3. Reinforced membrane
4. Bonding adhesive
5. Insulation
6. Polyester fleece layer
7. Sponge tube
8. Filler block

9. Mechanical fastener and plate
10. Concrete paving on pads
11. Filter layer
12. Lap seal
13. Provision for movement
14. Isolation layer
15. Deck
16. 20-40mm pebbles

Fig 13.5.10B(3) Abutment-accommodating movement

Inverted warm deck roof
- **EPDM**
- **Mechanically fixed**

1. Equipment
2. Plinth
3. Protection board
4. Concrete paving
5. Filter layer

6. Insulation
7. Membrane
8. Fleece layer
9. Deck

Fig 13.5.12 Plinth waterproofing layer
Additional load spreading is provided in the case of inverted roofs by the concrete paving slabs. The protection board may have simply a load-spreading function or it may be selected to reduce the transmission of vibration.

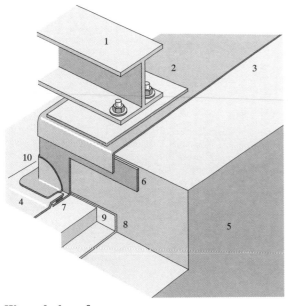

Warm deck roof.
- **PVC**
- **Mechanically fixed**

1. Cradle track
2. Sealing plate bedded in mastic
3. Code 5 lead flashing
4. Single-ply membrane
5. Plinth
6. Membrane coated metal box
7. Solvent weld
8. Vapour control layer
9. Insulation
10. Welded corner piece

Inverted warm deck roof.
- **CPE**
- **Ballasted**

1. Cradle track
2. Code 5 lead flashing
3. Sealing plate
4. Paving support
5. Plinth
6. Membrane coated metal strip
7. Membrane coated metal angle mechanically fixed to deck
8. Pebbles (20-40mm)
9. Concrete paving slabs on pads
10. Filter layer
11. Insulation
12. Membrane
13. Protection layer
14. Deck

Fig 13.5.13(1) Plinth

Bolt holes may require sealing individually or by the use of a bedded sealing plate.

Where the corners of the metal box have been cut they require sealing individually with welded corner pieces.

Fig No 13.5.13(2) Plinth

Additional protection to membrane upstands should be included where mechanical impact is likely. This may be lightweight fibre-cement-faced insulations, restrained behind a flashing or suitable protection board.

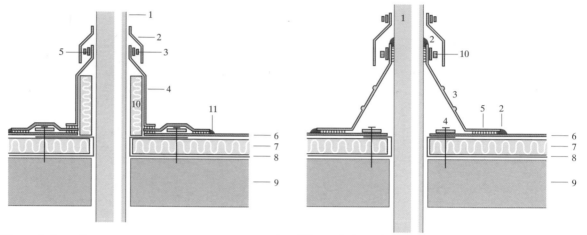

Warm deck roof.
- **PVC**
- **Mechanically fixed**

1. Service penetration (cold)
2. Weather collar secured to pipe
3. Membrane strapped to pipe
4. Membrane collar
5. Stainless steel clamp ring
6. Membrane

7. Insulation
8. Vapour control layer
9. Deck
10. Insulation collar
11. Lap sealant

Warm deck roof.
- **EPDM**
- **Mechanically fixed**

1. Service penetration (cold)
2. Lap sealant
3. Pre-moulded pipe seal
4. Mechanical fixing
5. Seal adhered to membrane

6. Membrane
7. Insulation
8. Vapour control layer
9. Deck
10. Stainless steel clamp

Fig 13.5.14A(1) Service penetration (cold)

To accommodate any possible movement between deck and service a number of alternative solutions are possible with single-ply membranes.

All solutions will generally use some form of pre-made upstand sleeve.

It is not necessary to sleeve the pipe with this method.

An insulation collar to the penetration is likely to be required only where the penetration has a high thermal conductivity, for example metals.

Effective vapour control of penetrations may involve the use of separate pieces of vapour control layer adhered to the roof field vapour control layer.

Fig 13.5.14A(2) Service penetration (cold) pre-formed collar

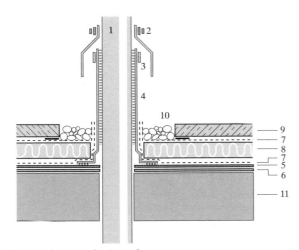

Inverted warm deck roof.
- **CSM**
- **Ballasted**

1. Service penetration (cold)
2. Weather collar secured to penetration
3. Stainless steel clamp ring
4. Unreinforced membrane collar adhered to penetration
5. Reinforced membrane heat-welded to collar pieces
6. Fleece isolation layer
7. Geotextile (filter) fleece layer
8. Insulation
9. Concrete paving
10. Pebbles (20-40mm)
11. Deck

Fig 13.5.14A(3) Service penetration (cold)

Warm deck roof.
- **EPDM**
- **Mechanically fixed**

1. Service penetration (hot)
2. Weather collar secured to pipe
3. Non-combustible insulation
4. Lap sealant
5. Membrane adhered to sleeve
6. Membrane
7. Insulation
8. Vapour control layer
9. Deck
10. Mechanical fixing
11. Metal sleeve secured to deck
12. Stainless steel clamp

Fig 13.5.14B Service penetration (hot)

Hot pipes such as flues must be sleeved and insulated with non-combustible insulation to prevent heat being transferred to the roof finish.

Particular care must be taken with timber decks to ensure sufficient separation is maintained. Metal hoods can also transmit heat to the waterproofing layer and adequate ventilation gaps between hood and finish must be kept.

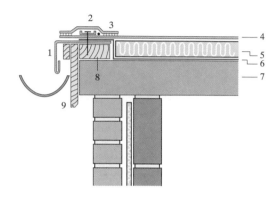

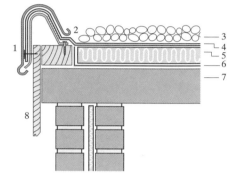

Warm deck roof.
- **PVC**
- **Mechanically fixed**

1. Membrane-coated metal profile
2. Welded membrane cover strip
3. Perimeter bar with mechanical fastener
4. Membrane
5. Insulation
6. Vapour control layer
7. Deck
8. Pre-treated timber bearer
9. Fascia

Warm deck roof.
- **EPDM**
- **Ballasted**

1. Snap-on membrane-coated metal trim on support profile
2. Membrane adhered to upstand
3. Ballast pebbles (20-40mm)
4. Membrane
5. Insulation
6. Vapour control layer
7. Deck
8. Fascia

Fig 13.5.15 Eaves with gutter

Eaves should be formed to ensure that water is discharged into the gutter via an adequate drip. Where continuous drips are formed in membrane coated metal profiles sleeving and sealing will be required at the junctions of lengths.

The fascia board should also be provided with a drip and stand clear of the face of the wall. If the fascia material is such as to require maintenance or replacement within the anticipated membrane lifetime it should be detailed and secured to allow access and/or removal without disturbing the drip profile.

Insulation should be protected at the edge by upstand fascia and timber bearer.

Consideration must be given to cold bridging to eaves, and insulation under the fascia and soffit board may be required.

In practice it is possible to construct this detail such as to eliminate edge ponding adjacent to the cover strip (2).

Fig 13.5.16 Eaves

Verges must provide an adequate check to prevent the discharge of water over the roof side, a minimum of 75mm upstand is recommended. Consideration should be given to the risk of wind scour of ballast at verges and the perimeter ballast pebbles selected accordingly.

A fleece separating layer may be required between the ballast and the membrane.

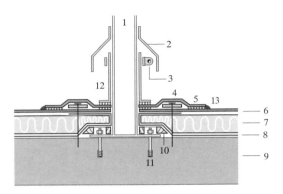

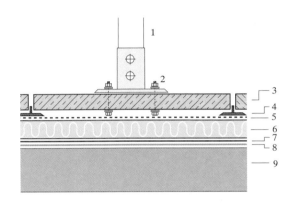

Warm deck roof.
* **PVC**
* **Mechanically fixed**

1. Balustrade post
2. Weather collar secured to post
3. Stainless steel clamp ring
4. Mechanical fixing
5. Heat weld
6. Membrane
7. Insulation
8. Vapour control layer
9. Deck
10. Pre-treated timber capping
11. Post fixing
12. Membrane collar, heat-welded to circular cover strip
13. Lap sealant

Fig 13.5.17(1) Balustrade fixing

Wherever possible, balustrades should be bolted to purpose made plinths structurally connected to the deck. This allows them to be removed without disturbance to the roof system. This is very important if the durability of the balustrade is expected to be less than that of the membrane. The bolt fixing plate must be protected with a timber cover plate to prevent any damage to the vapour control layer.

As the post passes through the insulation layer there is some risk of cold bridging. It must also be assumed that the post itself is waterproof.

Inverted warm deck roof.
* **PVC**
* **Mechanically fixed**

1. Balustrade post
2. Post mechanically-fixed to paving
3. Paving on pads
4. Pads
5. Filter layer
6. Insulation
7. Membrane
8. Fleece layer
9. Deck

Fig 13.5.17(2) Balustrade fixing

Designs incorporating independent bases must take into account *BS6399: Part 1 (1984)* and *The Building Regulations*, the effect of local loadings on the roof structure and the compressive strength of the insulation.

This arrangement is not suitable for safety barrier loadings, but may be useful for railings defining access ways.

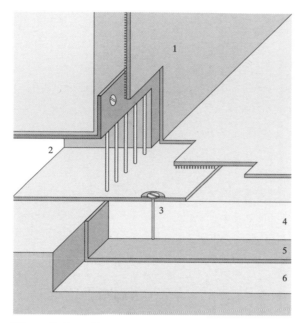

Warm deck roof.
- **PVC**
- **Mechanically fixed**

1. Membrane heat-welded to chute
2. PVC coated stainless steel chute with integral strainer
3. Mechanical fastener
4. Insulation
5. Vapour control layer
6. Deck

Fig No 13.5.18 Chute

Where possible the use of chutes should be avoided.

If they are to be used then they should be of sufficient size such that they can be adequately formed in the first instance and cleaned and maintained subsequently.

With single-ply membranes, chutes are generally pre-formed in membrane-coated stainless steel, to which the roof membrane will be welded.

The height of adjacent flashings should be consistent with the chute size.

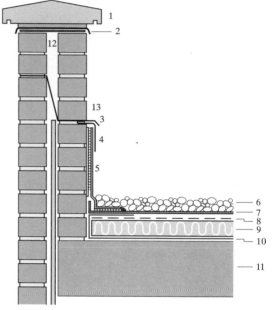

Warm deck roof.
- **PVC**
- **Ballasted**

1. Coping
2. Dpc
3. Cavity tray
4. Minimum code 4 lead or pre-formed metal cover flashing
5. Upstand membrane, solvent-welded to upstand, heat welded to roof sheet
6. Ballast pebbles (20-40mm)
7. Membrane
8. Separating layer (as required)
9. Insulation
10. Vapour control layer
11. Deck
12. Closer
13. Weepholes

Fig No 13.5.19A(1) Parapet abutment

Dpc under copings must be supported by slate or some other form of cavity closer.

Cavity trays must protrude over flashings and be sealed at laps which should be a minimum of 100mm. Weep holes should be provided at 900mm centres.

© BFRC / CIRIA: *Flat Roofing: Design and Good Practice. 1993*

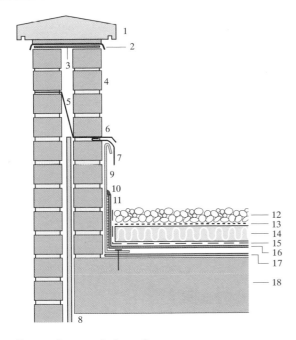

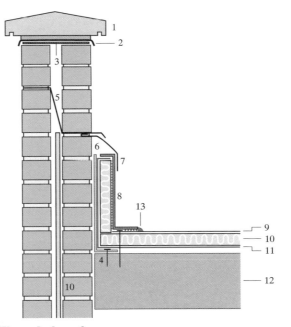

Inverted warm deck roof.
• **PVC**
• **Ballasted**

1. Coping
2. Dpc
3. Slate closer
4. Brickwork
5. Cavity tray
6. Weep holes
7. Code 4 lead flashing
8. Insulation
9. Membrane-coated metal upstand fixed to wall
10. Lap sealant
11. Membrane solvent-welded
12. Pebbles (20-40mm)
13. Filter layer
14. Insulation
15. Protection layer
16. Membrane
17. Protective fleece layer
18. Deck

Warm deck roof.
• **PVC**
• **Mechanically fixed**

1. Coping
2. Dpc
3. Closer
4. Metal support kerb secured to deck
5. Cavity tray
6. Membrane-coated metal profile secured through vapour control layer to kerb
7. Rigid metal cover flashing
8. Upstand membrane welded to insulation and metal profile
9. Roof field membrane
10. Insulation
11. Vapour control layer
12. Deck
13. Lap sealant

Fig No 13.5.19A(2) Parapet abutment

Copings should be weathered and provided with adequate overhangs and drips mechanical fixing of the copings may be necessary.

When adhered upstands are used a peel stop is generally provided through the horizontal membrane of the base. A cushion layer may be required if the upstand is not smooth.

Fig No 13.5.19B Parapet abutment – accommodating movement

Copper 14

14.1   General description

- Copper is used in both 'traditional' and 'longstrip' methods for the covering of flat roofs.
- Copper has useful mechanical properties and is malleable, making it suitable for various roof geometries.

Basis of technology

Copper has been used in roofing for over 2000 years. With its low thermal movement and excellent corrosion resistance, it can be used to produce very durable roofs.

A copper roof consists of a number of sheets jointed along their edges and held down onto the roof by means of cleats inserted in the folds. In the direction of the fall the joints are raised, while across the fall they are flattened to allow water to flow freely over the sheets. The use of copper in roofing is covered in *CP143: Part 12*, which should be checked for recent revisions.

Up until the late 1950s, copper roofing in the UK was carried out using the 'traditional method'. This consists of fully supported sheets of copper up to 600mm wide and up to 1.8m long being fixed to the roof in 'bays' or 'panels'.

'Longstrip' copper roofing was introduced to the UK from the continent. Longstrip copper roofing uses strips of copper up to 10m long compared to the 1.8m for traditional copper roofing. This greater length is made possible by use of a harder tempered copper sheet than traditional copper roofing and special cleats down the pitch of the roof. These cleats are designed to accommodate the increased thermal expansion associated with the longer strips of copper. Longstrip copper roofing is quicker to lay than traditional copper roofing as it require less jointing, and factory-made preformed trays can be used.

The longstrip method is only recommended for roofs with a pitch of not less than 3°, greater pitches are encouraged to speed the disposal of rainwater.

Constituent materials

The material used for 'traditional' and 'long strip' roofing is 99.90% pure copper as defined in *BS2870*, Section 7, Type C106.

Copper strip for traditional UK roofing should be fully annealed (softened). This corresponds to the 'O' condition of Type C106 to *BS 2870*. Copper for longstrip roofing should be tempered but not to more than half hard. This corresponds to the 'H' condition of Type C106 in *BS2870*.

Generic types

In addition to the traditional and long strip copper roofing described above, copper is also combined with together materials to form a range of proprietary roofing systems.

A number of examples are described here briefly, full technical details can be obtained from the manufacturers literature.

Copper-faced bitumen roofing felt.
The copper foil facing prevents evaporation of the essential oils from the bitumen, hence eliminating cracking and extending the life of the roof cover. This, together with protection from the harmful effects of the ultraviolet rays and oxidation, ensures that the bitumen remains supple. The copper finish will assume the green patina associated with traditional copper roofing.

The product is intended for used as a top (cap) sheet in built-up roofing (see **Chapter 11**).

Modified bitumen-backed embossed copper.
This consists of a copper foil with a modified bitumen backing. It combines the waterproofing characteristics of modified bitumen with the surface durability of copper sheet. The sheeting is always bonded onto an system of high performance bitumen sheets in a built-up roofing system.

Joints are made down the falls with standing seams or batten rolls and across the falls with single lock cross welts. Detailing of these top sheet follow traditional copper roofing practice (without drips or steps) but the rest of the specification is as for built-up roofing, (see **Chapter 11**).

Form / surface finish

The most important products for roofing are sheets and strip. Typical sheet thicknesses and sizes are given in Tables 14.1.1 and 14.1.2. Other product forms, such as tubes, may be of use for providing downpipes and guttering for the control of water run-off.

Tolerances in thickness, length and width of copper sheet and strip are to be as given in *BS 2870* (Table 1.8). The tolerance for straightness and other characteristics are not defined in the BS, but will be included in forthcoming CEN standards.

The natural colour of newly-produced copper is red (salmon pink). However, this changes with time and exposure, eventually to provide the familiar bright green colour often associated with 'old' copper. The ageing process is known as 'patination', the initial stage of which can be quite rapid. Full patination may not be achieved for a number of years.

Further reading:
CP 143: Part 12 Code of practice for sheet roof and wall coverings. Copper • CDA Copper in roofing—pocket book • BS 2870: Specification for rolled copper and copper alloys: sheet, strip and foil

• Copper develops a characteristic green colour through a weathering process known as patination.

During patination, the copper will change from red through dark brown and black to green. These are associated with changes over time in the chemistry of patina – a thin, stable insoluble film that is a combination of copper oxide, sulphate, carbonate and chlorides. The patina can self-heal when damaged, although this may result in a patchy appearance, because the damaged area will have to 'catch up' on the surrounding material.

The patination process usually will be more pronounced on flat surfaces than on the vertical. (In the latter case, the full green patina may only be achieved in marine locations). The patination time is also dependent on environmental conditions prevailing at a specific location. Table 14.1.3 gives typical times to full patination for a number of exposure conditions.

There are a number of ways in which the patina may be artificially formed to speed up this process. These are only appropriate for small areas; none of the commercially available techniques are recommended for large areas of roofing. Artificially prepatinated flat sheet copper is available for 'traditional' applications, however care must be taken during installation to avoid scratching and other surface damage.

Workability

The traditional and long strip panels are relatively lightweight compared to other roofing systems. They can, therefore, be easily transported and handled. Fully annealed copper used in traditional roofing is very malleable. It is easily worked and formed by hand using a range of plumber's tools. During cutting and forming operation the material will be locally work-hardened and the benefits of this will remain for the life of the roof.

Copper used for long strip roofing, is of a ¼ or ½ hard temper and hence less workable. However, much of the work carried out for long strip roofing is done mechanically. Forming machines are fairly portable and can be taken to the job site if necessary for manufacture of panels. The formation for standing seams is undertaken with electrically powered seaming machines. ∎

Table 14.1.1
Dimensions for traditional copper roofing

Sheet thickness mm	Sheet width mm	Bay width standing seam mm (nominal)	Bay width to centres of batten roll mm (nominal)	Maximum sheet length m
0.60	600	525	500[A]	1.8

Notes:
[A] Dimension given is the nominal dimension to centres of batten rolls, assuming the battens are 44mm wide.

Table 14.1.2
Dimensions for longstrip copper roofing

Strip thickness mm	Sheet width mm	Standing seam centres mm (nominal)	Length each bay m (maximum)
0.6/0.7	450	375[A]	10.0
0.6/0.7	600	525	10.0
0.6/0.7	670	595	10.0

Notes:
[A] For exposed locations.
Longstrip copper roofing bays may also be joined with batten rolls but standing seams are more generally used.

Table 14.1.3
Time for copper to form its mature patination

Atmospheric conditions	Time (Years)
Rural	30
Urban	15 to 20
City	8 to 12
Industrial	8 to 12
Marine	4 to 6

Critical factors

Further reading in the Guide:
11.1 - 11.4 Built-up roofing

14.2 Performance in use

- Copper is an inherently durable covering material for flat roofing.
- The interaction of copper with other materials must be carefully considered, both with regard to staining and corrosion.
- Bimetallic corrosion effects can occur with some metals.

Movement characteristics

The traditional and longstrip methods of laying copper on roofs have been developed to accommodate the movement characteristics of the material. Excessive and continued movement will however produce work hardening, which may cause the copper to split. Roofs must therefore be designed and installed to avoid this happening.

Key properties

The principal mechanical and physical properties of copper are summarised in Table 14.3.1. (see **Unit 14.3**)

Thermal performance

Being a good heat conductor, the thermal resistance of copper sheet is minimal. Copper is initially highly reflective but gradually loses this quality during the early stages of the formation of the patina. The mature patina is less reflective. The effects of solar heat therefore vary with time.

Fire resistance

The notional designation of roof coverings consisting of copper sheet is Ext SAA. The material may therefore be used without restriction.

Copper is non-combustible as defined by *BS476: Part 4*, and will not contribute to spread of flame. Fire-damaged copper should be scrapped and recycled.

Wind resistance

Copper roofing is vulnerable to wind uplift damage because of the light weight of the material and its un-profiled nature. Because wind uplift tends to be greatest at the edges of a roof, bay sizes at verges, and eaves should be evaluated. The width of verge bays should be less than 380mm. The centres of double lock cross welts on traditional applications should be reduced at ridge and eaves and the number of fixing cleats increased.

Traffic resistance

Copper roofing is not suitable for foot traffic other than for routine maintenance purposes but care must be taken to avoid flattening the standing seams.

If substantial traffic across the roof is envisaged for maintenance activities, batten rolls should be adopted and walkways be provided.

Similarly, heavy items of plant and equipment should not be placed directly on the roof covering. Appropriate upstanding platforms should be formed with suitable copper coverings and flashings.

Acoustic performance

Due to the light weight of copper roofing per square metre, it does not offer a good barrier to airborne or impact sound. The control of sound must be via the substrate and the underlay.

Durability

Expected life

Copper is highly resistant to corrosion in a wide variety of natural atmospheres and waters. This high resistance to corrosion means that copper roof can be expected to outperform many other membrane materials. If correctly designed and installed, a copper roof can be expected to last in excess of 25 years. Copper roofs may be seen which have been in service for 75 to 100 years.

Natural ageing

The changes in the surface appearance of copper are described in **Unit 14.1**.

Bimetallic corrosion

While copper is relatively immune to atmospheric corrosion, its effects on other metals to which it may be connected should not be ignored. When two dissimilar metals are electrically continuous in the presence of an electrolyte (e.g condensation, rain or seawater), bimetallic corrosion may result. This is rarely a problem for copper itself. However, the contact metal may rapidly suffer additional corrosion, particularly if it is steel, iron, zinc or aluminium.

Predicting the effects of bimetallic corrosion is difficult and expert advice should be sought. A recommended published guide is *PD6484*. The use of so-called tables of potential difference should be avoided, as these can only predict which metal may be adversely affected. They cannot predict whether additional corrosion will occur and, if it does, how severe it will be. In certain instances, the use of such tables can be misleading and erroneous. This is because rate of corrosion in a couple is dependent on surface films on the metal surface, metal temperature, electrolyte composition and, the relative areas of material. It is essentially independent of potential difference.

Further reading:
PD6484

© BFRC / CIRIA: Flat Roofing: Design and Good Practice. 1993

- Sulphur pollution in the atmosphere can be detrimental to copper.
- Care is required to avoid damage to completed copper roofs.

In general, it is best to avoid contact between copper and other metals. Where this cannot be avoided, the dissimilar metals should be electrically isolated, using nylon, or an other non-conducting separating layer. This is particularly important for flashings and lightning conductors.

Another area where corrosion can be a problem is with the presence of iron fillings and swarf from work on ferrous material. These may fall onto the roof and stain the roof as the ferrous material corrodes. This corrosion will itself be rapid due to the bimetallic effect. The rust deposit may initiate pitting below the deposit due to establishment of a differential aeration cell. This is best avoided by forbidding the cutting, drilling and welding of ferrous materials on or above a roof after the copper has been installed.

Atmospheric pollution
The specification of copper should be avoided on buildings that are to be located in environments containing excessively high concentration of sulphur. These are likely to arise from combustion products of power stations or industrial chimneys. These issues should received full consideration during the concept/scheme design and may affect the choice of roofing. During site evaluation, it may be necessary to carry out gas sampling of the local atmosphere over a period of time.

The potential for damage also exists with concentrated flue gases, from adjacent buildings or the building itself. This can be overcome, at least on the building being designed, by ensuring that flue openings terminate well above roof level. Here, it is important to consider:

- Type of flue gases
- Flue size and/or flue height restrictions
- Prevailing wind conditions and down draught.

Normal urban environments, whilst being polluted, should not be considered detrimental to the performance of copper. There are numerous examples of successful application of copper roofing in these environments.

Water run-off onto copper
Copper can also be adversely affected by adjacent overhanging roofs covered in bitumen felts or paints. The reaction of bitumen with ultra-violet light and water produces chemicals that are aggressive to copper. These chemicals not only can stain copper, which may be visually unacceptable, but also can cause serious corrosion. Water run-off from such roofs should therefore be avoided by the provision of suitable gutters.

Other building materials that can cause problems during construction include cement, concrete, lime and plaster. All can easily stain copper and may cause corrosion. This is best avoided by careful workmanship. Should any deposition occur, it should be removed immediately, by using a soft brush and tap water. On no account should any cleaning chemicals or materials be used, as they may leaves trace chemicals which will affect the patina development.

The leaching of chemicals from cedar shingles can cause staining and corrosion to copper roofs. Similar problems can arise from water run-off from tiled and felted roofs with moss or lichen colonies.

Lichen and moss
Copper will not support the growth of any living organisms or fungal growths. It is also resistant to all forms of attack by vermin and insects. It follows that wash-off from copper strips strategically placed above likely areas of moss and lichen colonies will maintain clear areas.

Water run-off from copper
It is important to ensure that details are correctly developed to deal with water run-off from copper roofs, as this run-off will contain copper compounds that may stain other materials and create a corrosion risk to other metals. Whilst staining is unlikely to have a detrimental effect on other non-metallic materials, it is undoubtedly unsightly and will detract from the appearance of the building as a whole. This problems is easily overcome, either by the provision of adequate guttering, which should itself be copper or copper-lined or by designing the roof to overhang other materials.

Similarly copper run-off should not be discharged into ponds contain plants, fish or other wild life without careful consideration of the relative dilution or the need to provide reactive filters. Copper is poisonous to many plants and run-off on to planted areas below the roof should also be avoided by the use of gutters.

Environmental impact
See **Unit 4.15** ■

Critical factors

Contact with other materials:

- in the atmosphere
- via water run-off
- from flue or other discharges
- in the building process
- once installed.

Further reading in the Guide:
4.15 Environmental impact of materials • 7.8 Lightning protection • 14.1 Copper: general description

14.3 Selection, design and application

- Well established details exist for the successful use of copper on flat roofing.
- The design of the fixing and jointing system must allow for the full effects of wind uplift and thermal movements.

Selection

Although copper as a base metal may be regarded as expensive in terms of costs per tonne, when considered in terms of installed costs, a copper roofing system can be an economically attractive option. This is particularly so when the ease of installation, adaptability and a relatively maintenance-free life are considered against first costs.

At pitches below 5° drainage of water from the roof may be retarded in high winds. For this situation the longstrip system is preferred with the seams sealed with non harding compounds. The properties of copper are summarised in Table 14.3.1.

Substructures

Substructures suitable for the support of copper roofing (see Table 14.3.2) must:

- have a smooth surface, free from nail heads, screws or other fixings
- be structurally sound and rigid enough to allow 'dressing' of the copper without springing
- be dimensionally stable and where significant have a low moisture content
- provide substrates of sufficient thickness for secure fixing for cleats and batten rolls
- be compatible with copper, particularly with respect to corrosion.

All substructures should be clean, dry and with a level surface.

The weight per unit area of copper sheeting is small compared to many other roofing materials and, in certain circumstances, advantage may be taken of this in designing the substructure.

For all cold roofs, adequate provision for ventilation beneath the roof structure to minimise the risk from condensation is required (see **Unit 4.7** and refer to information given in the *Pocket Book* published by CDA).

Application

Jointing

There are three basic types of joint for use with copper sheet and strip, these give roofs their characteristic form:

- Double lock standing seam – for use on both 'traditional' and 'longstrip'.

**Table 14.3.1
Physical and mechanical properties of copper**

Thickness	Approximate weight per square metre
0.60mm	5.4 kg/m²
0.70mm	6.3kg/m²
Tensile strength	
Annealed	210N/mm
Half-hard	245N/mm
Hard-wrought (up to 500mm width) (over 500mm width)	310N/mm 285N/mm
Coefficient of linear expansion	$17.4 \times 10^{-6}/°C$
Melting point	1083°C
Annealing temperature	600°C
Thermal conductivity	384W/m K
Elongation on 50mm:	
Annealed	35% minimum
Half-hard	15% minimum
Density	8900kg/m³

- Batten roll for 'traditional' method generally but also for longstrip.
- Double lock crosswelts for use with traditional method only.

The joints with the fall of the roof are formed using standing seams or batten rolls. Standing seams are suitable for roof pitches greater than 6°. Batten rolls are suitable for pitches down to the minimum recommended (3°), and should be used where there is more than occasional foot traffic. However, if standing seams are adopted they must be sealed for all flat roof pitches, with boiled linseed oil or a compatible non-hardening jointing

Further reading:

CDA Copper in roofing: pocket book

• It is good practice to lay a single layer of a waterproofing membrane below copper as a second line of defence.

Nani Nani office, Tokyo, Japan

compound. All standing seams should allow a gap at the base of the upstand to allow for thermal movement.

The maximum length of a standing seam in longstrip is 10m. For longer slopes a drip step should be introduced, a minimum 75mm deep. This is the only permissible method of jointing across the fall in longstrip construction to accommodate thermal movement.

The traditional system is vulnerable at the crosswelts and, when pitched below 6°, drip steps should be introduced in place of crosswelts. Any crosswelts should be sealed. Single lock crosswelts should not be adopted on flat roof pitches but may be used at junction with ridges, at eaves and drips. Where standing seams are used, crosswelts should be staggered in adjacent bays, but where batten rolls are adopted they may run in line.

Brazed joints (with silver or soft solder) are not recommended as a method of jointing for large roof areas. Brazing may be used for detail work to cesspools, gutter outlets, stop ends, expansion flashings, soil pipe flashings and minor repair work. For some work, there may be restrictions on the use of flame torches for soldering and brazing. *continued* ▶

Table 14.3.2
Substructures for copper roofing

Substructure material	Fixing for cleats and batten rolls	Comment
Cellular or foam concrete [A]	poor	Use treated wood battens 38mm x 50mm dovetailed and well spiked into deck with 24mm boarding or plywood deck overlay
Dense concrete [A]	good	as above
Screeded concrete	poor	as above, but with battens cast into screed at precise centres
Aluminium profiled decks	adequate	vapour control layer plus insulation board or compressed cork plus 18mm exterior WBP grade plywood to support over the troughs—all fixings to be in stainless steel to avoid interaction
Steel profiled	adequate	as above decks
Timber - T & G boarding [ABC]	good	boarding should be minimum 24mm thick
Timber - exterior plywood [C]	good	plywood should be WBP grade minimum 18mm thick
Woodwool slabs	not recommended	
Oriented strand board	good	Should have Agrément certification for roofing and be not less than 15mm thick

Notes:
[A] A layer of 3mm tempered hardboard may be laid over poor surfaced concrete or uneven timber boarding to provide a smooth surface for fixings such as cleats and batten rolls. All fixings must penetrate the hardboard and be securely anchored into the substructure. However, when laying hardboard over concrete or existing boarding attention should be given to the possibility of condensation.
[B] For slopes of less than 5°, all boarding should be laid in the direction of fall.
[C] Heads of nails must be punched in and screws countersunk.

Further reading in the Guide:
4.7 Condensation

Critical factors

• Ensure that the deck is suitable for copper roofing and is properly prepared.

• Minimise the number of penetrations as the execution of flashings requires great care.

Underlays

It is good practice to lay a bituminous or similar waterproof layer, with lapped and sealed joints, over the structural deck as a second line of defence and to guard against thermal pumping. A slip layer of non-woven 100% polyester geotextile or similar should be used between the waterproofing layer and the copper roofing.

The presence of an underlay will:

- lessen the possibility of abrasion between the copper and the substructure
- give a degree of thermal insulation
- prevent corrosion between the copper and any ferrous fixings in the substructure
- deaden impact sound form wind, rain or hail
- smooth out minor unevenness on the deck
- protect the copper from possible corrosion from elements in the substrate (some timber treatments can have a corrosive effect on metals).

Fixings

The methods used to fix copper to the substructure are very important in ensuring a long useful life. (see Figures 14.3.1, and 14.3.2)

Resistance to wind uplift must be allowed for within the design of standing seams and batten roll joints. The size and spacing of fixing cleats, as well as the maximum practical width for copper strip and sheet will also ensure adequate resistance to wind uplift. Details may be found in Copper Development Association *Copper in Roofing Pocket Book*.

Because the copper sheets must resist wind uplift it is important that the cleats and battens used to fix the sheets are themselves firmly and reliably fixed.

Cleats made of copper to *BS2870* or stainless steel to *BS 1449* are used to attach the copper sheet or strips to the sub-structure at the joints. Traditional roofing uses fixed cleats, while long strip roofing uses a combination of fixed cleats and 'expansion cleats'.

For traditional and longstrip roofing cleats should be spaced as given in Table 14.3.3. The arrangement of cleats is laid down in *CP143: Part 12*.

Treated wood should be used for all batten roll systems.

Nails for all fixings for copper sheet and strips must be copper or copper alloy to *BS2870* or stainless steel to *BS 1449* (minimum grade 304).

Table 14.3.3
Recommendations for cleats and fixings for use with standing seams, batten rolls and welts. Traditional and longstrip methods.

Height of building	Up to 8m	8 to 20m	20 to 100m
Width of strip (mm) Width of panels	450 600 670 375 525 595	450 600 670 375 525 595	450 600 375 525
Minimum thickness copper (mm)	0.6 0.6 0.6	0.6 0.6 0.6	0.6 0.6
In the plane of the roof Clip fixing centres (max.)	500 500 460	500 400 375	500 330
Roof edges and corners (1m wide zone) Clip fixing centres (max.)	500 500 460	500 330 305	280 250

Notes:

(1) Additional fixings may be necessary for conditions of high wind loading (wind speeds above 48m/sec).

(2) A clip pull-off load of 0.8kN and a safety factor of 2 are assumed.

Gutters

CP143: Part 12 gives advice with regard to dimensional details of insitu lined copper gutters. The thickness of copper should not be less than 0.6mm. Gutters should be laid to fall and should have a minimum depth of 75mm at the highest point. Steps in gutters should be avoided but where necessary should also be a minimum depth of 75mm.

Fabricated copper gutters are produced in heavier gauge material with brazed, joints permitting much longer and convenient lengths. Such gutters are specially produced to suit specific applications. Specialist fabricators and contractors will advise and manufacture to order.

Lightning

Although copper is a good electrical conductor, copper roofing should not be used as the air termination network for lightning protection (see **Unit 7.8**). The roofing components must, however, be bonded to the lightning protection system.

Further reading:
CP143: Part 12 Code of practice for sheet roof and wall coverings. Copper • BS2870: Specification for rolled copper and copper alloys: sheet strip and foil

---

© BFRC / CIRIA: Flat Roofing: Design and Good Practice. 1993

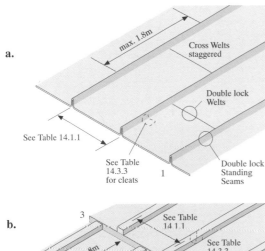

Figure 14.3.1
Traditional fixing

1. Standing seam
2. Batten roll
3. Drip step

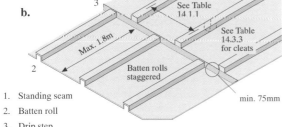

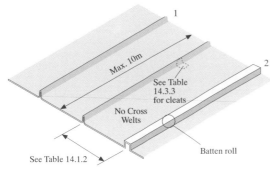

Figure 14.3.2
Longstrip system fixing

1. Standing seam
2. Batten roll

Standing seams

Copper components for lightning protection should be made from copper rod or section complying with *BS 2874*. Under no circumstances should other metals be used for lighting conductors in association with copper because of the problems of bimetallic corrosion (see below). The expert advice of a lightning protection specialist should always be sought to ensure complete build-up protection.

If the copper sheet roofing is effectively earthed, it will act as a barrier to electromagnetic radiation. It does not form a barrier against ionising radiation. Copper is an excellent conductor of electricity.

Protection

Copper roofing is not suitable for foot traffic other than for occasional maintenance work and should not be exposed at any time to concentrated loads or heavy foot traffic or equipment. Proper walkways are essential for regular traffic.

Safety issues

Copper is a relatively clean metal to handle, but care must be taken to wash before handling food. Being relatively thin, the sheet edges can be sharp and have barbs which can cause severe cuts. Gloves should be worn. ■

Critical factors

Further reading in the Guide:
7.8 Design for lightning protection

12 Mastic Asphalt	13 Polymeric Single Ply	14 Copper	15 Lead Sheet	16 Other Membranes	17 Thermal Insulants	18 Specification	19 Contracts & Procurement	20 Inspection	21 Maintenance	22 Bibliography	23 Index
263	301	331	353	375	383	393	399	413	429	437	455

14.4 Design details

- The nature and detailing of copper roofs is significantly different to that for the organic membranes.
- The information in this Unit provides guidance on the principles of detail design and provides specific examples of common conditions. **Unit 9.1** gives guidance on the broader performance principles of detail design.

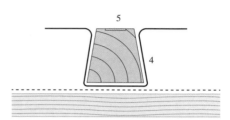

Fixing sequence - Stage 1

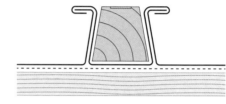

Stage 2

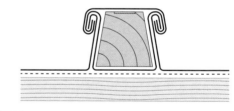

Stage 3

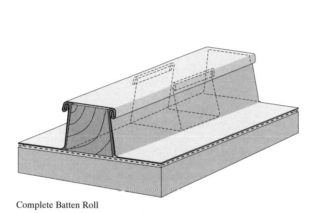

Complete Batten Roll

Fixing methods

Traditional system batten roll

This fixing method commonly seen on older and historic buildings enables a roof to appear structured with defined bays.

However, with modern installations and roof slopes in excess of 10 metres long provision must be made for the thermal expansion and contraction of the metal.

Batten roll joints are appropriate for lower pitched or roofs subject to foot traffic. A rectangular batten roll may be used if preferred.

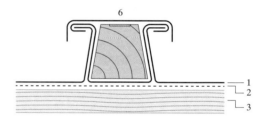

Stage 4

1. Copper sheet
2. Underlay
3. Deck
4. Fixing clip tacked to underside roll
5. Conical batten
6. Copper capping

Figure 14.4.1
Traditional system batten roll fixing and sequence

© BFRC / CIRIA: Flat Roofing: Design and Good Practice. 1993

- The details shown are generally for cold deck roofs
- The purpose of the details is to show the formation of the copper membrane and not the total system build-up

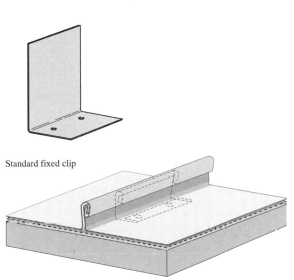

Standard fixed clip

Double lock standing seam

Figure 14.4.2
Traditional system standing seam

1. Copper sheet
2. Underlay
3. Deck
4. 3mm gap for thermal movement in cross direction

Traditional system standing seam.

Straight run standing seams should not exceed 10m in length. Where the length of the roof slope is greater, step drips should be provided across the slope, at not more than 10 m centres, to accommodate thermal movement.

Standing seams are normally 25mm high and are formed over and secured by standard fixed or fish-tail fixed clips. Sliding clips may be used if abnormal thermal movement is anticipated.

continued ▶

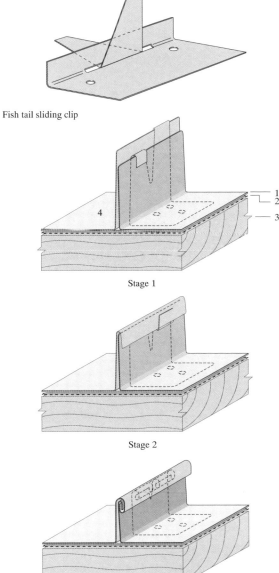

Fish tail sliding clip

Stage 1

Stage 2

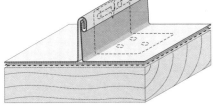

Stage 3

Fish tail fixed clip sequence

Figure 14.4.3
Longstrip system fixed and sliding fish tail clip seaming

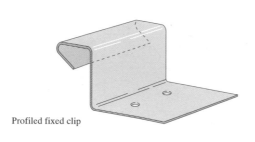

Profiled fixed clip

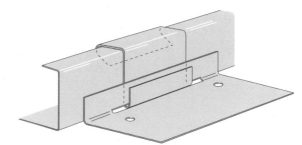

Stage 1

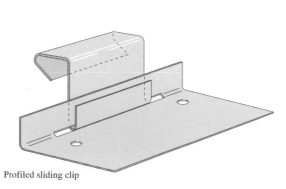

Profiled sliding clip

Figure 14.4.4
Longstrip system fixed and sliding profiled clips

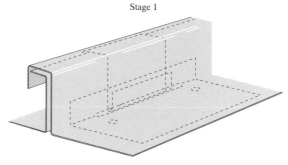

Stage 2

Longstrip seaming

Longstrip panels are generally secured with a combination
of fixed and sliding, standard or fish tail clips or with
fixed and sliding profiled clips. Fishtail clips are used
with panels having normal upstands of 45m on one side
and 35mm on the other.

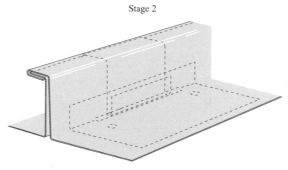

Stage 3

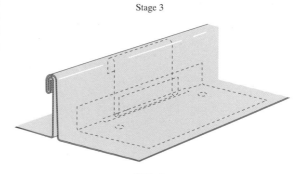

Stage 4

Figure 14.4.5
Long strip system, profiled sliding clip seaming

Chapter	1	2	3	4	5	6	7	8	9	10	11
Contents	Introduction	History	Regulatory Methods	Principles	Surveys	Constraints & Targets	Design Selection	Calculations	Detail Design Principles	Evaluation of Design	Built-up Roofing
Page	1	19	31	45	83	95	105	165	189	217	221

Forming methods

Ridges and hips

Where copper passes over the ridge, or hip, a batten timber not less than 38mm higher than the intersecting rolls or standing seams should be provided.

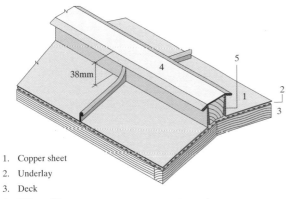

1. Copper sheet
2. Underlay
3. Deck
4. Ridge roll●
5. Expansion gap

Figure 14.4.6
Ridge

The following sequence of drawings indicate the methods of forming the termination of the eaves.

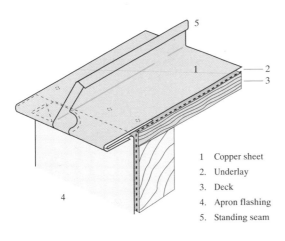

1 Copper sheet
2. Underlay
3. Deck
4. Apron flashing
5. Standing seam

Figure 14.4.7
Eaves detail: longstrip system splayed and eaves termination

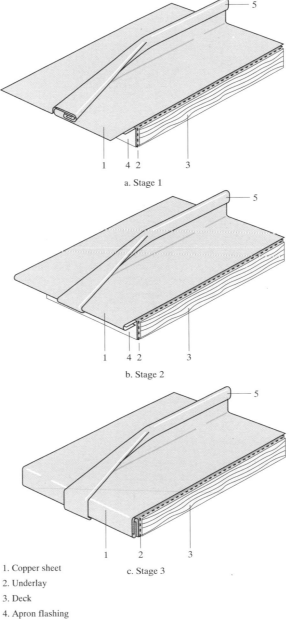

a. Stage 1

b. Stage 2

c. Stage 3

1. Copper sheet
2. Underlay
3. Deck
4. Apron flashing
5. Double lock standing seam

Figure 14.4.8
Standing seam eaves detail, traditional folding

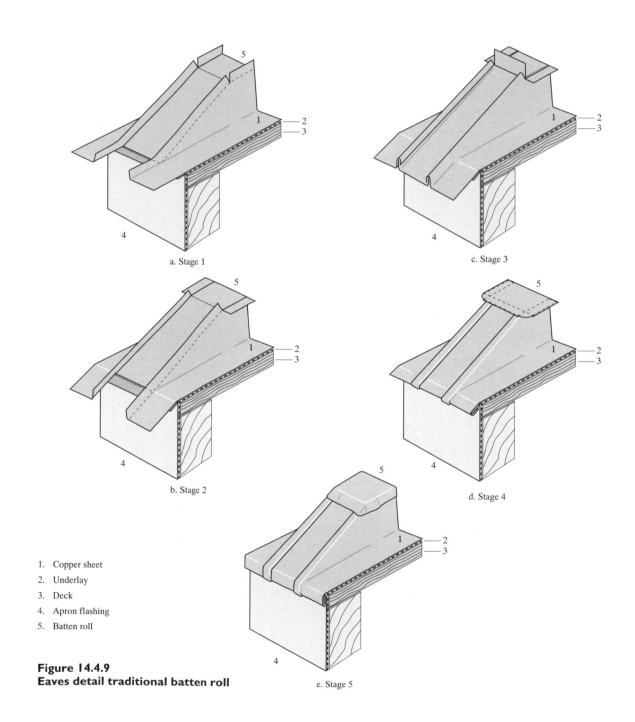

a. Stage 1

b. Stage 2

c. Stage 3

d. Stage 4

e. Stage 5

1. Copper sheet
2. Underlay
3. Deck
4. Apron flashing
5. Batten roll

Figure 14.4.9
Eaves detail traditional batten roll

Chapter	1	2	3	4	5	6	7	8	9	10	11
Contents	Introduction	History	Regulatory Methods	Principles	Surveys	Constraints & Targets	Design Selection	Calculations	Detail Design Principles	Evaluation of Design	Built-up Roofing
Page	1	19	31	45	83	95	105	165	189	217	221

344

© BFRC / CIRIA: Flat Roofing: Design and Good Practice. 1993

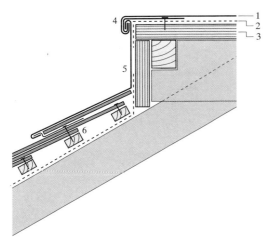

1.	Copper sheet	5.	Apron
2.	Underlay	6.	Copper under fastener secured
3.	Deck		with brass screws
4.	Welt		

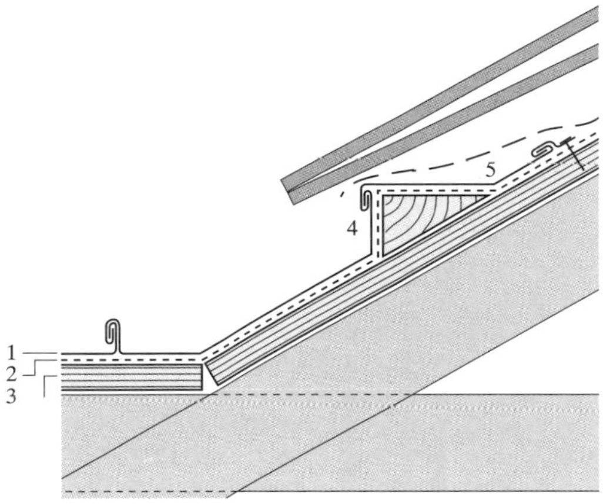

1.	Copper sheet	4.	Copper upstand dressed up
2.	Underlay		tilting fillet
3.	Deck	5.	Copper apron flashing

Fig 14.4.10 Flat roof junction with pitched roof

Where a copper flat roof discharges onto a tiled or slated roof, a drip should be formed by welting the edge of the copper to the vertical upstand of the copper apron.

The copper apron should be dressed with extreme care down over the sloping roof and fixed at the bottom with a copper under fastener beneath the top row of tiles or slates and fastened with brass or stainless steel screws into the tiling/slating battens.

There should be a minimum face to the copper upstand of 75mm.

This flashing is more conventionally formed in lead.

The consideration of ventilation to the roof is important and the incorporation carefully considered particularly if the pitched roof is not tiled or slated.

Fig 14.4.11 Upstand and apron beneath tile or slate eaves

Where tiled or slated roofs discharge onto a copper flat roof, a copper apron flashing should be clipped to the sloping roof, taken down over the tilting fillet, and welted to the copper flat upstand. The vapour control layers and insulation U-values must be consistent from pitched to flat areas. When the discharge is into the form of a gutter the gutter should be boxed if it exceeds 3m in length and the minimum depth of the gutter should be 75mm at its highest point.

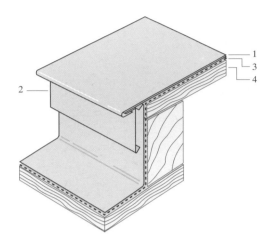

1. Copper sheet	3. Underlay
2. Weathering apron	4. Deck

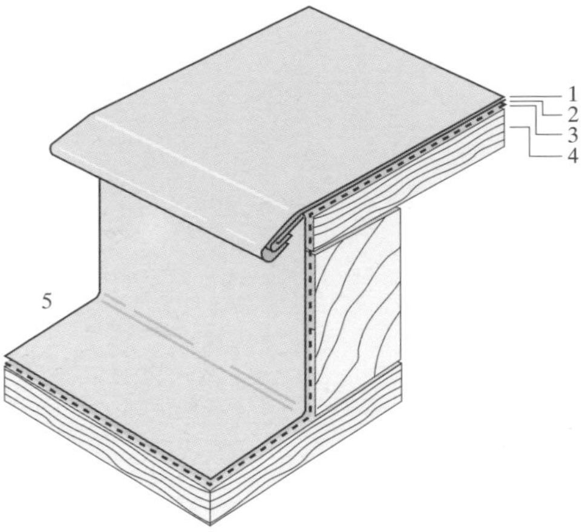 1. Copper sheet	4. Deck
2. Upstand restraint sheet	5. Gutter
3. Underlay	

Fig 14.4.12 Drip step with additional weather check

Where drips are constructed on a roof, the upper and lower bays are generally welted together with single lock welts at the drip edge. The turned up edges between the standing seam or batten roll being formed with dog ears.

However, on shallow pitched slopes a drip step with an additional weather check can be used to accommodate thermal movement in roofs on slopes in excess of 10 metres in length.

This step detail is not practical if the step is less than 100mm in overall depth.

Fig 14.4.13 Drip step into gutter

With standard construction, the (roof) side gutter upstand is joined to the roof sheeting with a single welt. For long strip the upstand is left free and weathered by a separate apron drip, itself welted to the roof sheeting. See Figure 14.4.12.

All individual lengths of parapet and box gutters, should be made in one piece with dog-eared corners i.e at drips, stop ends, sumps etc.

Tapered angle fillets should be incorporated in the gutter sole where it passes over a drip or discharges into a cesspool.

The maximum gutter width will be dependant on the girth and gauge of the copper sheet, the practical minimum is 150mm. However the gutter width must be related to outlet performance requirements and whether a cesspool is included.

Generally open ended box gutters are preferred to integral outlets.

Cesspools should be formed from one piece of copper, either by dog-ears or silver brazing at the corners. The sides of the cesspool should be taken up and welted to the surrounding copper work.

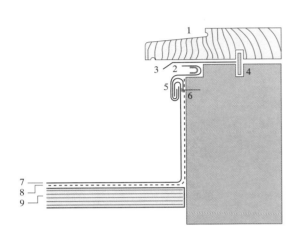

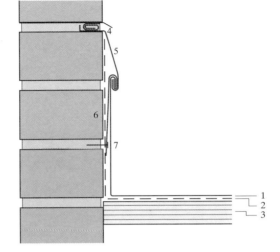

1.	Cill	5.	Copper flashing
2.	Copper or lead wedge and mastic pan	6.	Restraint apron
		7.	Copper sheet
3.	Flashing	8.	Underlay
4.	Water bar	9.	Deck

1.	Copper sheet	5.	Hanging flashing
2.	Underlay	6.	Copper clips
3.	Deck	7.	Copper upstand
4.	Copper wedge		

Fig 14.4.14 Opening onto roof

The detailing of the copper upstand is important in this situation to ensure water does not ingress under the cill. Other features such as cill trays, water bars and jamb dpc discharging over the cill tray should also be introduced.

Fig 14.4.15 Typical straight flashing to abutment

This detail is suitable for both longstrip and traditional systems. Where movement is anticipated the upstand copper may be turned up and fixed to a freestanding kerb.

The detail should ensure that the cavity tray or dpc discharges over the flashing.

All aprons and flashings to walls and abutments should consist of a separate strip of copper not more than 1800mm long.

The upper edge of the upstand should be tucked into the wall at least 25mm and with an upturn to act as a water stop. The flashing should be wedged with copper wedges and pointed with a mastic cement. The hanging flashing should have a beaded lower edge to stiffen it and to prevent wind uplift. Sufficient copper cleats should be used to anchor the roof upstand to the wall.

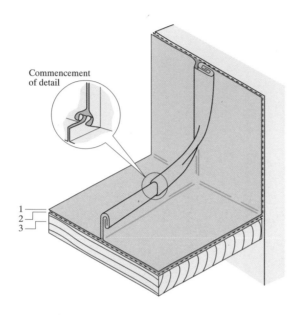

Commencement
of detail

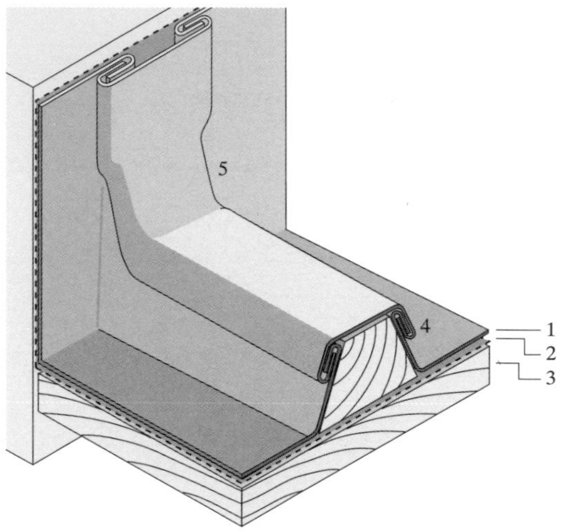

1. Copper sheet
2. Underlay
3. Deck

1. Copper sheet   4. Batten roll
2. Underlay   5. Timber fillet
3. Deck

Fig 14.4.16 Standing seam dog-ear termination to abutment

This detail is more suited to the traditional system, but can be worked on long strip panels.

Where a standing seam meets an abutment, the joint should either be dog-eared or depending on the pitch flattened to allow the metal to be formed in the upstand.

Fig 14.4.17 Batten roll dog-ear termination to abutment

This detail is suitable for traditional system only.

At the highest point of the roll and depending on the angle where it meets the abutment, a timber fillet should be fixed to the top of the roll.

A rectangular batten roll may be used if preferred.

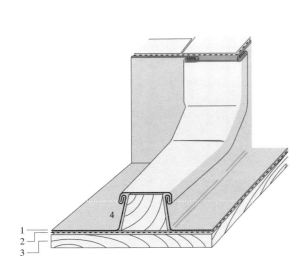

1. Copper sheet   3. Deck
2. Underlay   4. Batten roll

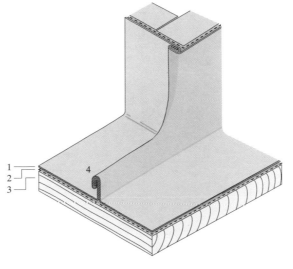

1. Copper sheet   3. Deck
2. Underlay   4. Standing Seam

Fig 14.4.18 Opening and rooflight upstand with batten roll

When forming a flashing around rooflight or any other roof opening the kerb must be 100mm minimum height.

Most roof openings have a width in excess of a copper panel width, requiring a back apron or other from of diversion to avoid ponding.

On shallow pitched roofs welts of the apron to the roof sheet are vulnerable. It is usual to provide a platform minimum 50mm high behind the opening and running up to the ridge. This platform will be pitched to the sides.

Fig 14.4.19 Rooflight upstand with graduated standing seam

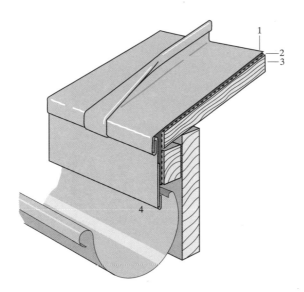

| 1. Copper sheet | 3. Deck |
| 2. Underlay | 4. Apron flashing |

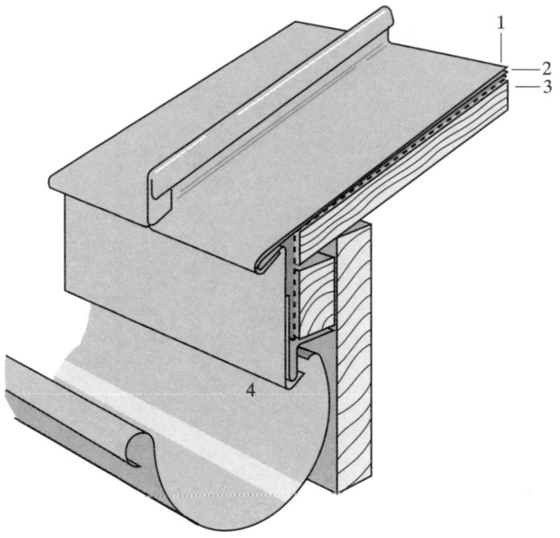 1. Copper sheet	4. Apron flashing
2. Underlay	
3. Deck	

Fig 14.4.20 Eaves detail with drop apron to gutter, traditional system

At the eaves, the main roof sheeting should be welted to an independent apron flashing, secured by a continuous fixing strip. Where batten is provided on the fascia or barge board for the continuous fixing strip, it should be securely fixed with brass or stainless steel screws.

Fig 14.4.21 Eaves detail with drop apron to gutter, longstrip system

This detail accommodates movement in all directions.

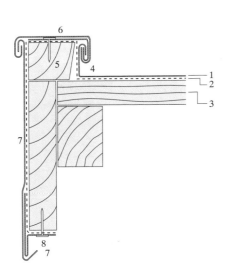

1. Copper sheet
2. Underlay
3. Deck
4. Gap to accommodate movement
5. Batten roll
6. Capping
7. Fascia apron
8. Apron restraint drip

Fig 14.4.22 Verge detail with roll upstand

In order to avoid rainwater being blown over a verge edge it is usual, but not essential to provide a check upstand. This illustration is typical for a traditional system application but may be formed as a seam upstand.

Depending on the exposure it may be advisable to reduce the width of a number of panels adjacent to the verge. On severely exposed situations closing down of the double lock cross welts might also be advisable.

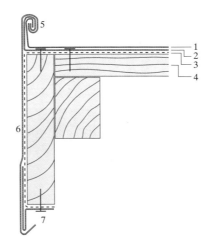

1. Copper sheet
2. Apron restraint sheet
3. Underlay
4. Deck
5. Standing seam
6. Fascia apron
7. Apron restraint drip

Fig 14.4.23 Verge detail with standing seam upstanding

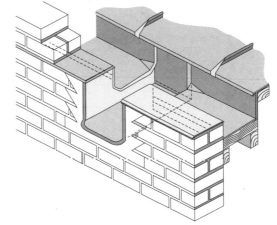

Fig 14.4.24 Chute

Chutes are only formed in conjunction with box gutters and the discharge should be so formed in copper to direct water into the hopper.

12 Mastic Asphalt	13 Polymeric Single Ply	14 Copper	15 Lead Sheet	16 Other Membranes	17 Thermal Insulants	18 Specification	19 Contracts & Procurement	20 Inspection	21 Maintenance	22 Bibliography	23 Index
263	301	331	353	375	383	393	399	413	429	437	455

Lead sheet 15

General description

- Lead has advantages which can be readily exploited in flat roof coverings.
- Well established methods of use have been developed over the years, but these have to be kept under review as the nature of building applications change.
- New conditions resulting from higher standards of comfort and higher internal relative air humidity require changes in traditional construction.

Basis of technology

Nature of material

Lead is a soft, heavy, bluish grey metal obtained from galena, an ore found in large deposits throughout the world. It has been used as a building material for around 7000 years. (The Babylonians are said to have used it to line their famous hanging gardens.) There are no lead covered roofs of such antiquity in existence today, although some that are have served their purpose for more than 400 years.

The properties of lead which are relevant to its use in roofing are given and discussed in the LSA *The Lead Sheet Manual*. For the vast majority of flat roofs, lead sheeting complying with *BS1178* will be appropriate.

General considerations

The geometry and form of the roof surface is dictated by lead's inherent characteristics:

- Its comparatively high coefficient of thermal expansion.
- Its comparatively low strength combined with its vulnerability to fatigue.
- Its particular jointing possibilities.

Stresses induced by thermal movement are controlled by limiting the size of sheets used; the thicker the sheet the bigger it can be. The traditional jointing system for flat roofs is the rolled joint, either hollow or with a wood core, following the slope, together with an overlapping stepped joint, or drip, across the slope. The finished flat roof is an assemblage of lead 'trays' with a very distinctive jointing pattern and appearance.

Appropriate construction

Experience of lead roofs in recent years has drawn attention to a weakness in both traditional and modern constructions. The weakness concerns condensation and, in particular, the failure of established roof types to prevent it occurring on the underside of the lead sheeting. The severity of the problem varies from building to building depending on the source, timing and duration of the condensation, the volume of the roofed space, the degree of ventilation and the presence of other cold surfaces, for example in walls and floors.

It is now generally recognised that the traditional lead roof should be used only in circumstances where the space below is unheated, has a relatively large volume and is well ventilated, so that the relative humidity of the air is not increased significantly in cold weather. When the rate of ventilation is inadequate or when more comfortable conditions are required then vapour control layers and thermal insulation must be introduced.

A solution to these problems is found with the two deck, 'ventilated warm deck roof', as proposed by the BRE, DoE, LSA and LCA and described in *BS5250*, clause 9.4.5. The deck, vapour control layer and insulation are in the usual position (for a warm roof) above the roof structure. There is a ventilated air space above the insulation and then a second deck, carrying the interlayer and the lead sheeting.

As yet, there is no published feedback on the performance of this form of construction.

Generic types

Milled lead sheet

Most lead sheet used in buildings is manufactured on rolling mills and is described as 'milled lead sheet'. Slabs of refined lead up to 125mm thick are first rolled out to a thickness of 25mm then cut into suitable sizes and passed backwards and forwards through the mill until reduced to the required thickness.

Milled lead sheet is manufactured to *BS 1178*, which lays down requirements that control the quality of the material, including stipulations that:

- the material be free from defects such as inclusions and laminations.
- the tolerance on thickness be not more than ± 5%.
- the chemical composition be not less than 99.9% lead.
- the grain structure have a uniform recrystallised form.

The preference, traditionally, has been that the composition of lead sheet should not contain any alloying elements that would significantly affect the characteristic softness and malleability. However, it is now recognised that a very small quantity of copper (in the range 0.03 to 0.06%) has the effect of enhancing the resistance of the lead sheet to thermal fatigue. This requirement was incorporated into the 1982 edition of *BS1178*.

Milled lead sheet is supplied by the manufacturer cut to dimensions as required, or as large sheets 2.4m wide and up to 12m in length. Lead strip is defined as material ready cut in widths from 75mm up to 600mm. Supplied in coils, this is a very convenient form of lead sheet for many flashing and weathering applications.

Further reading:
LSA The Lead Sheet Manual • BS1178: Specification for milled lead sheet for building purposes • BS334: Specification for compositional limits of chemical lead • BS5250: Code of practice for control of condensation in buildings • BS6915: Specification for the design and construction of fully supported lead sheet roof and wall coverings.

• Recent developments suggest that two-deck construction – with a well-ventilated cavity below the lead membrane – is an appropriate method.

Cast lead sheet

Cast lead sheet is still made as a craft operation by the traditional method of running molten lead over a bed of prepared sand. There is no British Standard for this material.

The available size of sheet is determined by the casting table and sizes of sheets made in recent years have varied from 2.75m x 1m to 5.5m x 2m. Skilled casters can cast sheets to an accuracy of 0.2mm thickness on average in a range of sizes corresponding to the standard sizes for milled lead sheet to Code Nos. 6, 7 and 8 (see below).

Machine-cast lead sheet

Lead sheet for building purposes is also produced by a continuous casting process. Machine cast lead sheet is formed on a rotating, cooled roller, the lower section of which is immersed in a bath of molten lead. The cooled lead sheet is taken off the roller onto a take-up spool. The thickness of the sheet is controlled by varying the speed of the roller and the depth of immersion. Lead sheet made by this process is produced in thicknesses between 0.45 and 3.85mm with a sheet width of between 150mm and 1.5m.

Form / surface finishes

Because the range of metric sizes corresponds closely to the traditional range (expressed in lb/ft^2), they have been given code numbers – 3,4,5,6,7 and 8. Thus, lead sheet is specified by its BS Code Number, or thickness in millimetres, e.g.. Code No. 4 lead sheet (thickness 1.80mm).The standard range of thicknesses is shown in Table 15.1.1.

Table 15.1.1
BS1178 **standard range of thicknesses of milled lead sheet**

BS Code No.	Thickness (mm)	Weight kg/m^2	Colour code
3	1.32	14.97	Green
4	1.80	20.41	Blue
5	2.24	25.40	Red
6	2.65	30.05	Black
7	3.15	35.72	White
8	3.55	40.26	Orange

When freshly cut and exposed to air, lead forms a surface film of oxide, which imparts a dark grey appearance. It will then slowly develop an even coloured and adherent patina by reaction with carbon dioxide and, more importantly, with sulphur dioxide in the atmosphere.

The initial patina may begin to form somewhat patchily, particularly in showery weather shortly after fixing. This initial patina is a lead carbonate which, while insoluble in atmospheric moisture, adheres only loosely and can wash off. Eventually, the permanent patina will develop and, in many forms of leadwork, the incidence of streaky initial patination will be of little consequence. But there are situations where it should be avoided, particularly when lead is used in conjunction with materials whose appearance may be marred by lead carbonate.

Traditionally, a smear coating of raw linseed oil, was applied to the surface of newly-fixed leadwork, to prevent the worst effects of this phenomenon. The modern treatment is to use an evenly-applied smear coating of a quick drying 'patination' oil.

Workability

Lead is the softest of the common metals and, in its refined form, it is very malleable and capable of being shaped with ease at ambient temperatures. It can readily be manipulated with hand tools and, using the technique of bossing, can be worked into the most complicated of shapes or dressed to fit the many types of deeply profiled shapes used in roofing.

Generally, the need for periodic softening or annealing during application is not necessary, since lead sheet does not appreciably work-harden. However, when using the thicker grades of sheet in winter conditions, an application of heat along the fold lines and bossing areas will make the work much easier and reduce the risk of creasing the lead during bossing. ∎

Critical factors

• Lead is vulnerable to corrosion from condensation on its underside, unless its recurrence is infrequent and its duration short term.

• Surface treatment with a patination oil prevents unsightly run-off onto other materials.

Further reading in the Guide:

15.2 Performance in use

- Lead, when patinated is very resistant to corrosion and weathering, but it needs protection from aggressive run-off and sulphates.
- Lead can normally be used in conjunction with other metals without significant risk of bimetallic corrosion.

Movement characteristics

Lead is susceptible to the phenomena of thermal fatigue and creep deformation, but, in building applications, provision is made for this by the appropriate sizing and fixing of the individual pieces of sheet. Resistance to thermal fatigue can be further improved by careful control of the chemical composition and hence the grain structure. To this end, *BS1178* specifies the inclusion of 0.03-0.06% copper, which promotes grain refinement and its associated benefits (see **Unit 15.1**).

'Creep' is the tendency of metals to stretch slowly in the course of time under sustained loading. However, experience has shown that significant creep will not occur with external leadwork, if the pieces are sized to normal recommendations.

Key properties

The physical properties of lead are set out in Table 15.2.1.

Thermal performance

The conductivity of lead is high and for practical purposes the effect of the lead sheeting on the roof can be ignored when calculating thermal resistance.

Fire resistance

Lead is incombustible. Lead roofs achieve the following ratings when tested to *BS476: Part 3*.

- Lead laid on square edged boarding: BA.
- Lead laid on T & G boarding or concrete: AA.

Wind resistance

In severe exposures, weight to help resist wind-uplift can be a factor requiring the specification of thicker lead sheet than normal.

Durability

Patination of external leadwork

Lead is extremely resistant to corrosion by the atmosphere whether in town, country or coastal areas. In time, lead develops a strongly adhering and highly insoluble patina, the natural colour of which is silver grey.

As will be seen from very many examples, the patina of old leadwork appears darker when there is a layer of grime. Parts of the surface that are less exposed than others to the scouring action of wind and rain, will appear darker. However, since grime forming emissions have been greatly reduced, leadwork can be expected to present a more natural weathered appearance in the future.

Table 15.2.1
Lead: physical data

Density	11340kg/m^3
Coefficient of thermal expansion	29.3 310^{-6}/°C
Thermal conductivity	34.76 W/m K
Melting point	327.4°C

Except in marine environments, the insolubility of the patina ensures that the run-off of rainwater from weathered surfaces takes nothing into solution to stain or harm adjoining materials, such as stonework.

Recent investigations have established that the permanent patina of external leadwork, even on leadwork many years old, is largely lead sulphate, irrespective of the exposure, whereas, in the past, it was thought to be predominately a lead carbonate.

Corrosion resistance

Although lead is very resistant to corrosion by atmospheric pollutants once the surface patina is developed, it is vulnerable to some alkalis, some acids and pure water. The agents most likely to attack its upper surface include:

- Water running off or dripping from a concrete surface.
- Water which has percolated through a concrete screed.
- Water running off a lichen or moss covered roof.
- Water running off cedar or oak shingles.

The attack on the upper surface is best treated by removing the agent at source or by diverting the aggressive run-off away from the lead. If the run-off cannot be diverted, the lead can be protected by overlaying it at the point of impact, for example in a lead lined gutter, with a sheet of sacrificial lead. A bituminous coating has sometimes been used instead, but it is not always effective due to the difficulties of achieving completeness of the film and resisting damage.

Condensation

Pure water in the form of condensation on the underside of lead sheet can cause significant corrosion by converting the metal to lead carbonate. It is important with new work to avoid the risk of condensation by designing in accordance with *BS 5250* and *BS 6229*. When renewing lead work on existing buildings there may be limitations on what can be done, but the provision of adequate ventilation will still be necessary.

Further reading:
MURDOCH, R and RAE, A S 'Avoiding corrosion under metal roofs' Building Technology and Management, Oct/Nov 1987 • BORDASS, W and FARRELL, D 'Corrosion control – sheet metal roofs, Architects Journal • ECCLESIASTICAL ARCHITECTS' AND SURVEYORS' ASSOCIATION, 'Corrosion Problems of Lead Roofing', Building Technical File • R H HILL The condensation corrosion of metal roofing materials.

Fortunately, the problem is one of degree. The historical record and recent research both indicate that lead can tolerate some water on its underside. Ameliorating conditions have not been investigated but experience suggests that damage is least if the exposure is short term and if air has reasonably free access.

Compatibility with other metals
Experience has shown that lead sheet can be used in contact with other metals such as copper, zinc, iron, aluminium and stainless steel in most normal environments, without risk of significant bi-metallic corrosion. For example, no problems arise in the traditional use of copper nails and clips as fixings for lead, and there is wide experience of the satisfactory use of lead flashings with aluminium glazing bars.

Extensive tests have been carried out to monitor the effect of run-off from lead to aluminium (and vice versa) in industrial, rural and exposed marine environments. Tests have also simulated crevice corrosion conditions. The results showed that in all environments – except marine – there was no significant increase in the aluminium corrosion rate when in contact with lead.

In the marine location, however, the chemical reaction between the lead oxide on the surface of the lead and the sodium chloride in salt water creates a caustic run-off which attacks aluminium, whether there is electrical contact or not. As severe corrosion can also occur in crevices, the use of lead sheet in juxtaposition with aluminium in marine environments is not recommended.

Compatibility with timber
Dilute solutions of organic acids from hardwoods, particularly oak, can cause lead to be slowly corroded. Where this cannot be avoided, designs should allow water to drain freely from the lead and not collect in pools on the surface.

This corrosion can be exacerbated in situations where condensation forms and takes up acid from the substrate. This potential problem, which is usually associated with old buildings, can be controlled by adequate ventilation and the use of a building paper underlay.

Investigation has shown that impregnation of softwoods with preservative and fire retardant solutions does not, in itself, increase the risk of corrosion. However, it is important to ensure that the substrate is dry before the lead sheet is laid.

Restoring historic lead sheet (superseded method)

Compatibility with sealants
Suitable sealants for joints between lead sheets and other materials are either polysulphide or silicone. Silicone sealants can accommodate greater movement and are available in two forms, acid cure and neutral cure. It is important to use only neutral cure silicone with lead work because acid cure can cause a white corrosion product to form on the surface of the lead.

Compatibility with concrete and mortars
Concretes and mortars made from Portland cement or lime can initiate a slow corrosive attack on lead in the presence of moisture. Direct contact between lead and new concrete or mortar should therefore be avoided. Lead sheet built into brickwork or concrete as a damp-proof course or impermeable membrane should be protected with a thick coat of bitumen paint.

When lead roof coverings and weatherings are applied to concrete surfaces, a sealing coat of hard-drying bitumen paint on the concrete, together with an underlay, gives adequate protection during the drying-out period.

Lichen and moss
Slow corrosion of lead by dilute organic acids can arise where there is lichen or moss growth on slated or tiled roofs. The rainwater picks up organic acid from the growth. At drip-off points, such as along a slated roof over a lead gutter lining, the acidic rainwater causes circular corrosion areas. After many years, this corrosion can penetrate through the lead.

Environmental impact
See **Unit 4.15**   ■

Further reading in the Guide:
4.15 Environmental impact • 15.1 Lead: general description

Critical factors

- Well established techniques and construction details have produced flat roofs which are satisfactory under traditional conditions.
- Lead may be laid on a variety of substructures, but timber is the most common.
- The choice of thickness of lead sheet will depend on joint spacing requirements and detailing considerations.

Selection

The appeal of lead is still strong today even though it now has to compete with cheaper materials less demanding of craftsmanship. It has particular advantages for flat roofs in the following circumstances:

- In areas where lead is established as a traditional roofing material.
- In areas where good corrosion resistance is required, for example, large cities, industrial areas and coastal belts.
- In buildings where the appearance of solidity and permanence are important characteristics.
- In buildings where materials will one day be re-cycled.
- In roofs where a visually strong pattern of joints is important.
- In roofs where a long life is intended.
- In roofs required to exclude or contain sound.
- In roofs required to exclude or contain ionising radiation.

The design and construction of fully supported lead sheet by roof coverings is covered in detail in *BS6915*.

The standard range of thicknesses, Code No. 3 to Code No. 8 (**see Unit 15.1**), will meet all normal needs in external leadwork – flashings, weatherings and roofing. Various factors need to be taken into account in choosing the best thickness to use for a specific application.

Generally, the thinnest lead sheet will outlast almost any roofing material, so far as atmospheric corrosion alone is concerned. Additional thickness is required in coping with thermal movement, for protection against mechanical damage, and to provide sufficient metal to dress, boss or leadweld the lead in shaping it.

The choice of joint spacings is related to the thickness of lead being used, as set out in Table 15.3.1.

Substructures

Most structural materials make suitable substrates for lead coverings. A smooth continuous surface, which is able to hold the necessary fixings, is an essential requirement. In practice, timber substructures are most common. Timber boards should be well seasoned. They should be wrought, tongued and grooved to give good resistance to warping. They should either be laid diagonally or in the direction of the fall.

Table 15.3.1
Joint spacings for lead sheet

Maximum spacing of joints for roof slopes up to and including 10°		
Thickness Code No. (see *BS1178*)	Joints across fall (mm)	Joints with fall (mm)
8	750	3000
7	675	2500
6	675	2250
5	600	2000
4	500	1500

Application

Underlays

The lead sheets are laid on a low friction, non-bonding interlayer, on a smooth deck, so that they are relatively free to move. They are kept in position by fixings across the top of each sheet and, when using wood-cored rolls, additional fixings in the top third of the undercloak. These fixings hold the sheets permanently in position while still allowing the lead to move freely when subjected to changes in temperature. This avoids over-stressing and fatigue, provided, of course, that the sheet size is compatible with the thickness (see *BS6915*, clause 5.1.2).

Traditionally, an impregnated felt complying with *BS747* Type 4A No.2 has been used as an underlay for lead. This has proved satisfactory on boarded, concrete and masonry surfaces provided that the type of felt used does not soften under solar head. This softening can cause bonding between the lead and the substrate thereby hindering free movement of the lead covering and making it vulnerable to thermal fatigue.

Building paper to *BS1521* Class A is a suitable underlay when the surface of the substrate is even and smooth, e.g. plywood.

An alternative underlay, recommended where there is any risk of condensation or moisture forming under lead work, is non-woven needle-punched polyester geotextile. This material will not rot if condensation does occasionally form under the lead and will also allow the air that circulates below the substrate to dry out moisture under the lead more readily. Geotextile underlays should have a weight of not less than 210g/m² (–5%).

Further reading:
BS6915 Specification for the design and construction of fully supported lead sheet roof and wall coverings • LSA Control of lead at work.

- Choice of underlay material between lead sheet and the supporting deck should be carefully considered.
- The use of lead on sites is coupled by the *Control of Lead at Work Regulations*

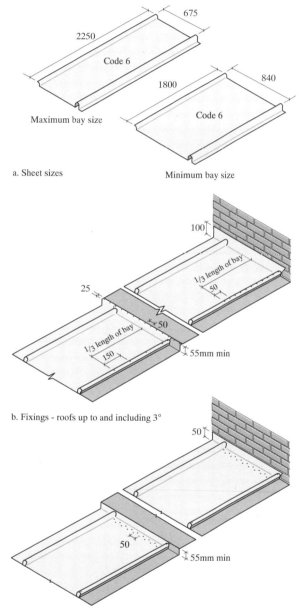

a. Sheet sizes

Maximum bay size

Minimum bay size

2250

675

Code 6

1800

840

Code 6

b. Fixings - roofs up to and including 3°

100

25

1/3 length of bay

50

50

1/3 length of bay

150

55mm min

c. Fixings - roofs above 3° up to and including 10°

50

50

55mm min

Figure 15.3.1
Sheet size and fixing key

Spacing of joints

Table 15.3.1 shows a fundamental principle for all sheet lead work: the thinner the lead, the smaller the piece. Situations sometimes occur where the length of a bay is less than the recommended maximum and, in these cases the width may be increased so that the bay is about the same area. For example, Figure 15.3.1a shows the maximum bay size when using Code 6 lead sheet. If the length is reduced to 1800mm, the girth can be increased to 840mm to provide a bay of about the same area. It is important to remember, however, that wood rolls are designed to prevent wind uplift as well as to allow for thermal movement. Therefore, in exposed positions, the width of bays should not be increased, as this could result in the lead lifting between the rolls during storm conditions. It is also very important that the length should never be increased beyond the maximum recommended for each code of lead even if the width is less than that recommended. Failure to observe these limits may result in fatigue induced cracking.

Methods of fixing

With roofs up to and including 3°, each bay of lead sheet is held in position by nailing the undercloak into a rebate in the drip at the top and nailing the undercloak to the wood roll at 150mm centres for the top third of its length, (Figure 15.3.1b). This method of fixing will hold the bay firmly and permanently in position while still allowing the sheet to move freely when subjected to changes in temperature. At abutments, the top of the bay is turned up against the wall. In this situation fixings, which should be spaced at 50mm centres in the top third of the roll, are sufficient to hold the bay in position.

For roof pitches over 3° however, experience has shown that these methods of fixing will not prevent the lead from moving downwards by gravity and, therefore, extra fixings will be required as shown in (Figure 15.3.1c). At drips, it is not necessary to turn the undercloak into a rebate at the top. The turn-up at abutments should be not less than 50mm. The splash laps or cover flashings at drips and abutments are extended to cover the copper nail fixings. As water will infiltrate the fixing area, it will be necessary to seal the nailheads by solder dabs or lead welding.

continued ▶

A ridge roll before capping.

Lead upstand around a rooflight, with welded corner mitre.

Welded roll end at abutment

Deep sided gutter with bossed roll ends.

Fixings in joints

Copper or stainless steel clips are incorporated into rolls, welts and standing seams to retain the lead work in position and to prevent the bays or panels from lifting under wind pressure or suction. Normally, the clips are spaced at 450mm centres, but may need to be closer in very exposed positions. Each clip is fixed to the substrate with three nails or two screws, and 0.6mm copper or 0.38mm stainless steel is an adequate thickness to use for most situations. However, in very exposed positions, a thicker material is recommended. When forming welts or standing seams, it is important not to dress the clip area too tightly, as this can cause the clip position to be seen on the surface of the lead.

Fixings on free edges

The free edges of lead work must be 'adequately clipped' to prevent lifting and distortion in high wind conditions. Adequate clipping will depend on the location, orientation and exposure of the building. In turn, these factors will determine the material used for the clips, their spacing and – most importantly – their method of fixing.

Table 15.3.2
Drip heights

Code	Minimum drip height (mm)
4	50
5	50
6	50
7	60
8	60

Drip

A drip is used across the fall of flat roofs, up to and including 10°, in conjunction with the wood-cored roll running with the fall. Drips are also used in lead-lined box, parapet and centre valley gutters. The height of a drip should normally be between 50mm and 65mm, depending on the thickness of lead sheet used for the roof covering or gutter lining.

In the past, 40mm drips incorporating an anti-capillary groove were sometimes used. Experience has shown that these grooves become ineffective, owing to the collection of atmospheric dust, etc., which make them vulnerable to water penetration in storm conditions. Also, 40mm drips are unsuitable for roll/drip abutments.

Roll/drip intersections

Rolls on the upper and lower roof areas at a drip can be either staggered or fixed in line. In either case, it is important that the finished roll height is not less than about 5mm below the height of the drip. To achieve this when using a standard 45mm high roll, the drip height will vary according to the thickness of lead sheet used. Table 15.3.2 shows the minimum drip height for Codes 4 to 8.

Safety issues

The *Control of Lead at Work Act* and the supporting Approved Code of Practice relate to the precautions required to protect people who are exposed to lead arising from work activities.

In most cases the use of lead sheet in building does not create a significant exposure to lead, although it is essential not to eat, drink or smoke in a place liable to be contaminated by lead and it is important to wash hands, arms and face thoroughly at the end of each working session.

When lead welding is carried out for short periods of time in the open air there is no significant hazard, but when stripping old lead sheet, where the underside is heavily corroded, or when lead welding in unventilated conditions additional precautions must be observed.

Further information is contained in the booklet *Control of Lead at Work*, available from the Lead Sheet Association.

Critical factors

15.4   Design details

- The nature and detailing of lead roofs is significantly different to that for the organic membranes.
- The information in this Unit provides guidance on the principles of detail design and specific examples of common conditions. **Unit 9.1** gives guidance on the broader performance principles of detailed design.

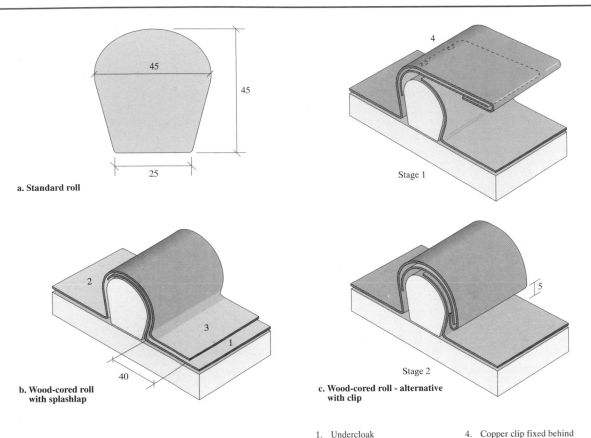

a. Standard roll

b. Wood-cored roll with splashlap

c. Wood-cored roll - alternative with clip

Stage 1

Stage 2

Fig 15.4.1
Wood cored roll jointing

1. Undercloak
2. Overcloak
3. Splash lap
4. Copper clip fixed behind undercloak
5. 5mm gap

Fixing methods

Wood-cored roll

This joint is suitable for flat roofing. Standard roll dimensions are shown in Figure 15.4.1a but bigger rolls are sometimes used to give a bolder appearance. The undercut at the base of the roll is designed to resist wind-uplift.

For flat roofing, the wood roll is the accepted joint, since it is not easily damaged by foot traffic. The undercloak is turned well over the top of the roll and then nailed to the roll, not more than one third of the length of the bay starting from the head. The overcloak is dressed fully over the roll and extended as a splash lap, which serves to stiffen the free edge and keep it in position (Figure 15.4.1b).

When using Codes 7 and 8 for flat roofing, in sheltered to moderate exposures, the traditional splash lap can be omitted and the overcloak finished about 5mm above the roof surface. However, in these cases, it will be necessary to extend the undercloak at the roll end to achieve an adequate lap.

An alternative wood-cored roll (Figure 15.4.1c) which is suitable for roofing is used when the splash lap is undesirable for aesthetic reasons. When using Codes 4-6 lead sheet, the splash lap is omitted and the edge of the overcloak welted around copper clips fixed behind the undercloak at 450mm centres.

• For clarity in the details, the underlay has been omitted.

Wood cored roll

With a 45mm roll, 75mm is added to the width of the bay for the undercloak and 175mm for the overcloak if there is a splash lap or 135mm for the overcloak if the splash lap is omitted. These measurements will allow for trimming of the overcloak to achieve a clean line along the free edge.

When using the alternative roll detail, the undercloak should finish at the top of the roll so that the copper nails do not penetrate the undercloak and cause a restriction on thermal movement. For this detail, an allowance of 65mm is made for the undercloak and 145mm for the overcloak.

Hollow roll

This joint can be used for flat roofs although it is more suitable for pitched roof coverings where laps are used for the joints across the fall and where there are few abutments or complicated joint intersections. To form a hollow roll, the undercloak is turned up 100mm, and 50mm wide copper clips – which have been previously fixed down the line of the roll at 450mm maximum centres – are turned over the top of the undercloak. The overcloak is turned up 125mm and the edge welted over the undercloak. The prepared and clipped upstand is then turned to form the hollow roll.

Drips

For roofs up to and including 3°, the undercloak is rebated into the timber substrate and nailed at 50mm intervals (see Figure 15.4.2a) However, where the pitch is over 3°, the fixings should be positioned (see Figure 15.4.2b) to prevent the roofing bays from slipping downwards. In these cases, it is not necessary to rebate the undercloak; but, to prevent water penetration through the fixing points the nails should be sealed over with a soldered or lead welded dot and the splash lap extended to conceal the fixings.   *continued* ▶

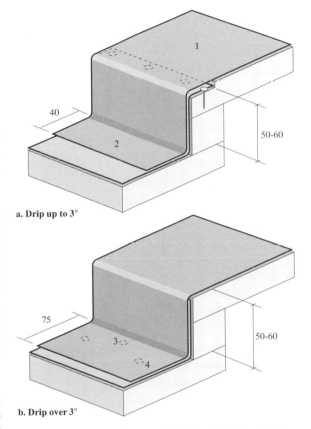

a. Drip up to 3°

b. Drip over 3°

1. Fixings on top of upstand
2. 40mm splash lap
3. Fixing soldered or welded over
4. Minimum 75mm splash lap

**Fig 15.4.2
Standard drip**

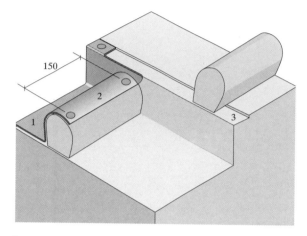

a.

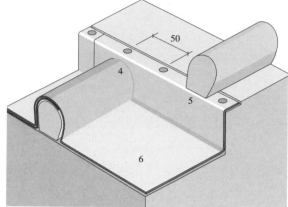

b.

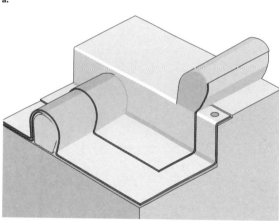

c.

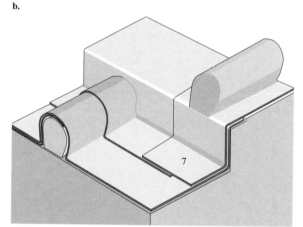

d.

Fig 15.4.3
Roll drip abutment: bossed staggered rolls up to 3°

1. Undercloak of lower bay	5. Splayed roll end
2. Fixings on top of roll	6. Overcloak of lower bay
3. Rebate	7. 40mm splash lap
4. Top of roll 5mm lower than drip height	

Roll/drip abutments – bossed

With lead-covered roofs having a pitch of 3° up to and including 10°, extra fixings are required to hold the bays firmly and permanently in position. As water will infiltrate the fixing area, it is necessary to seal the nailheads with solder or lead welding. For aesthetic reasons, the fixing area is covered by extending the splash lap to at least 75mm.

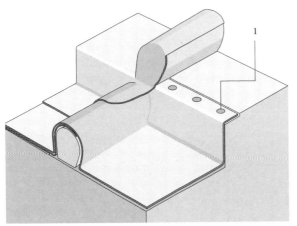

a. Undercloak of upper bay in position

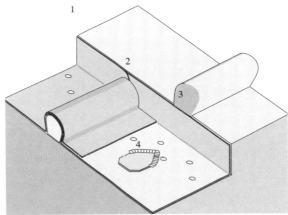

a. Lower bays in position

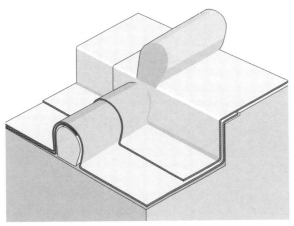

b. Completed work

1.Copper nails

Fig 15.4.4
Roll drip abutment: bossed rolls in line up to 3°

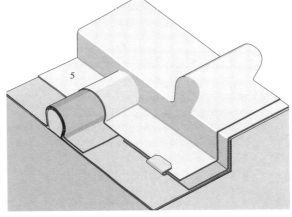

b. Completed roll/drip intersection

1. Upstand finished at top edge of drip
2. Top of roll 5mm lower than drip height
3. Splayed roll end
4. Lead clip welded to lower bay
5. 75mm splash lap to cover nail fixings

Fig 15.4.5
Roll drip abutment: bossed rolls 3°-10°

© BFRC / CIRIA: Flat Roofing: Design and Good Practice. 1993

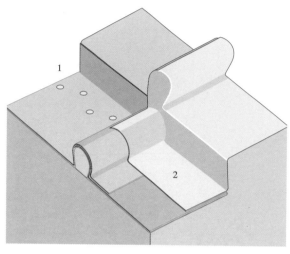

a. Undercloak of upper bay in position

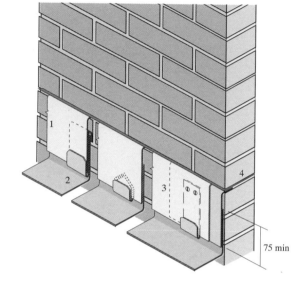

1. Lead flashing
2. Clips at 200mm to 450mm centres depending on exposure
3. 100-150mm lap at joints
4. Cavity tray

75 min

Fig 15.4.7
Cover flashings: roof pitches up to 3° – alternative clips

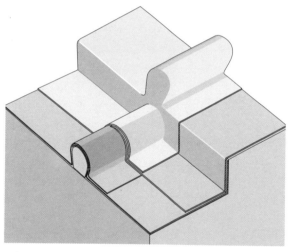

b. Completed work

1. Nail heads welded over
2. 75mm splash lap to cover nail fixings

Fig 15.4.6
Roof drip abutment-bossed rolls in line 3°-10°

Cover flashings at abutments 0°-3°

The type of flashing used at a horizontal abutment depends on the roof pitch. For roof pitches up to and including 3°, the bay is turned up at least 100mm against the wall and the flashing covers this upstand by 75mm minimum. Individual pieces of cover flashing should not exceed 1.5m in length, with laps between pieces not less than 100 mm. In severe exposures, the lap should be increased to 150mm. The top edge of the flashing is turned into a chase or groove in the masonry, not less than 25mm deep, and secured with lead wedges about 450mm apart. Clips are required along the lower edge at laps and not more than 500mm centres (Figure 15.4.7. Three alternative clips are shown).

Chapter	1	2	3	4	5	6	7	8	9	10	11
Contents	Introduction	History	Regulatory Methods	Principles	Surveys	Constraints & Targets	Design Selection	Calculations	Detail Design Principles	Evaluation of Design	Built-up Roofing
Page	1	19	31	45	83	95	105	165	189	217	221

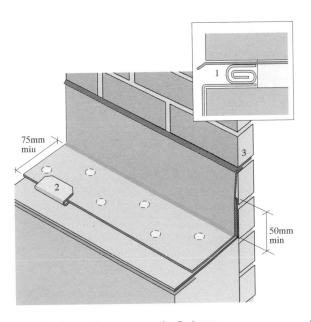

75mm min

50mm min

1. Lead wedges at 450mm maximum centres
2. 1 or 2 clips between rolls depending on exposure
3. Cavity tray

Fig 15.4.8
Cover flashings: roof pitches 3°-10°

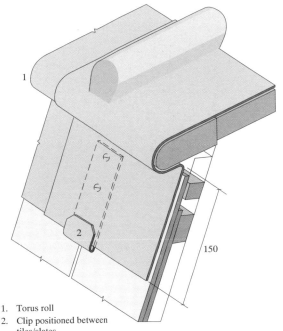

150

1. Torus roll
2. Clip positioned between tiles/slates

Fig 15.4.9
Flat roof junction with pitched roof

Cover flashings and abutments 3°-10°

For roof pitches above 3°, up to and including 10°, the flashing is extended to cover the fixings at the top of the roofing bays. Because this extension provides extra weathering, the upstand of the roofing bays can be reduced to not less than 50mm. Again, the flashing length must not exceed 1.5m with 100mm minimum laps between pieces. Lead clips, welded to the roofing bays, should be spaced along the free edge to suit the exposure.

Flat roof junction with pitched roof

Torus rolls are often used at the junction between a lead-covered flat roof and a mansard roof. Where a wood-cored roof finishes over a torus roll, the roll end is bossed or welded, but extra allowances are required for the turn down. This will depend on the size of the torus roll and the materials used for covering the mansard slope.

Where the extension down the mansard exceeds 150mm a separate flashing is used with a minimum cover of 100mm.

Although the spacing and fixing of clips along the free edge of all lead work is important, clips are particularly necessary below a torus roll because they also prevent the lead from sagging away from the underside of the roll.

© BFRC / CIRIA: Flat Roofing: Design and Good Practice. 1993

1
2
5
9
3
4
6
7
8

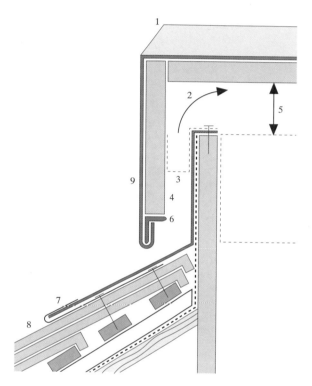

1. Splayed roll end
2. Ventilation through gap
3. Wire mesh screen
4. Minimum gap 25mm
5. Minimum gap 50mm
6. Continuous aluminium angle or fixing clip
7. Apron flashing (maximum 1.5m long) lapped 150mm onto pitched element
8. Copper or stainless steel clips 300-500mm centres
9. Overlap 75-100mm depending on exposure

Fig 15.4.10
Flat roof junction with pitched roof (ventilated)
The introduction of ventilation may be required at this point with a continuous 25mm ventilation slot between tiled/slated roof and lead flat roof.

100mm min
50mm min
225mm min
1. Tilting fillet
2. Underlay
3. Lead flashing
2
1
3
150mm max
75mm min

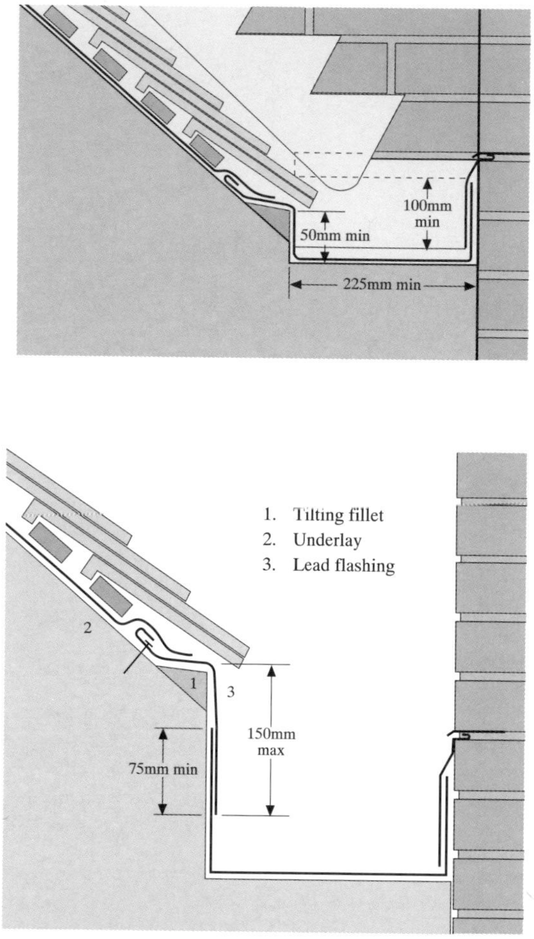

Fig 15.4.11
Pitched roof junction with box gutter
For practical reasons of construction, box gutters should not be less than 225mm wide and no less than 50mm deep at the highest point. The lead should be carried up the roof slope an additional height of 50mm to ensure an effective depth of 100mm.

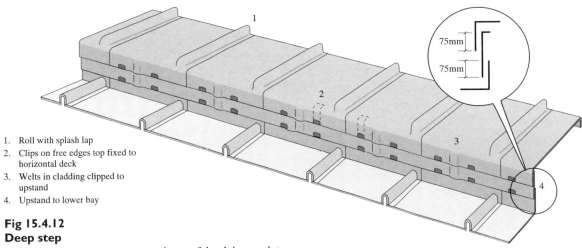

1. Roll with splash lap
2. Clips on free edges top fixed to horizontal deck
3. Welts in cladding clipped to upstand
4. Upstand to lower bay

Fig 15.4.12
Deep step

With deep steps a separate piece of lead is used to weather between the lower and upper levels. The upper, overlapping piece in each case, must lap the lower piece by a minimum of 75mm.

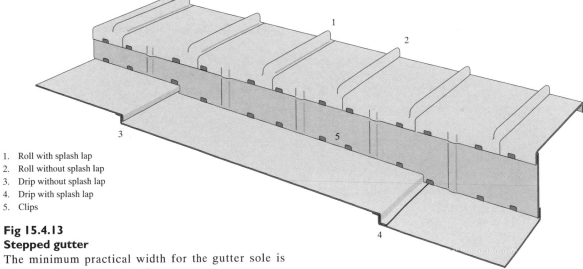

1. Roll with splash lap
2. Roll without splash lap
3. Drip without splash lap
4. Drip with splash lap
5. Clips

Fig 15.4.13
Stepped gutter

The minimum practical width for the gutter sole is 150mm if the gutter is tapered.

The number and spacing of clips will depend on the exposure criteria.

Step drips in the gutter should be a minimum of 50mm with or without splashlaps. However where rolls are used to divide wide tapering gutters the drip heights must be as Table 15.3.2. The drawing shows the configuration with and without splashlaps. The splash laps can only be omitted in sheltered conditions.

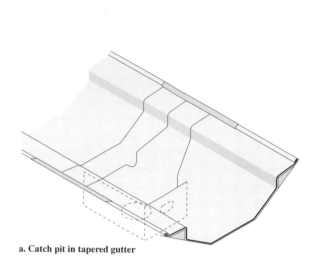

a. Catch pit in tapered gutter

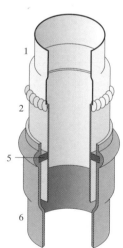

1.   Lead pipe
2.   Brass or copper sleeve
3.   Patent connector

4.   Cast iron downpipe
5.   Neoprene sealing ring
6.   Plastic downpipe

Fig 15.4.14
Downpipe connection to catchpit

In both conditions of the direct connection of the downpipe it is important that allowance for movement is given and the pipework adequately supported. A tapered connection is preferred.

The catchpit should always be equal to the width of the gutter sole.

b. Connection of downpipes

Chapter	1	2	3	4	5	6	7	8	9	10	11
Contents	Introduction	History	Regulatory Methods	Principles	Surveys	Constraints & Targets	Design Selection	Calculations	Detail Design Principles	Evaluation of Design	Built-up Roofing
Page	*1*	*19*	*31*	*45*	*83*	*95*	*105*	*165*	*189*	*217*	*221*

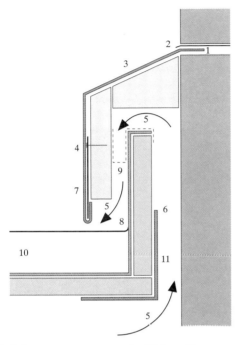

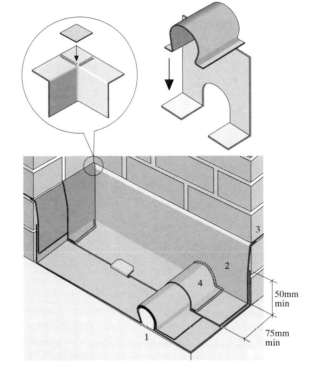

1. Cavity tray
2. Lead turn-in
3. Lead flashing maximum 1.5m lengths
4. Copper or stainless steel clips 300-500mm centres
5. Air flow
6. Minimum 25mm gap
7. Overlap 75mm-100mm
8. 150mm upstand
9. Wire mesh screed
10. Roll
11. Support angle

1. Roll with splash lap
2. Welded flashing
3. Cavity tray
4. Flashing cut over roll

Fig 15.4.15
Cover flashing at abutment – accommodating movement and ventilation
With roof pitches up to and including 3°, the upstand against this work should not be less than 100mm. The undercloak is nailed to the roll for the top third of the bay.

Fig 15.4.16
Corner abutment: 3°-10°
At an internal corner the flashing is cut to suit the roof pitch and welded with a lapped joint. A square gusset is inserted in the corner of the turn in.

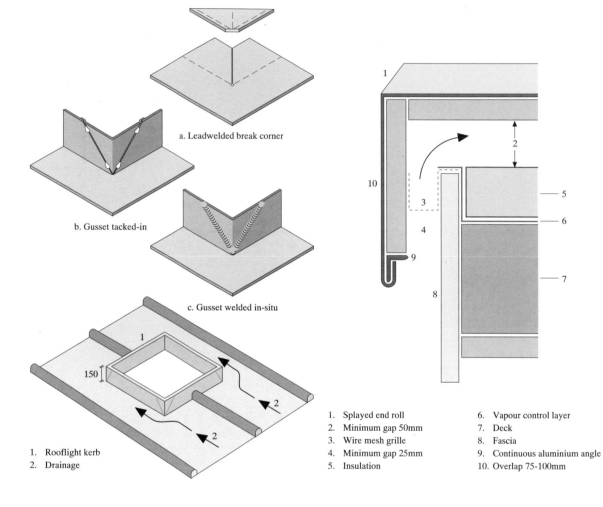

a. Leadwelded break corner

b. Gusset tacked-in

c. Gusset welded in-situ

150

1

2

2

1. Rooflight kerb
2. Drainage

1

10

2

3

4

9

8

5

6

7

1. Splayed end roll
2. Minimum gap 50mm
3. Wire mesh grille
4. Minimum gap 25mm
5. Insulation

6. Vapour control layer
7. Deck
8. Fascia
9. Continuous aluminium angle
10. Overlap 75-100mm

Fig 15.4.17
Rooflight abutment
It is important to avoid two rolls on the uphill side of the rooflight to abut the kerb, since this will cause flooding. If this is unavoidable, a back platform with a crossfall will be required. The lead can be turned over and nailed on the upstand kerbs.

Fig 15.4.18
Ventilated eaves

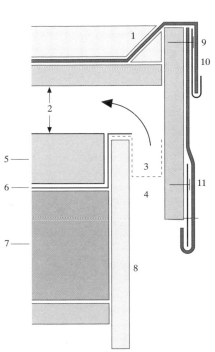

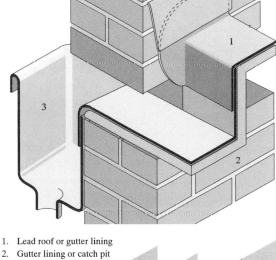

1. Lead roof or gutter lining
2. Gutter lining or catch pit
3. Hopper

1. Upstand fillet
2. Minimum gap 50mm
3. Wire mesh grille
4. Minimum gap 25mm
5. Insulation
6. Vapour control layer
7. Deck
8. Fascia

9. Copper or stainless steel clips at 300-500mm centres
10. Fascia cladding fixed with copper nails (75mm centres)
11. Overlap 75mm-100mm

Fig 15.4.19
Ventilated verge

It is important to note that water side flows will be limited by the roll discipline such that rainwater from one bay width only would be blown off a verge. The problem is therefore generally less than that provided for continuous waterproof membranes.

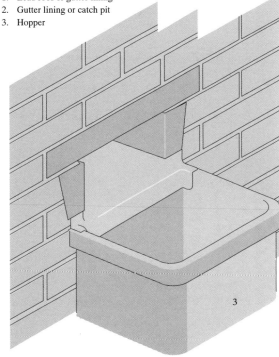

Fig 15.4.20
Chute

The opening for the hole is normally 150mm high with the lead dressed into the hopper head. ■

12 Mastic Asphalt	13 Polymeric Single Ply	14 Copper	15 Lead Sheet	16 Other Membranes	17 Thermal Insulants	18 Specification	19 Contracts & Procurement	20 Inspection	21 Maintenance	22 Bibliography	23 Index
263	301	331	353	375	383	393	399	413	429	437	455

Other membranes 16

16.1   Zinc

- Zinc is a traditional roofing material with a well developed vocabulary of use.
- The two grades now available give better properties with respect to creep resistance (Type A) and malleability for flashing work (Type B).
- Being harder, zinc is more difficult to work than lead, but the established detailing methods allow for this.

General Description

Zinc sheet for flat roofing has a long history. It was much used in the late 19th and early 20th centuries, as it provided a lightweight, relatively durable, yet widely available material.

The weathered matt grey appearance of zinc is considered by some to be less attractive than lead or copper. The material has, therefore, been viewed as more utilitarian. It can, however, been seen in many pitched, mansard and flat roofing applications in cities such as London and, particularly, Paris, where it remains popular in both new and remedial applications.

With its long history of use, there are well developed methods of working the material and executing the details. The relevant code of practice is *CP143: Part 5*. Although published in 1964, it remains current.

The relatively small use of zinc for flat roofing in recent years does mean that there is little feedback from 'non-traditional' applications which are not covered by the code. Care would be required to ensure that the material was used in a way that was appropriate to its characteristics. Advice should be sought.

Zinc for roofing applications used to be of ordinary commercial quality, with 98.5% purity, produced to *BS894*. This has now been superseded by material to *BS 6561*. Two grades of electrolytically refined zinc of higher purity are specified. Type A, a zinc/titanium alloy, has adequate creep strength and fatigue resistance for roofing applications. Type B, a zinc/lead alloy, is soft enough for it to be worked on site into flashing sections.

Zinc is available in sheet or strip. A minimum thickness of 0.7mm is used for roofing; 0.8mm is recommended for cladding and fascias. Various strip widths are available, particularly for Type B material. Lengths for individual strips of roofing material should not exceed 10m.

Performance in use

Zinc is non-combustible and will not contribute to fire spread. It achieves an AA rating to *BS476: Part 3*.

Zinc weathers to a distinct dull grey, which is quite different in colour to the natural colour of aluminium or lead. An adherent, protective layer of (mainly) basic zinc carbonate is formed. This is not dissolved by rainwater, unless it is acidic.

The life expectancy of zinc roof sheeting is related to the thickness and the exposure conditions. It is reasonable to expect a life in excess of 25 years. This relates to experience in urban areas. Assessing its life expectancy in a specific environment will not be easy, as the classifications 'urban', 'rural,' etc. are not good guides to the acidity of rainfall. A useful publication on which durability judgments can be based is a map produced by the Ministry of Agriculture Food and Fisheries and reproduced in the Zinc Development Association's *The Galvanisers' Guide*. It shows corrosion rates of zinc throughout the UK. It is updated at intervals, so care should be taken to obtain the most up-to-date version. Significant condensation (see **Unit 4.7**) forming on the underside of zinc roof sheets can lead to rapid corrosion. (See **Unit 15.1** for discussion of this problem in relation to lead roofs.)

Further reading:
CP143: Part 5 Code of practice for sheet roof and wall coverings. Zinc • BS656: Specification for zinc alloy sheet and strip for building • ZDA The Galvaniser's Guide.

- Durability is governed by thickness and exposure; acidic rainwater and the run off from some materials, notably copper and acidic timbers, is detrimental.

Application and design

Details of the traditional methods of laying zinc sheet are given in *CP143: Part 5*. The code covers the types of substructure, the use of underlays and details of the laying techniques involved. Diagrams are provided to show the essentials of the laying methods.

The coefficient of thermal expansion of zinc is greater than that of copper, but slightly less than lead. Care is therefore required to ensure that thermal movement can be accommodated. The traditional details given in the code of practice allow for this. It should be noted that these do not cover the use of thermal insulation immediately below the zinc, which would have the effect of increasing the thermal stressing of the zinc.

Although softer than aluminium, zinc is relatively hard compared to lead. It is less malleable than copper. There is now a preference for machine-forming the folds off-site, to ensure straightness.

The most common method of forming longitudinal joints between sheets is the roll cap system, using timber battens. Sheets may be soldered together up to 6m lengths. Strip material, of Type A, may be laid in longer lengths, depending on the strip width. Transverse joints are formed by a drip detail at a 65mm (minimum) step in the deck.

Fixings and ancillary metalwork are usually of galvanised steel. Nails which have been given a thick zinc coating by hot dip galvanising are preferred. Sheradising gives a thinner coating, and thus less protection; electroplating can only be considered for relatively temporary applications on roofs.

Technical information

Typical physical and mechanical properties are given in Table 16.1.1. ■

Table 16.1.1
Typical physical and mechanical properties of zinc

Properties	Zinc/titanium alloy type A (all applications)	Zinc/lead alloy type B (mainly flashings)
Physical		
Density (g/cm³)	7.2	7.2
Melting point (°C)	418 - 419	419.0
Coarse grain formation Temperature (°C)	>300	>180
Coefficient of thermal expansion ($\times 10^{-6}$°C)	21	29
Mechanical		
Tensile strength (MPa)		
Longitudinal	150 to 170	110 to 140
Transverse	200 to 220	140 to 170
Elongation		
Longitudinal	40 to 60	50 to 60
Transverse	20 to 25	40 to 50
Typical hardness (HV1)	40 to 45	33 to 36
Creep strength for 1% elongation/year at 20 ± 2 °C (MPa)	50 min	

Critical factors

- Dimensional constraints of the sheet sizes and jointing methods.
- Materials compatibility.
- Care required with non-traditional applications.

Further reading in the Guide:
4.7 Condensation • 15.1 Lead: general description

- Aluminium is available in narrow strips (450mm) for roofing, but can be used in lengths up to 7m between cross joints.
- Traditional details can be used, with the right grades of aluminium, but machine forming of seams is also an option.

Aluminium

General description

Although the first known use for aluminium in roofing dates from 1897, its more general use in this area is relatively recent. The use of aluminium for roofing is covered by *CP143: Part 15*.

Aluminium sheeting is laid in narrower strips between upstanding joints than is usual for the more traditional roofing metals. This gives it a distinct form, which it shares with stainless steel. The basic sheet width is 450mm and thickness 0.8mm, but wider strip widths are now available.

The code of practice recognises five grades of aluminium as suitable for roofing. Since it was last revised, the nomenclature for aluminium and its alloys has been changed. This is shown in Table 16.2.1. The most commonly used grade is 1050 A.

Design and application

Both the standing seam and batten roll jointing systems can be used with aluminium. The general principles are the same as for other metals. Joints across the fall, using the traditional 'drip' detail, should not exceed 3m spacing. A variation on the standing seam system is the long strip method, which enables lengths of up to 7m between drips.

Fixings are made using materials of aluminium or stainless steel. In some less demanding applications, galvanised steel nails are accepted.

Technical information

Aluminium comes in different conditions (temper), 'O' fully soft, H2 and H4, which are two grades of hardness. H4 material is only for use with machine formed seams. Table 16.2.1 also gives the recommended temper conditions for the different grades in the most common uses. Examples of the typical mechanical and physical properties of aluminium are given in Tables 16.2.2.

Table 16.2.1.
Grades of aluminium and recommended tempers

| Material and grade in accordance with *BS1470* | International system nomenclature | Thickness (mm) | Temper | | Standing seam and batten roll systems (traditional practice) |
| | | | Longstrip system | | |
			Hand formed	Machine formed	
S1 99.99 grade aluminium	No equivalent	0.8	H2	H2	H2
S1A 99.8 grade aluminium	1080A	0.8	O	H2	O
S1B 99.5 grade aluminium	1050A	0.8	O	H2	O
S1C 99 grade aluminium	1200	0.8	O	H2	O
NS3 aluminium alloy (0.8% to 1.5% manganese)	3103	0.8	O	H2	O

Performance in use

Aluminium is corrosion-resistant, but like zinc is affected by contact with, or run-off from, the same materials such as copper and acidic timbers.

The normal surface condition for aluminium is the 'mill finish'. No surface finish is required for durability, but factory applied coatings may be used for appearance reasons, if the weathered matt silver grey is not appropriate. The tones of grey of the weathered finish will vary in different locations and on different orientations on the same building.

Table 16.2.2
Physical properties of 1200 grade aluminium

Density	2710 kg/m^3
Melting point	658 °C (= 931K)
Specific heat (0 °C to 100 °C)	0.917 kJ/(kg K)
Coefficient of linear expansion	24 x 10^{-6} °C (between 20 °C and 100 °C)
Thermal conductivity	226 W/(m K)

Further reading:
CP143: Part 15 Aluminium • BS1449: Part 2 Specification for stainless and heat-resisting steel plate, sheet and strip

- Stainless steel is potentially the most durable roofing metal, but experience of its use in the UK is still limited.

- Traditional details can be used with stainless steel, but greater skill and experience is required.

Stainless steel

General description
Stainless steel is a relatively new material for roofing, although early examples can be found from the 1920s. Its inherent corrosion resistance offers the prospects of very durable roof covering. However, its high apparent price and greater difficulty of working still limit its application. It is used in much thinner sheet than any of the other metals (0.38 and 0.46mm). The normal coil width is 460mm, but wider sheets are now available and sheet lengths up to 15m are possible.

The ductility and tensile strength of stainless steel make it more resistant than other roofing metals to the stresses associated with thermal movements and to the consequent fatigue problems.

There is no code of practice covering the use of this material for roofing.

Performance in use
It is important to distinguish the issues of surface staining and basic corrosion resistance when dealing with stainless steel. Despite its name, most grades of the material are not 'stainless' in external exposures. Of the grades used for roofing, only Type 316 will remain reasonably stain free. The others will show surface discolouration that will vary in different atmospheres. In some cases it can look distinctly 'rusty'.

These surface effects do not indicate that corrosion is occurring which will compromise the integrity of the sheet, in normal atmospheres. However, in marine environments, chlorides are present, which can produce forms of pitting corrosion. This can lead to penetration of the sheet. With the details used for metal roofs, there must be a danger of significant chloride concentrations accumulating at some of the joint folds. This could limit the life of the material in marine locations, and care should be taken before specifying the material.

Stainless steel is not susceptible to problems from contact with, or run-off from, other materials.

Design and application
In the absence of a code of practice specifically for stainless steel, the general principles of those for zinc (CP143: Part 5) and aluminium (CP143: Part 15) may be followed (see Unit 16.1).

Table 16.2.3
Roofing grades of stainless steel

Type	
304 S16	Standard quality, 18% chromium, 10% nickel alloy
316 S16	2.5% molybdenum in addition to chromium and nickel, for greater durability
Surface finishes	
2D	Cold rolled, softened and descaled- a uniform matt finish
2B	Cold rolled, softened, descaled, lightly rolled on polishing rolls- a smooth finish for general applications, brighter than 2D
2A	Cold rolled, bright annealed- a reflective cold rolled finish

Table 16.2.4
Indicative physical properties of stainless steel

Density	7900 kg/m^3
Melting point	1400 °C
Coefficient of linear expansion	17 x 10^6 °C
Thermal conductivity	14.2 W/(m K)

Hand tools can be used to form the various welts and seams, but specialist skills are required for successful results. The roll cap system is normally easier to carry out than standing seams.

Fixings should be made from stainless steel. Soldering can be carried out to join sheets, but the degree of difficulty varies with the surface condition. Fluxes used with stainless steel are necessarily aggressive to the substrate. It is therefore essential that they are used sparingly and any excess is removed. Failure to do so can initiate localised corrosion.

Greater care is required in handling strips of stainless steel, particularly after they have been cut, compared to other roofing metals.

Technical information
BS1449: Part 2: 1983 gives the grades of stainless steel and the various surface finishes. The information relevant to flat roofing applications is summarised in Table 16.2.3. Some properties are given in Table 16.2.4. ∎

Critical factors

- Aluminium: contact with other materials or the run off from them.

- Stainless steel surfaces are not fully 'stainless'; surface staining should not be confused with damaging corrosion.

- Use of stainless steel in a marine environment requires special consideration.

Further reading in the Guide:
16.1 Zinc

16.3 Liquid applied membranes

- The term 'liquid membrane' covers a wide range of chemical types, with or without reinforcements for which no standards exist.
- The products are offered for both new work and for remedial applications.
- Agrément Certificates provide a source of detailed information on specific proprietary products.
- The performance of these materials is particularly sensitive to site conditions and workmanship.

General description

A further category of materials, different from any other described in this Guide, is the thin membrane that is formed insitu, known collectively as 'liquid applied membranes'. The idea of forming a seamless membrane from materials that can be brought to site in drums has certain attractions, but there are disadvantages as well as advantages, particularly in the control necessary to achieve a defect-free membrane of consistent thickness.

These materials are described briefly in this Unit.

A range of quite different materials and methods of application are covered by the generic description 'liquid applied membranes'. Reference should be made to the manufacturers for detailed information. Ten products carry current Agrément Certificates, and reference should be made to these for the relevant information.

Table 16.4.1 gives the summary descriptions taken from the Agrément Certificates.

- Some are reinforced over their whole area with either glass-fibre or polyester fleece.
- Others only use reinforcement over discontinuities in the substrate.
- Most are cold applied, but one involves hot application.
- One-component products avoid the need for mixing, but two part ones offer the more controlled chemical curing.
- Hybrid systems are available which combine sheet and liquid applied material. In one of these, the self-adhesive sheets are applied first, followed by a two-part sprayed modified bitumen.

These materials are offered both for new roofs and for remedial applications. Some are specifically targeted at the refurbishment market, where their ability to extend the life of asphalt and bitumen felt roofs can be advantageous in some circumstances.

Whilst normally used for flat roofs that are only accessible for maintenance, some systems are designed to receive traffic, for example, in car parks.

Table 16.3.1
Liquid membranes: system descriptions

A glass-fibre reinforced polyester resin, cold applied on site by the hand lay - up process.
Cold liquid applied, unsaturated polyester coating reinforced with a polyester fleece.
A single component, liquid applied, aliphatic polyurethane system for spray, roller or brush application.
A black, two-part, cold liquid applied, extended urethane roof waterproofing system, reinforced with a woven polyester scrim.
A one-component moisture-curing polyurethane elastomer, for use as a cold, liquid applied membrane.
A one-part, hot-applied rubberised bituminous membrane for use in protected roofing system.
A cold-applied, chemically curing two-part pitch-polyurethane compound for protected roofing.
A self-adhesive membrane coated on site with two-part self curing bitumen/polymer liquid (a hybrid system)

Note: The above descriptions are drawn from the Agrément Certificates for specific proprietary products.

© BFRC / CIRIA: Flat Roofing: Design and Good Practice. 1993

- The life expectancy most often quoted is ten years, but this can be exceeded by careful choice of material and detail of use.

Performance in use

Given the diverse range of materials covered in this section, it is not possible to give specific guidance on durability. In any case, the absence of standards means that the performance of each proprietary material must be evaluated, taking care that long-term data has not been invalidated by changes in formulation.

The best guides to life expectancy are to be found in the Agrément Certificates. A figure of 10 years is most commonly quoted. Some are thought to achieve longer lives, say 15 years, even when fully exposed. Others can survive longer in protected conditions, i.e. when not exposed to ultra violet light or extremes of temperature.

Substrate movement is a common cause of premature failure, even where reinforcing materials have been used. Difficulties of application at upstands and penetrations are another source of water penetration.

Design and application

Liquid systems are designed to be fully bonded to the substrate. Not all substrates are suitable for all the different materials. Their application to insulation materials can present problems and polystyrene is normally considered to be an unsuitable base. Some systems require specific primers for some substrates.

All systems require application in more than one layer, with two or three being most common. Reinforced systems have one layer of glass-fibre or polyester fleece. Some require substrate discontinuities to be treated with membrane and reinforcement before the main application. Others include this as part of the main application work.

The site conditions and weather during application can be critical. There are usually specific time constraints for one coat to follow another, if good inter-coat adhesion is to be obtained.

The quoted minimum finished thicknesses tend to be in the range 1 to 3mm. Thicknesses are often stated to surprising degrees of accuracy (e.g. 'the first layer should have a minimum thickness of 2.3mm'). A few products are designed to be applied more thickly.

Some materials are only suitable for use under protection, such as paving, screeds or ballasted insulation. Others have additional finish coats to provide non-slip surfaces in areas which may be trafficked.

The formation of a thin membrane on site requires great care, if pinholes and other defects which would disrupt the integrity of the membrane, are to be avoided. The high standard of workmanship that is needed is seen by many as a significant drawback, limiting the wider use of these systems.

From an assessment of the site conditions, the nature of the material being used, and the expected weather, the amount that can be covered in a day must be evaluated. Surface preparation should be thorough, bearing in mind that these are bonded systems. Given that the finished membranes are relatively thin, it is essential to ensure that grit and other contaminants are removed, so that they do not cause membrane defects.

For two-part materials, the pot life after mixing can be a limiting factor. Application times between coats must be within the limits stated by the suppliers.

The methods of application vary. Some products are offered in different grades to suit airless spray, trowelling or self-levelling. Others come in one grade which can be applied by spray, roller or brush.

Reinforcing materials are normally bedded in the first fully applied coat of the membrane. The techniques used are intended to ensure that the reinforcement is fully encapsulated in the first and second coats of the membrane. Care is required to ensure that trapped air is eliminated.

The execution of details at upstands and roof penetrations requires care. The systems vary in the approach used to deal with these situations. Many require additional reinforcement. Some use special grades of the material which are more easily applied on vertical surfaces.

The timing of the application of the membrane in relation to other site activities must be carefully considered, as many of the products are not robust and can be damaged relatively easily. ■

Critical factors

- Design should allow for the thin nature of the materials.
- Care must be taken that the application conditions are appropriate to the particular product being used.

Further reading in the Guide:

12 Mastic Asphalt	13 Polymeric Single Ply	14 Copper	15 Lead Sheet	16 Other Membranes	17 Thermal Insulants	18 Specification	19 Contracts & Procurement	20 Inspection	21 Maintenance	22 Bibliography	23 Index
263	301	331	353	375	383	393	399	413	429	437	455

Thermal insulants 17

17.1 Selection of insulants

- Many types of materials have useful insulating properties.
- Insulating materials can be classified in different ways, but such classifications can mask beneficial properties of individual insulants.
- The essential performance of insulants, when incorporated into a roof, is governed by more than just the thermal performance.

Types of materials

Insulating materials for incorporation into the roof can be formed from many types of materials and in different configurations. When considering such a diverse array of possible materials some designers may find it helpful to group them into categories so that, as far as possible, their general properties may be more easily compared. There are a number of different ways of categorising the available insulants, for example:

- foam/non-foam
- organic/inorganic
- natural/synthetic
- combustible/non-combustible
- environmentally friendly, or not
- single component/composite.

These various categorisations have varying advantages depending on the situation. There are dangers from such rigidity in approach which may mask individual characteristics of insulants. Designers may wish to make their comparison or selection using one of these, or other, categorisations. For this Guide no specific formal split into categories is proposed, although, where appropriate, properties which are common to more than one type are discussed together.

Some aspects of the properties and performance of insulants in a roof are given elsewhere in this Guide. The principles of thermal insulation and the effects on roofs are given in **Units 4.5 and 4.6**. A design selection procedure including consideration of the interactions with other roof components is shown in **Unit 7.6**. The calculations of thermal performance and of condensation risks are described in **Units 8.1 and 8.2**.

Insulation products

Unit 17.2 gives more information about the materials and products which make up the most commonly encountered insulants in flat roofing. The information in those units is based upon that available from manufacturers and British Standards. No attempt is made to list all the variations available within insulant types, nor the manufacturers producing such products. Listings of current manufacturers for each type of insulation can usually be found in trade catalogues or from the appropriate manufacturers associations.

The majority of insulation products will be used in slab or sheet form. Some products, however, combine other features such as the ability to be brought to site in roll form, which can increase installation speed. Others may have channels or depressions formed within them to allow ventilation or drainage. Such 'specials' are not discussed further in this Guide.

Comparison of thermal insulation products can be made using data from different sources including manufacturers, British Standards and Agrément Certificates, or from data contained in this Guide. The most specific data is that available from manufactures and should be used in any final, detailed, evaluation of the complete roofing system. More generalised data such as that reproduced here is usually sufficient to allow a selection and initial evaluation of the potential performance of a roof construction. Within specific product types where products are available from more than one manufacturing source e.g. polyurethane, the sources of raw materials and the nature of the manufacturing process can lead to differences in actual properties. This increases the importance for the designer to carry out any evaluation based upon manufacturers current data.

Factors for selection

Thermal performance

The key requirement when selecting an insulant to be incorporated in a roof is its thermal performance. Table 17.1.1 lists the more commonly encountered products and shows their approximate thermal conductivity values. It is useful to see at a glance the approximate thickness that might be needed to achieve certain U-values. Further general information on the types of insulant considered in this Guide is shown in Table 17.1.2 (overleaf).

continued ▶

Further reading:
BS3837: Part 1 Boards from expanded beads • BS4841: Part 3 Boards with auto-adhesively bonded facings for built-up roofs
BS3837: Part 2 Extruded polystyrene boards

- Selection of an insulant requires aspects of: thermal, mechanical, fire and possibly environmental considerations.
- Some insulant types are covered by British Standards.
- Insulation and energy savings are prominent in the environmental debate.

Table 17.1.1
Comparison of typical thermal properties of insulants.

Material	Fully aged thermal conductivity (W/mK) (design value used in U value calculation)	Density (kg/m³)	Approximate thickness for U value of 0.25W/m²K (WDRT)	0.45W/m²K (WDRC)
Rigid urethane foam[A]	0.025 (0.022)	30-40	75	41
Extruded polystyrene[A]	0.034 (0.028)	35	96	72[B]
Expanded polystyrene	0.033	24	113	62
Phenolic foam[A]	0.036	48	123	67
	0.025	48	86	46
Cellular glass	0.042	125	144	73
Mineral wool (rigid)	0.036	180	123	67
Perlite/fibre	0.055	175	188	102
Woodfibre	0.048	300	164	89
Cork	0.041	120	140	76
Foamed concrete	0.28	800	–	515

Notes:
(WDRC) Assumes warm deck roof on 150mm dense concrete deck with allowances for surface resistances, and vapour control layer and membrane.
(WDRT) Assumes warm deck roof on 20mm plywood deck with allowances for surface resistances, vapour control layer and membrane.

It is not implied that all insulants listed are suitable for this type of roof construction. The values are given for comparison purposes only.

[A] The thermal conductivity values of these foamed plastics may vary with differing blowing agents.
[B] Inverted roof on 150mm dense aggregate concrete roof with 50mm concrete paving plus allowance for water film at insulation.

Critical factors

- Selection on combination of properties.
- Balance of benefits for the environment.

Further reading in the Guide:
4.5 Thermal transmission • 4.6 Solar radiation and thermal effects • 7.6 Design for thermal performance • 8.2 Calculation of thermal performance • 17.2 Insulants: materials

Table 17.1.2
Comparison of principal characteristics of insulants

	British Standard	Density (kg/m³)	Thermal conductivity (W/mK)	10% compression strength (kPa)	Trough deck spanning (distance between crowns)
Rigid urethane foam	BS4841 pt 3	32–48	0.022-0.025[A]	175–205	See B.S.
Phenolic foam	—	48	0.025–0.036	175	—
Extruded polystyrene	BS3837 pt 2	32–34	0.028[A]	150–700	N/A
Expanded bead polystyrene	BS3837 pt 1	21–25	0.033 / 0.033	110 / 150	—
Mineral wool	—	180	0.036	120-180	2.0–2.5 × Thickness ≥ Span
Perlite	—	150–175	0.055	230–320	2.1–2.5 × Thickness ≥ Span
Cellular Glass	—	125	0.042	230-500	1.6–2.04 × Thickness ≥ Span
Cork	—	80-120	0.041	100-200	1.7–3.0 × Thickness ≥ Span

Notes:

This table is intended as a design aid only. It is not definitive and the properties for a specific insulant design should be checked with manufacturers.

The ranges of values shown are for products typically available and may not correspond to the ranges quoted in relevant British Standards.

Mechanical performance

Where the membrane is supported directly by the insulant, the insulant must be able to resist any imposed loads without causing distress to the membrane. A particular consideration in this may be the compression behaviour of insulants.

Compression loads on foamed plastics give three modes of deformation. Compression is initially by elastic deformation in the cell walls, subsequently buckling and collapse of the cells give a large increase in strain for little increase in load, finally the foam becomes a 'solid' and deformation continues within the plastic itself. This behaviour makes it inappropriate to use a true compression strength. Instead it is more common to quote a load for a given compression strain – usually 10%. Other non-foamed materials also use a similar approach to quoting compression resistance. The 10% compression loads are shown in Table 17.1.2.

Fire behaviour

Unit 7.9 discussed the design for fire behaviour of roofs and drew attention to shortcomings in the use of Approved Document notional fire ratings. Designers, clients, or others, may have perceptions about how various materials will behave in a fire. These may encompass: ease of ignition, rate of flame spread, smoke and possible toxic fume generation. The behaviour of an insulant alone can be modified considerably when incorporated into a roof. It is reasonable to conclude that all of the organic insulant materials will be in some way combustible. This may or may not be significant for the roof as a whole. Many of the foamed plastics materials may have fire retardant grades available or have tests in the relevant British Standards for fire resistance. This information is unlikely to be useful in flat roof design. Designers will need to discuss the particular behaviour with product manufacturers where appropriate.

Further reading:
BS3837: Part 1 Boards from expanded polystyrene beads • BS4841: Part 3 Rigid urethane boards with autoadhesively bonded facings for built-up roofs • BS3837: Part 2 Extruded polystyrene boards

Restriction to roof configuration?	Composite board available?	Membrane compatible	Moisture susceptible[C]	Cut to falls boards?	Environmental considerations[B]
Cold and warm decks only	Yes	Some grades not for asphalt Special facings for single ply	No	Yes	Effects of CFC blowing agents on atmosphere but non-CFC agents available
,,	Yes	Needs facing for single ply	No	Yes	,,
Inverted warm or cold deck only	Yes for finishes	All	No	No	,,
Cold and warm deck only	Yes	Care with some single ply, needs composite for mastic asphalt	No	Yes	Non CFC products available
No restriction	No	May need isolating board under asphalt	No	Yes	Non-renewable resource used
Cold and warm decks only	Yes	All	Need to keep dry	No	,,
,,	No	All	No	Yes	No CFC blowing agents
,,	Yes	All	No	Yes	Renewable resource in limited quantity

[A] Design values for use in thermal performance calculations.

[B] See text for further discussion.

[C] See Tables 7.7.1 and 8.3.2 for data on moisture transmission

Critical factors

- Consult manufacturers or suppliers.

Peel/lamination strength

The design of roofs to resist wind up-lift is described in **Units 7.10 and 8.4**. Where a roof construction is fully bonded the wind up-lift resistance has to be transmitted through the insulation. This requires a certain level of peel, lamination or tensile strength from the insulant. At present there are many different methods of determining such properties in British and other standards. As such it is not currently possible to give coherent advice on the performance of the range of insulants available. Manufacturers' advice on the most appropriate methods and properties should be sought, together with data from the performance of existing roofs.

Environmental considerations

'The environment' is a large subject and one which generates much debate about the effects of the building process on it. **Unit 4.15** describes some of the general issues and gives some introduction to the relevant aspects of insulants. A general conclusion is that the use of insulants to conserve energy, outweighs many of the disadvantages of depletion of resources. One particular issue is that of CFC blowing agents. These are used to create the bubbles in the plastic foam, and help to give the foam a low thermal conductivity (see **Unit 4.5**). In the past, some of the CFCs used had a high ozone depletion potential, with concerns about effects on the atmosphere. As the result of the Montreal Protocol the substitution of less potentially damaging agents has come about. There are still some concerns about the real effects of these ozone-friendly gases. It is important with all environmental concerns to assess real data rather than emotive statements. All materials use resources and energy in their recovery and manufacture. ■

Further reading in the Guide:
4.5 Thermal transmission • 4.6 Solar radiation and thermal effects • 7.6 Design for thermal performance • 8.2 Calculation of thermal performance • 17.2 Insulant materials

12 Mastic Asphalt	13 Polymeric Single Ply	14 Copper	15 Lead Sheet	16 Other Membranes	17 Thermal Insulants	18 Specification	19 Contracts & Procurement	20 Inspection	21 Maintenance	22 Bibliography	23 Index
263	301	331	353	375	383	393	399	413	429	437	455

17.2　Insulants: materials

- Many materials have useful insulating properties and are available as proprietary products.
- Foamed plastics insulants are perhaps the most widely used of the thermal insulants.

Many materials have useful insulating properties and are also available as proprietary products. Such products may have properties in common. Where products are of the same generic type (e.g. rigid urethane foams), there are likely to be detailed differences between them, in either construction or constituents. This Unit gives general considerations for the commonly available materials so that a preliminary selection can be made. Once selected, designers should confirm the specific product properties with the manufacturers. Tables 17.1.1 and 17.1.2 in **Unit 17.1** show some properties of the various insulant types. These will augment the specific commentary in this unit. Composite products, where more than one type of insulant is used in combination, are now more widely available. Where appropriate, comment on specific combinations is given.

Perhaps the most widely used category of insulants for flat roof are foam plastics materials. This is because a low thermal conductivity can be achieved, allowing a target thermal resistance to be achieved with minimum board thickness. The thermal conductivity of the individual polymers does not vary greatly: the differences between such materials result from the foam cell structure – size and distribution – and the gas within the cells. Insulants not made from foamed plastics, are generally less thermally efficient than the foam plastics. However, for some considerations, such as fire behaviour, they may be viewed as having more desirable performance.

Rigid urethane foams (RUF)

Rigid urethane foam is the term now used to cover products previously described, separately, as polyurethane (PU) and polyisocyanurate (PIR) foams. Although different in the detailed chemistry of the resin system, the similarities in overall chemistry and characteristics are sufficiently great for these materials to be discussed together. The manufacture is similar in that two resin components react to form a third 'stable' resin. They are perhaps the highest efficiency insulants – at least in their 'unaged' condition – used in flat roofing, because of the low thermal conductivity halogenated hydrocarbon gases used as the blowing agents. In the past these were CFC materials but many manufacturers have now changed to HCFC. They are covered by *BS4841: Part 3*. The standard gives requirements for properties, in addition to thermal performance, important for the performance of the roof or useful for control of the manufacturing process.

The standard requires that foamed boards are faced with reinforcing materials by 'auto-adhesion', in which the facings are bonded to the foam core during the foaming process, not by separate adhesives. A variety of facings are used to make them suitable to different roof membranes. Bitumen coated glass and glass tissue/polyethylene/glass tissue facings are described in the British Standard, but others (such as bitumen felt or aluminium foil) are available.

RUF insulants are predominantly used in warm deck roofs although they could be used in cold deck roofs, particularly where a laminate with plasterboard is used.

Gas blowing agents can migrate from the cells; and their effects on the thermal performance are described in **Unit 4.5**. This release of gas has caused concern about the risks of blistering of a fully adhered membrane system and spot bonding using a Type 3G felt was used to reduce the risks. The use of a composite insulation board with cork, woodfibre or other material also allowed full bonding with less risk of blistering from gases. Current formulations have however largely eliminated this problem.

The one significant difference between the two types of RUF board is relative temperature stability. Boards with a higher polyurethane content generally have a lower maximum operating temperature. This is of little significance during the service life of the roof, but is important during construction. With mastic asphalt the greater quantity of heat stored within the asphalt during laying can cause damage to boards with a higher urethane content. For such roofs, foams with a higher isocyanurate content should be selected, or a board with, say, a cork or fibreboard overlay used.

RUF foams can be ignited and their combustion rates may be high. Direct application of flames during installation, maintenance or repairs should be avoided. Although a measurement of burning characteristics is included in *BS4841*, this test is intended for laboratory testing of product consistency and is not helpful in assessing the performance in a fire on a roof. Manufacturers can, partially, modify the ease of ignition and fire spread characteristics of the insulation board, some products of this general type have received approvals from insurance-related assessments for performance in a fire of the whole roof.

Further reading:
BS3837: Expanded polystyrene beads: Parts 1 and 2 • BS4841: Part 3 Laminated board with auto-adhesively bonded reinforcing facings for use as roofboard thermal insulation

• The primary advantage of foamed plastics is good thermal efficiency; their disadvantage is the perception of fire performance.

Phenolic foams

The property which has promoted the development of phenol formaldehyde resin (phenolic) foams is behaviour in fire. Unlike the other foamed plastics, phenolics do not readily ignite and, if burnt, less smoke is produced. Previously, some phenolic foams had unsatisfactory long term mechanical properties, tending to be brittle and friable, and increasing corrosion risks of metals in contact because of the low pH of water extracts. Much development has taken place to improve resin systems and products. Concerns about possible corrosion of metal components in contact with damp phenolic insulants have been reduced with current manufacturing methods and because of the essentially closed cell nature of the insulants produced. However, specific data should be sought from manufacturers in relation to the risk of transient condensation or other sources of moisture for a particular roof design. These products are not covered by a British Standard. A range of facings can be produced which make them suitable for roofs using the organic waterproofing membranes. The thermal performance of phenolic foams is broadly comparable with RUF insulants when similar types of blowing agents (CFC or HCFC) are used.

Extruded expanded polystyrene

These products are produced by combining polystyrene polymer with a volatile blowing agent under pressure and extruding through a die. On release from the die the reduced external pressure generates an expansive force within the polymer which creates the foam. They can be produced with either CFC or HCFC blowing agents.

The properties of extruded expanded polystyrene are covered by *BS3837: Part 2* which lists grades E1 - E7. Grades E2 - E4 are appropriate for various flat roof applications. Manufacturers have a wider range of product grades than those suggested in the Standard but also may not manufacture products to each of the grades listed. The Standard does not list compressive strengths but the recommended uses do cover the likely range of traffic conditions. Such traffic loadings may in the case of heavy vehicles be accommodated, by using concrete load spreading layers (see **Unit 7.11**).

These types of insulant are principally used for inverted warm deck roofs or its variants. For roofing, the boards are used with the skins, formed during manufacture, in place.

This enhances the low water absorption of the closed cell foam thus improving its retention of thermal properties when exposed. Losses of thermal performance by water absorption and from water percolating between the insulant and the membrane, are compensated for by using an increased thickness of insulant board (see **Unit 8.2**).

Extruded polystyrene ignites when exposed to a flame and will burn freely if flame contact is maintained, with the consequent release of black smoke. When subjected to heat, extruded polystyrene undergoes melting shrinkage which 'pulls' it away from the source of the heat. The maximum recommended continuous service temperature is 75°C, which is lower than for many other foam plastics.

As extruded polystyrene boards are used in the 'inverted' configuration, the use of boards cut to falls is not appropriate – falls must be provided beneath the membrane.

Expanded bead polystyrene

Expanded bead polystyrene is made into boards or blocks by heating, using moisture to expand the individual beads, and thus fusing them with adjoining beads. The thermal conductivity is not as low as other foamed plastics. The foaming process is not dependent on low thermal conductivity gases, so there is no significant ageing or diminution of properties with time. Thus in the longer term the effective thermal performance is closer to that of 'aged' extruded polystyrene and some of the other plastics foams. The non-use of CFC or HCFC in the manufacture of these materials is environmentally welcome.

The properties of the materials are covered by *BS3837: Part 1* which has five grades. Of these, two grades HD and EHD – high duty and extra high duty – are used for roofing. The insulant is primarily used for a warm deck roof configuration. The application of heat or solvents to expanded bead polystyrene can lead to softening and collapse of the foam structure and should therefore be avoided. For use with built-up membranes, boards are available factory pre-felted (partial bond required) or as a composite board(for full bonding). Alternatively, a separate overlay of wood fibre board, cork or perlite can be bonded to the pre-felted board to enable full bonding. The combination of expanded bead polystyrene with an overlay of fibreboard, corkboard or similar, also provides a suitable substrate for a mastic asphalt membrane. *continued* ▶

Critical factors

• Thermal performance over time.

• Fire behaviour.

• Load carrying.

• Moisture susceptibility.

• Check with manufacturers or suppliers on specific properties of their products.

Further reading in the Guide:
4.5 Thermal transmission • 4.6 Solar radiation and thermal effects • 4.15 Environmental impact of materials • 7.6 Design for thermal performance • 7.11 design for traffic and loadspreading • 8.2 Calculation of thermal performance • 17.1 Selection of insulants

- Many insulant products are covered by British Standards or Agrément certification.
- Some insulants are made from renewable sources or have other benefits when considering the use of non-renewable resources.

Particular care is needed with mastic asphalt at upstand details to ensure the mastic asphalt does not come into contact with the edge of the polystyrene board. The necessary vertical support to the asphalt should be provided by a sand cement infill or similar.

Some polymeric single ply membranes, such as PVC, can have deleterious chemical interactions with the polystyrene. If such a combination is desired for other reasons an interlay between membrane and insulant should be provided.

Like extruded expanded polystyrene, the expanded material is combustible and can be ignited when subject to a flame. *BS3837:Part 1* lists two sub-divisions for each strength grade; N for normal fire grade and A for an improved fire retardant grade.

Mineral wools

Mineral wool is defined in *BS3533:* as insulation materials manufactured from mineral sources, either rock or glass. The more common mineral wool is that based on rock. Mineral wool boards are manufactured from natural rocks, synthetic minerals, or a combination of both, which are heated until molten and then spun into a fibrous mat or wool.

This conglomerate is then treated with a resin (phenolic or other) and other additives which bind the board and impart properties such water repellency.

During the resin curing, the board is compressed to achieve the required strength and density properties. Facings, such as glass tissue, are also incorporated during the pressing and curing process. Other surface treatments are applied by manufacturers to aid construction, such as bonding with bitumen. Glass-based wools are made by essentially the same process but using molten glass.

No British Standards exist for mineral wools used in flat roofing applications. Some products have Agrément Certification.

Mineral wool boards are widely used in warm deck roofs, with all types of membrane, and for cold deck roofs. More recently a grade of mineral wool board has been developed for use in inverted warm deck roofs. There are no special compatibility requirements when incorporating mineral wool boards under built-up roofing or polymeric single ply membranes.

Where used under mastic asphalt, a protective overlay of a bitumen impregnated woodfibre board may be necessary. Fixing the boards to the roof construction can be by bonding in hot bitumen or mechanical fixings, or both, depending on the membrane type and the wind uplift exposure for the roof. The main use of glass fibre wools is in quilted form for cold roofs.

The major component of mineral wool boards is non-combustible and generates little smoke in a fire. If a fire were severe, loss in mechanical properties through loss of binder might be expected.

Cellular glass

Cellular glass is made by mixing crushed glass and carbon which is then heated to 1000°C: when the carbon oxidises it creates a foam. The manufacture is carried out in moulds or boxes which can then be cut or shaped as required. The insulant is not covered by a British Standard but some grades have Agrément certification. Varying grades are available with differing compressive strengths and some differences in thermal conductivity.

Cellular glass is used primarily for warm roofs although it could be used for cold deck roofs, particularly with under-slab insulation. It is not suitable for inverted warm deck roofs, although it is a closed cell material with low water take up, because there are concerns about long term damage to surface cells by exposure to the weather.

The high compressive strength of the insulant makes it particularly suited for roofs with substantial finishes, or where good resistance (to traffic loads or damage by root growth) is required.

Cellular glass is essentially non-combustible, has very low water absorption and low water vapour transmission properties. The low water vapour transmission, when coupled with the bitumen bonding, provides a layer which, if complete, has a vapour resistance greater than many separate vapour control layers (which may then be omitted).

Cellular glass is bonded to the deck in hot bitumen. Mechanical fixings are discouraged because of risk of damage to the vapour resistance properties. Larger boards of slabs, bonded together, can be fixed with a cold bitumen adhesive. These slabs can increase installation speed. The waterproofing layer is fixed by torching on a built-up system. Polymeric single ply membranes can be used with

Further reading:
BS1142: Specification for fibre building boards • BS 3533 • BS3837: Expanded polystyrene beads: Parts 1 and 2 • BS4841: Part 3 Laminated board with auto-adhesively bonded reinforcing facings for use as roofboard thermal insulation

Chapter	1	2	3	4	5	6	7	8	9	10	11
Contents	Introduction	History	Regulatory Methods	Principles	Surveys	Constraints & Targets	Design Selection	Calculations	Detail Design Principles	Evaluation of Design	Built-up Roofing
Page	1	19	31	45	83	95	105	165	189	217	221

• Consideration of the chemical, mechanical or temperature compatibility with the membrane may restrict selection.

Bofill office, Barcelona, Spain

cellular glass insulants, but must either be compatible with bitumen or a separation layer used.

Perlite

Perlite is a volcanic mineral naturally containing some water. When powdered and subjected to high temperatures it expands (10-20 times the original volume). The expanded granules are then combined with mineral fibres and binders to form a board. The resulting board has good fire performance – low ignitability and smoke evolution. Boards are treated to improve water repellency and rot resistance. Perlite boards are frequently used either compositely with or as an overlay to, foam plastics boards. They are not covered by a British Standard but some products have Agrément certification.

Perlite boards are principally used for warm roofs and are compatible with the main membrane types. Fixing can be achieved by bitumen bonding or mechanical fixing to the structural deck.

Woodfibre softboard

Bitumen impregnated wood fibre boards have been used in flat roof construction for many years but became less common when higher insulation standards were required. The boards are made by a felting process which removes layers of random fibres as a mat from a suspension of wood and vegetable fibres in water. This mat is then compressed to form the final board. The bitumen impregnation gives improved water resistance and dimensional stability. Even with improved water resistance the boards are still vulnerable to loss in properties if persistently, or frequently, wetted in storage or in the roof construction. Generally wood fibre building boards are covered by *BS1142* but specific proprietary products also have Agrément certification.

The relatively soft nature of the board is helpful where a slightly irregular substrate is to be covered, and indeed much of the market for these boards is for overlays to other materials to provide a smooth surface upon which to install the membrane or other layer. Fixing can be bitumen bonded or mechanical, although the peel resistance to wind uplift should be carefully examined if only bonded.

The boards can be used with mastic asphalt, built-up membranes or polymeric single-ply if specific compatibility has been confirmed with the manufacturers.

Cork

Cork board insulants are produced from raw materials cut from a tree – Quercus Suber. They therefore have gained a reputation for having environmental merit. However the cork stripped from the tree has to be granulated, compressed, steam baked and then cut into the final shapes; much of the energy for this is derived from burning waste cork. The adhesive holding the granules together is a natural cork gum.

Cork boards are not made to a British Standard but products may have Agrément certification. Cork is principally used for warm roofs. The insulant can be used with built-up membranes, mastic asphalt or polymeric single ply, if the specific compatibility is confirmed with manufacturers. The boards can be friable when being handled but, once properly incorporated in the roof, it can take foot traffic without damage.

Composite insulants

Table 17.1.2 indicated that a number of insulants for flat roofing are available as composite boards. The combination of two different insulating materials can help to optimise the overall performance of the insulant in the roof. For example, the higher thermal performance of a foamed plastic can be augmented by the better fire performance of a perlite board. Similarly, the combination of a foamed plastic and another type can give increased suitability for hot applied membrane materials. The overall performance of the products and the preferred orientation should be checked with manufacturers. ■

Further reading in the Guide:
4.5 Thermal transmission • 4.6 Solar radiation and thermal effects • 4.15 Environmental impact of materials • 7.6 Design for thermal performance
8.2 Calculation of thermal performance • 17.1 Selection of insulants

Specification 18

18.1 Specification writing

- The principal intention of the specification whether by performance or prescription, is to convey the instructions of the design/specifier, under the contract, to the contractor/constructor.
- A specification should be:
  - Complete
  - Precise
  - Co-ordinated with other project information
  - Clear and unambiguous
  - Enforceable.

General

The specification is a document included in the Contract Documents, the purpose of which is to convey the instructions of the design/specifier, under the contract, to the contractor/constructor. It may include, alone or in combination, requirements for materials, workmanship or performance.

A specification for the construction of a roof (or for any other element of the building) should be a document that is:

- **Complete**, identifying all performance criteria or materials and products to be used and describing standards of workmanship to ensure that the quality requirements are clear.
- **Clear** and unambiguous, as brief as possible, containing no irrelevant clauses and making use where necessary of up-to-date references.
- **Precise** in requirements, including those of performance and testing.
- **Enforceable**.
- **Co-ordinated** with other project information and arranged for easy dissemination (see also **Unit 3.5**).

Main principles

The status of the specification within the Contract Documents must be clearly established and understood. Different forms of contract give different status to the specification. The specification should be prepared in all cases by a technically competent designer, familiar with the project.

The specification should aim to contribute to the quality of the finished product and the efficiency of the construction. It should aim to eliminate defects in completed work and claims for additional cost by the completeness and accuracy of the information contained therein.

The specification where possible should:

- Be clear, concise and comprehensive.
- Be co-ordinated and not conflict with drawn information.
- Contain no conflicting clauses.

- Use up-to-date references (e.g. British Standards).
- Incorporate current good practice.
- Contain all necessary information to tender and execute the works.
- Be constructive and practical.
- Be presented in a standardised format
- Not repeat or compound existing errors (e.g. in specifications from previous contracts).

Forms of specification

The form of the specification may be one of two types, although in many instances a combination of the two exists. The two broad types are specification by **performance** or specification by **prescription**.

Performance

With a performance specification, the contractor will be responsible for the design and material selection in response to criteria laid down by the designer. Performance specifications can lead to a vast range of alternative solutions, for example offering:

- Warm deck roof
- Cold deck roof
- Inverted warm deck roof.

with many options for membrane material.

The solution may depend on several criteria, apart from performance and 'pure' design, for example:

- Speed of construction
- Prevailing weather
- Cost parameters (and whether these can be assessed in life-cycle costing)
- Available production resources of the contractor
- Availability of materials or subcontractors

Prescription

Specification by prescription is the more traditional 'materials and workmanship' specification, where all materials are described together with any reference standards, and the required quality of workmanship is clearly specified with reference to Codes of Practice, accepted industry standards, samples, etc. if appropriate.

Further reading:
National Building Specification • Specification

- The contractual aspects of responsibility for design should be addressed before those responsibilities are discharged.
- This unit is provided to assist specifiers in organising their work. It does seek to define or extend their terms of appointment.

Selection of specification approach

Selection of specification approach is influenced by a number of factors other than the 'ideal' principles underlying their description. At present, the body of established research data is not really adequate to enable a true performance approach. For such specifications there will be instances where the designer may, by establishing certain key requirements, seek to reduce the options available to the tenderer. Where values for specific properties are used (for either specification approach), the properties required for individual components of the roof should be those which are relevant to the performance of the roof system as a whole: e.g. elongation figures for the sheeting itself are unlikely to be significant for the performance of the whole roof in the majority of cases. A similar case can be made for not using specification restrictions on roof sheet constituents. A further point to consider is that any criteria laid down should be checkable to show conformance to the requirement.

The onus of assessment with either route is significant. With prescriptive specifications, the designer will be required to check the proposals against the standards set down. With performance specifications, varying solutions will have to be checked against the established performance criteria. Where possible, these should involve a common terminology, defined service environment, criteria of acceptance, agreed data and methods of assessment.

The designer should exercise reasonable skill and care in the selection of materials and in the specification of workmanship. It is important that documentary evidence of the method of selection is kept. The contractor's design submission, in response to performance specifications, must be positively and carefully reviewed and any deviation agreed with the employer.

Where the design is being undertaken by a specialist contractor, the designer must obtain the client/ employer's agreement to delegate design duties and obtain financial security of this relationship.

Preparation

The preparation of the specification should be undertaken by a person qualified to do so.

A programme should be prepared for document production, indicating when input will be required, particularly where there are various contributing authors.

Drafts should be established early in the design process and, as design decisions and material selection take place, the information should be incorporated into the draft. The selection at any early stage will enable cross-referencing to drawings to be more easily undertaken.

It is important that a new specification is produced from a sound base specification, perhaps from a library of pre-written clauses. This base should be regularly updated both by feedback from previous projects and by reference to British Standards, Regulations, Codes of Practice, etc. Uncritical copying of previous specifications can compound previous errors, introduce new errors and make reference to obsolete or inappropriate standards.

Some design offices will be large enough to prepare and maintain their own libraries of clauses. For others, it will be necessary to subscribe to commercially available libraries, e.g. National Building Specification (NBS).

Where specifications are produced by reference to other documents, care must be taken to ensure that:

- Mass reference is not made to Codes of Practice, etc., which contain a variety of options, without selecting the options required.
- Where possible, the relevant aspect of a reference is included if it is only a small part of the overall document.
- Ready access will be available to reference material for all parties at the relevant times.

Content

The specification must draw together all the relevant information on which the tender and subsequent execution of the work is based. **The specification should**:

- Identify the constraints under which the work will be undertaken. For example, the form of contract, the method of tendering, the control of the works, temporary works and services (Preliminaries).
- Establish any performance requirements, even in a 'materials and workmanship' approach. *continued* ▶

continued ▶

Critical factors

- Form of specification.
- Competent designers to produce the project specification.
- Up-to-date base specification and reference material.
- Co-ordinate with other project documents.

Further reading in the Guide:
3.1 Standards and certification: a framework • 3.5 Organisation of technical information • Chapter 19 Contracts and procurement

12 Mastic Asphalt	13 Polymeric Single Ply	14 Copper	15 Lead Sheet	16 Other Membranes	17 Thermal Insulants	18 Specification	19 Contracts & Procurement	20 Inspection	21 Maintenance	22 Bibliography	23 Index
263	301	331	353	375	383	393	399	413	429	437	455

- Specifications should be co-ordinated, consistent and cross-referenced with other project information, e.g. drawings, bills of quantities.
- Some aspects of a specification will be common to different roof types and materials. Other clauses will need to be specific to an approach.
- Checklists for each membrane material can give a prompt for aspects to be considered.

- Identify extent of information to be supplied by the tenderers, in order to assess their proposals.
- Establish criteria by which assessment should be made.
- Identify the relevant drawings and any other relevant information.
- Identify the properties and characteristics of the completed work and should establish the standards of workmanship and materials.
- Contain sufficient information or refer to accessible documents, to enable inspection and supervision of the work to be satisfactorily undertaken.
- Be the sole place for the full description of information. Drawings, Bills, etc. should then make reference to the specification items.

Presentation

The presentation of the specification should be such that the document is easily read, referred to and sub-divided (if it is anticipated that a contract will obtain separate sub-contract tenders).

Specifications produced in the common arrangement of work sections (CAWS), developed by the Co-ordinating Committee for Project Information, combine 'materials and workmanship' clauses, facilitating the splitting up of documents. Specifications with combined 'materials and workmanship' clauses, as in NBS and CAWS, facilitate cross-referencing from drawings and Bills of Quantities to the specification (see **Unit 3.5**).

Co-ordination

Specification information can be found in various places, in some project specifications, on drawings and in the Bills or Schedules. The specification document should be the sole place for the description of information.

If a consistent approach is not adopted, and the information is spread over various sources, problems may arise, including:

- The preparation of tenders.
- The assessment of tenders.
- Ordering of materials.
- Quality Control and Quality Assurance.
- The use of one source without reference to another.
- Conflict between two sources, if information is provided in each.
- Identifying unintended variations to specifications.

Compliance

The specification should not contain requirements that cannot be achieved, or for which it is not possible to ascertain if the requirements have been achieved. Any performance clauses should be such that the Contractor's response to these clauses is capable of being assessed by the specifier as complying with the specification. Testing requirements should establish the exact responsibility, should tests fail.

The specifier should ensure that, at the time of submission of tenders, the Contractor has provided the necessary information to enable their proposals to be checked against the standards set down and that the checking is undertaken and recorded.

Aspects other than direct technical compliance and cost may have to be taken into account in the evaluation of tenders. These might include:

- Building/element life
- Ease of installation
- Installation programme
- Ease of testing
- Ease of replacement.

Materials checklist

Specifications will have many clauses which are the same, independent of membrane type (e.g. location and description of the building). Other clauses will be material-specific and will reflect the particular requirements of the material. A full specification library is outside the scope of this Guide. The following are some key factors for the principal membrane types covered to assist the specifier.

Built-up roofing
- Substrate condition
  - type, attachment, moisture, smoothness.
- Substrate preparation
  - drying, priming.
- Underlayer specification
  - product name & supplier (if appropriate), or
  - BS classification, or
  - base composition, base weight, coating type.
  - method of attachment
    - general areas/specific details,
    - bonding bitumen grade/fixing type.

Further reading:
National Building Specification • Specification

© BFRC / CIRIA: *Flat Roofing: Design and Good Practice.* 1993

- Specifications with combined materials and workmanship clauses facilitate splitting up the documentation and cross-referencing to other project information.

- Top layer specification
  - product name and supplier (if appropriate), or
  - BS classification, or
  - base composition, base weight, coating type, finish type.
  - method of attachment
    - general areas/specific details.
    - bonding bitumen type/BS grade
- Surface protection
  - type (e.g. chippings/paving/ballast)
  - application density (for chippings)
  - bonding materials (if appropriate).

Mastic asphalt
- Substrate condition
  - type, attachment, moisture, smoothness.
- Substrate preparation
  - surface laitence removal? (from concrete)
  - priming/surface sealing (if required)
  - fixing of expanded metal lathe - type/fixing
  - formation of keys in masonry.
- Separating layer specification
  - type and quality (BS, glass tissue weight etc.).
  - application and laps
- Mastic asphalt specification
  - grade (from BS or other), or
  - product name and supplier (for polymer-modified)
  - thickness, number of coats, tolerance,
    - general areas/specific details
  - maximum temperature of application
  - forming of fillets and legs
  - formation of bay joints
  - surface finish.
- Surface protection
  - type and supplier
  - application density (for chippings)
  - bonding materials (for other than chippings)

Polymeric single ply
- Substrate condition
  - type, attachment, condition, smoothness.
- Substrate preparation
  - drying, sealing, taping.
- Isolation layer specification (if required)
  - Product name/supplier
  - direction of laying
  - method of attachment

- Membrane specification
  - product name/supplier, or
  - reference to certification (e.g. Agrément)
  - method of fixing, mechanical/adhesive/ballasted
    - number and type
    - variation in fixings across roof/details
    - adhesive type
    - application details
    - type and quantity of ballast
- Jointing and lap sealing method(s)
  - weld (heat or solvent)
  - tape interlayer
- Surface protection specification (for traffic roofs)
  - paving type, paviour/slab
  - dimensions
  - support system

Copper
- Substrate type and condition
- Material specification
  - gauge (mm)
  - temper
  - type and grade *(BS2870)*
- Membrane system
  - traditional/longstrip
  - seam or batten roll centres
- Type of roof configuration
  - warm deck/cold deck
- Protection to membrane
  - short/long term

Lead
- Substrate
  - type, condition, smoothness
- Underlay
  - type, quality
- Material specification for main roof area and details
  - type
  - BS Code number/sheet size, thickness
- Membrane system
  - dimensional disciplines/spacing of joints
  - type and dimensions of joints: standing seam, wood cored rolls, drip steps
  - fixing methods: type, material, spacing
  - sealants (if necessary)
- Protection of membrane
  - weathering oil
  - temporary and permanent protection.

Further reading in the Guide:
3.1 Standards and certification: a framework • 3.5 Organisation of technical information • Chapter 19 Contract and procurement

12 Mastic Asphalt	13 Polymeric Single Ply	14 Copper	15 Lead Sheet	16 Other Membranes	17 Thermal Insulants	18 Specification	19 Contracts & Procurement	20 Inspection	21 Maintenance	22 Bibliography	23 Index
263	301	331	353	375	383	393	399	413	429	437	455

Contract and procurement 19

Special Notes:

1 The provision of general guidance is intended to assist Architects and other agents of the Employer or building client/owner in understanding the implications of the various standard forms of contract. The construction of any particular contract is governed by its particular terms.

2 This chapter distinguishes between (i) the 'consultant designer' be he or she Architect or Civil Engineer, and (ii) the 'specialist designer' being a designer employed by a specialist sub-contractor.

Approaches to contract

- The principal intention of a contract is to set down the rights and obligations of the parties.
- The consultant designer will need to assess the options of specialist design input, and the resulting contractual implications.
- Procurement can be 'traditional' where the design, tendering and construction are consecutive activities, or 'fast track' where design and construction overlay.

General

The exact duties of the consultant designer will depend on his or her terms of appointment, but essentially these will provide for the consultant designer to design all or part of the project and to exercise skill and care in that work.

The consultant designer will be held responsible for the design, unless the express agreement of the client is obtained to delegate the design of a particular part of the work. The involvement of a specialist firm which provides an element of design input does not in itself relieve the consultant designer of responsibility for the overall design.

The extent of design carried out by the consultant designer and that required of a specialist designer will vary according to the nature and complexity of the complete roofing system. The identification of the extent and correct timing of the specialist design input can have a significant influence on the choice of an appropriate form of contract and the tender procedures to be adopted.

Liability

There are many standard forms of contract and associated subcontracts and warranties in common use by the construction industry; guidance on the principal forms is given later in this chapter.

In recommending a particular form of contract, the consultant designer should be aware of the allocation of risk in the event of the contractor or sub-contractor being in default.

Acceptance of risk

It is clearly advisable that the client understands and accepts the allocation of risk under a form of contract or subcontract prior to adopting it for the work.

If the particular design introduces anything of an innovatory nature, the consultant designer should consider informing his client of the risk likely to be involved and obtain the client's consent before proceeding.

Knowledge and expertise

The consultant designer must be clear as to whether or not the practice has the requisite knowledge and experience to select and design the roofing element. If not, the consultant designer should advise the client that specialist advice is required, where it may be available, and how it might be procured.

For the simpler type of roof construction, advice may be obtained from roofing material manufacturers or from specialist roofing firms, usually without payment but with an undertaking by the consultant designer to include that product and/or the name of the specialist firm 'in the specification'. The advice obtained by this method is used by the consultant designer at his or her own risk, as it is unlikely that the provider of such information would accept responsibility for any subsequent failure.

Specialist design

When specialist design input is required, the input has to be obtained at the correct time in the design process. If obtained later, or otherwise out of sequence, then it is likely that variations will arise on other already-designed work.

To obtain specialist design input, prior to letting the contract for the main construction or for management, it may be necessary to select the appropriate firm and for the client to enter into a contractual commitment for payment for any work done prior to signing of the principal construction or management contract.

Where a main contractor is used, the bringing in of a specialist firm to assist in the design process on a contractual basis inevitably means that issues are raised in respect of the selection of an appropriate firm, prior to the appointment of the main contractor. These issues are less likely to arise when supplying firms are selected on a competitive tender basis against a full specification.

Further reading:
NEDO: Faster Building for Commerce • JCT: Practice Note 20: Deciding on the appropriate form of JCT Main Contract • JCT: Guide to the Standard form of Building Contract 1980 Edition • CASEC: Contract Manual–Guide JCT 1980 Forms of contract • CASEC: Nomination and the Building Process • HMSO: Guidance Notes on Sub-Contract GW/S • POWELL-SMITH, V and CHAPPELL, D. JCT Minor Works Form of Contract (MW80). A Practical Guide

- A contract should be:
  - Concise
  - Unambiguous
  - Co-ordinated with other project documentation
  - Enforceable
  - Explicit

Tendering and contractual arrangements

If the contractor has ultimate control over the selection of the roofing specialist, the contractor is likely to be totally responsible for the specialist work as if it were their own. Where the consultant designer selects the specialist firm or takes part in the selection process, the client generally takes a degree of responsibility for the performance of the specialist firm.

A firm selected by the contractor is referred to as a 'domestic' subcontractor, a firm selected by the consultant designer is said to be 'nominated', and there are variations to this e.g. 'named' subcontractors under the *JCT Intermediate Form of Contract (IFC84)*. Under a management contract, the roofing contractor would be termed a 'works package contractor'.

Different arrangements for the allocation of risk vary under the many different forms of contract and subcontract in everyday use by the industry.

Procurement procedures

The term **'traditional procedure'** is used in this Guide where design, tendering, and construction are consecutive activities.

Contracts relating to traditional procedures to procure building work are therefore generally based on the premise that the design is 100% complete before the work is made the subject of tendering or negotiation and, once let, such contracts are subject to change only by authorised variation. In practice, it is rare for the design to be 100% complete at tender stage. This may lead to variations, applications to extend the contract period, and all the disputes which naturally arise when a form of contract designed for one situation is used in different circumstances.

'Fast track' procedures, are generally understood to be those which overlap the design and construction processes. They can reduce the procurement period from that required by the traditional consecutive procedure.

The overlapping of design and construction requires detailed planning and experienced management of the design and procurement process to be effective. Although variations due to incomplete design being tendered are not unknown in traditional sequential working, the effect on fast track work where construction is close up behind the design can be very disruptive to the progress of the works and very expensive.

The consultant designer should advise his or her client as to the most appropriate manner to procure the roofing element, and be prepared to give reasons for their recommendation. The following is given to guide the designer on the more commonly used forms available.

Standard forms of contract and sub-contract

Table 19.1.1 lists the more common forms. This list is given for guidance only and is not intended to be comprehensive. Consultant designers should ensure that when using a particular form, all current amendments are included and their significance understood.

Maintenance and minor repairs

For the work on maintenance and repairs, and for minor new works, there are several contract forms of a relatively simple nature (e.g. JCT contracts for jobbing work – *JA/C90* – for Renovation Grant works, the *Measured Term Contract,* and the non-JCT *Building work (1986).* All these forms are for use on uncomplicated work and would require amendment should specialist design input be required on roofing works.

continued ▶

Critical factors

- Clarify liabilities and allocation of risk.
- Ensure use of current versions of terms of contract and that implications of recent amendments are understood.
- Contractual relationships where specialist design input is obtained prior to letting of main contract.

Further reading in the Guide:
3.1 Standards and certification: a framework • 3.3 Quality management • 19.2 Review of contracts and sub-contracts

12 Mastic Asphalt	13 Polymeric Single Ply	14 Copper	15 Lead Sheet	16 Other Membranes	17 Thermal Insulants	18 Specification	19 Contracts & Procurement	20 Inspection	21 Maintenance	22 Bibliography	23 Index
263	301	331	353	375	383	393	399	413	429	437	455

- Many forms of building contract are available for building works
- The various forms cover different aspects of work or are more or less elaborate for varying size and complexity of work.

Table 19.1.1
Commonly-used standard forms of contract and related sub-contracts

Main contract forms	Related sub-contract forms
Forms published by RIBA Publications Ltd	
Joint Contracts Tribunal forms:	**Joint Contracts Tribunal forms:**
1. Standard Form of Contract 1980 (JCT80) (Private and Local Authority editions, each in three versions: with quantities, with approximate quantities and without quantities) Supplements and amendments Note specifically: Contractor's Designed Portion Supplement	1a. Sub-Contract Forms (Nominated) published by RIBA Publications Ltd; Tender NSC/T Agreement NSC/A Conditions NSC/C Agreement NSC/W Nomination NSC/N 1b. Sub-Contract Form (Domestic) published by Building Employers Confederation, Articles and Conditions DOM/1
2. Intermediate Form of Contract (IFC84)	2a. Sub-Contract Form (Named) published by Building Employers Confederation: Conditions NAM/SC 2b Sub-Contract Form (Named) Published by RIBA Publications Ltd: Tender and Agreement NAM/T 2c Sub-Contract Form (Named) Published by RIBA Publications Ltd. and the Committee of Associations of Specialist Engineering Contractors: Form of Employer/Specialist Agreement ESA/1 2d. Sub-contract Form (Domestic) published by Building Employers Confederation: Articles and Conditions IN/SC
3. Agreement for Minor Works (MW80)	3. No provisions for sub-contracting specialist works
4. Standard Form of Contract With Contractors Design (CD81)	4. Sub-contractor Form (Domestic) published by Building Employers Confederation: Articles and Conditions DOM/2
5. Management Contract (MAN 87) Supplements and amendments to the contract documentation	5. Works Contracts Published by RIBA Publications Ltd: Invitation to Tender WKS1/1 Tender by Works Contractor WKS1/2 Agreement WKS1/3 Conditions of Contract WKS/2 Employer/Works Contract Agreement WKS/3
6. Fixed Fee Form of Prime Cost Contract (now superseded)	–
7. The Standard Form of Prime Cost Contract 1992	7. Conditions NSC/C (PCC)
8. Conditions of contract for building work of a jobbing character (JA/C90)	8. No provision for sub-contracting works
9. Agreement for Renovation Grant works (where an architect/ supervision officer is appointed.	9. No Sub-contract form
10. Measured term contract	10. No Sub-contract form

Further reading:
JCT: IFC/84 Practice Note IN/1 • JCT: MC/1: Management Contracts under the JCT Documentation • JCT: MC/2: Commentaries (on MC87) • FRANKS, J. Building Procurement Systems Edition 2 • TURNER, D. F, Building Sub-Contract Forms • POWELL SMITH, V and CHAPPELL, D, JCT Intermediate Forms of Contract (IFC 84) A Practical Guide

- Simple forms of contract for uncomplicated works may require care where specialist design input is required.

Table 19.1.1
Commonly-used standard forms of contract and related sub-contracts *(continued)*

Critical factors

- Choose form of contract appropriate for project.

Forms published by the National Federation of Building Trades Employers.

Joint Contract Tribunal Forms:

1. Agreement for Renovation Grant works (where no Architect/Supervising Officer is appointed).

1. No Sub-contract form

Forms published by HMSO

1. General Conditions of Government Contracts for Building and Civil Engineering Works Edition 3 (GC WORKS/1) (Versions with quantities and without quantities, plus amendments)

1. Sub-contracts form published by HMSO: Contract Sub-contract Conditions. Articles and Appendix GW/S

2. General Conditions of Government Contracts of Minor Works (GC WORKS/2)

2. No sub-contract form specifically provided

Forms published by the Institution of Civil Engineers

1. Conditions of Contract and Forms of Tender Agreement and Bond of Works of Civil Engineering Construction (Edition 6)

1. Sub-contract form published by the Federation of Civil Engineering Contractors
   2HH: Articles and Conditions known as the 'Blue Form'

2. Conditions of Contract, Agreement and Contract Schedule for use in connection with Minor Works of Civil Engineering Construction

2. No provisions for sub-contacting specialist works

Forms published by the British Property Federation

1. BPF Edition of ACA Form of Building Agreement (revised 1990)

2. No sub-contract form published

Forms published by the Architects and Surveyors Institute

1. Building Contract (1986 Edition)

1. Sub-contracts published by the Architects and Surveyors Institute

2. Small works contract (1989 Edition)

   - Sub-contract (1981 Edition)
   - Domestic Sub-contract (1991 Edition)

3. Small works contract with supplementary conditions for quantities

---

Further reading in the Guide:
3.1 Standards and certification: a framework • 3.3 Quality management • 19.2 Review of contracts and sub-contracts

12 Mastic Asphalt	13 Polymeric Single Ply	14 Copper	15 Lead Sheet	16 Other Membranes	17 Thermal Insulants	18 Specification	19 Contracts & Procurement	20 Inspection	21 Maintenance	22 Bibliography	23 Index
263	301	331	353	375	383	393	399	413	429	437	455

- Traditional procedures and contracts are used where the design, tendering and construction process are sequential.
- Tenders in traditional procedures are intended to be based on a completed design.
- Traditional procedures do not in principle allow for specialist design input on a contracted basis.

General

There are several bodies who have produced standard forms for construction contracts, the principal one being the Joint Contracts Tribunal (JCT). The JCT is made up of representatives of clients, consultants, contractors and specialist firms, and the forms of contract issued are generally accepted by all parts of the construction industry.

Standard forms of contract related to traditional procedures

The various standard forms of construction contract produced by the JCT related to traditional procedure comprise the JCT 80 series, the *Intermediate Form of Contract* (IFC 84) suitable for works of simple content, and the *Agreement for Minor Building Works* (1980).

The JCT 80 series and IFC 84 forms permit the engagement of sub-contractors for work of a specialist nature, but the minor works form has no sub-contact provisions.

Sub-contracts under JCT 80

Under JCT 80, sub-contractors may be nominated using the standard documentation listed in **Unit 19.1**.

A **nominated sub-contractor** (NSC), under NSC/W, warrants that he has exercised, and will exercise, all reasonable skill and care in the design, selection of materials and the satisfaction of any performance specification in so far as his work is concerned with design etc. Following a recent legal case concerning materials and goods satisfaction, it is recommended that workmanship is also included under this warranty.

Tenders may be called on the basis of a complete design with a specification of materials and workmanship, or upon a performance specification, the work being included in the main contract documents as a Prime Cost (PC) Sum.

Nomination under the JCT 80 may seem a somewhat complex process but it provides a good management tool, document control and a record of decisions made.

Under Clause 19.3 of JCT80, the specialist work may be let on a domestic basis by inclusion in the main tender documents either as measured work or as otherwise described. The consultant designer names a minimum of three firms from whom the contractor shall at their sole discretion select one to execute the work. The contractor may however add one or more firms of their own, at any time prior to the execution of a binding sub-contract agreement, subject to the consultant designer's approval.

For domestic sub-contracts a standard form, DOM/1, is available with terms entirely consistent with JCT 80, but neither the contractor nor the sub-contractor is obliged to use it.

Liability for nominated and domestic sub-contractors

Where a sub-contractor has been nominated under JCT 80, the Contractor's liability for the nominated sub-contractor is restricted in some respects, leaving the Employer's remedy for certain defaults against the nominated sub-contractor under a direct warranty. Thus the Contractor is not generally liable for the nominated sub-contractor's delay. The Contractor is not responsible for the nominated sub-contractor's design, although he remains responsible for bad workmanship and materials. If a nominated sub-contractor, during the course of the works, repudiates his sub-contract, the Employer has a duty to re-nominate a new sub-contractor, bearing any increased costs resulting from such a re-nomination and becoming liable to pay damages to the Contractor for any delay he suffers awaiting a re-nomination.

Where, on the other hand, the Contractor himself selects a sub-contractor, the Contractor remains entirely responsible for the work carried out by that domestic sub-contractor as if it were his own work, even if the contractor has chosen one of the firms named by the consultant designer. Default of a domestic sub-contractor in no way limits the rights of the client against the contractor. Should such a default occur, the client can claim liquidated damages for any delay so caused to the completion of the main contract.

Sub-contracts under JCT IFC 84

Under the JCT IFC 84, with the approval of the client, the consultant designer may require the main contractor to sub-contract specialist works to a **'named sub-contractor'** using standard forms NAM/T and NAM/SC. When the sub-contract includes a design element, the form ESA/1 should be signed by the client and the sub-contractor to provide a warranty in similar terms to NSC/W.

The IFC 84 form, being for work of a simpler nature than that envisaged under JCT 80, makes no explicit provision

Further reading:
PARRIS, J: (1985) Default by Sub-Contractors and Suppliers • POWELL SMITH, V and CHAPPELL, D: JCT Minor Works form of Contract (MW 80) A Practical Guide • POWELL SMITH, V and CHAPPELL, D: Building Contracts Compared and Tabulated

- The construction of the roofing element will in almost all cases be sub-contracted to a specialist firm.
- The main standard forms of contract are produced by the Joint Contracts Tribunal.
- There are special forms of contract for government work.

St John's College, Oxford, UK

for engagement of named sub-contractors prior to obtaining main contractors' tenders. However, the form of *Employer/Specialist Agreement* ESA/1 allows for named sub-contractors to be so engaged directly by the Employer if so required, prior to appointment of a main contractor.

Where a named sub-contractor is so appointed, the work of the sub-contractor is defined and included in the main tender document for pricing by the main contractor with the name of the sub-contractor given.

The contractor may also propose sub-letting part of the work to a domestic sub-contractor, but cannot add names to those listed in the tender for identified specialist work.

Liability for delays to progress by IFC 84 sub-contractors

Where the employment of a sub-contractor who has been named under JCT IFC 84 is determined, the client bears the extra cost of employing the new sub-contractor (excluding the value of any remedial works) and lose their right to liquidated damages for delay, whilst the main contractor carries the cost of any remedial works and the costs of the extended contract period.

Contracts for government agencies

Contracts placed by the Government are let on the General Conditions of Government Contracts for Building and Civil Engineering GC/Works/1 (currently edition 3), GC/Works/2 being the form for minor works. Both these forms make provision for the engagement of sub-contractors.

Sub-contracts under GC/Works/1

Under GC/Works/1 Edition 3 (latest revision 1992), sub-contractors can be nominated by the consultant designer, the work being included in the bills of quantities as a PC sum. Where the sub-contractor is engaged prior to the main tender, his name should be stated in the main tender document. A standard sub-contract form GW/S is provided but currently (October 1991) this only applies to Edition 2 of GC/Works/1. Whilst the sub-contractor indemnifies the main contractor in respect of any default in design, no provision is made in the documentation for the sub-contractor to provide a warranty to the client.

Under GC/Works/1 the contractor may sub-let any part of the works to a sub-contractor of their own choice with the approval of the client. However, as opposed to the JCT 80 series, the main contract has mandatory provisions requiring the contractor to enter into sub-contracts whose terms will enable them to fulfil their obligations under the contract, and states explicitly that certain provisions must be included.

GC/Works/1 allows the consultant designer to specify that certain work included in the contract documents is to be sub-contracted but there are no provisions to allow the designer to propose names (other than to nominate under a PC sum).

Liability for delays to progress by GC/Works/1 sub-contractors.

Where a sub-contractor who has been nominated under GC/Works/1 fails to complete the sub-contract on time, or at all, the client, i.e. the authority, has the liability to reimburse the contractor an amount equal to the difference between (i) any cost the contractor has incurred in securing the completion of the sub-contract which exceeds the cost to them of completion under the original sub-contract and (ii) the amount which, by using their best endeavours, they have or should have recovered from the original sub-contractor. *continued* ▶

Critical factors

- The roofing element under a management contract will be, or be part of, a Works Contract.
- Procurement procedures which overlap design tendering and construction of various elements of the work are termed 'Fast Track' procedures.
- The most common form of fast track procurement is the management contract, each specialist being engaged under a Works Contract.

Standard Forms of Contract related to fast track procedures

Management Contracts

In Management Contracts the 'main contractor' is called the 'Management Contractor' and the sub-contractors are called 'Works Contractors'. The Management Contractor does not itself carry out any construction work. All construction work is carried out by the Works Contractors employed by the Management Contractor.

The JCT has a comprehensive set of standard documents for a Management Contract known as JCT MAN 87.

Works Contracts under JCT MAN 87

The full package of documents produced by the JCT is:

- The Standard Form of Management Contract itself.
- A standard set of documents for the procurement of Works Contracts, comprising an invitation to tender, form of tender and articles of agreement (collectively Form of Works Contract/1).
- A standard form of Employer/Works Contract Agreement (in effect, a design warranty), to establish a direct contractual relationship between the employer and a works contractor.
- A set of Works Contract formula rules where Works Contracts are to be on the basis of formula price adjustment.
- Phased completion supplements for the Management Contract and Works Contract.

Using this method of procurement, the specialist element would be subject of a Works Contract, the management contractor co-operating with the professional team in the selection of appropriate firms to tender for the work, and in programming its execution.

The management contractor is responsible for ensuring that the works contractor carries out the work in accordance with the project specification and with the Works Contract. Should a works contractor default, the management contractor must pursue every endeavour – including litigation if necessary – to obtain a sum equal to the losses incurred by himself, by other works contractors, and by the client in remedying the breach. Should the management contractor fail to recoup part or all of the monies due, then the client has the ultimate obligation to reimburse any unrecovered losses incurred by the management contractor and the other works contractors.

Works contracts under other forms of management contract

Some private – i.e. non-standard forms – of management contract are based on terms similar to JCT MAN 87. These may include provisions which effectively convert it to a lump sum basis and make the management contractor directly responsible for delay for any reason, with payment of liquidated damages, rather than only for delay brought about by breach or negligence in performance by the management contractor of his management duties. This is generally known in the construction industry as a 'hard' version, as opposed to a 'soft' form of management contract, e.g. JCT MAN 87.

These non-standard forms of management contract often impose liabilities on the management contractor in respect of works contractors similar to those in the JCT 80 series for domestic sub-contractors.

Construction management

A significant alternative to the management contract procedure is the construction management process. In this a construction manager is appointed to take responsibility for the procurement of the work, but the individual works contractors each enter into a contract directly with the client. No standard forms are available for construction management, but the construction manager can adopt any of the standard forms available and adapt them to suit the nature of the work packages.

The construction manager, generally in consultation with the architect, will select the specialist roofing works contractor, and the terms under which this works contractor enters into a contract with the client should include a design warranty in terms similar to JCT NSC/W if this is appropriate.

In adapting a standard form for the roofing element on a specific project, care should be taken to ensure that the interfaces of responsibilities between client and the various works contractors are harmonised.

Further reading:
POWELL SMITH, V and CHAPPELL, D: JCT Minor Works form of Contract (MW 80) A Practical Guide • CIRIA Special Publication 81 Roles, responsibilities and risks in management contracting

- Design-and-construct contracts offer clients a comprehensive approach under one contract. Construction firms offering such an approach may have in-house designers or use consultants.

- Standard forms of contract are produced by other organisations, including the British Property Federation and the Institution of Civil Engineers.

Design-and-construct contracts

Although not strictly fast-track, the industry offers clients a comprehensive design-and-construct basis under contract to one firm. The firms offering this service may offer an in-house design facility, but, in some cases, the design may be sub-contracted to consultant designers.

Sub-contractors in design and construction contracts

The *JCT Standard Form of Building Contract with Contractor's Design 1981* allows the client to obtain tenders based on a statement of 'Employer's Requirements'. Under this procedure the contractor is entirely responsible for the design, selection of materials and quality of workmanship and is free to choose the sub-contractor for any specialist element.

However, the client may name a specialist in the statement of Employer's Requirements. A form, DOM/2, is available to employ a sub-contractor with a design input but, like DOM/1, neither party is obliged to use it.

Unless the contract expressly provides that the contractor's obligation in relation to design is equivalent to that of a professional designer (which JCT 81 does), the courts may imply an absolute obligation for the contractor to produce a building that is 'fit for the purpose'.

Consultant designers engaged by design and build contractor may be inadvertently be caught up by an obligation of 'fitness for purpose'. A fitness for purpose obligation is unlikely to be covered by professional indemnity insurance.

The British Property Federation System

The British Property Federation (BPF) has produced its own form of consultant agreement and form of construction contract, the essence of which is that at an early stage of the procurement process, the contractor takes over and completes the design.

Sub-contracts under the BPF Contract System

Under the BPF system, the designer may include one or more names in the tender documents to design and execute certain works. These become 'named sub-contractors', for whose performance the contractor is made entirely responsible, including any design undertaken by them.

The contractor may, in addition, propose names of sub-contractors to execute other works by listing them in his tender. Client acceptance of the tender confirms acceptance of the listed firms as domestic sub-contractors for whom the main contractor takes total responsibility.

Civil engineering work under the ICE Forms

Contracts relating to traditional procedures to procure civil engineering work are based on the premise that, whilst the design is effectively complete, the full extent of the work is unknown before the work is made the subject of tendering or negotiation, and, once let, the work as executed is subject to remeasurement.

Sub-contracts under the ICE Form

The consultant designer may nominate a specialist roofing sub-contractor under the ICE Form, the work being covered in the contract document as a PC sum.

Under the ICE Form 6th Edition, any design requirements must be expressly stated in both the main contract and in the appropriate nominated sub-contract.

The ICE Form of contract allows the contractor to sub-let any part of the work to a sub-contractor of his own choice provided the written consent of the client is first obtained. Such consent is stated as not relieving the contractor from any liability or obligation under the contract. There are no provisions which enable the consultant designer to state that roofing work included in the contract documents is to be sub-let to a sub-contractor, named or otherwise.

When a sub-contractor who has been nominated under the ICE Form defaults, the contractor looks first to the defaulting sub-contractor to recover all costs, including the client's costs, arising from the default. Should recovery be incomplete, or impossible, the client is liable to reimburse the contractor his unrecovered expenses.

Minor civil engineering work

It should be noted that only the main ICE Form makes provision for the engagement of sub-contractors. ∎

Critical factors

Further reading in the Guide:
19.1 Approaches to contract • 19.3 Tendering, certificates, warranties, insurance and defects

19.3 Tendering, certificates, warranties, insurance and defects

- The procurement procedure will be determined largely by the size of the project and the extent to which specialist design is required, and the placement of risk.
- The consultant designer must exercise skill and care in the selection of a specialist roofing firm.
- Where a specialist design input is required, a warranty in respect of design should be entered into between the client and the specialist roofing contractor.

General

This Unit gives a brief overview of significant aspects related to the procurement of the roofing element to the satisfaction of the consultant designer and ultimately the client.

Selection of specialist firms

Consultant designers must ensure that appropriate and competent firms are selected to execute the work. The qualification procedure should be rigorous and consultant designers should satisfy themselves that firms on the tender list, named in tender documents, or proposed by the main contractor, have the technical ability and resources, including management expertise, to execute the work to the standard required, including any appropriate design work.

Consultant designers should ascertain what similar work has been satisfactorily completed in the immediate past, obtain clients' references and/or be prepared to inspect their previous projects. Similarly roofing contractors, when tendering should also satisfy themselves that they have the necessary skills and resources.

The specialist's financial standing should be examined. Whilst the financial assessment may be in the hands of the quantity surveyor, the consultant designer retains his general responsibility for the appointment of a satisfactory firm.

Tendering procedures

The various forms of contract in general set the tendering procedure for specialist work.

When the work is to be contracted on a **'domestic'** basis, the consultant designer should ensure that the tender and contract documents issued to the main contractor clearly identify the workmanship and material requirements. In practice, domestic sub-contracts often include an element of design and it is advisable for this also to be clearly identified.

Where the work is to be contracted on a **'nominated'** basis, or equivalent, the consultant designer should ensure that the tender documentation is comprehensive and fully describes the work which is the subject of the tender. Procedures set out in the standard forms (e.g. Amendment 10 to the JCT 80) should be strictly followed to avoid confusion.

Certificates generally

Certificates are required for various purposes under all forms of contract. The consultant designer should check the specific form of contract and sub-contract, other than 'domestic', on each project, for the requirements of each type of certificate, and which other members of the consultancy team may be involved in preparation thereof.

The following is given for general guidance only, each standard form has particular definitions and requirements.

Payment certificates

The value of work executed should only include work which is properly executed in accordance with the contract and goods properly brought to site but not yet fixed.

Certificate of Practical Completion

The person named in the contract must issue this when, in their opinion, the works are practically complete; individual certificates of Practical Completion are also required in respect of each nominated sub-contractor under JCT 80.

The date of issue of the Certificates of Practical Completion is the date from which the defects liability period runs, for the period stated in the appendix to the contract.

It is in addition the date on which responsibility for the building passes from the contractor to the owner.

Further reading:
CORNES, D L. Design Liability in the Construction Industry • CECIL, R: Professional Liability

© BFRC / CIRIA: Flat Roofing: Design and Good Practice. 1993

- All contractual obligations on the part of the specialist roofing contractor should be discharged before the issue of the final certificate.
- The law relating to construction is complex and develops by both statute, and by case law.
- Consultant designers are advised to seek legal advice if there is any uncertainty in the provisions of agreements and contracts.
- Many roofing product manufacturers and specialist contractors offer guarantees.

Certificate of Making Good Defects

The person named in the contract should issue this certificate when all defects properly notified and remedied have been made good. The completion of making good defects is normally deemed to have taken place on the day named in the certificate.

Final Certificate

This states the sum of the amounts previously certified, and the contract sum (adjusted as required under the terms of the contract), the balance being stated as the amount due from the client to the contractor, or vice versa.

The Final Certificate clause in every form of contract will give rules as to its issue and the effect these have if arbitration or other proceedings have been commenced.

If, and to the extent that it is provided in the contract documents, the materials and workmanship are to be to the nominated person's satisfaction, the Final Certificate is conclusive evidence that, in respect of those matters, the contractor and all sub-contractors have fulfilled their contractual obligations.

The certifier should therefore not issue the Final Certificate purely for payment purposes, but must first satisfy himself that all contractual obligations have been satisfied in general and particularly any residual obligations in respect of the roofing elements.

Design warranties

Sub-contractors' Warranty to Employer

When a sub-contract under any form of contract provides a design input to the roofing element, it is recommended that the specialist firm enters into a warranty agreement, termed a collateral warranty, direct with the employer in terms similar to the following from NSC/W:

'The sub-contractor warrants that he has exercised and will exercise all reasonable skill and care in:

1. The design of the Sub-contract Works insofar as the Sub-contract Works have been or will be designed by the sub-contractor, and

2. The selection of materials and goods and quality of workmanship for the Sub-contract Works insofar as such materials and goods and workmanship have been or will be selected or determined by the sub-contractor, and

3. The satisfaction of any performance specification or requirement insofar as such performance specification or requirement is included or referred to in the description of the Sub-contract Works included in or annexed to the Tender:

Nothing in the above clause shall be construed so as to affect the obligations of the sub-contractor in regard to the supply under the sub-contract of workmanship, materials and goods.'

The effect of such a warranty is to provide a contractual line of recourse and it identifies a design responsibility separate from that of the consultant designer. In practice, both may have a degree of design responsibility. Diagrammatic representation of the relationships under a warranty is shown in Figure 19.3.2.

Manufacturers' and specialist contractors' guarantees
Many roofing product manufacturers and specialist contractors now offer guarantees which cover more than the performance of materials or workmanship in isolation. These guarantees may include design, materials and workmanship, as a package, for varying periods, perhaps up to 15 to 20 years. Such warranties may be linked to the restriction of product specified, a regular maintenance contract or other conditions. These warranties can, however, demonstrate supplier/contractor confidence in their proposals and may in some cases be supported by insurance. There are, as yet, no standardised conditions or benefits, among the guarantees offered. Clients/designers should therefore, carefully assess the terms of guarantees to consider the scope of protection they offer.

Consultant Designers warranty to a third party
In the case of consultant designers, two standard forms of duty of care agreements are published by the British Property Federation. One relates to funders, and the other to purchasers and tenants. Both these forms have the agreement of the RIBA, RICS and ACE. *continued* ▶

Critical factors

- Contractual responsibilities of named persons in contract.
- Warranties create contractual links where otherwise there would be be none.
- Careful assessment of manufacturers and contractors guarantees

---

Further reading in the Guide:
5.2 Surveying buildings: scope • 5.3 Surveying buildings: roofs • 19.1 Approaches to contract • 19.2 Review of contracts and sub-contracts • 21.2 Diagnosing defects and remedies

12 Mastic Asphalt	13 Polymeric Single Ply	14 Copper	15 Lead Sheet	16 Other Membranes	17 Thermal Insulants	18 Specification	19 Contracts & Procurement	20 Inspection	21 Maintenance	22 Bibliography	23 Index
263	301	331	353	375	383	393	399	413	429	437	455

- Professional liability can arise in contract, in tort or under some particular statute.
- Implied contract term (where not explicitly stated) that services will be carried out with reasonable skill and care.

Insurance

Consultant design practices should carry Professional Indemnity Insurance (PII) in respect of the legal liability for negligence arising from their professional activities.

Specialist sub-contractors will rarely carry Professional Indemnity Insurance and consequently other forms of financial security should be considered.

Defects

When a defect is detected in the roofing element an investigation must take place to determine the cause, and to find out where and how often the defect has occurred and its effect.

Investigation of problems in flat roofs can be particularly difficult to carry out (see also **Unit 21.2**). A typical example of this is the leak point in the roof deck being remote from the entry point through the waterproofing membrane or associated building perimeter details. This may be further confused when condensation gives the impression of a 'leak'. Where investigation is required to resolve contractual obligations, special care will be needed. Investigations may form part of resolving a contractual dispute. Any investigation should be impartial and concern itself with the facts (see also **Unit 5.1**), rather than support one particular view. Records should be kept, together with drawings and photographs where appropriate. Where opening up is necessary, sequential photographs can be useful. Such records have increased real value when debate and argument continue between parties for long periods – even years.

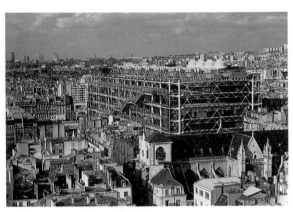

Centre Pompidou, Paris, France

Salzmann House, USA

Further reading:

Chapter	1	2	3	4	5	6	7	8	9	10	11
Contents	Introduction	History	Regulatory Methods	Principles	Surveys	Constraints & Targets	Design Selection	Calculations	Detail Design Principles	Evaluation of Design	Built-up Roofing
Page	1	19	31	45	83	95	105	165	189	217	221

- Construction law is complex and develops by case law and legislation.
- Consultant designers should keep up to date with new forms to contracts, case law and legislation.

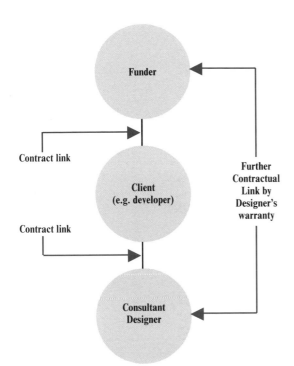

Figure 19.3.1
Relationships between client and consultant designer

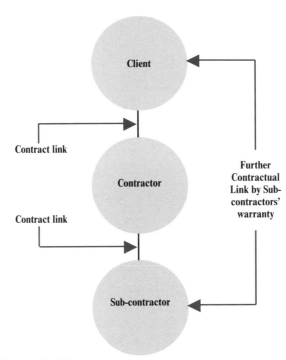

Figure 19.3.2
Relationships between client and sub-contractor

Critical factors

- Investigation of defects for cause and responsibility

Once the investigation has been completed, and the results made known to the investigator's client, and others as appropriate, the questions are then posed: is the defect caused by materials and workmanship not being in accordance with the contract? or has a performance specification not been satisfactorily fulfilled? alternatively, was the design defective?

Liability for defects
In many cases the answer is clear, and responsibility can rest with one defaulting party. In other cases it is found that responsibility must be apportioned between the parties involved.

Difficulty can be experienced by the client who may not know that a defect has occurred until the effects begin to appear a considerable time later. The period during which a specialist contractor or consultant designer can be sued is governed by law. In contract, the period is six years for contracts under hand or twelve years for contracts as a deed. For negligence cases – i.e. for claims in tort – in each case it is generally six years (except for personal injury where it is three years). Under the *Defective Premises Act 1972*, the time for actions runs from the date upon which the premises are completed. ∎

Further reading in the Guide:
5.2 Surveying buildings: scope • 5.3 Surveying buildings: roofs • 19.1 Approaches to contract • 19.2 Review of contract and sub-contracts • 21.2 Diagnosing defects and remedies

12 Mastic Asphalt	13 Polymeric Single Ply	14 Copper	15 Lead Sheet	16 Other Membranes	17 Thermal Insulants	18 Specification	19 Contracts & Procurement	20 Inspection	21 Maintenance	22 Bibliography	23 Index
263	301	331	353	375	383	393	399	413	429	437	455

Inspection 20

Special Note:
The provision of detailed guidance is intended to assist Architects, Clerks of Works, Superintending Officers, Surveyors, or other agents of the Employer or building client/owner, where they have a duty to inspect the works, in identifying which matters require attention in their particular circumstances. This Chapter should not be interpreted as defining their duties or as extending their duties beyond those in their terms of employment.

20.1 Inspection of the works

- Inspection of the works is different from supervision. It can overlap the function of supervision, in that the same work has also to be scrutinised by the contractor, but the actions and responsibilities differ if the work is unsatisfactory.

- The aim of inspection of the works is to determine as far as possible that the installation is carried out in accordance with the contract. For convenience, the person carrying out this task is here termed 'the Inspector'.

The term 'inspection' as a distinct activity is here restricted to 'inspection of the works'. It is distinct from maintenance surveys (see **Units 5.1** and **21.1**). Although inspection and supervision are sometimes regarded as the same, they are taken as different in this Guide (see also **Unit 5.1**).

Inspection of the works

This is the inspection of current construction works, on or off site, by someone acting as Agent for the client or Employer – such as an architect or other Superintending Officer or a Clerk of Works. It may form a basis for certification.

The task is solely to determine whether or not the works have been carried out in accordance with the requirements of the Contract. It may result in an instruction being given to the contractor, but does not involve instructions directly to the workforce. In this sense, 'inspection' is different from 'supervision'. This Guide offers some guidance on inspection, but not explicitly on supervision.

The 'Inspector'

The term 'Inspector' is used solely for convenience in this Guide, and refers to a person acting as agent of the Employer. No general legal meaning is assumed here and the special note on the Chapter head page is relevant.

The quality of the finished roof will be directly related to the quality of workmanship and supervision. The inspection of these areas must be competent, thorough and undertaken by suitably qualified personnel.

Pre-construction

Where possible, the Inspector should prepare for inspection. This might include:

- Study of the contract drawings, details, specifications and bills of quantities, and related standards, manufacturers' information, etc., to judge whether there is adequate information available to execute the works.
- Advice to the designer of information requirements, including possible design errors, omissions and ambiguities.
- Establish with the design team and/or contractor (as appropriate) – and maintain – a consistent policy on acceptable standards of materials and workmanship.
- Record any agreed deviation from the contract documentation.

- Establish what training/experience is appropriate for makers/installers of the specified system.
- Establish that test equipment will be to hand at the appropriate time.
- Establish procedures with the contractor to provide satisfactory inspection.
- If a flood test is envisaged, check with the structural consultant and the designer on the implications.
- Arrange, co-ordinate and monitor the receipt and despatch of relevant information and correspondence.
- Develop a standard reporting format, maintained and circulated as appropriate. This can be followed up with a similar or extended format for report during construction (see below). It might include:
  - diary for the project
  - instructions/variations received
  - quality control system
  - instruction or directions given
  - test reports
  - works visit reports.
- Agree any attendance at progress meetings.

During construction

The Inspector's duties during site operations may include the following:

- Inspect systematically the works in progress, to determine compliance with the contract.
- Inspect critical details, joints and junctions.
- Inspect proprietary items, to determine whether fixed and fitted in accordance with manufacturer's instructions (where specified).
- Inform design team of work not conforming to the requirements of the contract documents; where authorised, issue instructions for the removal or remedy of unsatisfactory work.
- Inspect materials delivered to site.
- Arrange for testing of materials as required (see **Unit 20.6**).
- Witness tests undertaken on the works.
- Keep records of completed but inaccessible work.
- Check temporary protection of completed roof.
- Comment upon the contractors' progress report, where possible prior to the progress meeting.
- Approve and record samples of materials.
- Approve and record samples of workmanship.

Further reading:
CLARK, T. Developing the Clerk of Works professional function • HOLLAND, R., MONTGOMERY-SMITH, B.E. & MOORE, J.F.A. Appraisal and repair of building structures

- The Inspector should compile a written record of the inspections and any tests carried out both on and off site, during or immediately after such an event (where possible).
- Guidance here covers a comprehensive range of advice, from which the Inspector may select according to need and the terms of appointment. Any inspection does not relieve any supplier or contractor of their contractual obligations.

- Monitor the contractors' arrangements for safety, security, cleanliness and conformity with appropriate regulations (e.g. COSHH).
- Records (which may be extension of report format from pre-construction phase – see above) might include:
  - site diary
  - weather and working conditions
  - all delays, with reasons where known
  - instructions/variations
  - tests undertaken
  - mock-up examination (and any visual record – e.g. photographs)
  - off-site visits
  - inspections carried out to sectional completion of areas and notes on any deviations from the contract requirements.
- Carry out defects inspection of completed work, including final snagging and at completion of contract.
- Observe whether protection is put in place to finished work and as required elsewhere.
- Ensure that other staff and replacements are adequately notified and briefed during the Inspector's absences from site.

Critical activities

Each contract will have its critical activities which, if not considered properly, can lead to severe problems later on. These might include:

- Pressure to progress works out of sequence or prematurely.
- Roofing commences too early to complete, requiring return visits.
- Work activities carrying on above or around the roofing during its installation, leading to subsequent damaged to the roof system.
- Inadequate consideration given to the method and sequence of the overall building construction. Particular concerns are:
  - construction access over the roof, before, during or after the laying of the roofing system
  - storage of materials, equipment, facilities on areas of completed work
  - location of equipment hoists, cranes, etc., in positions which do not enable work to be satisfactorily done, finished or tested
  - late instructions for service penetrations.

- Protection inadequate, especially to:
  - work area prior to commencement, with potential contamination of the base
  - work area during laying
  - completed work area after testing has been done.
- The workface not proceeding as a uniform work front – leaving preceding layers exposed for long periods.
- Subsequent loading of the roofing system (e.g. during remedial works).

Inspection priorities

A number of factors have outcomes which can be incorporated as priorities into the inspection procedures. Items can include:

- Correct falls incorporated in base.
- Correct preparation of base.
- For profiled metal decking, location of fixings etc. on crown of deck.
- Integrity and full support of the VCL.
- Seal of VCL around perimeters and penetrations in roof and ceiling.
- Integrity and completeness of separating layers.
- Bonding/securing, staggering of insulation.
- Roof/wall junction of insulation.
- Use of non-compressible insulant under membrane.
- Physical securing of finish.
- Correctly formed movement joints.
- Fillets and chamfers formed and in place.
- Depth and quality of any ballast.
- Temporary protection.
- Physical protection of roof for more than light foot traffic.
- Testing of the completed roof (e.g. flood test).
- Inspection of each stage for physical damage.
- Not laying in adverse weather conditions.

Testing

Testing of completed work, trial or completed repair areas must be considered an integral aspect of the installation process (see **Units 5.3** and **20.6**).

Record keeping

Future benefits will result from comprehensive completion of record information, such as the sound basis for planned maintenance (see **Unit 21.1**). These may draw upon Inspector's reports compiled during the contract. ■

Critical factors

- Systematic inspection of the works in progress, to agreed criteria and standards.
- Testing of the works.
- Recording of all matters relating to inspections of the works.
- Information from the contractor.
- Identify priority items for checking.
- Agree installation procedure and monitoring.
- Agree and follow documentation of procedure and monitoring.
- Inspection of all interfaces with other elements

Further reading in the Guide:
5.1 Types of survey and inspection • 5.3 Surveying buildings: roofs • 20.6 Site processes: remedial works and testing • 21.1 Planned maintenance

12 Mastic Asphalt	13 Polymeric Single Ply	14 Copper	15 Lead Sheet	16 Other Membranes	17 Thermal Insulants	18 Specification	19 Contracts & Procurement	20 Inspection	21 Maintenance	22 Bibliography	23 Index
263	301	331	353	375	383	393	399	413	429	437	455

20.2 The role of the contractor

- The main contractor may have responsibility for providing information relevant to inspection and for checking the preceding works and advising the Inspector.
- Attention to the suitability and quality of the preceding and associated works is important, to ensure satisfactory and progressive installation of the roofing. .

It is often the responsibility of the contractor to check various items and to advise the Inspector before commencing work. Examples may include information and preceding works.

Information required to facilitate inspection

To facilitate inspection, information/actions may be required from the contractor, particularly where the contractor is responsible for design. During the pre-construction period, and depending on the terms of the contract, the Inspector should seek to obtain information which may include:

- Detailed specification – to facilitate observing compliance with the contract specification, including:
  - specification of materials and source
  - certification of compliance with standards
  - method of compliance with specific performance requirements (e.g. trafficking of roof, unusual processes or materials).
- Detailed working drawings – covering all areas of the contract works, including all areas of roof to be covered, cross referenced to details.
- Samples of materials to be used (see also below), including:
  - certification of compliance
  - confirmation of material compatibility.
- Detailed programme – co-ordinated with the main contract programme, including:
  - manufacture
  - activity programme – co-ordinated with material delivery and handling
  - possession and handover dates
  - completion
  - proposals for protection or isolation of completed roof areas.
- Method statements – to be prepared and submitted for approval, where appropriate, including factory/off-site activities:
  - material production
  - certification
  - compliance with standards
  - material identification (e.g. production date, run number, checker)
  - storage and handling
  - transportation
  - material sampling
  - protection
  - health and safety regulations (e.g. COSHH).
- Method statements which include site activities, such as:
  - delivery/tickets/checking
  - storage/security/weather and physical protection
  - handling
  - loading of structure
  - system of supervision of preceding work, work under way, completed work
  - temporary rainwater disposal, temporary weather protection
  - sampling, testing, remedials, re-testing
  - health and safety regulations
  - protection of preceding works, daywork joints, completed work.

Preceding works – general

A number of generally applicable items should be checked by the contractor (and the Inspector advised). These may include checking that:

- The base has been properly laid to the specified falls, tolerance and finish.
- The base is sound, sufficiently dry, physically secure, and free from contaminants (e.g. oil, grease, dirt, even milk in the case of built-up roofing).
- Any moisture trapped in the roof deck or cementitious screed has a suitable escape route.
- All upstand and membrane penetration details have been completed, to enable a complete area of the roof to be addressed.
- All flashings and other metal work have been correctly installed.
- All outlets have been installed, fixed and located at the correct height relative to the base to accommodate the particular finish.
- Vertical surfaces have been correctly prepared.
- Movement joints are in place.
- All cut and preformed chases are complete.
- Any required preformed fillets are in place.
- Agreed details are in place, including:
  - flues
  - lightning protection
  - cleaning equipment bases and tracks
  - plant and equipment bases and mountings

Further reading:

Chapter	1	2	3	4	5	6	7	8	9	10	11
Contents	Introduction	History	Regulatory Methods	Principles	Surveys	Constraints & Targets	Design Selection	Calculations	Detail Design Principles	Evaluation of Design	Built-up Roofing
Page	1	19	31	45	83	95	105	165	189	217	221

© BFRC / CIRIA: Flat Roofing: Design and Good Practice. 1993

- Samples and mock-ups can demonstrate conformity with the design intent. They can also allow the resolution of difficult details, as well as providing a reference for quality management on site.
- Guidance here covers a comprehensive range of advice, from which the Inspector may select according to need and their terms of appointment. Any inspection does not relieve any supplier or contractor of their contractual obligations.

- rooflights, louvres and ventilation ducts
- handrail fixings
- any other fixing that penetrates the membrane.

Preceding works – membrane materials

The following membrane material specific items may have to be checked:

Built-up roofing:
- Substrates should be in a condition, particularly with regard to moisture, which will allow adequate bond to be obtained. A test sheet should be used to check this, where necessary.

Mastic asphalt:
- Concrete screeds or decks should receive the equivalent of a wood float finish.
- The agreed form of key proposed is in place on vertical and sloping work.

Polymeric single-ply:
- The surfaces of all substrates should be checked for smoothness and be free of any loose material or debris.

Copper sheet:
- The surface of all substructures should be checked for smoothness and rigidity.
- Where substructures are covered with boarding or plywood the surface should be checked for flushness and any protruding nail or screw heads. Where these are evident, they must be punched in or countersunk respectively.

Lead sheet:
- Check that substrates provide a continuous smooth surface strong enough to support the lead, and will hold the fixings firmly and permanently. Timber decking should preferably be tongue-and-grooved: check that it is wrought, seasoned, fixed in the direction of the fall or diagonally. (More usually, external quality plywood may be used.)
- Nails should be punched well home, screws counter sunk and any sharp corners smoothed off.
- Check that concrete decking is smooth, with an underlay. Any materials used to take fixings should not be vulnerable to decay through the presence of retained moisture or condensation.

Samples/mock-ups

Samples and/or mock-ups may be required on site during the contract, for example to agree a standard of finishes. The contractor should arrange them for inspection and approval, before they are used as a reference.

The use of samples or mock-ups should be considered during the design process (see also **Unit 7.1**), but sometimes the full benefits only become apparent when planning the inspection of the works. Both are important, as design choices may also arise during construction, especially when working on existing buildings.

Suppliers will normally be able to provide designer/specifiers with samples of their membrane material and prototype accessory products, such as roof outlets, trim sections, etc. This can be a particularly useful service to both the designer and to those on site.

These samples should be carefully kept as references against the product specified but should be made available to the contractor in order to ensure that the correct product is installed.

For any of these provisions, where appropriate, the site sample of a roofing system should incorporate:

- any additional base preparation
- base construction
- priming
- separating membrane and laps
- VCL and laps
- insulation bonding, butting, securing
- upstand, edge trim, outlet, movement joint
- laying, joints, welds, welts, seams, rolls cappings etc.
- daywork joint, finish, protection
- any special or unusual features.

Using mock-ups and samples in the building process – both for new build and for work to existing buildings – can substantially assist in discussions between designers, suppliers, contractors, and in some cases with statutory authorities, etc. They can also help the designer to show the client what is intended. In some circumstances, the extensive use of mock-ups is advisable, in which case appropriate time and budget should be planned accordingly. ∎

Critical factors

- Condition of the substrate.
- Preparatory work carried out correctly and completely.
- Establish need for approved samples of materials and systems.
- Establish critical information, its distribution and timing.
- Limit traffic, working and loading on complete roof.

Further reading in the Guide:
7.1 Design selection: general approach • 20.1 Inspection of the works

12 Mastic Asphalt	13 Polymeric Single Ply	14 Copper	15 Lead Sheet	16 Other Membranes	17 Thermal Insulants	18 Specification	19 Contracts & Procurement	20 Inspection	21 Maintenance	22 Bibliography	23 Index
263	301	331	353	375	383	393	399	413	429	437	455

20.3 Health and safety

- The importance of safety in operations on roofs cannot be over-emphasised.
- Some requirements, such as those affecting storage, arise for reasons of health and safety as well as for reasons of ensuring the quality of the installed products.
- The combination of working at height with heavy, awkward and, in some cases, hot or flammable materials, is potentially dangerous.

General

Health and safety factors must be considered throughout the process of design and construction (see also **Unit 3.4**). They should also be taken into account in considering the duties of the Inspector, for that person's own well-being and insofar as they have a duty of care to those involved with or affected by the works in progress.

Manufacturers' health and safety data sheets should be available on site and their contents drawn to the attention of all operatives.

The working environment should comply with the relevant requirements of the *Health and Safety at Work etc. Act*, COSHH and the local Factory Inspectorate.

Operatives should be required to exercise disciplines appropriate to the situation and should be aware of their own responsibility for their own and their colleagues' health and safety.

Some requirements, such as those for storage, arise for reasons of health and safety as well as for reasons of ensuring the quality of the installed products. It may be helpful to consult relevant suppliers for their advice.

Arrangements for work

It may be necessary to consider restrictions on work methods where the use of hot materials and/or equipment which produces naked flames might present an unacceptable risk – either to people or to building fabric (e.g. work to existing buildings of historic or architectural interest). In such cases, requirements of insurance companies may also restrict the acceptable methods of working.

Adequate safety guards generally and guarded landing platforms should be provided. The area below any hoist should be guarded off, to prevent operatives standing directly below. The arrangements for fixing, working around and providing access to hoists and other mechanical handling equipment require particular attention.

The roof area should be kept clear of all materials other than those being used, unless this cannot be reasonably avoided; in all cases, temporary storage areas should be checked to prevent overloading.

All tools and machines should be maintained in good condition and stored in a safe area when not in use. Electrical supplies should be disconnected and all gas-fired equipment turned off when not in use. Cable runs should be avoided where possible, but, otherwise, should be protected and marked.

Built-up roofing

Where hot-poured bitumen is used, particular safety issues arise. For example:

- Care is needed in setting up the boiler and in the arrangements for placing, drawing upon and controlling the gas supply.
- The boiler should not be transported or towed if it contains hot bitumen or if the burner is alight.
- The boiler and its performance should be monitored at all times by a responsible and competent person.
- Temperatures of oxidised bonding bitumen should never exceed 260°C or the flash point less 15°C, whichever is lowest.
- Boilers should designed and manufactured to suitable standards; the manufacturers' instructions for safe use should always be followed.
- Appropriate fire-fighting equipment and materials should always be within easy reach of those operating the equipment.

Mastic asphalt

Because of its weight and need to be poured as a hot charge (factors which arise in achieving its merits as a membrane material), particular precautions are needed in handling and using mastic asphalt:

Site operatives

Operatives should always wear strong flame-proof gloves and working boots with non-slip soles. When applying primer and reflective paints, face masks should be worn.

Block form

When mastic asphalt is supplied on pallets, the pallets and strapping are not usually sufficient for safe crane handling. Special purpose lifting tackle and caging or netting are usually required, to form part of the operation, in accordance with current safety requirements. Blocks should be transported in high sided vehicles or netted.

Further reading:
Health and Safety at Work etc. Act • The Factories Act • SI 1972 No 917 High Flammable Liquids and LPG Regulations; • COSHH Regulations • BSCP144: Part 3 Built-up bitumen felt; Part 4 Mastic asphalt • BS2092: Eye protectors • FRCAB/NFRC Information Sheet 18: Code of practice for safe handling of hot bitumen for roofing purposes • LSA Control of lead at work, • Publications from time to time by the HEALTH AND SAFETY EXECUTIVE

- The contractor and all operatives should comply with all safety directives, on site and where appropriate in the factory. Site helmets and other relevant protective clothing should be worn at all times.
- Guidance here covers a comprehensive range of advice, from which the Inspector may select according to need and their terms of appointment. Any inspection does not relieve any supplier or contractor of their contractual obligations.

'Hot charge' form

Hot charge mastic asphalt is delivered at a maximum temperature of 230°C. The major hazard is that of skin burns. Exposed areas of skin should be reduced to the minimum. Heat-resistant gloves and eye protection (to *BS2092*) should be worn where splashing is foreseeable.

General

A number of other considerations can be mentioned:

- Heating and melting should be carried out to procedures under the Working Rule Agreement.
- Temperatures should never exceed 230°C (as specified in *CP144, Part 4*).
- Excessive fume generation results when the material is overheated; prolonged overheating can cause reduction in the bitumen content and in the hardness of the installed material, thus affecting long-term performance (see also **Unit 4.13**).
- If mastic asphalt is to be applied in a confined situation, potential exposure to bitumen fumes will be higher. Adequate ventilation should be provided and suitable respiratory protection worn. As mastic asphalt is non-toxic and generally suitable for use, including possible contact with potable water, it should not present special problems in this regard during works in the open on site.
- Where asphalt has to be heated at a lower level and then hoisted to the roof by rope or pulley, it must be kept clear of scaffolding.
- All necessary precautions should be strictly observed. Fuel bottles and cauldrons should be at least 10m apart and a fire extinguisher should be within easy reach.

Polymeric single-ply

Particular issues arise from the safe storage of materials at the workplace (as well as for site storage before use – see also **Unit 20.4**). For example:

- Single-ply materials should be stored under cover and generally in accordance with the relevant regulations, e.g. the *Factories Act, Health and Safety at Work etc. Act, High Flammable Liquids and LPG Regulations* and *COSHH Regulations*. Contamination with other products, particularly those based on hydrocarbons, must be avoided.
- Roll stock of membranes should be chocked to prevent rolling and, until required during that work period,

should be stored in an area of the roof not in use (subject to not over-loading the roof structure and to being capable of safe handling to the workplace).
- The solvent adhesives typically used should be stored with lids firmly secured. When in use, only sufficient material for immediate use should be exposed. Adhesive should be decanted into smaller containers and the lid replaced and securely fastened. When maintained on the roof, these materials should be stored securely in an area not in use and away from exposed edges.

Fire safety is also an issue which requires attention, for example:

- Naked flames should not be used where they may come into contact with single-ply membranes, and should not exist on the roof when solvent-based adhesives are present or in use.
- Water may be used to extinguish a fire affecting the membrane but water must not be used to extinguish solvent fires. In the event of a solvent fire, carbon dioxide powder or sand should be used to smother the flame. All those on site should avoid breathing the fumes.

Lead sheet

The approved Code of Practice, *Control of Lead at Work*, and *SI 1980 No.1258*, '*The Control of Lead at Work Regulations*', require employers of workers or operatives in contact with lead to take safety precautions. Some immediate considerations include:

- Bossing is not defined as 'significant' exposure but the abrading of lead is.
- In most cases the use of lead sheet in building does not create a significant exposure to lead, although it is essential not to eat, drink or smoke in a place liable to be contaminated by lead and it is important to wash hands, arms and face thoroughly at the end of each working session.
- When lead welding is carried out for short periods of time in the open air there is no significant hazard, but when stripping old lead sheet, where the underside is heavily corroded, or when lead welding in unventilated conditions additional precautions must be observed.

Further information is contained in the booklet *Control of Lead at Work*, available from the Lead Sheet Association.

■

Critical factors

- Establish the applicable safety requirements.
- Decide how the procedures are to be implemented.
- Check installation Company safety policy, both general and applicable to the contract.
- Ensure copy available on site.
- Reports of any safety officer's visits to be obtained and stored.

Further reading in the Guide:
3.4 Health and safety • 5.1 Types of survey and inspection • 7.1 Design selection: General approach • 20.1 Inspection of the works
20.4 Materials handling and storage • 22.2 Health and safety bibliography

12 Mastic Asphalt	13 Polymeric Single Ply	14 Copper	15 Lead Sheet	16 Other Membranes	17 Thermal Insulants	18 Specification	19 Contracts & Procurement	20 Inspection	21 Maintenance	22 Bibliography	23 Index
263	301	331	353	375	383	393	399	413	429	437	455

- Some requirements, such as those affecting storage, arise for reasons of health and safety as well as for reasons of ensuring the quality of the installed products.
- Suppliers and manufacturers may be able to advise on storage and handling.
- Guidance here covers a comprehensive range of advice, from which the Inspector may select according to need and their terms of appointment. This advice does not relieve any supplier or contractor of their contractual obligations.

General

Building materials and components may experience their most demanding conditions before they reach their final service destination in the building. The local stresses they experience while being handled, or their vulnerability while laying in a temporary storage area just before installation, can lead to significant damage. This can affect their performance in use (and hence is an issue for inspection), and thus requires remedy. Delays occurring just before installation can be particularly difficult for the contractor to resolve without affecting the whole programme.

Further effects can be surprising. Moisture and/or temperature conditions, which the materials can comfortably resist in service, can sometimes provide problems if experienced in the vulnerable condition before installation.

Some requirements, such as storage, arise for health and safety reasons as well as for ensuring the quality of the installed products.

It may be necessary to consider restrictions on work methods where the use of hot materials and/or equipment which produces naked flames might present an unacceptable risk. In such cases, requirements of insurance companies may also restrict the acceptable methods of working.

Information

Information should be made available to those responsible for organising delivery of materials. It may include:

- exact delivery address and any special restrictions of time, access points, use of pavements, etc.
- height from ground level and particulars of access to the roof area
- details of hoisting and cranage on site
- compound areas
- phasing of the works
- any special or unusual features (e.g. safety, ease of immediate road access).

Designers and specifiers can draw on the considerable expertise of suppliers and manufacturers by reference to their instructions and recommendations for good practice, as published with their products and services. They should wherever possible have specified that suppliers' or manufacturers' instructions are to be followed, rather than leave it to be inferred. Where doubt arises, this should be raised formally with the supplier.

Certificates of conformity

Suppliers who hold Agrément Certificates can be expected to provide material conforming in all respects to that covered by the certificate. It is possible to obtain certificates of conformity from suppliers, especially those who operate a *BS5750* Quality Assurance Scheme, as assurance that the product meets the product specification.

Condition at arrival on site

All materials should arrive on site un-opened in their original containers or wrappers. All products should be clearly identified by the manufacturer's name and batch code: damaged or unrecognisable materials should not be used and should be removed from site as soon as possible.

All materials should be checked; where appropriate, they should be properly labelled with the appropriate BS Kitemark or the CE mark (see also **Unit 3.1**).

Correct storage and handling of materials is a prerequisite of satisfactory installation.

Preparation for workplace

Materials required for the installation should be accumulated and checked for quality and quantity before work commences on site.

Materials and items in general should not be left on the roof. Where this reasonably cannot be avoided, materials should be adequately protected against wind and weather, and access to the roof should be removed or prevented at times when the roof is unattended.

Storage of materials should be only in the locations and to the loadings agreed with the structural consultant prior to the commencement of work on site.

Specific materials

Apart from general guidance on storage of materials and equipment, including those materials (such as adhesives) which are 'consumed' in the process of installing a roof, certain materials have particular considerations.

Vapour control materials

Despite the toughness of modern vapour control materials, it is still all too easy to damage them on site. With many of the sheet materials typically in use, it can be difficult to identify small holes or similar damage – but these can lead to condensation problems once installed. Suppliers' recommendations are the most obvious detailed guidance available and should be sought at the time when their

---

Further reading:
CIRIA Special Publication 57 Handling of materials on site

Chapter	1	2	3	4	5	6	7	8	9	10	11
Contents	Introduction	History	Regulatory Methods	Principles	Surveys	Constraints & Targets	Design Selection	Calculations	Detail Design Principles	Evaluation of Design	Built-up Roofing
Page	1	19	31	45	83	95	105	165	189	217	221

- Certain aspects of material handling are critical to the eventual quality of the finished product:
  - storage conditions, particularly of those materials that can be damaged physically or by weather
  - handling methods, including any protections and/or temporary packaging
  - distances from point of mixing to point of placing of hot *insitu* applied materials
  - avoiding spillage of liquid materials e.g. solvents, which may cause damage

product is being considered.

Ballast

Apart from any recommendations by suppliers, three things should be kept in mind:

- Structural loadings on whatever supports the ballast.
- The stability of the ballast materials as a pile – angle of repose to prevent slippage, etc.
- Prevention of contamination of the ballast with materials which might damage components beneath it, once in place, or might affect its ability to be placed properly.

Thermal insulants

There is an advantage that, by their nature, many such materials will appear potentially fragile, despite often surprising toughness. Particular issues are:

- Minor damage – e.g. to corners – when the components are accidentally dropped.
- Crushing during handling.
- Spilling liquid materials which may interact chemically.
- Allowing the materials to get wet (even where the insulants are intended for use in inverted warm deck roofs, and therefore will often have water around them in use).
- Vulnerability to high winds

Built-up roofing

Unless otherwise recommended by the manufacturer, bituminous roofing materials should be stored vertically, on end, on level surfaces, and not so that one roll rests on another. They should be protected from moisture. It is good practice for rolls to be stored on supply pallets.

In cold conditions, rolls of oxidised bitumen-coated intermediate layers and cap sheets should be stored in conditions with background heat, to ease workability.

Mastic asphalt

The materials and the mixer should be stored as closely as possible to the access point of the roof. Gas-fired equipment should be stored in a secure compound.

Storage and handling features are of particular concern:

- Temperatures should never exceed 230°C (as specified in *CP144, Part 4*).
- Excessive fume generation results when the material is overheated; prolonged overheating can cause reduction in the bitumen content and in the hardness of the installed material, thus affecting long-term performance (see also **Unit 4.13**).

- Hot charge mastic asphalt deliveries are available, supplying up to 16 tonnes of material. All deliveries are made in specially designed thermostatically-controlled agitation machines.

Polymeric single-ply

Rolls of single-ply material should be stored flat and stacked no more than three high, chocked to prevent movement. Rolls should not be stacked vertically on end.

Single-ply material should be hoisted to the roof only by roll cores, webbing straps or stacked horizontally on pallets. They should not be uncovered or unwrapped until ready for use.

Where the covering is prefabricated, it will be delivered folded and will require equipment to lift it to the roof, where it is unfolded. For large roofs, the folded membrane will constitute a substantial point load.

Mechanical handling is usually by means of fork-lift trucks, as most materials and accessories are palletised. These may be lifted to roof level by crane, although care must be taken to avoid localised overload of the deck.

Copper sheet

This must be transported flat on pallets and delivered in a dry condition. All copper strip, in coil form, should preferably be transported on edge in crates or palletised and delivered in a dry condition. Care must be exercised to avoid any damage to the surface.

Copper sheet and strip should be stored in an enclosed building that is dry. Copper roofing materials should never be stored in the open air. When material is delivered on pallets, they should be stored so that there is adequate space for the circulation of air around all sides of the stack.

Lead sheet

Coils of lead sheet must be protected from water and delivered in dry condition. Lead sheet must be stored off the ground and in a well-ventilated dry enclosure. (Lead sheet is particularly vulnerable to the action of pure water, which arises in condensate.)

Care must be exercised in the transport, unloading and storage of lead sheet, to avoid damage to the surfaces: otherwise, the effect can be an unacceptable appearance when the roof is completed. ■

Critical factors

- Safe non-detrimental handling of materials from factory to the workplace.
- The quality of the installed roof, and its long-term performance, from appropriate materials handling and storage.
- Role of inspection in checking materials handling and storage as part of contractual requirements.
- If suppliers' or manufacturers' instructions are to be followed, this should be stated explicitly.
- Approved method statement procedure to be followed.
- Materials kept in dry and well-ventilated enclosures.

Further reading in the Guide:
3.1 Standards and certification: a framework • 4.13 Durability of materials • 18.1 Specification writing • 20.3 Health and safety

20.5   Site processes: general

- Works on site require certain conditions to be established by the contractors at the commencement of − and during − the execution of the roof construction:
  - correct sequencing of the inter-related trades, to ensure continuity of roofing operations.
  - correct programming of the roofing installation, to ensure no back-tracking over completed work.
  - sufficient time allowance for testing, with contingency for any required remedial work and subsequent re-testing.

General

This Unit deals with general guidance which is intended to assist the Inspector by providing some indicators of good site practice. They may also be helpful to supervisors. Where such practices are absent or are plainly not followed, there may be cause for enquiry: they can thus serve as early warnings.

Information

As soon as practicable, there should be full exchange of information between the general and roofing contractors.

Protection from overhead works

It is usually desirable that all work above roof level be completed before the roofing is installed. If not, provision should be made for complete−and safe−protection of the roof by the main contractor. This should include for all temporary works by other operatives.

Scaffolding

It is normal practice for the main contractor to provide adequate scaffolding, edge protection and hoisting facilities. Early consultation is essential.

Control of the working areas

The working area should be maintained in a clean and tidy condition at all times.

It is essential to close the roof to prevent water ingress in the event of unexpected rain. All perimeters, interruptions and the working edge should have overnight security against wind and water. Temporary disposal of rainwater may be necessary.

Loose covers should not be stored on the roof or weighted down with items likely to be displaced. This particularly applies to adhesive products, where spilled material may seriously damage the roof.

Other trades

The roofing contractor may require the cooperation of other trades, for example:

- scaffolders etc. to install scaffolds and hoists
- carpenters, plumbers, other metal craftsmen, in constructing kerbs, upstands, free-standing collars
- plumbers for the fixing of outlets
- bricklayers for repointing chases and in planning arrangements of dpc flashings, etc.
- operatives involved in making the deck/substrates, in planning fixing methods and in protection of works

- any other work associated with removal of unacceptable work and its remedy.

Installation of the waterproof membrane

Materials should be checked and, where appropriate, tested on delivery to site (see also **Unit 20.6**).

Any preliminary construction work, such as rooflight plinths, removal of units or their casings, clearing and cutting chases and installation of lead cover flashing, etc., should be done before installing the membrane.

The method of checking membrane joints, etc., should not risk damage (e.g. avoid sharp tools in testing bonds).

The good practice on site should be related to the detailed joints and junctions specific to the different membrane options (see **Units 9.1, 11.5, 12.5, 13.5, 14.4, 15.4**).

Issues specific to particular materials are given below, which should be considered with the general approach to designing the roof (**see Unit 7.1**) and the material-specific chapters (see **Units 11.1, 12.1, 13.1, 14.1, 15.1, 17.1**).

Built-up roofing

VCL, insulation, and built-up roofing should not be laid until traffic over the roof has ceased. If the roof has to be used as a building or storage platform, a temporary waterproofing membrane (such as *BS747* Type 5U) should be laid−including fillets and upstands.

Bitumen sheets, underlays, VCL and insulation should be labelled and in accordance with the specification. They should be stored correctly in a dry location until needed.

Plant

A suitable level surface is required for the bitumen heater. It should be placed to minimise the transfer time of hot bitumen to the work area, but should also be arranged so that it does not impede other works or traffic.

The bitumen kettle should be thermostatically-controlled or equipped with a thermometer, so that the temperature of the bitumen can be monitored at all times. Bitumen should not be heated to over 260°C or above flashpoint less 15°C whichever is the lowest. It should not be maintained at high temperatures for long periods as this will lead to loss of volatile components and change the properties of the bitumen.

Further reading:
BS747: Specification for roofing felts

© BFRC / CIRIA: Flat Roofing: Design and Good Practice. 1993

- It is preferable for all work above roof level to be completed prior to roof installation. If not, roof protection should be provided.
- Works requiring hot materials and on-site heating plant should be handled with particular care.
- Guidance here covers a comprehensive range of advice, from which the Inspector may select according to need and their terms of appointment. Any inspection does not relieve any supplier or contractor of their contractual obligations.

Fixing and laying
Oxidised bonding bitumen is generally of the correct viscosity for roofing applications at a temperature of approximately 240°C and is unlikely to be suitable below 220°C. Adequate adhesion should be ensured on non-ballasted roofs, to prevent wind uplift.

Joints/laps between sheets should be staggered for each successive layer (see Table 11.3.1). Sheeting should commence at the bottom of the slope and work up. Lap dimensions and adhesion should be regularly inspected. No cutting should occur on the finished surface.

Bitumen buckets, hot tools, etc., should not be placed on the finished surface.

Particular indications
Inspectors on completion should check for physical damage or for indications such as:

- blisters
- inadequately sealed laps
- solar finish complete
- collars of service penetrations incorrectly formed.

Mastic asphalt

VCL, insulation and mastic asphalt should not be laid until traffic over the roof has ceased. If the roof has to be used as a building or storage platform, a temporary waterproofing membrane, such as 12mm thick single-coat roofing grade mastic asphalt (including all upstands and fillets), should be laid. This can be repaired subsequently, and may be used as the VCL (if properly designed).

Blocks of asphalt should be checked on arrival to see if the coding complies either with any Agrément Certificate or with the British Standard grade specified for the works.

Location of plant
A suitable level surface for the mixer or cauldron and blocks is required as close as practicable to the work and the hoist, ensuring they do not impede other works or traffic.

The temperature of mixing asphalt should be monitored to ensure it is not heated to more than 230°C.

Distance from heating asphalt to point of work should be such that over-cooling of asphalt does not occur.

Fixing and laying
The separating layer should be lapped at all points.

Upstands should be keyed and inspected to ensure that slumping does not occur.

Great care is required to dress asphalt over trims of lead or sheet aluminium, and adequate keying should be carried out.

Torching of joints instead of poulticing, for continuing from day joints, should not occur. All traces of timber from stop ends should be removed as this may lead to opening of the joint.

Blows or damage to the surface should be pierced and made good while the mastic asphalt is still warm.

Sand (for rubbing to prevent crazing) should be removed prior to the formation of an upstand or continuation from a day joint. Otherwise, bonding will be inadequate. Removal should be by poulticing with hot asphalt, cutting away and bonding, while the asphalt is still hot.

Precautions should be in place to ensure the prevention of droppings passing into rainwater outlets.

Particular indications
Inspection on completion should check for:

- cracking/splits
- blisters
- slumping/rippling
- softening
- ponding
- completeness of solar protection.

Polymeric single-ply

Materials arriving on site should be checked to ensure they comply with the specifications. CSM should also be checked for date of manufacture – it has limited life (in terms of weldability) as low as 6 to 9 months. Material should be kept in its original packing until use on site.

The supplier's recommendations should be made available to the architects or specifiers, main contractors, specialist contractors.

Where polymer-coated metal sheeting is specified for roof perimeters, etc., this should be cut and preformed.

Refurbishment
Scarifying and removal of existing bituminous products and contamination should take place prior to installation of the membrane to avoid contamination of its surface.

continued ▶

Critical factors

- Correct sequencing of the works and trades.
- Completion of preliminary work before roof work commences.
- Systematic and continuous process, inspection at stages in the construction.
- Temporary protection of roof finish during construction and when completed.

- Fixing and laying should be carried out on a clean surface, free of debris or materials which might contaminate the membrane.
- Protection of incomplete work is essential.
- Any ventilation paths should be kept clear.

Fixing and laying

Joints and openings should be sealed, according to specification. Temporary joints and covers may be attached for subsequent removal. Contractors should seek supplier's instructions on procedures.

Installations should, where practicable, commence at the point furthest away from the access. Soft shoes (non-scuffing soles) should be worn by operatives during installation. Shoes contaminated by bitumen should not be worn on the roof works.

Particular indications

The following require particular attention:

- Adequate mechanical or adhesive fixing of the build-up and membrane. Mechanical fixings should be checked early to confirm the fixing adequacy of the substrate.
- On fully bonded systems, avoid puddles or blobs of adhesive. They may lead to punctures or difficulty with welding joints.
- Entrapped air should be removed from bonded systems, to avoid later punctures.
- Poor welding technique, or equipment leading to unsatisfactory welds (particularly at junctions).
- Solvent-welding at low temperatures.
- Joint sealing being delayed after the membrane is laid.
- Site forming of the three-directional junction penetrations. In these situations, preformed assemblies may be used.

Some materials are extremely sensitive to repair work; guidance must be obtained from the suppliers on method and timing. Replacement should always be considered.

On completion inspect carefully (to avoid damage) for:

- physical damage
- rucking at seams
- badly sealed seams
- air bubbles
- inadequate fixing
- welding/seaming at laps and junctions.

Copper sheet

The method of setting out the work will depend on whether the roofing work is traditional or longstrip system.

Materials checks

Copper sheet arriving on the site or being prefabricated in a factory should be checked for the following:

- That it is in accordance with the relevant parts of *BS2870*.
- Thickness of the sheet by weighing a sample and confirming it against Table 1 of *BS2870*.
- Ductility.
- Freedom from surface damage.
- A valid rolling mill certificate.

Fixing and laying

Ensure that the base is smooth and has nails and screws fully driven.

Avoid contact with materials which may attack copper or cause electrolytic or electrochemical action (see **Unit 13.1**).

All copper roofing should be laid flat on the substructure and show no undue signs of surface irregularity.

All standing seams and batten rolls should be accurately formed, visually straight, of even height and width throughout without irregularities or deformation.

All pointing to flashings should be complete and secure and showing no signs of cracking.

All aprons and flashing should be adequately secured against wind uplift.

Ensure ventilation paths are clear.

Particular indications

On completion, Inspectors should check for:

- Signs of splitting or cracking caused by cold or excessive working of the material.
- Adequate provision for thermal movement at seams, welts and rolls.
- Number, types and locations of fixing used.
- Surplus materials that may otherwise be trodden onto or damage the surface if not removed.

Lead sheet

Lead sheet arriving on site, should be checked for compliance with the thickness or weight specified and ordered.

Materials checks

In most cases, lead will be colour-coded (see Table 20.5.1). *BS1178* allows for a thickness variation of ±5%. Care should be taken when measuring the thickness of lead sheet because of its softness. A micrometer with a thimble ratchet and flat-faced anvil of 6-7mm diameter should be used, to prevent indentation: the sheet should be flattened and measurements taken away from free edges

---

Further reading:
BS1178: Milled sheet lead for building purposes • BS2870: Rolled copper and copper alloys: sheet, strip and foil

- Materials should be checked on arrival on site for conformity with the specifications, in particular metal sheet should be checked for thickness.
- Maintenance of good site practice will help to ensure that the works conform to the contract requirements

where burrs, physical markings and creases may be present. At least three evenly-spaced measurements should be taken across the sheet and five along its length, at 100mm intervals. These should be representative of the sample.

Because lead is soft, measurement by a micrometer may be difficult. *BS1178* gives a convenient alternative.

Lead sheet should be free from surface damage, inclusions, laminations and pinholes (most important for sand cast lead). It should be checked for impurities such as bitumen and solder (possible in recast sheet).

Contact with oak/elm/cedar should be avoided, as they contain natural compounds which may attack lead.

Fixing and laying
The base should be capable of holding nails and screws.

Roofs should be clear of debris before lead sheet is laid.

The substrate should be protected from rain or other water during the laying of lead sheet.

Avoid bonding of the lead to the base, by the use of the correct underlay. Some bitumen underlays cause local adhesion between underlay and base and between underlay and lead sheet. This can cause splitting of the lead sheet due to restrained thermal movement.

Ventilation paths should be clear.

Lead sheet should be laid as flat as possible to minimise the voids between it and the deck (see also **Unit 4.8**).

Particular indications
Inspection on completion should check for:

- Signs of stretching, thinning, buckling or splitting of the lead on bossed or welded work.
- Undercutting in lead welding, as this can cause reduced thickness of lead adjacent to welds.
- Adequate provision for thermal movement at rolls, welts and seams.
- Number, types and locations of fixings used.
- Applications of patination oil, if specified.

As with most roofs, the most vulnerable parts are eaves, gutters, joints, changes in direction and fixings.

Table 20.5.1
Colour coding of lead sheet

Code	Thickness (mm)	Colour
8	3.55	orange
7	3.15	white
6	2.65	black
5	2.24	red
4	1.80	blue
3	1.32	green

Insulation

Insulation should be staggered and run in a different direction – ideally diagonal – to the proposed membrane system. The insulation should be laid to ensure continuity, evenness and consistency of finish and should be protected prior to laying the membrane.

Fixing of insulation, and the application of any adhesive used in the system, should be thorough, particularly on warm deck roofs where the membrane is laid directly over the insulant, as movement here will be the greatest.

Testing the satisfactory adhesion of fully-bonded insulation may be carried out informally by a person physically pulling up the insulation slab. If it comes up easily, it is inadequately bonded; if only with difficulty, then a satisfactory bond has taken place.

Some insulants (e.g. cellular glass) can provide a VCL themselves. Random inspection of the junctions between a slab and at penetrations is important to ensure that full depth bitumen between panels is present, ensuring continuity of the VCL.

Vapour control layer

The installation of the VCL will need to take account of the nature of the material (e.g. robustness), of the deck (e.g. degree of support) and the required performance for control of vapour required. ∎

Critical factors

- Refer to 'particular indications'.
- Checking of bonds, etc., should be done without damaging the works.

Further reading in the Guide:
13.1 Polymeric single-ply: general description • 13.5 Polymeric single-ply: design details • 14.1 Copper: general description • 14.4, Copper: design details • 15.1 Lead sheet: general description • 15.4 Lead sheet: design details

Site processes: remedial works and testing

- The specification of remedial work should follow a proper diagnostic sequence.

- Where the remedial works involve refurbishment, design checks should be carried out as for a new roof.

- Testing on materials is only worth instigating if action will be taken as a result of the tests. Therefore, the methods and criteria for testing should be clearly established and agreed in good time.

General

Once a defect or failure has occurred, it must be subject to a proper diagnostic process (**see Unit 21.2**). Only on that basis can remedial works be specified with precision and confidence.

Repairs should only be carried out after the type and extent of any defects have been noted and their underlying cause identified. The intention of repair work should be to restore the roof to its original condition and to ensure its continuing satisfactory performance. All repairs should therefore be carried out in materials and with accessories and a standard of workmanship comparable with the original installation, unless it is the intention to upgrade the performance or other qualities of the roof.

The extent of repair work will depend on the nature of the fault. Some faults due to underlying problems may require extensive opening up, in order to correct defects in the substrate or insulation.

When carrying out any repairs to roofs, precautions must be taken during the site operations to protect the waterproof layer and any underlay and, in the case of warm deck roof construction, the insulation.

In considering the repair of the waterproof membrane, it is advisable to check the various perimeter and boundary conditions of the roof. For example, defective pointing should be broken out and renewed. Split or broken non-ferrous metal cover flashings should be repaired or renewed as necessary.

Additions and refurbishment

Where the remedial works involve significant addition or refurbishment, design checks should be carried out as for a new roof (see **Units 7.1, 10.1**).

Addition of rooflights or the forming of penetrations will require connection to the existing waterproofing and should be carried out in a similar manner.

Built-up roofing

Minor defects such as blisters can be repaired by star cutting the affected area, re-bonding and patching over the area, and finishing with the solar protective treatment. Tears, splits, etc., will be treated by cutting back the membrane over the area in staggered layers and ensuring that the whole area is dry, before relaying the complete system.

In some circumstances, repairs can be undertaken by torch-on membrane.

Mastic asphalt

All remedial work should be carried out in accordance with *CP144: Part 4*.

Any surface treatment that has been damaged or displaced should be made good to match the existing.

Where movement of edge trims has caused stress failure of the mastic asphalt, the cracks may be cut out and renewed with fresh asphalt. It is not normally possible to remove asphalt from edge trims and re-use the same trim, as warping or breakage usually occurs.

Small blisters may often be left undisturbed but remedial action is simple and effective. Large blisters in excess of 150mm square are usually indicative of more serious underlying problems. They should be cut out and the substrate examined to establish the cause.

Cutting out defective areas, cracks, stress fractures or cutting to line between new and existing asphalt may be carried out with an electrical or mechanical cutter. If it is necessary to remove an area of mastic asphalt, the lines of the cuts should be covered with molten mastic asphalt until the underlying material has softened. The asphalt should not be removed until this has taken place. In no circumstances should a hammer and chisel be used to cut cold mastic asphalt.

The cut edge of the existing mastic asphalt should be softened using molten mastic asphalt, and removed to half its depth for a width of approximately 75mm. A proper lapped joint with the re-laid mastic asphalt can then be formed.

Refurbishment

Refurbishment of mastic asphalt roofs sometimes can be carried out by repairing the existing membrane to create a VCL. Insulation is then placed over the old asphalt and the new asphalt applied on top of the insulation. Design checks as for a new roof (see **Units 7.1, 10.1**) should be carried out.

Inverted roofs can also be created by adding insulation and ballast to a repaired roof. Checks will have to be made for the additional load being applied.

Further reading:
BS2870: Rolled copper and copper alloys: sheet, strip and foil • BS5284: Sampling and testing of mastic asphalt and pitchmastic • BSCP144: Part 4 Roof coverings: mastic asphalt • BS6925: Mastic asphalt for building and civil engineering • BS1447: Mastic asphalt for roads, footways and paving in buildings • BS5750: Quality systems

© BFRC / CIRIA: Flat Roofing: Design and Good Practice. 1993

- Guidance here covers a comprehensive range of advice, from which the Inspector may select according to need and their terms of appointment. Any inspection does not relieve any supplier or contractor of their contractual obligations.
- Prior to undertaking any repair work, checks should be made that:
  - the surrounding material is sound and that other components can be satisfactorily connected to it.
  - the underlying cause of the defect has been resolved.

Polymeric single-ply

If mechanical damage does occur to the membrane, repair is usually undertaken by welding a patch of new material over the fault. The patch should have rounded corners and be larger than the damaged area by at least 50mm in each direction.

Water that has entered through the damaged area should be removed or allowed to escape.

The surfaces to be welded must be clean and dry. Some materials may require a solvent cleaner and abrading of the surface.

Remedial works may also be needed to deal with the effects of chemicals on the membrane (e.g. services discharges).

Copper

Small holes in copper sheet can be repaired with a copper patch, soft soldered over the defect. Larger repairs should be made by cutting out the damaged section of roof and inserting a new copper sheet patch with a dog-tooth joint to hold the edges of the old and new sheets together. This process is only possible where the existing sheet can be lifted to insert the patch.

Where the damage is extensive, the whole panel should be removed and replaced. This involves the opening of standing seams and batten rolls as appropriate and should be undertaken with great care. Where there is evidence of extensive star-cracking, the existing bay should be replaced by two half-length bays.

Lead

Lead is relatively easy to repair with lead-welded patches.

Where there are a number of repairs required in a single bay, the bay should be replaced.

It is usually not practical or advisable to patch repair lead sheet which has significant underside corrosion (e.g. due to condensation); this condition should be checked as part of the diagnostic process.

Testing of materials

In carrying out repair work, the appointed contractor should collect samples from each delivery of materials made to site, in order that these may be compared against the reference samples (see also **Unit 20.5**).

The designer may also specify that once remedial works have been installed, they are to be tested. The test methods may be those used for testing during surveys (see **Unit 5.2**).

Testing on materials is only worth instigating if action will be taken as a result of the tests. Therefore, the methods and criteria for testing should be clearly established and agreed in good time.

Mastic asphalt
Sampling and testing of mastic asphalt is covered by BS5284.

Member companies within the Mastic Asphalt Producers' Association (MAPA) operate under Quality Management schemes approved to BS5750, ensuring product quality at both the manufacturing stage and delivery to site.

Testing of the material once laid is not normal practice, but if such testing is sought, reference should be made to BS5284: Parts 4,5, CP144, BS6925, BS1447.

Copper sheet
Testing of all samples of copper sheet and strip should be made in accordance with the relevant parts of BS2870. Any quality management procedures should refer to this explicitly.

The suppliers of all copper sheet and strip should certify that the materials comply with the specification given in BS2870, where applicable.

The ductility of copper should be checked by the double bend test given in BS2870.

The thickness of copper sheet and strip should be checked by weighing a sample and confirming against figure given in Table 1 of BS2870: 1980, or by gauging.

All copper sheet should be inspected for quality and freedom from surface damage and accompanied by a valid certificate from the rolling mill.

Testing of complete roofs

An approach to the testing of roofs for defects is given in **Unit 21.2**. Information on methods of testing for watertightness/integrity is given in **Unit 5.3**. ∎

Critical factors

- Repairs should be carried out only when the defects and their causes have been identified.
- Allow sufficient time for testing.

Further reading in the Guide:
5.2 Surveying buildings: scope • 5.3 Surveying buildings: roofs • 7.10 Design for wind resistance • 10.1 Evaluation checklist • 20.2 The role of the contractor • 20.3 Health and safety • 20.5 Site processes: general • 21.2 Diagnosing defects and remedies

12 Mastic Asphalt	13 Polymeric Single Ply	14 Copper	15 Lead Sheet	16 Other Membranes	17 Thermal Insulants	18 Specification	19 Contracts & Procurement	20 Inspection	21 Maintenance	22 Bibliography	23 Index
263	301	331	353	375	383	393	399	413	429	437	455

Maintenance 21

Special Note: *the provision of detailed guidance is intended to assist Architects, Clerks of Works, Superintending Officers, Surveyors, or other agents of the Employer or building client/owner who may have a duty to inspect the works for maintenance, in identifying which matters require attention in the particular circumstances. Any duties of inspection will be governed in each case by the terms of appointment and this guidance should not be interpreted as a description or definition of such duties.*

21.1 Planned maintenance

- A comprehensive maintenance programme and budget should exist for the whole building.
- The roof is one of the larger depreciating elements in a building and probably the most significant in terms of the building fabric.
- The roof maintenance regime will significantly affect its performance-in-use over building life, and should be considered in the design process.

Maintenance of the building fabric and services should be taken into account throughout the initial design of a building (see **Unit 7.12**), throughout its use and as part of the further design work involved whenever there are changes to the building fabric (repairs, refurbishment or replacement).

Maintenance should always be considered within a general framework of quality building performance over time and of life-cycle costing.

Durability and general performance in use is presented in **Unit 4.13**, and **Unit 4.14** introduces an outline explanation of life-cycle costing methods.

It is recommended that a planned and comprehensive maintenance programme be compiled for every building, part of which of course would deal with the roof. This is likely to be both more cost-effective and reduce disruption to building owners and users, as compared with an approach where matters are investigated only when a building defect or even failure occurs (such as leaking of water into the building). Any form of maintenance programme will be founded on a programme of different forms of survey or inspection (see **Units 5.1, 5.2**).

Even with a planned maintenance programme, there can also be occasions when an unexpected problem arises. For this reason, two forms of maintenance action arise: 'pro-active' or preventative and 're-active' or problem-solving. These are described below.

Pro-active maintenance

Pro-active maintenance is concerned with forward planning and sensible anticipation of potential problems, seeking to prevent or at least minimise their effects.

The building owner/tenant should where possible:

- Assess the current construction and design against ongoing needs.
- Consolidate earlier information, as set out in **Unit 5.3**, perhaps held in a maintenance manual (see below).
- Have in place a maintenance contract for the roof element.
- Budget for annual maintenance and repair costs.
- Budget for replacement at the end of the anticipated life of the roof system.
- Undertake regular surveys (see **Unit 5.4**) of the roof, using a checklist which should cover such aspects as:
  - integrity of solar protection
  - ponding (is there any change from previous survey?)
  - spongy areas underfoot
  - cracks, tears, splits, ripples, rucks
  - blisters, delamination
  - pitting cracking, sagging
  - punctures, rips, scores and any physical damage
  - softening of surface
  - corrosion
  - wind uplift
  - accommodation of silt, vegetation, leaves, rubbish
  - damage or movement to copings/flashings/penetrations
  - integrity of gaskets and sealants.
- Carry out surveys after major storms.
- Carry out the following principal tasks, preferably twice yearly:
  - clear the roof areas of deposited materials deleterious to performance(particularly late autumn leaves)
  - clean out rainwater outlets and check the whole drainage system for blockages and leaks
  - reinstate any damaged or disturbed solar protection.

Re-active maintenance

There will be occasions during the life of even the best maintained building when a problem will develop. The building owner/tenant should then:

- address the problem as quickly as possible
- make temporary repairs if necessary to prevent unnecessary damage to substrates or internal finishes
- investigate/survey to ascertain the extent of problem.
- instigate permanent remedial work where appropriate.

Following a period of work on the roof to relocate or change services and/or plant, there should be a thorough survey of the roof condition after the works – in addition to inspection and supervision of those works – to ensure that no consequential damage has occurred.

Maintenance manuals

For many clients, whether they are owners or tenants (with 'repairing leases'), it can be of great assistance to have a maintenance manual prepared by their professional consultants, as an extra service. The concept is quite similar to the User's Manual and Logbook for a car. It is preferable that it be prepared at the time of initial construction, but it can be done later – although some of the relevant information may be difficult to establish at

Further reading:
BICKERDIKE ALLEN PARTNERS. Flat Roof Manual

- Roof maintenance will usually fall into one or both of two categories: **pro-active** (preventative) and **re-active** (problem solving).
- A maintenance manual is recommended as a guidance document and aid for building owners and tenants. Maintenance contracts should be considered.
- Special requirements of warranties and guarantees must be taken into account in any maintenance programme.

---

that time. Such a manual should include basic information and guidance to the maintenance items and scheduling, for example:

- A set of 'as built' drawings, to which 'as built' drawings of any subsequent changes should be added. A dated schedule of works over the life of the building, including any repairs, etc., can be helpful as a fast reference system.
- A set of specifications, relevant calculations and dates of controlling documents used (e.g. *The Building Regulations*).
- Copy records of any surveys or tests carried out on the building systems (e.g. flood tests of the roof), whether before handover or after occupation.
- A list of designers, contractors, sub-contractors and suppliers involved.
- Copies of any warranties, guarantees, etc, with a schedule of any requirements (e.g. maintenance) arising therefrom.
- Checklists and timetables of suggested maintenance tasks, e.g. items to be checked each year, each five years, etc. according to the types of inspection or survey envisaged (see also **Unit 5.1**).
- Simple pro formas to help keep the maintenance records in good order, including provision for record photographs (see also **Units 5.2** and **5.3**).
- Information on the general use of the building, noting any special features of the internal environment (e.g. uses leading to exceptionally high relative humidity, areas subject to high loadings, etc.).
- Records of any reported or discovered defects and what action followed (see also **Unit 21.2**).
- Copies of any maintenance contracts (see below), with a schedule identifying any requirements arising therefrom.
- In the case of a 'repairing lease', preferably a Schedule of Condition from the beginning of the term and, in any event, a clear description of the legal liability for the condition of disrepair.
- Incorporate guidance from pro-active and re-active maintenance (see above).

Maintenance contracts

Building owners may wish to enter into a maintenance contract with the roof installers. Building owners willingly invest significant sums on maintenance contracts

for building plant and equipment; by entering into a contract for preventative maintenance of the roof, the owners are acknowledging the importance of continuing roof maintenance.

Two levels of maintenance contracts can be considered - service contracts and maintenance agreements.

Service contracts
Here there is an arrangement for the prompt attention to faults on a call out basis. No guarantee is involved other than the work will be done competently, quickly and at a known cost rate.

Maintenance agreements
This form of agreement can be taken out when a new building is completed or following a detailed survey during the life of the building. The building owner pays an annual charge to the contractor to maintain the roof and ensure that it remains 'free from leaks', undertaking any necessary work to comply. The maintenance agreement should include for regular surveys (pro-active maintenance – see above) in order to anticipate possible problems.

Guarantees and warranties

Guarantees and warranties of materials or workmanship may be available only on condition that a defined standard or arrangement for maintenance is ensured. In contemplating maintenance arrangements, full attention must be paid to any stipulations of guarantees or warranties and these should be incorporated into that programme.

The warranty may be void if specified changes occur without the warrantor being notified: these should be noted specially. It is essential that the consequences of any limitations of a warranty or guarantee are fully recognised in any maintenance programme and in any maintenance and repairs budgeting (see also **Unit 4.14** and **7.12**).

When the contractor or sub-contractor is required to complete the detailed design of the roof construction, a warranty covering design obligations may be desirable. A warranty is unlikely to cover all items; any maintenance programme therefore should recognise these limitations.

∎

Critical factors

- Programmed maintenance activities undertaken.
- Regular inspections of the roof.
- Early and correct attention to defects or failures.
- Establish procedures for maintenance and records.

Further reading in the Guide:
4.13 Durability of materials • 4.14 Life-cycle costing • 5.1 Types of survey and inspection • 5.2 Surveying buildings: scope • 5.3 Surveying buildings: roofs • 5.4 Surveying buildings: roof materials and details • 7.12 Design for maintenance • 20.1 Inspection of the works • 20.6 Site processes: remedial work and testing • 21.2 Diagnosing defects and remedies

12 Mastic Asphalt	13 Polymeric Single Ply	14 Copper	15 Lead Sheet	16 Other Membranes	17 Thermal Insulants	18 Specification	19 Contracts & Procurement	20 Inspection	21 Maintenance	22 Bibliography	23 Index
263	301	331	353	375	383	393	399	413	429	437	455

21.2   Diagnosing defects and remedies

- Before any remedial action is taken, defects should be diagnosed to determine the cause and extent of failure
- Diagnosis of defects or failures can be a complex matter and should be approached systematically.
- Diagnosis starts with a survey; checklists may form a useful aid.

Defects in buildings generally – and the roof in particular – may be discovered (e.g. via maintenance or other survey) or reported (e.g. because occupants have seen direct evidence of failure, such as water appearing internally). At this point, the building owner or tenant will need to decide what is to be done. To do so, the defect has first to be diagnosed and then the options for remedy considered. This Unit summarises the main issues raised in this process which is initiated by the fact of a defect or failure.

Diagnostic purposes

Any diagnosis must begin with thorough investigation as to what facts can be discovered - a survey or inspection (see also **Unit 5.1**).

Clear diagnosis

Clear definition of the diagnosis of roof defects requires attention to:

- The facts which lead one to think there is a defect or failure.
- Whether a detailed survey or inspection would be appropriate, both to make clear the nature of the failure (e.g. is the appearance of water internally a sign of leakage or of condensation?) and to gather relevant information to establish its cause.
- Whether some form of opening up and/or non-destructive testing would be appropriate (see also **Unit 5.3**).
- The analysis of the problem, its nature, extent, seriousness and likelihood of having further implications (e.g. leading to more severe problems in an associated area of construction).
- Given the available facts, and a clear description of the symptoms of failure, diagnosis of the possible cause(s) and the originating defects or faults.
- If a defect arises during or soon after construction, the extent to which the remedy is the responsibility of the contractor or sub-contractor (e.g. does it fall within the scope of the defects liability under the Contract?).
- Whether the failure gives cause to consider the failure in terms of latent defects, or of a design and/or construction mistake, with the known legal implications.

Competing or combined explanations

Where a symptom is likely to involve several plausible but different originating faults (e.g. signs of water appearing inside the building), these investigations may need to consider the broader issues of:

- Understanding how the system and materials perform, both in isolation and in their relation with one another.
- Understanding how the system works in isolation from the substrate.
- Testing of core samples to ascertain that they are the original materials specified and that they were installed correctly in the first place.
- Spray or flood testing the roof area (see also **Unit 5.3**), to check hypotheses of failure mechanisms.
- Other possible reasons for indications of water penetration, such as:
  - water entrapped during construction
  - defective cavity trays at upstands or other junctions
  - joints within and between dpc and cavity trays
  - condensation (see also **Units 4.7, 4.8**)
  - pipework leaks
  - curtain walling leaks as the origin of water penetration which may otherwise appear to come from the roof.
- The timing as well as the location of failure patterns, for example:
  - whether the symptoms appear after rainstorms, or in cold weather.
  - whether they appear at likely openings in the VCL such as light fittings, or at junctions near a likely cold bridge. - etc.
- The potential effect of long-term failure of a roof finish on the structural integrity of the substrate. Timber structures, for example, can suffer extensive attack by rot (fungal attack) in warm moist conditions, giving rise to potential structural problems. Even with inverted warm deck roofs, where the thermal insulant is notionally accessible, maintenance of insulation is unlikely to be required, let alone possible. During regular maintenance inspections, any unusual changes in the level of the finished surface should be noted and investigated where appropriate: they might indicate failure of the insulant to support the membrane (warm deck roof) or the surfacing (inverted warm deck roof).

Analysis

During the survey and investigation process, information will have been compiled that, with knowledge of the material and system performance, will usually be sufficient to develop explanations for the failure.

Further reading:
BICKERDIKE ALLEN PARTNERS. Flat Roof Manual

Chapter	1	2	3	4	5	6	7	8	9	10	11
Contents	Introduction	History	Regulatory Methods	Principles	Surveys	Constraints & Targets	Design Selection	Calculations	Detail Design Principles	Evaluation of Design	Built-up Roofing
Page	1	19	31	45	83	95	105	165	189	217	221

- Analysis of local defects should ascertain if they are related to the complete installation or solely to a detailed issue. They should also be considered in relation to the anticipated building life.
- Design proposals should always be checked and evaluated as new design work, within a life-cycle cost framework.

It may be possible to identify the remedial work that would be necessary to cure individual problems. However, only when all the defects are considered, should the decision on the way to proceed be adopted. Table 21.2.1 suggests how a typical defect analysis might develop.

The analysis of the defect chart will indicate whether faults exist with the system as a whole, or whether faults are of a local nature, which can be dealt with by local repair. However, the local faults may be so widespread as to require total refurbishment or replacement of the roof.

The correct diagnosis of the fault is of vital importance, as an apparently similar defect can be caused by either a detailed problem or a system fault.

Once the analysis has been concluded, and the fault and cause identified – and perhaps tested to verify the conclusion – the designer will need to examine the options for remedy of the defect or failure.

The remedy is as much a matter of design as was the new building and equally should be considered in a life-cycle cost framework.

Options

Following the thorough inspection, investigation and analysis of the roof faults, the options available to the owner/tenant must be assessed.

The investigation analysis will have identified to what extent (if any) the roof is suffering from inherent system faults.

System faults indicate that problems could arise in the future on any part of the roof surface and therefore weigh more heavily in considering refurbishment or replacement of the roof. Local faults, if they are not widespread and appear without any system faults, would imply favouring local repair.

Considerations

The owner must consider a number of other matters in parallel:

- The practicality of the site works involved (see **Unit 20.6**).
- The urgency of the need for remedy (i.e. can they live with it a while longer?).
- The anticipated remaining life of the roof.
- The current cost of remedial works in relation to the nuisance caused. Some processes and functions can tolerate minor water penetrations; for other operations, the smallest failure could be catastrophic.

Table 21.2.1
Illustrative defect chart
(built-up roofing in this example)

Location[A]	Observed symptom	Cause concluded	Originating fault	Type of fault		Proposed repair[B]
			Description	local	system	
A22	Blister surface	Moisture from deck in between layers of felt	entrapped moisture in slab	Yes		B1
A43 A47 A52 A60	Splits in surface	Movement in deck not catered for in membrane	Material bonded to deck no provision for movement		Yes	B2
A80 A81	Punctures in surface	Heavy foot traffic	Unprotected access ways	Yes		B1 plus protection
A102	Ponding	Inadequate damage	Outlet blocked	Yes		B3

Notes:

A   Location keyed to plan, sections etc. of inspected roof

B   Repair method (brief description)
   B1 – Cut out locally, allow to dry and re-felt.
   B2 – Take up existing felt and relay, incorporating partially-bonded layer and movement joints.
   B3 – Clean outlet. Provide protection for future if possible.

- Whether taking the opportunity to introduce other improvements during remedial works, such as the thermal and/or acoustic performance of the roof, is a benefit that would improve the overall cost-effectiveness of the works.
- The structural capacity of the roof and building to take any form of enhanced or different roof finish.
- Whether simultaneous improvements in safety/maintenance access can be achieved.
- The roof plant configuration and how easily it lends itself to one course of action or another.
- The effects on the drainage system.
- Consequential effects, such as having to upgrade parapet or abutment waterproofing (e.g. insertion of new dpc or cavity trays, etc.).   continued ▶

Critical factors

- Assessment of the scale and urgency of any problem.
- Comprehensive survey to diagnose cause and extent.
- Refer to previous maintenance and repair records.
- Safety issues during inspections.
- Assessment of existing construction and drainage.
- Assessment of nature of fault – local or system.
- Analysis of options.

Further reading in the Guide:
4.7 Condensation • 4.8 Condensation: pumping • 4.15 Environmental impact of materials • 5.1 Types of survey and inspection • 5.3 Surveying buildings: roofs • 6.1 Design requirements: constraints and targets • 7.1 Design selection: general approach • 20.6 Site processes: remedial works and testing

- Options available in the event of a defect all involve **design decisions** and in summary are:
  - no action
  - refurbish
  - repair
  - replacement.
- Remedial work to occupied buildings may impose constraints on the remedial action selected and the programme

---

Work to buildings in occupation

With repair, refurbishment or replacement works, it is likely that the building concerned will be occupied – partly or wholly – or that it is vacant only for a limited period. This can be an important constraint (see also **Unit 6.1**), affecting design choices and the works programme. Full consultation is necessary with all those affected, taking into account the effects on:

- contract start and finish dates
- hours of working
- health and safety
- acceptability of certain equipment on site
- restrictions on noisy operations or other disturbances
- site conduct
- site access
- storage facilities, location, access, security, etc.
- supply of electricity, water, gas for the works
- sequence of trades
- timing of any decanting of people and/or equipment and furniture
- temporary connections of services (e.g. telephones).

In circumstances where it is essential that no water be allowed to enter the building while the works are in progress (e.g. above a maintained computer installation), it may be necessary to consider the provision of a temporary waterproof structure over the roof scheduled for remedial works.

These factors may prove also to have significant effects on the life-cycle cost analysis (see also **Unit 4.14**) of the total project.

Advice from suppliers

It should be remembered that considerable expertise in all forms of roofing works to existing buildings exists amongst the specialist sub-contractors and suppliers. Indeed, some clients prefer to return to a known system and/or supplier for precisely this reason. Designers also can benefit greatly from the advisory services offered by suppliers, including considering the implications of their different options. This reinforces the need to carry out design checks and evaluation (see **Unit 10.1**) as noted.

House, Ticino, Switzerland

Four options

In this context, the client and their designer will have to contemplate one or more of four options:

- no action
- repairs
- refurbishment (perhaps incorporating other less urgent refurbishment at the same time)
- replacement (again perhaps incorporating other less urgent works).

Design checks

All but the first of these four options require design decisions and, usually, should be accompanied by the tasks set out for design generally (see **Unit 7.1**). The design requirements – the constraints and targets (see **Unit 6.1**) – should be identified for this design task. Designers should certainly use the suggested evaluation framework (see **Unit 10.1**) to satisfy themselves that they know that thermal and condensation checks have been satisfied. They should also be conscious of the fact that many options for remedying defects involve adding extra material to the roof construction – and the roof loadings must be checked accordingly.

Further reading:
BICKERDIKE ALLEN PARTNERS Flat Roof Manual

• Within the refurbish and replacement options the opportunity may be available to alter the roof system completely. The principal options are:
  • replace system or components on a like-for-like basis
  • replace with a warm deck roof.
  • replace with an inverted warm deck roof.

Repairs

It is not always easy to undertake satisfactory repair work without major disruption to the surrounding building fabric. Access to restricted areas – around services, buildings as a whole, especially parapets – is sometimes very constrained.

When repairing to adjacent fatigued areas, satisfactory results are not always guaranteed, for example:

• Working old lead or copper can result in splitting.
• Solvent welding/adhering to vulcanised single-ply membranes is not always satisfactory.
• The removal of mastic asphalt can, if done on cold asphalt, cause cracking further from the area of repair.

Considerations of this kind can sometimes lead the designer to recommend works more extensive than simple repair.

Refurbishment

Refurbishment usually involves either significant restoration of a previous system or even upgrading beyond what was originally built. Certain consequences should be remembered:

• It is not always possible to leave the existing roof membrane in place.
• In other cases, the existing membrane can sometimes be used, or repaired and used, as a VCL for a new waterproofing membrane.
• Upgrading a roof with the addition of ballasted insulation, although a way of creating an inverted roof, can cause problems with:
  - overloading of the structure by dead weight
  - overloading of the structure by snow retained longer by the performance of the additional insulation
  - interrupting the drainage on the roof
  - height of upstands at parapets, junctions, details, etc.
• It is possible to use insulation cut to create the required falls and to lay a new finish on the insulation

• Some single-ply membranes can be laid over the top of existing roofs without the need for stripping (this should be checked with the potential supplier). There may be a requirement for a separation layer. All existing fixings would be required to be checked for soundness.
• Consideration can be given to converting the existing roof configuration to an alternative e.g. a cold deck roof to a warm deck roof. In such circumstances it is essential to check the thermal performance and condensation risk.

Replacement

Replacement is a much more radical option. Here it is assumed to mean replacement of the complete roof system, whilst retaining the principal loadbearing structure. There are a number of possible replacement options of which the principal flat roof options are:

• Replace like-for-like.
• Replace a cold deck roof with a warm deck roof or an inverted warm deck roof.
• Replace a warm deck roof with an inverted warm deck roof.

In each case, the consequences of retaining or changing a particular roof system must be examined, especially if there is an intended change of use of the building.

It is essential in designing the replacement roof to properly check the thermal performance and condensation risk.

In many instances, because of the constraints applied by the existing building structure or configurations, it may not be possible to explore several options: it may be that only one option is feasible. ∎

Critical factors

• Design checks and evaluation of proposals.
• Advice from specialist suppliers.
• Constraints affecting choice of remedial option.

Further reading in the Guide:
4.14 Life-cycle costing • 4.15 Environmental impact of materials • 5.1 Types of survey and inspection • 6.1 Design requirements: constraints and targets • 7.1 Design selection: general approach • 10.1 Evaluation checklist

Bibliography 22

22.1 Bibliography

This Unit is a general bibliography, covering the design and construction of flat roofs. An additional and specialised bibliography on Health & Safety follows in (**Unit 22.2**).

A

Alexander, W. and Street, A. (1989): *Metals in the service of man*. Penguin.

Anderson, J.M. and Gill, J.R. (1988): *Rainscreen cladding a guide to design principles and practice*. CIRIA

André, J. (1988). Special issue. Roofing. *Building, 253* (4), supplement, 22 January pp.3-55.

Anon. (1984). Flat roofs, selection is the key. *Construction News Products, (9)*, pp.12-14.

Anon. (1985). Flat roof construction. *Civil Engineering*, September, p.48-49.

Anon. (1985). Improving flat roofs. *Civil Engineering*, (March), pp.23-24, 28.

Anon. (1986). Fire safety in thermally insulated roofs with trapezoidal steel profiles. Part II. Recommendations for restricting the spread of fire of nonventilated, thermally insulated flat roofs with trapezoidal steel profiles (April 1984). *Fire Safety Journal, 10* (2), March, pp.149-154.

Anon. (1986). Wind load and the single ply solution. *Civil Engineering*, November/December, pp.27-28

Anon. (1986). Construction risks and remedies. Thermal insulation. Part 2 - the remedies. *Architects Journal, 183* (25), 18 June, pp.61-62.

Anon. (1989). Way to build up layers. *Building Design*, suppl., February, pp.40-42.

Anon. (1990). Flat roofing. *Building, 255* (16), suppl., 20 April, p.3-50.

Anon. (1990). Roofing: how to get what you want in a roof. *Construction Specifier, 43* (11), pp.49-138.

Approved Documents. see Department of the Environment

Architects' Journal Focus. (1988). Flat and pitched roofing. *Architects' Journal Focus, 2* (1), pp.29-31, 34, 35-37,40-41.

Architects' Journal. (1986). Seven Soho schemes [Dean Street Centre competition, London]. *Architects' Journal, 184* (43), 22 October, pp.26-31.

Architects' Journal. (1986). Construction risks and remedies. Thermal insulation: 1. The risks. *Architects' Journal, 183* (24), 11 June, pp.51-64.

Association Française de Normalisation. NFG 37. *Coated fabrics*. AFDN.

Association Française de Normalisation. (1971): NFT: 54-102: 1971. *Plastic materials - sheets - determination of tensile characteristics*. AFDN.

Association Française de Normalisation. (1971): NFT 54-108: 1971. *Plastic materials - thin plastic sheets determination of the resistance to tear propogation*. AFDN.

Association Française de Normalisation. (1988): NFP 84-352: 1988. *Waterproofing - sheeting for roofing and damp proofing - static penetration test*. AFDN.

Association of Consultant Architects. (1984): *Guide to the ACA Form of Building Agreement*.

Aston, R. (1984). The successful flat roof - product of research and modern technology. *Building Technology and Management, 22* (6), February, p.25.

Aston, R. (1985). The successful flat roof. *Plan, 16* (2), February, p.35.

Aston, R. (1986). Pointers to a rooftop decision. *Civil Engineering*, (April), pp.35-38.

Aston, R. & Dood, K. Roofing. (1987) *Architect & Surveyor, 62* (3), June/July, pp.21, 23-24.

B

Barrick, A. (1989). Flat roof council launchs first major study for 10 years. *Building Design*, no.965, (8 December), p.5.

Beattie, T. (1990). Defect detection. *Building* Roofing Supplement, (July), p.43

Beaumont-Markland, A. (1981). Flat roofs: avoiding failure. *RIBA Journal, 88* (2), pp.58, 63.

Beech, J.C. & Baud, M.J. (1984): The durability of bituminous built-up flat roof membranes. *Third International Conference on the Durability of Building Materials and Components, 2*.

Beech, J.C. & Saunders, G.K. (1984). The movement of foam plastics insulants in flat roofs. *Building and Environment, 19* (2), pp.65-74

Beech, J.C. & Saunders, G.K. (1989). Performance characteristics of mastic asphalt used as the weatherproof layer in flat roofs. *Construction and Building Materials, 3* (2), pp.81-85.

Beech, J. & Turner, C.H.C. (1985). Flat roof systems: a more promising future. *What's New in Building*, (May), pp.117-120.

Bellamy, J. (1988). Flat to pitched roofing: key factors in design. *Concept in Wood*, (February/March), pp.11-12.

Bickerdike Allen Partners. (1985): *Flat roof manual: a guide to the repair and replacement of built-up felt roofs*. NHS Continuing Education Unit.

© BFRC / CIRIA: *Flat Roofing: Design and Good Practice. 1993*

Bone, S. (1986). Flat roofing: a classic detailing conundrum. *RIBA Journal, 93* (11), November, pp.59-73.

Booth, R.J. (1991): Design, repair and maintenance of flat roofing systems for the pulp and paper industry. *Pulp & Paper Canada, 92* (1) 53-56.

Bordass, W., Farrel, D. and Dickin, G. (1989). Corrosion control: sheet metal roofs. *Architects Journal, 190* (22), pp.71-75.

BPIC. Coordinated Project Information. (1987) *Common arrangement of work sections for building works*, Building Project Information Committee.

BPIC. Coordinated Project Information. (1987) *Production drawings. A code of procedure for building works*, Building Project Information Committee.

BPIC. Coordinated Project Information. (1987) *Project Specification. A code of procedure for building works*, Building Project Information Committee.

BRE see Building Research Establishment.

Briggs Amasco. (1984). Design and maintenance of flat roofs. *Civil Engineering*, (May), pp.25-26, 68.

British Flat Roofing Council. (1983): *Built-up roofing: construction details*. Technical Information Sheet No 13. BFRC.

British Flat Roofing Council. (1983): *Built-up roofing: methods of attachment*. Technical Information Sheet No 4. BFRC.

British Flat Roofing Council. (1983): *Design and selection of flat roof decks*. Technical Information Sheet No 11. BFRC.

British Flat Roofing Council. (1983): *Estimating condensation risk*. Technical Information Sheet No 5. BFRC.

British Flat Roofing Council. (1983): *Flat roofs: maintenance and repairs*. Technical Information Sheet No 6. BFRC.

British Flat Roofing Council. (1983): *Polyester based: high performance materials. Amendments to BS747:1977*. Technical Information Sheet No. 12. BFRC.

British Flat Roofing Council. (1983): *Flat roofs: selection of materials for built-up roofing*. Technical Information Sheet No 7. BFRC.

British Flat Roofing Council. (1983): *Thermal design*. Technical Information Sheet No 2. BFRC.

British Flat Roofing Council. (1983): *Types of flat roof*. Technical Information Sheet No.1. BFRC.

British Flat Roofing Council. (1983): *Guide to new BS Code of Practice for flat roofs with continuously supported coverings - BS 6229*. Technical Information Sheet No 3. BFRC.

British Flat Roofing Council. (1984). Inspection, maintenance and repair of flat roofs. Part 1. The treatment of condensation damage. *Roofing Contractor, 33* (224), pp.14-15.

British Flat Roofing Council. (1984). Inspection, maintenance and repair of flat roofs. Part 2. Leakage and repair. *Roofing Contractor, 33* (225), p.12.

British Flat Roofing Council. (1984): *Falls and drainage. Flat Roof Design and Construction*. Technical Information Sheet No 8. BFRC.

British Flat Roofing Council. (1985). Flat roof repair. *Building, 248* (14), 5 April, pp.53, 57, 59.

British Flat Roofing Council. (1985). *Flat roofing - inspection and quality control on site*. Bituminous Roofing Council Technical Information Sheet No 9. BFRC.

British Flat Roofing Council. (1985): *Flat roofs of dwellings*. Bituminous Roofing Council Technical Information Sheet No.10, BFRC.

British Flat Roofing Council. (1987): Model Specification Sheet C.N.1. *Built-up Roofing: Concrete Deck*. BFRC.

British Flat Roofing Council. (1987): Model Specification Sheet P.L.1. *Built-up Roofing: Plywood Deck*. BRFC.

British Flat Roofing Council. (1987): Model Specification Sheet T.B.1. *Built-up Roofing: Timber Boarded Deck*. BFRC.

British Flat Roofing Council. (1987): Model Specification Sheet M.D.1. *Built-up Roofing: Metal Deck*. BFRC.

British Flat Roofing Council. (1987): Model Specification Sheet W.W.1. *Built-up Roofing: Woodwool Deck*. BFRC.

British Standards Institution. (1989): BS 219: 1977 (1989). *Specification for soft solders*. BSI.

British Standards Institution. (1989): BS 334: 1982 (1989). *Specification for compositional limits of chemical lead*. BSI.

British Standards Institution. (1981): BS 460: 1964 (1981). *Specification for cast iron rainwater goods*. BSI.

British Standards Institution. (1975): BS 476: Pt.3: 1975. *Fire tests on building materials and structures. External fire exposure roof test*. BSI.

British Standards Institution. (1970): BS 476: Pt.4: 1970. *Fire tests on building materials and structures. Non-combustibility test for material*. BSI.

British Standards Institution. (1989): BS 476: Pt.6: 1989. *Fire tests on building materials and structures. Method of test for fire propagation for products*. BSI.

British Standards Institution. (1987): BS 476: Pt.7: 1987. *Fire tests on building materials and structures. Method for classification of the surface spread of flame of products*. BSI.

British Standards Institution. (1988): BS 476: Pt.11: 1982 (1988). *Fire tests on building materials and structures. Method for assessing the heat emission from building materials*. BSI.

British Standards Institution. (1987): BS 476: Pt.20: 1987. *Fire tests on building materials and structures. Method for determination of the fire resistance of elements of construction*. BSI.

British Standards Institution. (1987): BS 476: Pt.21: 1987. *Fire tests on building materials and structures. Methods for determination of the fire resistance of loadbearing elements of construction* . BSI.

British Standards Institution. (1987): BS 476: Pt.22: 1987. *Fire tests on building materials and structures. Methods for determination of the fire resistance of non-loadbearing elements of construction.* BSI.

British Standards Institution. (1987): BS 476: Pt.23: 1987. *Fire tests on building materials and structures. Methods for determination of the contribution of components to the fire resistance of a structure.* BSI.

British Standards Institution. (1987): BS 569: 1973 (1987). *Specification for asbestos - cement rainwater goods.* BSI.

British Standards Institution. (1964): BS 648: 1964. *Schedule of weights of building materials.* BSI.

British Standards Institution. (1986): BS 747: 1977 (1986). *Specification for roofing felts.* BSI.

British Standards Institution. (1939): BS 849: 1939. *Code of practice for plain sheet zinc roofing.* BSI.

British Standards Institution. (1983): BS 882: 1983. *Specification for aggregates from natural sources for concrete.* BSI.

British Standards Institution. (1980): BS 1091: 1963 (1980). *Specification for pressed steel gutters, rainwater pipes, fittings and accessories.* BSI.

British Standards Institution. (1981): BS 1105: 1981. *Specification for wood cement slabs up to 125mm thick.* BSI.

British Standards Institution. (1989): BS 1142: 1989. *Specification for fibre building boards.* BSI.

British Standards Institution. (1982): BS 1178: 1982. *Specification for milled lead sheet for building purposes.* BSI.

British Standards Institution. (1974): BS 1202: Pt.2: 1974. *Copper nails.* BSI.

British Standards Institution. (1963): BS 1210: 1963. *Specification for wood screws.* BSI.

British Standards Institution. (1987): BS 1369: Pt.1: 1987. *Specification for expanded metal and ribbed lathing.* BSI.

British Standards Institution. (1980): BS 1431: 1960 (1980). *Specification for wrought copper and wrought zinc rainwater goods.* BSI.

British Standards Institution. (1990): BS 1446: 1973 (1990). *Specification for mastic asphalt (natural rock asphalt fine aggregate) for roads and footings.* BSI.

British Standards Institution. (1988): BS 1447: 1988. *Specification for mastic asphalt (limestone fine aggregate). for roads, footways and pavings in buildings.* BSI.

British Standards Institution. (1983): BS 1449: Pt.2: 1983. *Specification for stainless and heat-resisting steel plate, sheet and strip.* BSI.

British Standards Institution. (1987): BS 1470: 1987. *Specification for wrought aluminium and aluiminium alloys for general engineering purposes: plate, sheet and strip.* BSI.

British Standards Institution. (1987): BS 2092: 1987. *Specification for eye-protection for industrial and non-industrial uses.* BSI.

British Standards Institution. (1970): BS 2782: 1970. *Methods of testing plastics.* BSI.

British Standards Institution. (1976): BS 2782: Pt.3: Methods 320A to 320F: 1976. *Tensile strength, elongation and elastic modulus.* BSI.

British Standards Institution. (1991): BS 2782: Pt.3: Method 360B: 1991. *Determination of tear resistance of plastics film and sheeting by the trouser tear method.* BSI.

British Standards Institution. (1980): BS 2870: 1980. *Specification for rolled copper and copper alloys: sheet, strip and foil.* BSI.

British Standards Institution. (1986): BS 2874: 1986. *Specification for copper and copper alloy rods and sections (other than forging stock).* BSI.

British Standards Institution. (1980): BS 2997: 1958 (1980). *Specification for aluminium rainwater goods.* BSI.

British Standards Institution. (1988): BS 3083: 1988. *Specification for hot-dip zinc coated and hot-dip aluminium/zinc coated corrugated steel sheets for general purposes.* BSI.

British Standards Institution (1981). BS 3533; 1981. *Glossary of thermal insulation terms.* BSI.

British Standards Institution. (1990): BS 3690: Pt.1: 1989. *Bitumens for building and civil engineering. Specification for bitumens for roads and other paved areas.* BSI.

British Standards Institution. (1989): BS 3690: Pt.2: 1989. *Bitumens for building and civil engineering. Specification for bitumens for industrial purposes.* BSI.

British Standards Institution. (1990): BS 3690: Pt.3: 1990. *Bitumens for building and civil engineering. Specification for mixtures of bitumen with pitch, tar and Trinidad lake asphalt.* BSI.

British Standards Institution. (1986): BS 3837: Pt.1: 1986. *Expanded polystyrene boards. Part 1. Specification for boards manufactured from expandable beads.* BSI.

British Standards Institution. (1990): BS 3837: Pt.2: 1990. *Expanded polystyrene boards. Part 2. Specification for extruded boards.* BSI.

British Standards Institution. (1988): BS 4370: Pt 1:1988. *Methods of test for rigid cellular materials. Part 1. Methods 1 to 5.* BSI.

British Standards Institution. (1973): BS 4370: Pt. 2:1973. *Methods of test for rigid cellular materials. Part 2. Methods 6-10.* BSI.

British Standards Institution. (1988): BS 4370: Pt. 3:1988. *Methods of test for rigid cellular materials. Part 3. Methods 12 and 13.* BSI.

British Standards Institution. (1991): BS 4370: Pt. 4: 1991. *Methods of test for rigid cellular materials.* **Part 4. Method 14.** *Determination of flexural properties.* BSI.

British Standards Institution. (1989): BS 4576: Pt.1: 1989. *Half-round gutters and pipes of circular cross-section.* BSI.

British Standards Institution. (1987): BS 4778: Pt.1: 1987. *Quality vocabulary. International terms.* BSI.

British Standards Institution. (1991): BS 4778: Pt.2: 1991. *Quality vocabulary. Quality concepts and related definitions.* BSI.

British Standards Institution. (1991): BS 4778: Sec.3.1: 1991. *Quality vocabulary. Guide to concepts and related definitions.* BSI.

British Standards Institution. (1991): BS 4778: Sec.3.2: 1991. *Quality vocabulary. Glossary of international terms.* BSI.

British Standards Institution. (1975): BS 4841: Pt.1: 1975. *Rigid polyurethane (PUR) and polyisocyranurate(PIR) foam for building purposes. Laminated board for building purposes.* BSI.

British Standards Institution. (1975): BS 4841: Pt.2: 1975. *Laminated board for use as a wall and ceiling insulation.* BSI.

British Standards Institution. (1987): BS 4841: Pt.3: 1987. *Specification for two types of laminated board (roofboards) with auto-adhesively bonded reinforcing facings for use as roofboard thermal insulation for built up roofs.* BSI.

British Standards Institution. (1972): BS 4868: 1972. *Specification for profiled aluminium sheet for building.* BSI.

British Standards Institution. (1975): BS 5234: 1975. *Code of practice. Internal non-loadbearing partitioning.* BSI.

British Standards Institution. (1989): BS 5250: 1989. *Code of practice for control of condensation in buildings.* BSI.

British Standards Institution. (1978): BS 5268: Pt.4: Sect.4.1: 1978. *Recommendations for calculating fire resistance of timber members.* BSI.

British Standards Institution. (1989): BS 5268: Pt.5: 1989. *Code of practice for the preservative treatment of structural timber.* BSI.

British Standards Institution. (1989): BS 5268: Pt.7: Sect.7.2: 1989. *Recommendations for calculating fire resistance of timber members. Joists for flat roofs.* BSI.

British Standards Institution. (1976): BS 5284: 1976. *Methods. Sampling and testing of mastic asphalt and pitchmastic used in building.* BSI.

British Standards Institution (1991). BS 5306; Part 0; 1986. *Fire extinguishing installations and equipment on premises.* BSI

British Standards Institution. (1991): BS 5328: Pt.1: 1991. *Concrete. Part 1. Guide to specifying concrete.* BSI.

British Standards Institution. (1991): BS 5328: Pt.2: 1991. *Concrete. Part 2. Methods for specifying concrete mixes.* BSI.

British Standards Institution. (1990): BS 5328: Pt.3: 1990. *Concrete. Specification for the procedures to be used in producing and transporting concrete.* BSI.

British Standards Institution. (1990): BS 5328: Pt.4: 1990. *Concrete. Specificatin for the procedures to be used in producing and transporting concrete.* BSI.

British Standards Institution. (1984): BS 5395: Pt.1: 1977 (1984). *Staris, ladders and walkways. Code of practice for the design of straight stairs.* BSI.

British Standards Institution. (1985): BS 5395: Pt.3: 1985. *Stairs, ladders and walkways. Code of practice for the design of industrial type staris, permanent ladders and walkways.* BSI.

British Standards Institution. (1978): BS 5400: Pt.2: 1978. *Steel, concrete and composite bridges. Specification for loads.* BSI.

British Standards Institution (1990). BS 5588; Part 1; 1990. *Fire precautions in the design, construction and use of buildings. Part 1: Code of practice for residential buildings.* BSI

British Standards Institution. (1989): BS 5669: Pt.1: 1989. *Particle board. Methods of sampling, conditioning and test.* BSI.

British Standards Institution. (1989): BS 5669: Pt.2: 1989. *Particle board. Specification for wood chipboard.* BSI.

British Standards Institution. (1989): BS 5669: Pt.4: 1989. *Particle board. Specification for cement bonded particle board.* BSI.

British Standards Institution. (1989): BS 5669: Pt.5: 1989. *Particle board. Code of practice for the selection and application of particle boards for specific purposes.* BSI.

British Standards Institution. (1987): BS 5750: Part 0: Section 0.1: 1987. *Quality systems. Guide to selection and use.* BSI.

British Standards Institution. (1991): BS 5925: 1991. *Code of practice for design of buildings: ventilation principles and design for natural ventilation.* BSI.

British Standards Institution. (1987): BS 6100: Sec.1.3.2: 1987. *Building and civil engineering terms. Roofs and roofing.* BSI.

British Standards Institution. (1982): BS 6229: 1982. *Code of practice for flat roofs with continuously supported coverings.* BSI.

British Standards Institution. (1991): BS 6268: Pt.2: 1991. *Structural use of timber code of practice for premissible stress design, materials and workmanship.* BSI.

British Standards Institution. (1983): BS 6367: 1983. *Code of practice for drainage of roofs and paved areas.* BSI.

British Standards Institution. (1984): BS 6399: Pt.1: 1984. *Code of practice for dead and imposed loads.* BSI.

British Standards Institution. (1988): BS 6399: Pt.3: 1988. *Code of practice for imposed roof loads.* BSI.

British Standards Institution. (1985): BS 6561: 1985 (1991). *Specification for zinc alloy sheet and strip for building*. BSI.

British Standards Institution. (1985): BS 6566: Pt.1: 1985. *Plywood. Specification for construction of panels and characteristics of piles including marking*. BSI.

British Standards Institution. (1985): BS 6566: Pt.2: 1985. *Plywood. Glossary of terms*. BSI.

British Standards Institution. (1985): BS 6566: Pt.3: 1985. *Plywood. Specification for acceptance levels for post-manufacture batch testing including sampling*. BSI.

British Standards Institution. (1985): BS 6566: Pt.4: 1985. *Plywood. Specification for tolerances on the dimensions of plywood panels*. BSI.

British Standards Institution. (1985): BS 6566: Pt.5: 1985. *Plywood. Specification for moisture content*. BSI.

British Standards Institution. (1985): BS 6566: Pt.6.1985. *Plywood. Specification for limits of defects for the classification of plywood by appearance*. BSI.

British Standards Institution. (1985): BS 6566: Pt.7: 1985. *Plywood. Specification for the classification of resistance to fungal decay and wood borer attack*. BSI.

British Standards Institution. (1985): BS 6566: Pt.8: 1985. *Plywood. Specification for bond performance of veneer plywood*. BSI.

British Standards Institution. (1985): BS 6577: 1985. *Specification for mastic asphalt for building (natural rock asphalt aggregate)*. BSI.

British Standards Institution. (1990): BS 6651: 1990. *Code of practice for protection of structures against lightning*. BSI.

British Standards Institution. (1986): BS 6677: Pt.1: 1986. *Clay and calcium silicate pavers for flexible pavements. Part 1. Specification for pavers*. BSI.

British Standards Institution. (1986): BS 6677: Pt.2: 1986. *Clay and calcium silicate pavers for flexible pavements. Part 2. Code of practice for design of lightly trafficked pavements*. BSI.

British Standards Institution. (1986): BS 6677: Pt.3: 1986. *Clay and calcium silicate pavers for flexible pavements. Part 3. Method for construction of pavements*. BSI.

British Standards Institution. (1986): BS 6717: Pt.1: 1986. *Precast concrete paving blocks. Part 1. Specification for paving blocks*. BSI.

British Standards Institution: (1989): BS 6717: Pt.3: 1989. *Precast concrete paving blocks. Part 3. Code of practice for laying*. BSI.

British Standards Institution. (1988): BS 6915: 1988. *Specification for the design and construction of fully supported lead sheet roof and wall coverings*. BSI.

British Standards Institution. (1988): BS 6925: 1988. *Specification for mastic asphalt for building and civil engineering (limestone aggregate)*. BSI.

British Standards Institution. (1988): BS 6931: 1988. *Glossary of terms for copper and copper alloys*. BSI.

British Standards Institution. (1989): BS 7021: 1989. *Code of practice for thermal insulation of roofs externally by means of sprayed rigid polyurethane (PUR) or polyisocyanurate (PIR) foam*. BSI.

British Standards Institution. (1990): BS 7263: Pt.1: 1990. *Precast concrete flags, kerbs channels edgings and quadrants. Specification*. BSI.

British Standards Institution. (1990): BS 7263: Pt.2: 1990. *Precast concrete flags, kerbs channels edgings and quadrants. Code of practice for laying*. BSI.

British Standards Institution. (1992): BS 7543: 1992. *Guide to durability of buildings and building elements, products and components*. BSI.

British Standards Institution. (1989): BS 8000: Pt.4: 1989. *Workmanship on building sites. Code of practice for water-proofing*. BSI.

British Standards Institution. (1990): BS 8102: 1990. *Code of practice for protection of structures against water from the ground*. BSI.

British Standards Institution. (1987): BS 8204: Pt.2: 1987. *In-situ floorings. Code of practice for concrete wearing surfaces*. BSI.

British Standards Institution. (1987): BS 8233: 1987. *Code of practice for sound insulation and noise reduction for buildings*. BSI.

British Standards Institution. (1991): BS 8290: Pt.1: 1991. *Suspended ceilings. Code of practice for design*. BSI.

British Standards Institution. (1991): BS 8290: Pt.2: 1991. *Suspended ceilings. Specification for performance of components and assemblies*. BSI.

British Standards Institution. (1991): BS 8290: Pt.3: 1991. *Suspended ceilings. Code of practice for installation and maintenance*. BSI.

British Standards Institution. (1972): CP 3: Ch.V: Pt.2: 1972. *Wind loads*. BSI.

British Standards Institution. (1958): CP 143: Pt.1: 1958. *Code of practice for sheet roof and wall coverings. Aluminium, corrugated and troughed*. BSI.

British Standards Institution. (1964): CP 143: Pt.5: 1964. *Code of practice for sheet roof and wall coverings. Zinc*. BSI.

British Standards Institution. (1973): CP 143: Pt.10: 1973. *Code of Practice for sheet roof. Galvanized corrugated steel. Metric units*. BSI.

British Standards Institution. (1970): CP 143: Pt.11: 1970. *Lead. Metric units*. BSI [WITHDRAWN].

British Standards Institution. (1988): CP 143: Pt.12: 1970 (1988). *Code of practice for sheet roof and wall coverings. Copper. Metric units*. BSI.

British Standards Institution. (1973): CP 143: Pt.15: 1973 (1986). *Aluminium. Metric units*. BSI.

British Standards Institution. (1970): CP 144: Pt.3: 1970. *Built-up bitumen felt metric units*. BSI.

British Standards Institution. (1970): CP144: Pt.4: 1970. *Roof coverings. Mastic asphalt. Metric Units*. BSI.

© BFRC / CIRIA: Flat Roofing: Design and Good Practice. 1993

British Standards Institution. (1982): DD 73: 1982. *Basic data for the design of building: Daylight*. BSI.

British Standards Institution. (1979): PD 6484: 1979. *Commentary on corrosion at bimetallic contacts and its alleviation*. BSI.

BSI see British Standards Institution.

Building. (1985): Flat roof repair. *Building, 248* (14), pp.53,57,59-65+.

Building. (1988): Roof repairs. *Building, 253* (51), pp.59-77.

Building. (1988): Bradford's Sloane Square revamped as low cost housing. *Building, 253* (10), p.7.

Building. (1989): Roofing. *Building, 254* (4), pp.3-63.

Building Act 1984 (1984). *Building Act 1984. Chapter 55*. HMSO.

Building Maintenance Cost Information Service. (1986): Occasional Paper No.153. *Design/Performance Data. Building Owner's Reports: 2 Flat Roofs*.

Building Regulations see Department of the Environment

Building Research Establishment. (1981): Current Paper 4/81. Holmes, R, Marvin, H.E, Banks. W.B, Kroll, M.E. & Newman, P.L. *Maintenance Costs of Flat Roofs*. BRE.

Building Research Establishment. (1983): *Defect Action Sheet DAS 33. Flat Roofs: Built-up Bitumen Felt - Remedying Rain Penetration* BRE.

Building Research Establishment. (1983): *Defect Action Sheet DAS 34. Flat Roofs: Built-up Bitumen Felt - Remedying Rain Penetration at Abutments and Upstands*. BRE.

Building Research Establishment. (1984): *Defect Action Sheet DAS 59. Felted cold deck roofs: remedying condensation by converting to warm deck*. BRE.

Building Research Establishment. (1987): *Defect Action Sheet DAS 107. Cavity Parapets - Installation of copings, dpc's, trays and flashings*. BRE.

Building Research Establishment. (1972): Digest 144. *Asphalt and built-up felt roofings: durability*. BRE.

Building Research Establishment. (1989): Digest 247. *Sound insulation basic principles*. BRE.

Building Research Establishment. (1983): Digest 270. *Condensation in insulated domestic roofs*. BRE.

Building Research Establishment. (1984): Digest 282. *Structural appraisal of building with long-span roofs*. BRE.

Building Research Establishment. (1985): Digest 295. *Stability under wind load of loos-laid external roof insulation boards*. BRE.

Building Research Establishment. (1986): Digest 311. *Wind scour of gravel ballast on roofs*. BRE.

Building Research Establishment. (1986): Digest 312. *Flat roof design: the technical options*. BRE.

Building Research Establishment. (1987): Digest 324. *Flat roof design: thermal insulation*. BRE.

Building Research Establishment. (1988): Digest 332. *Loads on roofs from snow drifting against vertical obstructions in valleys*. BRE.

Building Research Establishment. (1988): Digest 336. *Swimming pool roofs: minimising the risk of condensation using warm-deck roofing*. BRE.

Building Research Establishment. (1988): Digest 337. *Sound insulation basic principles*. BRE.

Building Research Establishment. (1988): Digest 338. *Insulation against external noise*. BRE.

Building Research Establishment. (1989): Digest 346. *The assessment of wind loads. Part 2. Classification of structures*. BRE.

Building Research Establishment. (1992): Digest 372. *Flat roof design: waterproof membranes*. BRE.

Building Research Establishment. (1979): Information Paper IP 35/79 McIntyre, I.S. *Moisture in a timber-based flat roof of cold deck construction*. BRE.

Building Research Establishment. (1980): Information Paper IP 2/80 Read, R.E.H. and Hinkley, P.L. *Roofs as barriers to fire*. BRE.

Building Research Establishment. (1980): Information Paper IP 3/80 Read, R.E.H. and Hinkley, P.L. *The effects of a roof on a fire within a buiding*. BRE.

Building Research Establishment. (1980): Information Paper IP 25/80 Rogowski, B and Sutcliffe, R.J. *Fire performance of loft insulating materials*. BRE.

Building Research Establishment. (1981): Information Paper IP 3/81 Anderson, B.R. *The assessment of U-values for insulated roofs*. BRE.

Building Research Establishment. (1982): Information Paper IP 15/82 Hide, W.T. *Inspection and maintenance of flat and low pitched timber roofs*. BRE.

Building Research Establishment. (1982): Information Paper IP 19/82 McIntyre, I.S and Birch, D.P *Considerations in the design of timber flat roofs*. BRE.

Building Research Establishment. (1984): Information Paper IP 6/84 Beech, J.C. and Saunders, G.K. *The movement of foam plastics insulants in warm deck flat roofs*. BRE.

Building Research Establishment. (1986): Information Paper IP 15/86 Edwards, M.J. *Waterproof joints in large panel system: 4. Flat roofs, balconies and deck accessways 1986*. BRE.

Building Research Establishment. (1987): Information Paper IP 13/87 Beech, J.C. and Ubevoi, S. *Ventilating cold deck flat roofs*. BRE.

Building Research Establishment. (1989): Information Paper IP 2/89 Beech, J.C. and Saunders, J.K. *Thermal performance of lightweight inverted warm deck flat roofs*. BRE.

Building Research Establishment. (1991): Information Paper IP 8/91 Beech, J.C. and Saunders, G.K. *Mastic asphalt for flat roofs: testing for quality assurance*. BRE.

Building Research Establishment. (1989): BRE Report BR143. *Thermal insulation: avoiding risks. A guide to good practice building construction.* BRE.

Building Research Establishment Report. *BREEAM: an environmental assessment* (versions 1/93 for new office design, version 2/91 for new superstores and supermarkets, version 3/91 for new homes). BRE.

Building Research Establishment (1993) BRE Report BR238: *Sound control for homes.* BRE/CIRIA.

Building Research Station. (1959): *Principles of modern building. Volume 1.* 3rd ed. HMSO.

Building Research Station. (1961): *Principles of modern building. Volume 2. Floors and roofs.* HMSO.

Building (Scotland) Act 1959 (1959): *Building (Scotland) Act 1959. Chapter 24.* HMSO.

Burberry, P. (1990). Controlling the risk: Code for condensation. *Architects Journal, 192* (13), pp.60-63.

Burn, K.N. & Roux, R. (1982). Insulating existing flat roofs: design and construction details. *Journal of Thermal Insulation, 5,* (April), pp.209-228.

C

CASEC see Committee of Associations of Specialist Engineering Contractors

Catt, R. (1990). Crowning glories. *Chartered Quantity Surveyor, 12* (7), pp.36-39

Cecil,R. (1991): *Professional liability.* 3rd ed. Legal Studies and Services (Publishing) Ltd.

Chappel, D. and Powell-Smith, V. (1991): *JCT Intermediate Form of Contract: a practical guide.* 2nd ed. Legal Studies and Services (Publishing) Ltd.

Chappell, D. and Powell-Smith, V. (1991): *JCT Minor Works Form of Contract: a practical guide.* 2nd ed. Legal Studies and Services (Publishing) Ltd.

Chartered Institute of Building. (1990): *Building procurement systems - a guide to building project management; with additional material provided by P.Harlow.* 2nd ed. CIOB.

Chartered Institution of Building Services Engineers. (1986). CIBSE Guide, Volume A, Design data. Section A3 *Thermal properties of building structures.* 5th CIBSE.

Chartered Institution of Building Services Engineers. (1986). CIBSE Guide, Volume A, Design Data. Section A10 *Moisture transfer and condensation.* 5th ed. CIBSE.

Clark T.(1991). *Developing the clerk of works professional function.* University of York.

Clifton-Taylor, A. (1972): *The pattern of English building.* Faber

Coad, J.R. & Rosaman, D. (1984). Failures involving site-applied adhesives - A study of BR Advisory Service Site Investigations. *Building Technical File, (7),* pp.57-62.

Coates, D.T. (1983). The seamier side of roofing [Standing seam roofing]. *Building Technology and Management, 21* (2), p.24.

Committee of Associations of Specialist Engineering Contractors. (1981): *CASEC guide to the JCT Standard Form of Nominated Sub-Contract Tender and Agreement 1980 (NSC/1).* CASEC

Committee of Associations of Specialist Engineering Contractors. (1986): *CASEC guide to the JCT Intermediate Form of Building Contract (IFC84).* CASEC

Confederation of Associations of Specialist Engineering Contractors. (1985): *Nomination and the building process.* CASEC.

Construction Industry Research and Information Association. (1985). CIRIA Technical Note 121. *Sample quality assurance documents.* CIRIA.

Construction Industry Research and Information Association. (1993) CIRIA Report 127: *Sound control for homes.* CIRIA/BRE.

Construction Industry Research and Information Association. (1988). CIRIA Special Publication 57. *Handling of materials on site.* CIRIA/CIOB.

Construction Industry Research and Information Association. (1989). CIRIA Special Publications 63 and 64. *Quality assurance in construction* (video and booklet). CIRIA

Construction Industry Research and Information Association. (1989). CIRIA Special Publication 72. *Quality management in construction - certification of product quality and quality management systems.* CIRIA.

Construction Industry Research and Information Association. (1990). CIRIA Special Publication 74. *Quality management in construction - interpretations of BS 5750(1987) - "Quality systems" for the construction industry.* CIRIA

Construction Industry Research and Information Association. (1991). CIRIA Report 122. *Life cycle costing.* CIRIA.

Construction Industry Research and Information Association. (1991). CIRIA Special Publication 81. *Roles responsibilities and risk management in contracting.* CIRIA.

Construction Industry Research and Information Association. (1992). CIRIA Special Publication 84. *Quality management in construction - contractual aspects.* CIRIA

Construction Industry Research and Information Association. (1992). CIRIA Special Publication 88. *Quality management in construction - implement-ation in design services organisations.* CIRIA.

Coordinated Project Information, (1988) *SMM7. Standard Method of Measurement of building works,* 7th edn. RICS/BEC.

Chapter	1	2	3	4	5	6	7	8	9	10	11
Contents	Introduction	History	Regulatory Methods	Principles	Surveys	Constraints & Targets	Design Selection	Calculations	Detail Design Principles	Evaluation of Design	Built-up Roofing
Page	1	19	31	45	83	95	105	165	189	217	221

Copper and Brass Extended Uses Council. (1927). *Copper in architecture: A treatise for the information of architects, builders and lovers of good building.* CBEUC.

Copper Development Association. (1987): Information Sheet 4. *Roofing and cladding: Private house, Chirk, Clwyd, Wales.* CDA.

Copper Development Association. (1987): Information Sheet 8. *Roofing and cladding: Roman Catholic Church, Bracknell.* CDA.

Copper Development Association. (1987): Technical Note 9. *Copper and copper alloys - composition and properties.* CDA.

Copper Development Assoication. (1987): Technical Note 25. *Joining of copper and copper alloys,* CDA.

Copper Development Association. (1987): Technical Notes 32. *Copper in Roofing - design and installation.* CDA.

Copper Development Association. (1987): Information Sheet 3. *Central Mosque Regents' Park.* CDA.

Copper Development Association. (1987): Information Sheet 25. *Roofing and cladding: Central Bank of Ireland, Dublin.* CDA.

Copper Development Association. (1989): *Introduction to copper.* CDA.

Cornes, D.L. (1989): *Design liability in the construction industry.* 3rd ed. BSP Professional Books.

Council of the European Communities. (1971): *CEC Directive 71/305/EEC. Council Directive concerning the co-ordination of procedures for the award of public works.*

Council of the European Communities. (1989): *CEC Directive 89/106/EEC. On the approximation of laws, regulations and administrative provisions of member states relating to construction products.* CEC.

Council of the European Communties. (1989): *CEC Directive 89/440/EEC. Council Directive concerning the co-ordingation of procedures for the award of public works. CEC.* [Amending directive 71/305 CEC]

CPI - see BPIC and Coordinated Project Information.

Cunningham, M.J. (1987): *Drying of construction moisture in timber-framed flat roofs, Low air leakage. ASHRAE Trans.,* 93, Part 2, pp.153-170.

Curwell, S. et al (1990): *Buildings and Health. The Rosehaugh Guide to the design, construction and management of buildings.* RIBA.

Curwell, S. and March, C. (1986): *Hazardous building materials. A guide to the selection of alternatives.* E&FN Spon.

D

Davey, N. (1972): *A history of building materials.* Phoenix House

Davis, G and Ventre, F.T. (1990): *Performance of building and serviceability of facilities.* STP 1029. ASTM.

Deeble, V.C. & Probert, S.D. (1986). Optimising the thickness of thermal insulant to be used in the walls and flat roof of a building. *Applied Energy,* 25 (4), pp.299-308.

Department of Education and Science. (1985). Design Note 46. *Maintenance and Renewal in Educational Buildings. Flat Roof. Criteria and Methods of Assessment, Repair and Replacement.* DES

Department of the Environment. (1991): *The Building Regulations 1991. Approved document A. Structure. 1992.* HMSO.

Department of the Environment. (1991): *The Building Regulations 1991. Approved document B. Fire safety. 1992.* HMSO.

Department of the Environment. (1991): *The Building Regulations 1991. Approved document C. Site preparation and resistance to moisture. 1992.* HMSO.

Department of the Environment. (1989): *The Building Regulations 1985. Approved documents F. Ventilation. F1. Means of ventilation. F2. Condensation.* 2nd ed. *1990.* HMSO.

Department of the Environment. (1989): *The Building Regulations 1985. Approved documents H. Drainage and waste disposal.* 2nd ed. *1990.* HMSO.

Department of the Environment. (1991): *The Building Regulations 1991. Approved document K. Stairs, ramps and guards. 1992.* HMSO.

Department of the Environment. (1991): *The Building Regulations 1985. Approved document L. Conservation of fuel and power.* 2nd ed. *1990.* HMSO.

Department of the Environment. PSA Special Services:1991. *Costs-in-use tables* 3rd ed. HMSO.

Department of Transport. (1984): Departmental Standard BD21/84. *The assessment of highway bridges and structures.* DTp.

Desmond, T. (1986). Special issue. Roofing. *Building,* 253 (30), supplement, 22 July, pp. 5-73.

Deutsche Institut für Normung. (1986): DIN 16730 (1986). *Plasticized polyvinyl chloride (PVC-P) roofing felt incompatible with bitumen: requirements.* DIN.

Deutsche Institut für Normung. (1988): DIN 17650 (1988). *Copper sheet and strip for use in building construction; technical delivery conditions.* DIN.

Deutsche Institut für Normung. (1981): DIN 53354 (1981). *Testing of artifical leather; tensile test.* DIN.

Deutsche Institut für Normung. (1981): DIN 53455 (1981). *Testing of plastics; tensile test.* DIN.

Deutsche Institut für Normung. (1969): DIN 53363 (1969). *Testing of plastic films tear propagation test on trapezoidal specimens with a slit.* DIN.

Deutsche Institut für Normung. (1983): DIN RAL RG 717/1 (1983). *Roofing sheets of PVC soft, without bitumenous resistance, without support; quality assurance.* DIN.

DOE see Department of the Environment.

12	13	14	15	16	17	18	19	20	21	22	23
Mastic Asphalt	Polymeric Single Ply	Copper	Lead Sheet	Other Membranes	Thermal Insulants	Specification	Contracts & Procurement	Inspection	Maintenance	Bibliography	Index
263	301	331	353	375	383	393	399	413	429	437	455

E

EC   see Council of the European Community

Ecclesiastical Architects' and Surveyors' Association. (1987). Corrosion problems of lead roofing. *Building Technical File No.18*, p.41-46.

Edwards, M.J. (1988). Performance of thermally upgraded flat roofs. *Building Technical File, No.23*, 11-16.

Edwards, R.M. (1981). The selection of components for flat roofs. *Building Specification*, October, pp.61-62.

Estenssoro, L.F. (1989): Two roof failures due to water ponding and related code requirements. *Journal of Performance of Constructed Facilities, 3* (3), pp.184-190.

Eurisol U.K. (1982). Insulation Fact Sheet No.12A. *Thermal insulation of flat roofs - cold roof*. EURISOL UK.

Eurisol U.K. (1982): Insulation Fact Sheet No.12B. *Thermal insulation of flat roofs - cold roof*. EURISOL UK.

F

Factories Act (1961): *Factories Act 1961*. HMSO.

Fazio, P & Gowri, K. (1989). Knowledge-based system for the selection and design of roof systems. *Bâtiment International/Building Research & Practice, 22* (5), September/October, pp.294-298.

Felt Roofing Contractors Advisory Board. (1981). *Calculation of thermal transmittances (U-Values) for flat roofs*. FRCAB.

Flanagan, R. et al (1989): *Life cycle costing. Theory and practice*. BSP Professional Books.

Flat Roofing Contractors Advisory Board. (1988). *Roofing Handbook*. FRCAB.

Flat Roofing Contractors Advisory Board. (1989). Condensation and vapour control layers. *Building Technical File No.24*, January, pp.27-29.

Forsyth, M. (1985): *Buildings for music*. Cambridge University Press.

Fox, A. and Murrell, R. (1989): *Green design. A guide to the environmental impact of building materials*. Architectural Design and Technology Press.

G

Gallagher, A. (1989). Flat roofs: maintenance and repair. *Plan: Architecture + Interior Design in Ireland, 21* (5), May, p.35.

Galvanizers Association. (n.d.): *Steelwork protection guide*. Galvanizers Association

Genge, G.R. (1987). Roofing and waterproofing update. *Canadian Architect, 32* (7), July, pp.47-49.

Gillan, G.J. (1980). Trafficked flat roofs water-proofed with mastic asphalt. *Quantity Surveyor, 36* (10), pp.193-1944.

Greater London Council. *Materials and Development Bulletin No. 43 (2nd series)* 1971.

Griffin C. W. (1982) *Manual of built-up roof systems*. McGraw Hill, New York.

Groák, S. (1992): *The idea of building*. E&FN Spon.

Grover, R. (1985). Flat roof construction. *RIBA Journal, 92* (11), November, pp.100-112.

Guedes, P. (1979): *The Macmillan encyclopaedia of architecture and technological change*. Macmillan

H

Haden, J.A. (1985). Prevention's better than cure in flat roof maintenance. *Surveyor, 165* (4833), 28 February 1985, pp.13-15.

Hansen, A.T. (1963). Points to watch when insulating wood framed flat roofs. *Canadian Builder, 13* (7), p.66.

Health and safety see below and Unit 22.2

Health and Safety Commission. (1981): *Control of lead at work: approved code of practice*. HMSO.

Health and Safety Commission. (1992): *Proposals for construction (Design and Management) Regulations and approved code of practice. Consultative document*. HSE

Health and Safety Executive Publications see alsoUnit 22.2

Health and Safety Executive. (1987). HS(G)33. *Safety in roofwork*. HSE.

Health and Safety Executive. (1977). HSW6B. *Safety in construction work: roofing*, 2nd ed. HSE.

Health and Safety at Work Act. (1974): *Health and safety at work etc Act 1974*. HMSO

Hedlin, C.P. (1987). Seasonal variations in the modes of heat transfer in a moist porous thermal insulation in a flat roof. *Journal of Thermal Insulation*, pp.11, 54-66.

Hens, H. L. & Vaes, F. (1986). An inverted roof with mineral wool. *Bâtiment International, 14* (4), pp.245-251.

Hill R.H. (1982). *The condensation control of metal roofing materials*. Lead Industries Group Ltd.

Hoeglund, I, Espling R. & Hindling, G. (1989). Functional studies of flat roofs covered with membranes of butyl rubber. *Bâtiment International, 22* (5), pp.309-312.

Holland, R., Montgomery-Smith, B.E. and Moore, J.F.A. (1992): *Introduction to appraisal and repair of buildings*. Thomas Telford.

Hollis, M. (1983). The survey and inspection of modern timber framed property. *Structural Survey, 2* (2), pp.158-63.

Hollis, M. (1988): *Surveying for dilapidations*. Estates Gazette

© BFRC / CIRIA: Flat Roofing: Design and Good Practice. 1993

Hollis, M. and Gibson, C. (1983): *Surveying buildings*. RICS Surveyor Publications.

Holton, B. (1984). The design of the modern flat roof. *Clerk of Works, 102 (1210)*, pp.8-10, 12-13.

Holton, B. (1985). The design of the modern flat roof. *Roofing Contractor, 34 (235)*, March, pp.13-14, 16.

Home Office (1971): *Fire precautions act 1971. Chapter 40*. HMSO.

Hunter-Cairns, A. (1982). The going on the flat: a review of current practices in flat roof insulation. *Roofing, Cladding and Insulation*, February, pp.13, 16, 38.

Hunter-Cairns, A. (1986). Avoiding the pitfalls of upgrading a flat roof. *Building Trades Journal, 191 (5649)*, pp.28-34.

Hutchison, D. Special issue. Roofing. *AJ Focus, 3 (1)*, January, pp.19-51.

I

Institution of Civil Engineers (1985): *Design life of buildings*. Thomas Telford.

International Organization for Standardization. ISO/9000: 1987. *Quality management and quality assurance standards - guidelines for selection and use*. ISO.

International Organization for Standardization. ISO/R527: 1966. *Plastics: Determination of tensile properties*. ISO.

J

Johnson, K.A. (1989) The calculation of interstitial condensation risk. *Building Technical File, (26)*, pp.23-30

Joint Contracts Tribunal for the Standard Form of Building Contract. (1990): *Intermediate Form of Building Contract 1984 edition. Practice note IN/1. Revised December 1990. Introductory notes on the Intermediate form of building contract IFC 84*. RIBA.

Joint Contracts Tribunal for the Standard Form of Building Contract. (1980): *JCT Guide to the standard form of building contract 1980 edition, and to the JCT nominated sub-contract documents*. RIBA.

Joint Contracts Tribunal for the Standard Form of Building Contract. (1987): *Management contract documentation 1987. Practice note MC/1. Management contracts under the JCT documentation*. BEC.

Joint Contracts Tribunal for the Standard Form of Building Contract. (19): *Practice Note MC/2. Commentaries on the JCT Management Contract Documentation*.

Joint Contracts Tribunal for the Standard Form of Building Contract. (1988): *Standard form of building contract 1980 edition. Practice note 20. Deciding on the appropiate form of JCT Main contract*. Revised July 1988. RIBA.

Joint Contracts Tribunal for the Standard Form of Building Contract. (1992): *Guide to the Standard Form of Agreement for the Appointment of an Architect for Design and Build*. RIBA

Jones, G.V.H. (1981). Modern ways with flat roofs. *Building Specification*, October, pp.55-56.

K

Keyworth, B. (1987). Flat roof construction. *Structural Survey, 6 (2)*, pp.119-123.

Korsgaard, V. (1985). Ventilation of timber flat roofs. *Building Research & Practice, 13 (4)*, July/August, pp.211-219.

Korsgaard, V, Christensen, G, Prebensen, K & Bunch-Nielsen, T. (1985). Ventilation of timber flat roofs. *Bâtiment International, 18 (4)*, July/August, pp.211-219.

L

Labs, K. (1990). Roofs for use. *Progressive Architecture, 71 (7)*, pp.36-42.

Lead Development Association/Lead Sheet Association. (1990): *The lead sheet manual: a guide to good building practice. Vol.1. Lead sheet flashings*. LDA/LSA.

Lead Development Association/Lead Sheet Association. (1992): *The lead sheet manual: a guide to good building practice. Vol.2*. LDA / LSA.

Lead Sheet Association. (1989). *Lead sheet in building*. LSA.

Lowe, S. (1987). Special issue. Roofing. *Building, 252 (42)*, October, pp.8-64.

M

Mann, E. (1984). Facing flat roof failure. (Roofing supplement) *Building*, 22 June, pp.26-27.

March, P. (1985). Special issue. Roofing and cladding supplement. *Building Design*, Supplement, March, pp.1-56.

Marsh, P. (1981). Should flat roofs be the last resort? *Building Trades Journal, (5397)*, 3 April, pp.28,30.

Marshall, R. (1985). Flat roof maintenance & refurbishment. *Architectural Technology*, no.72, 1985 March, p.20.

Mastic Asphalt Council and Employers' Federation (1969): *Trapped water in roofs*, Technical Information Sheet No.2. MACEF.

Mastic Asphalt Council and Employers' Federation (1980): *Paving Handbook* MACEF.

Mastic Asphalt Council and Employers' Federation (1980): *Roofing handbook*. MACEF

May, J.O. (1988). *The roof and roofing: new materials, industrial applications, uses and performance*. Ellis Horwood.

Bibliography *continued*

McDonald, T.B. (1987). Upside-down roofs. Architecture. *The AIA Journal, 76* (1), pp.105-107.

Murdoch, R. and Rae, A.J. (1987). Avoiding corrosion under metal roofs. *Building Technology and Management, 25* (5), pp.4-6, 11.

Murray, J. (1984). Compatibility of components in flat roof construction. *Roofing Cladding and Insulation,* October 29, pp.32-34 and November, p.32, p.34

Murray, J. (1985). The maintenance of flat roofs on commercial buildings. *Structural Survey, 3* (4), pp.349-358.

Muttock, J. (1990). The structure of flat roofs. *Building Today, 199* (5858), pp.19-20.

Muttock, J. (1990). Thermal insulation and condensation. *Building Today, 199* (5863), pp.24-25.

Muttock, J. (1990). Speedy removal of rainwater. *Building Today, 199* (5860), pp.28-29.

N

National House-Building Council. (1981). *Construction of Flat Roofs and pitched roofs with a fully supported continuous weatherproofing membrane. Practice Note 13.* NHBC.

National Economic Development Office. (1988): *Faster building for commerce.* 3rd ed. NEDO.

National Federation of Roofing Contractors. (1992): Information Sheet 18. *Code of practice for safe handling of hot bitumen for roofing purposes.* NFRC

Naujoks, V. (1986). *Highly durable insulation systems using roofing membranes based on high polymers. German Plastics, 76* (1), January, pp.28-29.

NBS Services Ltd. (1988): *The National Building Specification. Full, Intermediate and Minor Works versions.* Updated regularly. NBS Services Ltd

Newman, P. (1990). Flat roofing: a new era. *RIBA Journal, 97* (10), October, pp.89-93.

O

Osbourne, J. (1990). Flat roofing. *Building, 255* (16), Supplement, April 20, pp.10-47.

P

Parkin, P. and Humphreys, H. (1979): *Acoustics, noise and buildings.* Faber and Faber.

Parris, J. (1985): *Default by sub-contractors and suppliers.* Collins.

Potter, J. (1981). The art of construction. Flat roofs. Part 1. Elements and principles. *Architects Journal, 174* (39), pp.613-623.

Potter, J. (1981). The art of construction. Flat roofs. Part 2. Case study of inverted roofs. *Architects Journal, 174* (39), pp.657-665.

Potter, J. (1981). The art of construction. Flat roofs. Part 3. Case study of inverted roofs. *Architects Journal, 174* (39), pp.657-669.

Potter, J. & Kennedy, I. (1987). Element design guide. Roofs: 7. Flat roof construction. *Architects' Journal, 185* (16), pp. 51-59.

Powell-Smith, V. and Chappell, D. (1990): *Building contracts compared and tabulated.* 2nd ed. Legal Studies and Services (Publishing) Ltd.

Prebensen, K., Christensen, G. & Korsgaard, V. (1981). Combating moisture in timber flat roofs. *Building Research and Practice, 9* (2), pp.84-96.

Property Services Agency. (1989): *Defects in building.* HMSO

Property Services Agency. (1987): *Technical guide to flat roofing. Volumes 1 & 2.* PSA

Puterman, M., Soroka, I. & Bentur, A. (1985). Deterioration of externally exposed waterproofing systems of flat roofs. *Durability of Building Materials, 2* (3), pp.275.

R

Raeber, J.A. (1989). Evaluating traffic-bearing waterproofing systems. *Constr.Specifier, 42* (5), pp.29-31.

Reading University. *Life cycle costs for architects. A draft design manual.* Reading University.

Reffell, S. (1985). How to design a successful flat roof. *Building Trades Journal, 189* (5602), 25 April, pp.37-38.

Reid, M. (1986). Flat roof waterproofing: a decade of development. *Architectural Technology* No.80, July, pp.16-17.

Rosehaugh Guide - see *Curwell, S et al.*

Roay, M. & Robinson, P. (1985): *Re-Roofing. A Guide to Flat Roof Maintenance and Refurbishment.* Euroroof Ltd.

Royal Institution of Chartered Surveyors. (1985). *A practical approach to flat roof covering problems: guidance note - the Building Surveyors Division of the Royal Institution of Chartered Surveyors.* Surveyors Publications.

Royal Institute of British Architects (1988): *Architects' job book.* 5th ed. RIBA

Royal Institute of British Architects (1983): *Flat roofs today.* A conference held at the Royal Institute of British Architects, 19th October 1983. RIBA

Ruberoid Contracts Limited (1982): *Built-up roofing handbook.* Ruberoid Contracts Ltd

S

Sanders, C.H. (1980). Condensation and its treatment. *Building Technology and Management, 18* (11), pp.35-38.

© BFRC / CIRIA: Flat Roofing: Design and Good Practice. 1993

Sax, N. and Lewis, R. (1989): *Dangerous properties of industrial materials*. Van Nostrand Reinhold.

Schoepe, R. (1988). Plastics roofing membranes under testing. *Kunststoffe - German Plastics, 78* (7), July, pp.26-29.

Sherlock, D. (1987). Special issue. Property maintenance. *Planning & Building Developments, 92,* July, pp.49-90.

Singapore Institute of Architects' Journal. (1986). Special Issue. Flat Roofs. *Singapore Institute of Architects' Journal, 137,* (July/August), pp.4-29.

Single Ply Roofing Association. (1990): *Guide on design criteria for single ply roofing membranes.* SPRA.

Smith, J. (1987). Building Technology Special. Flat roof repair. *Building, 252* (15), 10 April, pp.55-65.

Smith, J. et al (1987). Flat Roof Repair. *Building, 252* (15), pp.55-65.

Smith, P. (1989). Special issue. Roofing. *Building, 254* (4), supplement, 27 January, pp.5-63.

SMM7 - *see Coordinated Project Information*

Society for Chief QS in Local Government. (1984): *Life cycle cost planning. A guide to life cycle costing and financial appraisal of local authority property and new construction.* The Society.

Somerville, G. (1987): *Design life of concrete structures.* Cement & Concrete Association.

Specification (1992): *Specification 1992. Technical volume. Product volume. Clauses volume.* MBC Architectural Press and Building Publications.

Stathopoulos, T. and Baskaran, A. (1987). Wind pressures on flat roofs with parapets. *ASCE Journal of Structural Engineering, 113* (11), pp.2166-2180.

Stathopoulos, T., Surry, D. and Davenport, A.G. (1981). Effective wind loads on flat roofs. *Journal of the Structural Division ASCE, 107* (ST2), pp.281-298.

Statutory Instruments. (1972): SI 1972 No.917. *Factories. The Highly Flammable Liquids and Liquefied Petroleum Gases Regulations.* HMSO.

Statutory Instruments. (1980): SI 1988 No.1258. *The Control of Lead at Work Regulations.* HMSO.

Statutory Instruments. (1988): SI 1988 No.1657. *Health and Safety. Control of Substances Hazardous to Health Regulations. (COSHH Regulations).* HMSO

Statutory Instruments. (1991): SI 1990 No. 2179 (S.187). *Building and buildings. The building standards (Scotland) regulations 1990.* HMSO.

Statutory Instruments. (1991): SI 1991 No. 1620. *Building and Buildings. The Construction Products Regulations 1991.* HMSO.

Stranks, J. (1990): *A manager's guide to health and safety at work.* Kogan Page

Surry, D. and Stopar, E.M.F. (1989). Wind loading of large low buildings. *Canadian Journal of Civil Engineering, 16* (4), August, pp.526-542.

Swedish Finnish Timber Council. (1986): *Span tables for flat roof joists and domestic floor joists of Swedish and Finnish redwood and whitewood.* The Swedish Finnish Timber Council.

T

Tarmac. (1983): *Flat roofing: a guide to good practice.* 2nd ed. Tarmac Ltd

Thomas, A. (1989). Roofing tests. *RIBA Journal, 96(10),* pp.87-107

Thompson, J. and Day, C. (1990). The greening of the roof. *Architecture Today,* (11), pp.74-79.

Thorp, D. (1989). Early warning: a moisture monitor intended to boost the popularity of flat roofing systems. *Building Design,* February, suppl., p.9.

Tiwari, G.N. (1985). Influence of the thermal trap material on the performance of a roof as an inexpensive collector/storage system. *Applied Energy, 20* (2), pp.117-121.

Turner, D.F. (1985): *Building Sub-Contract Forms.* Collins.

Twiston-Davies, J.C.D. (1987). Flat roofs: success and failure. *RIBA Journal, 95* (11), November, pp.123, 127, 131, 135, 137-138.

V

Venmore-Rowland, P. et al (1991): *Investment, procurement and performance in construction.* E&FN Spon.

W

Weaver, L (1909): *English leadwork: its art and history.* Batsford

Woolaston, A.K. (1987). Roofing with copper a contemporary tradition. *Building Trades Journal,* 23 April, pp.42-44. ■

22.2 Health and safety bibliography

B

British Standards Institution (1988): DD 175: 1988. Draft for Development. *Code of practice for the identification of potentially contaminated land and its investigation.* BSI.

British Standards Institution (1979): BS1397:1979. *Specification for industrial safety belts, harness and safety lanyards.* BSI.

British Standards Institution (1986): BS1870: Part 2:1976 (1986). *Specification for lined rubber safety boots.* BSI.

British Standards Institution (1988): BS1870: Part 1: 1988. *Specification for safety footwear other than all-rubber and all-plastics moulded types.* BSI.

British Standards Institution (1981): BS1870: Part 3 1981. *Specification for polyvinyl chloride moulded safety footwear.* BSI.

British Standards Institution (1984): BS5228: Part 1:1984. *Noise control on construction and open sites. Code of practice for basic information and procedures for noise control* BSI.

British Standards Institution (1987): BS5240: Part 1: 1987. *Industrial safety helmets. Specification for Construction and Performance.* BSI.

British Standards Institution (1984): BS5528: Part 2:1984. *Noise control on construction and open sites. Guide to noise control legislation for construction and demolition, including road construction and maintenance.* BSI.

British Standards Institution (1990): BS5973: 1990. *Code of practice for access and working scaffolds and special scaffold structures in steel* BSI.

British Standards Institution (1990): BS5974: 1990. *Code of practice for temporarily installed suspended scaffolds and access equipment* BSI.

British Standards Institution (1982): BS6187: 1982. *Code of practice for demolition.* BSI.

C

Construction Industry Research and Information Association (1981): Special Publication16. *A guide to the safe use of chemicals in construction.* CIRIA

F

Factories Act (1961): *Factories Act 1961.* HMSO.

Federation of Civil Engineering Contractors (1986): *Supervisor's safety booklet. 5th ed.* FCEC.

H

Health and Safety at Work Act (1974): *Health and Safety at Work etc. Act 1974* HMSO.

Health and Safety Commission (1975): HSC 3. *Advice to employers.* HMSO.

Health and Safety Commission (1975): *Health and Safety at Work etc. Act: The Act outlined* HMSO

Health and Safety Commission (1976): HSC 8. *Safety committees. Guidance to employers whose employees are not members of recognised independent trade unions.* HMSO.

Health and Safety Commission (1976): HSC 7. *Regulations, approved codes of practice and guidance literature.* HMSO.

Health and Safety Commission (1987): HSC 6. *Writing a safety policy statement: Advice to Employers* HMSO.

Health and Safety Commission (1975): HSC 5. *Health and Safety at Work etc. Act: Advice to Employees.* HMSO.

Health and Safety Executive (1988): *Blackspot construction: A study of five years fatal accidents in the building and civil engineering industries.* HMSO.

Health and Safety Executive (1988): *Construction site safety checklist.* HMSO.

Health and Safety Executive (1991): *Construction industry: list of HSC/E information.* HMSO.

Health and Safety Executive (1988): COP 1. *Safety representatives and safety committees. (The Brown Book).* HMSO.

Health and Safety Executive (1985): COP 2. *Control of lead a work: approved code of practice: revised june 1985 (in support of 51 1980 No. 1248).* HMSO.

Health and Safety Executive (1988): *COSHH assessments: a step by step guide to assessments and the skills needed for it. Control of Substances Hazardous to Health Regulations.* HMSO.

Health and Safety Executive (1981): CS 6. *Storage and use of LPG on construction sites.* HMSO.

Health and Safety Executive (1985): *Deadly maintenance: A study of fatal accidents at work.* HMSO.

Health and Safety Executive (1977): EH 7. *Petroleum-based adhesives in building operations.* HMSO.

Health and Safety Executive (1990): EH 10. *Asbestos – exposure limits and measurement of airborne dust concentrations.* HMSO.

Health and Safety Executive (1986): EH 28. *Control of lead: air sampling techniques and strategies.* HMSO.

Health and Safety Executive (1981): EH 29. *Control of lead: outside workers.* HMSO.

Health and Safety Executive (1989): EH 35. *Probable asbestos dust concentrations at construction processes.* HMSO.

Health and Safety Executive (1990): EH 36. *Work with asbestos cement.* HMSO.

Health and Safety Executive (1989): EH 37. *Work with asbestos insulating board* HMSO.

Health and Safety Executive (1991): EH 40. *Occupational exposure limits 1991: containing the lists of maximum exposure limits and occupational exposure standards for use with The Control of Substances Hazardous to Health Regulations 1988.* HMSO.

Health and Safety Executive (1984): EH 43. *Carbon monoxide.* HMSO.

Health and Safety Executive (1990): EH 47. *Provision, use and maintenance of hygiene facilities for work with asbestos insulation and coatings.* HMSO.

Health and Safety Executive (1988): EH 50. *Training operatives and supervisors for work with asbestos insulation and coatings.* HMSO.

Health and Safety Executive (1977): GS 5. *Entry into confined spaces.* HMSO.

Health and Safety Executive (1989): GS 7. *Accidents to children on construction sites.* HMSO.

Health and Safety Executive (1980): GS 10. *Roofwork—Prevention of falls.* HMSO.

Health and Safety Executive (1982): GS 15. *General access scaffolds.* HMSO.

Health and Safety Executive (1988): GS 29/1. *Health and safety in demolition work Part 1: preparation and planning.* HMSO.

Health and Safety Executive (1988): GS 29/2. *Health and safety in demolition work Part 2: legislation.* HMSO.

Health and Safety Executive (1988): GS 29/3. *Health and safety in demolition work Part 3: techniques.* HMSO.

Health and Safety Executive (1988): GS 29/4. *Health and safety in demolition work Part 4: health hazards.* HMSO.

Health and Safety Executive (1984): GS 31. *Safe use of ladders, step ladders and trestles.* HMSO.

Health and Safety Executive (1987): GS 42. *Tower scaffolds.* HMSO.

Health and Safety Executive (1983): *Guidance on health and safety advisory services for the construction industry. Part 1. The need for advice and the services available.* HMSO.

Health and Safety Executive (1983): *Guidance on health and safety advisory services for the construction industry. Part 2. The safety adviser; selection, training and professional standards.* HMSO.

Health and Safety Executive (1982): HS(G) 19. *Safety in working with power-operated mobile work platform.* HMSO.

Health and Safety Executive (1991): HS(G) 65. *Successful health and safety management.* HMSO.

Health and Safety Executive (1991): HSE 4. *Employers Liability (Compulsory Insurance) Act 1969: A short guide.* HMSO.

Health and Safety Executive (1986): HSE 11. *Reporting and injury or a dangerous occurrence.* HMSO.

Health and Safety Executive (1988): HSE 21. *Report that accident: RIDDOR The Reporting of Injuries, Diseases and Dangerous Occurrences Regulations 1985.* HMSO.

Health and Safety Executive (1978): HSW 6 *Safety in Construction Work. General Site Safety Practice.* HMSO.

Health and Safety Executive (1977): HSW 6B. *Safety in construction work. Roofing.* HMSO.

Health and Safety Executive (1988): HSW 6E. *Safety in Construction Work. Demolitions.* HMSO.

Health and Safety Executive (1974): HSW 25. *Noise and the worker.* HMSO.

Health and Safety Executive (1971): HSW 47. *Safety in the stacking of materials.* HMSO.

Health and Safety Executive (1978): HSW 50. *Welding and Flame Cutting using Compressed Gases.* HMSO.

Health and Safety Executive (1991): IND(G) I(L). *Articles and Substances used at work: the legal duties of designers, manufacturers, importers and suppliers and erectors and installers.* HMSO.

Health and Safety Executive (1989): IND(G) 73(L). *Working alone in safety: controlling the risks of solitary work* HMSO.

Health and Safety Executive (1990): IND(G) 80(L). *Construction: head protection regulations and you.* HMSO.

Health and Safety Executive (1990): IND(G) 92(L). *Dangerous substances on site: notification and warning signs.* HMSO.

Health and Safety Executive (1990): IND(G) 97(L). *COSHH and section 6 of the Health and Safety at Work Act.* HMSO.

Health and Safety Executive (1991): IND(G) 107(L). *Asbestos and you.* HMSO.

Health and Safety Executive (1988): *Managing health and safety in construction: management contracting.* HMSO.

Health and Safety Executive (1987): *Managing health and safety in construction: principles and application to main contractor/sub-contractor projects.* HMSO.

Health and Safety Executive (1986): *Noise in construction: guidance on noise control and hearing conservation measures* HMSO.

H *(continued)*

Health and Safety Executive (1991): OL 1. *The Construction Regulations: an open learning course.* HMSO.

Health and Safety Executive (1991): OL 2. *COSHH: an open learning course.* HMSO.

Health and Safety Executive (1990): *Organisations concerned with health and safety information.* HMSO.

Health and Safety Executive (1983): PM 30. *Suspended access equipment.* HMSO.

Health and Safety Executive (1979): *Safety in demolition.* HMSO.

Health and Safety Executive (1974): *Safety of scaffolding* HMSO.

Health and Safety Executive (1988): SS 1. *General legal requirements.* HMSO.

Health and Safety Executive (1988): SS 2. *Safe use of ladders.* HMSO.

Health and Safety Executive (1988): SS 3. *General access scaffolds.* HMSO.

Health and Safety Executive (1988): SS 4. *Safety in roofwork.* HMSO.

Health and Safety Executive (1988): SS 5. *Suspended cradles and small lifting appliances.* HMSO.

Health and Safety Executive (1988): SS 6. *Use of portable electric tools and equipment on construction sites.* HMSO.

Health and Safety Executive (1988): SS 10. *Tower scaffolds.* HMSO.

Health and Safety Executive (1988): SS 11. *Safe use of propane and other LPG cylinders.* HMSO.

Health and Safety Executive (1988): SS 13. *Construction goods hoists.* HMSO.

Health and Safety Executive (1988): SS 15. *Confined spaces.* HMSO.

Health and Safety Executive (1989): SS 16. *The Control of Substances Hazardous to Health Regulations 1988 (COSHH).* HMSO.

Health and Safety Executive (1991): SS 18. *Provision of toilet, washing and general welfare arrangements at small fixed sites.* HMSO.

Health and Safety Executive (1991): SS 19. *Safe use of mobile cranes on construction sites.* HMSO.

Health and Safety Executive (1989): *Standards significant to health and safety at work.* HMSO.

Health and Safety Executive (1989): *The control of substances hazardous to health in the construction industry.* HMSO.

Health and Safety Executive (1989): *Writing your health and safety policy statement: our health and safety policy statement: a guide to preparing a safety policy statement for a small business.* HMSO.

R

Rosehaugh Guide - see Curwell, S et al (Unit 21.1).

Royal Society for the Prevention of Accidents (1987): *The supervisors guide to the Construction Regulations.* ROSPA.

S

Statutory Instruments (1958): SI 1958 No. 61. *Work in compressed air special regulations 1958.* HMSO.

Statutory Instruments (1961): SI 1961 No. 1580. *The Construction (General Provisions) Regulations 1961.* HMSO.

Statutory Instruments (1966): SI 1961 No. 1581. *The Construction (Lifting Operations) Regulations 1961.* HMSO.

Statutory Instruments (1966): SI 1966 No. 94. *The Construction (Working Places) Regulations 1966.* HMSO.

Statutory Instruments (1966): SI 1966 No. 95. *The Construction (Health & Welfare) Regulations 1966.* HMSO.

Statutory Instruments (1969): SI 1969 No. 690. *Asbestos Regulations 1969.* HMSO.

Statutory Instruments (1974): SI 1974 No. 1681. *The protection of eyes regulations 1974* HMSO.

Statutory Instruments (1980): SI 1980 No. 1258. *Control of Lead at Work Act 1980:* HMSO.

Statutory Instruments (1983): SI 1983 No. 1649. *Asbestos (Licensing) Regulations 1983.* HMSO.

Statutory Instruments (1984): SI 1984 No. 1358. *Gas Safety (Installation and Use) Regulations 1984* HMSO.

Statutory Instruments (1985): SI 1985 No. 2023. *The reporting of injuries, diseases and dangerous occurrences regulations 1985.* HMSO.

Statutory Instruments (1988): SI 1988 No. 1657. *Control of Substances Hazardous to Health Regulations 1988 (COSHH).* HMSO.

Statutory Instruments (1989): SI 1989 No. 682. *The Health and Safety Information for Employees Regulations 1989.* HMSO.

Statutory Instruments (1990): SI 1989 No. 2209. *The Construction (Head Protection) Regulations 1989.* HMSO. ∎

Index and further sources of information 23

23.1 Index

This index gives the principal location in the Guide of the key subjects in the design and performance of flat roofs.

The index does not try to give a comprehensive listing of all terms and subjects within the Guide.

The Unit numbers and page references will enable the user to find information on the subject; the cross referencing and further reading information within each Unit will then enable other relevant information to be found.

The Guide contents listing (**Unit 1.2**) and the Unit references in the Glossary of terms (**Unit 1.3**) will also help the reader to locate relevant information in the Guide.

© BFRC / CIRIA: *Flat Roofing: Design and Good Practice.* 1993

Further sources of information

• BRITISH FLAT ROOFING COUNCIL

38 Bridlesmith Gate, Nottingham NG1 2GQ
Tel: 0602 507733   Fax: 0602 504122

Contact: ....
Notes: ....
....
....

• CONTRACTORS' ORGANISATIONS

Flat Roofing Contractors Advisory Board
Fields House, Gower Road, Haywards Heath,
West Sussex RH16 4PL
Tel: 0444 440027   Fax: 0444 415616

Contact: ....
Notes: ....
....
....

National Federation of Roofing Contractors
24 Weymouth Street, London W1N 3FA
Tel: 071 436 0387   Fax: 071 637 5215

Contact: ....
Notes: ....
....
....

• PRODUCT ASSESSMENT ORGANISATIONS

British Board of Agrément
PO Box 195, Bucknalls Lane,
Watford WD2 7NG
Tel: 0923 670844   Fax: 0923 662133

Contact: ....
Notes: ....
....
....

• MATERIALS TRADE ASSOCIATIONS

Association of British Roofing Felt Manufacturers
38 Bridlesmith Gate, Nottingham NG1 2GQ
Tel: 0602 589209   Fax: 0602 504122

Contact: ....
Notes: ....
....

Mastic Asphalt Technical Advisory Centre
Leslie House, 6/8 Broadway,
Bexleyheath DA6 7LE
Tel: 081 298 0414   Fax: 081 298 0381

Contact: ....
Notes: ....
....

Single Ply Roofing Association
38 Bridlesmith Gate, Nottingham NG1 2GQ
Tel: 0602 240499   Fax: 0602 504122

Contact: ....
Notes: ....
....

Copper Development Association
Orchard House, Mutton Lane, Potters Barr,
Herts EN6 3AP
Tel: 0707 650711   Fax: 0707 642769

Contact: ....
Notes: ....
....

Lead Sheet Association
St. John's Road, Tunbridge Wells,
Kent TN4 9XA
Tel: 0892 513553   Fax: 0892 535028

Contact: ....
Notes: ....
....

Zinc Development Association
42 Weymouth Street, London W1N 3LQ
Tel: 071 499 6636   Fax: 071 493 1555

Contact: ....
Notes: ....
....

Notes